Health, Illness, and Medicine in Canada

Eighth edition

Health, Illness, and Medicine in Canada

Juanne Nancarrow Clarke

OXFORD

UNIVERSITY PRESS

Oxford University Press is a department of the University of Oxford.
It furthers the University's objective of excellence in research, scholarship,
and education by publishing worldwide. Oxford is a registered trade mark of
Oxford University Press in the UK and in certain other countries.

Published in Canada by
Oxford University Press
8 Sampson Mews, Suite 204,
Don Mills, Ontario M3C 0H5 Canada

www.oupcanada.com

Library and Archives Canada Cataloguing in Publication
Title: Health, illness, and medicine in Canada / Juanne Nancarrow Clarke.
Names: Clarke, Juanne N. (Juanne Nancarrow), 1944- author.
Description: Eighth edition. | Includes bibliographical references and index.
Identifiers: Canadiana (print) 2020027547X | Canadiana (ebook) 20200275496 | ISBN 9780199035908
(softcover) | ISBN 9780199035939 (ebook)
Subjects: LCSH: Social medicine—Canada.
Classification: LCC RA418.3.C3 C53 2020 | DDC 306.4/610971—dc23

Cover image: Chinnapong/Shutterstock.com
Cover design: Sherill Chapman
Interior design: Sherill Chapman

Oxford University Press is committed to our environment.
Wherever possible, our books are printed on paper which comes from
responsible sources

Printed and bound in Canada

5 6 7 — 24 23 22

Contents

Part III • Sociology of Medicine 193

9   A Brief History of Medicine and the Development and Critique of Modern Medicalization 216

10   The Social Democratic and Current History of Medicare: Privatization and the State of Medicare in Canada 239

11   The Medical Profession, Autonomy, and Medical Error 263

Figures, Tables, and Boxes

Figures

Tables

Boxes

Canada in a Global Context

Critical Thinking

Highlighted Issues

Remembering Our History

Spotlight on Ethics

Preface

The fundamentals of the health of Canadians continue to be threatened. Significant changes in the medical care system and in the degree of inequality in the Canadian population continue. Perhaps the most basic change confronting Canadians in terms of medical care today is the challenge to a universal medical care system. As contested federal transfer payments decrease and the responsibility for medical care shifts to the provinces, the likelihood grows of inequality in the availability of particular services across the nation. Universal medical care is threatened as Canada shifts to the political right in the context of economic globalization. Unless the direction in which we are heading alters dramatically, inequality in medical services among provinces, between the rich and the poor, among racialized and ethnic groups, and between women and men will continue to grow. In the context of the globalization of neo-liberal ideology and policy, health differences resulting from inequalities in the social determinants of health will increase.

Some argue that this crisis in the provision of allopathic medical care may have positive effects on the health of the population. The argument is that as the near-monopoly in allopathic medical care is weakened, complementary and alternative care strategies will grow in their availability for the population. In fact, already about 40 per cent of the US and Canadian populations use alternative or complementary health care. To the extent that the current medical care crisis destabilizes the hegemonic status of allopathic medicine and, in turn, other types of health care take up positions as possible health-care strategies for Canadians, this crisis in medical care could be seen as an opportunity.

Investments in health promotion and disease prevention are a significant part of the overall thinking about the health of Canadians. These strategies have resulted in some benefits. They are also problematic at times because they individualize health problems that result from social-structural inequalities and may lead to "blaming the victim." Focusing on individual choice with respect to prevention issues such as seat-belt use, quitting smoking, moderation in alcohol consumption, low-fat diets, and exercise obscures the social, cultural, and structural constraints within which such choices occur. By contrast, the social determinants of health perspective spotlights systemic and structural issues such as social class, education, occupation, employment, literacy, and racialization as precursors to illness or well-being. We discuss the social determinants of health at some length. In particular we concentrate on the health of Indigenous Canadians in this new edition.

Concern appears to be deepening about environmental issues such as climate change, especially after the leadership of the child activist, Greta Thunberg, who has invigorated a global movement for change. Actions taken by citizens on an individual basis, such as recycling paper, metal, glass, and cardboard, and reducing and reusing whenever possible, have only a minor effect in an industrial and corporate context where environmental controls compete with profitability. Major environmental challenges, such as global warming, chlorinated water, and the pervasive use of bleach in manufacturing, the widespread use of pesticides, herbicides, and fertilizers in agriculture, the continued use of fossil fuels and nuclear energy, and the widespread consumption of meat, especially beef and pork, all continue to affect the health of the population and threaten to do so in the future.

Wars and political violence, along with massive shifts in populations of people who are political and environmental refugees, are growing around the world. With these processes come new and increased levels of mental and physical illness as well as death.

Many have noted that sociology is approached from different theoretical perspectives: structural-functional, conflict, social constructionist, feminist, critical race, and post-structural. Each of these is based on different assumptions, asks different questions, and uses different methods and rules of evidence. This book is organized into three major sections. The first part, Chapter 1, addresses some theoretical and methodological issues, and discusses some of the theories behind each of the sociological perspectives. Included in this chapter are illustrations of each perspective as applied to concrete studies.

The second part, Chapters 2 to 7, explores the meaning and measurement of health and illness. Chapter 2 examines Canadian mortality in historical and cross-cultural contexts. It examines questions such as: What are the chief causes of death and disease in the developing world and in Canada today? What were the chief causes of death 150 years ago? Why has the difference between male and female mortality rates increased over time?

Chapter 3 examines the impact on health of environmental, occupational, and other health and safety issues, as well as violence in society. It asks questions such as: What are the major threats to the environment? What do we know about their impact on the health of the population? Are the health effects of environmental degradation spread equally across Canada and throughout the global community? What occupations are safe? Is shift work bad for our health? Does violence affect the health of Canadians?

Chapter 4 focuses on the social determinants of health, that is, the impact of unequal social statuses on the health of the population. In particular, it looks at the effects of processes such as inclusion and exclusion. This chapter sets out the theoretical approaches that are discussed empirically in the next chapter. Questions such as the following are asked: Are poorer people more likely to be sick? Is education an important prerequisite to health? How do political forces relate to health outcomes?

Chapter 5 examines specific aspects of inequity in the social system—age, gender, racialization, and ethnicity. Pertinent questions include: Is there evidence of ethnic differences in morbidity and mortality? Do people of different genders, ages, and "race"/ethnic backgrounds experience different health and life changes? The second half of this chapter concentrates on Indigenous people and their health.

Chapter 6 looks at the social and psychological antecedents to illness and disease and considers such questions as: What is the relationship between stress and illness? Can the loss of a loved one lead to serious illness? Is the inability to express anger sometimes implicated in the onset of cancer? Can social support minimize the effects and shorten the duration of an illness?

Chapter 7 concerns the phenomenological experience of illness and answers questions such as: How does epilepsy, cancer, or multiple sclerosis affect the everyday life of patients and family members? Do diseases have social meanings?

The third part of the book, "Sociology of Medicine," deals with medical research and practice, the pharmaceutical industry, and the organization of the Canadian medical care system. It also looks at three medical systems around the world. It addresses questions such as: Does a universal medical care insurance scheme guarantee universal accessibility? Why has the number of malpractice suits increased? What is the impact of the increasing number of female doctors? What is the fate of idealism in medical school? How does Canada's system compare with others in a global context?

Chapter 8 discusses the social basis of medical science and medical research. It also examines some strategies of lay resistance to conventional medicine. Questions asked include: Is allopathic medical practice entirely based on the findings of traditional medical science research? Is medical science objective? Are new medical technologies necessarily better? When and why do people sometimes resist medical prescriptions and diagnoses?

Chapter 9 examines the relationship between medicine and religion in cross-cultural and historical contexts. It considers questions such as the following: Is medicalization increasing? Is medical practice an art or a science? Do physicians act as moral entrepreneurs? What sort of ethical dilemmas do doctors face as they do their work?

Chapter 10 examines the history of universal medical care insurance in Canada. What is the impact of universal medical insurance on class-based differences in health status? What is the future of extra-billing? What role did Tommy Douglas play in the foundation of Canada's universal medical care system?

Chapter 11 examines medical practice as an occupation, and seeks to answer such questions as: Is medicine a profession? What is a profession? How do doctors handle mistakes? What is medical culture?

Chapter 12 describes other health-care providers—nurses and midwives. Typical questions are: What is the importance of Florence Nightingale for nursing work today? What are the consequences of the bureaucratic work organization of the hospital on the work of nurses? What is the status of the midwife in Canada?

Chapter 13 examines the place of complementary and alternative health care in Canadian and other Western industrialized societies. In-depth examinations of two alternative forms of health care, chiropractic and naturopathy, are included.

Chapter 14 examines the pharmaceutical industry as one component of the medical-industrial complex. It considers questions such as: How does the pharmaceutical industry maintain its position as one of the lowest-risk and highest-profit industries in Canada today? What is the role of doctors and pharmacists in prescribing drugs? Which Canadians are most likely to use mood-altering drugs?

Discussion of the Canadian medical care system is followed by a new concluding chapter. Chapter 15 looks at health care in international perspective and in the context of globalization, with particular focus on the health-care systems of Brazil, the United States, and the United Kingdom as well as an early view of the impacts of coronavirus pandemic in 2020.

Acknowledgements

Many people have contributed to this eighth edition, first of all my students, who have asked questions, shown enthusiasm, and made suggestions for the inclusion of new material. In addition, colleagues both at Laurier and at universities across the country have supported the previous editions and suggested new topics, amplifying innovative directions. In particular, I would like to thank the following reviewers, whose thoughtful comments have helped shape this edition:

Andrea Bundon, University of British Columbia
Meredith Burles, University of Saskatchewan
Lisa F. Carver, Queen's University
Sarath Chandrasekere, University of Toronto

Linda Cohen, Memorial University of Newfoundland
Margaret K. Dechman, Cape Breton University
Ryan Higgit, University of New Brunswick
Kerry-Anne Hogan, University of Ottawa
Cynthia Levine-Rasky, Queen's University
Alison Luke, University of New Brunswick, Saint John
Alissa Overend, MacEwan University

I am especially grateful to Mariah Fleetham at Oxford University Press for her close reading and thinking about the topics covered in this book. Finally, Richard Tallman and Laurna Tallman, the fine editors for Oxford, have helped enormously, especially at the final stages, by noticing a myriad of small details and larger questions of substance and meaning that needed to be attended to before publication. I am also very grateful to have had their continued work on this book from the first edition because their interest in and engagement with many of the ideas improves my thinking and clarity and makes my reading of their responses both fun and challenging.

Part I

Sociological Perspectives

This book is divided into three sections. The first is comprised of Chapter 1. In Chapter 1 we discuss some of the most important theoretical underpinnings of the sociological study of health, illness, and medicine. They include (1) structural functionalism, (2) conflict theory, (3) social constructionism/interpretive theory, (4) feminism, (5) critical race theory, and (6) post-structuralism. All of these theoretical approaches are included throughout the text in the different studies brought to bear on the specific arguments made. In Part II we discuss issues of relevance to the branch of the field called the sociology of health and illness. Here we focus particularly on the social causes of death and disease around the world and in Canada. We especially examine inequality and inequity as the major social determinants of health. The health issues of Indigenous peoples also are examined. In Part III we focus on both the historical and contemporary features of the Canadian medical care system within the contexts of medicalization and biomedicalization. This first part, then, covers some of the basic concerns of the whole field of the sociology of health, illness, and medicine as it explains and illustrates six principal sociological perspectives.

Ways of Thinking Sociologically about Health, Illness, and Medicine

1

Chapter Overview

- There are many different approaches to research and analysis in the field of sociology.
- In this book we have divided these into six different theoretical perspectives: (1) structural-functional, (2) conflict, (3) interpretive/social constructionist, (4) feminist, (5) critical race theory, and (6) post-structuralism.
- Each perspective involves a fundamentally different paradigm or way of seeing the important issues in health and medical sociology as well as some distinct methodological strategies.

- Structural functionalism, based initially on the work of Émile Durkheim, sees society as a system of interlocking and functional parts.
- Conflict theories, from the work of Karl Marx, are concerned about the documentation and elimination of injustices, particularly those based on economic inequities.
- Interpretive or social constructivist sociologies, based initially on the writing of Max Weber, see sociology as the study of social action insofar as it is socially meaningful.

- Feminist theories are more recent, dating from the latter part of the last century. Gender, as distinct from sex, was the original core concept for critical analysis. The work of Canadian sociologist Dorothy Smith is used to exemplify feminism.
- Studies based on critical race theory have much in common with critical feminist studies in that they

focus on structural problems within society and its institutions. The work of a Canadian, George Sefa Dei, is used to illustrate anti-racist theories.
- The post-structuralist focus on how power produces effects through reflexive and circulating discourses is based initially on the work of Michel Foucault.

Introduction

Almost all of us have been sick at some time in our lives. When do we acknowledge that we are sick? Is it when we stay in bed for a day or two? Is it perhaps when we feel a pain or have a fever but use over-the-counter medicines purchased from the drugstore and go on with the day as planned? Or perhaps we may not truly claim sickness unless we go to the doctor to find a name for the unusual way we feel. All of us experience illness in a social context. We recognize it because we have developed a vocabulary that allows us to think and talk about it with others in our immediate circle or in the larger social world. We learn what to do about it as we interact with friends and families, at times with the formal medical system, and with our society through television, newspapers, magazines, and various social media and online websites.

Health and illness are socially patterned. Are you aware of the relationship between ethnicity and sickle-cell anemia? Sickle-cell anemia is more common among people of African or Mediterranean background. Did you know that unemployment is often followed by ill health? Most types of morbidity and mortality are inversely related to income. That is, it is statistically correct to say that the lower the income, the higher the rates of sickness, disability, and death. What are the health consequences of the global spread of **neo-liberalism**? In many ways and in many places the gap between the rich and the poor has increased within individual countries. Increased inequality has limited progress towards better health and health care. The early and dramatic spread of HIV/AIDS among some of the poorest

workers and their families in Africa is a case in point. It happened in part because male workers frequently had to travel away from their homes and families for an extended period of time in order to make a living. During time away they engaged in sex with strangers, including sex workers. When they went home they unknowingly spread the disease to family and friends. The experiences or meanings of symptoms are constructed differently in various societies, classes, and cultures. Socio-psychological factors are linked to various diagnoses. These are the sorts of issues discussed in the sociology of health and illness. The sociology of health and illness seeks to describe and explain some of the social causes and consequences of illness, disease, disability, and death; to show the ways lay people and medical professionals construct their own distinct categories of disease and illness; and to describe the identities and experiences associated with illness and wellness. Table 1.1 lists examples of relevant topics.

When we think that we are sick, what do we do? Some of us treat ourselves with our favourite home remedies such as bed rest, lemon tea, or chicken soup. Some of us seek advice from friends or family members. Some of us visit our general practitioner, a medical specialist, or a pharmacist. A few head off to the emergency room of the nearest hospital. Others seek alternative health care such as homeopathy or acupuncture. When you seek the advice of a doctor, do you think you would receive better medical care from a physician who works in a fee-for-service setting or from one on a salary paid by the state, a corporation, or a clinic? Do practitioners in group practice provide better care than those in practice on their own? Does the

Canadian government have adequate drug safety procedures to protect Canadians against another drug disaster such as thalidomide? Why does the universal medical insurance scheme provide guaranteed funds for medical practitioners and pharmaceuticals when in hospital but only limited funds for outpatient pharmaceuticals. Why are complementary and alternative health-care providers excluded from medicare? How does medical care financing vary around the world? Do you think that medicine sometimes is used to fulfill dreams and aspirations or is it simply for treatment of disease? These are some of the questions we ponder in the second half of this text.

The sociology of medicine is the study of the ways the institutionalized medical systems construct what they consider to be illness out of what they recognize as signs and symptoms, and what they constitute as their responses to such "illness" through the treatments they prescribe (see Table 1.1). The medical care system also has to respond, sometimes with diagnoses and particular treatments, to the everyday demands of patients,

the bidding of the disease-related support and advocacy groups, pharmaceutical regulations and advertising, the requests of governments and health insurance companies, and the innovations of medical device corporations, among other external forces. Sociology of medicine examines and offers explanations for such issues as **medicalization**, **biomedicalization**, the varying types of medical practice and medical **discourses**, the ideology and organization of medicine, different ways of financing medical care, the structure and operation of the hospital, the pharmaceutical industry, and the occupational worlds of nurses, doctors, and myriad other health-care workers. It also attempts to explain the relationships among the different types of health care and the role of the medical care system in the context of the culture, the political economy of states, and the globalizing world.

Sociologists study the social world from a variety of perspectives. Depending on their perspective, they focus on some aspects of social life and ignore others, and ask different questions and

Table 1.1   Examples of Topics within the Sociology of Medicine and of Health and Illness

Sociology of Medicine	Sociology of Health and Illness
Medicalization and biomedicalization	The construction and distribution of disease and death in the context of medicalization and biomedicalization
The organization of the Canadian medical care system in the context of medicalization and biomedicalization	Disease and death in socio-historical context
	Socio-demographic explanations for disease and death
The profession of medicine (and auxiliary and competing health-care professionals)	Class, patriarchy, racism, and sexism as explanations for disease and death
Alternative health-care providers	Socio-psychological explanations for disease and death
The financing of medical care	
The medico-industrial complex	Experiencing and talking about disease and death
Class, racism, and sexism and the organization and provision of medical care	Ways people construct or label certain signs as symptoms of disease
The health-promotion and prevention industries	Environmental conditions and health, occupational health, safety issues, and health consequences
Medical care around the globe	
The development and perpetuation of medical discourse and ideology	Health and illness around the globe

use different ways to answer them. Sociologists have approached both the sociology of health and illness and of medicine with different or even contradictory assumptions. At times, different sociologists have described or analyzed an aspect of illness or medicine from such widely differing points of view that they appear to be discussing different phenomena. Among sociologists you will find some agreement, amid a lot of debate, that the various perspectives can be distilled into six distinct paradigms. The present convention is to call these perspectives structural-functional theory, conflict theory, social constructionist/interpretive theory, feminist and anti-racist theories, and post-structuralism. Table 1.2 outlines the principal characteristics of each approach. In this chapter we will begin to learn about the research and writing from each of these theoretical perspectives.

Structural Functionalism

Structural functionalism dominated North American sociology for many years. It had been the reigning paradigm, the "normal" science of the discipline (Kuhn, 1962). Many sociological studies published in North America have adopted this perspective. The American field of the sociology of medicine was founded on it (see, for instance, the major journal in health sociology in the United States, the *Journal of Health and Social Behavior,* as well as publications and research in the fields of mainstream public health and **epidemiology**, for continuing examples of the dominance of this perspective). Auguste Comte (1798–1857), who first gave the name of "sociology" to the science of society, thought that sociology's goal was to better society so that it might become orderly and progressive. He might be called the godfather of sociology. Émile Durkheim (1858–1917) provided both the theoretical and methodological models for structural functionalism. Durkheim defined sociology as a science of social facts. Social facts, he said, were to be treated and studied as if they were real, external to individuals, and yet capable of constraining and directing human behaviour and thought. The subject matter of sociology was

these social facts and their impact on human behaviour. Constrained by the external world, human beings, in Durkheim's view, were predictable and controllable through the power of social facts that exist as norms in their own right, aside from their manifestations in individuals.

Sociology in the Durkheimian tradition is often called structural functionalism. It assumes that the proper level of study for the sociologist is the system. The social system is composed of parts, institutions that function to maintain order. Just as the organs in the human body are inextricably tied to one another and function as interrelated components, so, too, do the parts or the institutions of society—the family, the economy, the polity, and the educational, welfare, justice, military, and medical care systems. All of these institutions operate interdependently to keep the society functioning. The goal of maintaining a good working order in society motivates theorizing and research in this sociological perspective.

Structural-functional theory is associated with positivist methodologies. Positivists view sociology as a science in the same way that physicists view physics as a science. Positivists assume that social scientists should and can remain objective and value-free while observing, recording, and measuring external social facts and their impacts on people. Just as the natural sciences seek universally true, causal explanations of relationships in the natural world, so do positivist sociologists in the social world. As well, since positivists believe that social facts are to be treated as real and external, they tend to rely on data that are assumed to be objective, collected from interviews and questionnaires, administered to individuals in survey research, and analyzed and organized to reflect the probability of the occurrence of particular behaviours among a certain aggregate of individuals.

Five principles distinguish structural functionalism from the other perspectives. They are the assumptions that: (1) sociology aims to discover and to explain the impact of social facts on human behaviour, attitudes, and feelings; (2) social facts are to be treated as things that are real and external to human actions, and that determine

Table 1.2   The Six Central Sociological Perspectives

	Structural Functionalism	Conflict Theory	Interpretive/Social Constructionist Theory	Feminist Theory	Critical Race Theory	Post-Structuralism
Exemplar	Émile Durkheim	Karl Marx	Max Weber	Dorothy Smith	George Sefa Dei	Michel Foucault
Model of subject matter	Society is a social system of interlocking and interrelated parts of institutions.	Society is a system of classes.	Society is composed of selves who make their social lives meaningful through interaction.	To truly understand society, we must be keenly aware of inequity, social organization, structure, power, and knowledge from women's perspective.	Understanding how racism affects inequity, social organization, and power is necessary to understanding society.	There is no single reality; we need to interrogate key social concerns through fundamental concepts: biopower, medical gaze, power/knowledge, governmentality, and technologies of the self/subjectivities.
Model of the subject matter in process	Institutions perform (dys)functions that are both manifest and latent in the interest of the (dis)continuation of the social system in equilibrium.	Power groups with contradictory purposes, based on their relationship to the basic economic structures.	Selves create reality anew from situation to situation in interaction with others.	Selves and identities are tied to the relations of ruling. Feminist and anti-racist research has change as one of its goals. They emphasize critical analysis and transformation of patriarchal and racist social system.		Circulating discourses infuse everyday practices through power/knowledge, governmentality, technologies of the self, and subjectivities.

Ways of doing sociological analysis	System explainable and predictable through a series of "if x . . . then y" causal statements; x and y are social facts.	Power groups are understandable from a committed stance examining the conflicts in historical context.	Selves' world views and symbols arise out of interaction and are made understandable through process of interpretive, empathetic understanding—*verstehen*.	All methods of data collection may be used but a collaborative approach (between researcher and subjects of research) is advocated. Triangulation is suggested. Language is gender appropriate.	All methods of data collection may be used but a collaborative approach (between researcher and subjects of research) is advocated. Triangulation is suggested. Language is anti-racist.	Research is archaeological, genealogical, and historical discourse analysis as well as contemporary discourse analysis.
Objectivity/ subjectivity	Necessary to be objective and to study the social world objectively.	Value-committed perspective necessary.	Acknowledgement of the inevitability of contextual reflexivity of knower and known.	Focuses on and begins with the experience of women. Impossible to be objective. Therefore important to clarify standpoint and acknowledge reflexivity.	Focuses on and begins with the experience of racialized people along with other marginalized identities. Impossible to be objective. Therefore important to clarify standpoint and acknowledge reflexivity.	Objectivity is not possible because of the irreducible connection between power/knowledge.
Image of human nature	Human beings believe, think/ feel, and do as the result of external constraining forces.	Human beings are alienated from self, others, and meaningful work, and need the liberation that would come from revolutionary change.	Human beings continually construct reality as they interact with others in their social worlds.	Differences by racialization, class, gender/power, sexual orientation, dis/ability limit generalization.	Differences by racialization, class, gender/power, sexual orientation, dis/ability limit generalization.	Subjectivity is continually recreated and resisted through the technologies of the self-infused with power/knowledge.

human behaviour; (3) social facts can be seen in aspects of the social structure such as the norms associated with structural locations (e.g., gender, race, status, class) that guide behaviour through roles enacted in social institutions such as the family or the economy, and in social behaviours such as those in relationships, in marriage, or at work; (4) sociology is a science that seeks to describe the world in a series of universal causal laws related to the operations of social facts; and (5) this science considers that human behaviour is objectively and quantitatively measurable through methods such as experiments and survey research.

One of the most influential contributions to medical sociology from a structural-functional point of view is Talcott Parsons's work on the **sick role** (Parsons, 1951, pp. 428–79). To understand Parsons's concept of a sick role, it is necessary to think that each individual plays a number of roles in society. Roles are linked to norms. Roles and norms arise out of the institutions with which the individual is associated. An individual may play a variety of work roles, community roles, family roles, friendship roles, and so on. All roles reflect something of the intermeshing of the individual in society and are guided by behavioural norms. The idea of role is pivotal for conceptualizing the relationship between the individual and society in structural functionalism.

Parsons's main concern was to describe the processes that maintain societal institutions and thus the stable workings of society. His notion of the sick role should be looked at in this context. Sickness, if not somehow integrated into social institutions, could lead to societal breakdown. This would result from the inability of the sick to fulfill their necessary social roles. Therefore sickness must be managed, and must be accorded a special position. However, this sick role legitimation is only temporary and is contingent on the fulfillment of certain obligations by the individual who claims the sick role. The sick role has four components. The first two are rights; the second two are duties. Both the rights and duties of the sick role must be fulfilled if the equilibrium of society is to be maintained.

(1) The sick person is exempt from "normal" social roles.

The truly sick individual has a legitimate excuse for missing an exam or a major presentation at work, for staying in bed all day and neglecting household chores, or for staying home from work. In order to win exemption, the individual may need formal, medical acknowledgement. The sick person may have to obtain an official diagnosis and even a medical certificate as proof of illness. Exemptions from examinations, for instance, generally require a formal written note from a physician.

(2) The sick person is not responsible for his or her condition.

The sickness must be the result of circumstances beyond the control of the individual if that person is to be accorded the sick role. Thus, the individual is not to be blamed or punished. Influenza, a cold, and a broken leg are usually considered the results of misfortune, not of personal will or desire. Therefore, sympathy rather than blame is considered the appropriate reaction of others.

(3) The sick person should try to get well.

The sick role exemption is only temporary. The person who is given the legitimacy of the sick role is duty bound to try to get well. If an individual does not want to get well or does not try to get well, then the sick role is no longer considered legitimate. Thus, if a person has received a diagnosis of pneumonia, he or she must do what the doctor orders. If not, the legitimacy of the sick role deteriorates into the shame of such a label as "foolish," "careless," "immoral," or a "malingerer."

(4) The sick person should seek technically competent help and co-operate with the physician.

The duties associated with the sick role also require that the ill person seek "appropriate" medical attention and comply with the treatment provided.

For example, a person with HIV/AIDS or another sexually transmitted infection who refuses both to accept medical care and to change certain sexual interactions would not be accorded the rights of the sick role and could be subject to legal punishment.

From the viewpoint of Parsons, illness is a form of deviance. It is a potential threat to the ongoing social system unless it is managed for its benefit. Medicine is the institution responsible for providing legitimation. It is also responsible for bringing the sick back to wellness or "normality." Medical institutions can be seen as agents of social control in much the same way as are religious institutions and the criminal justice system.

Parsons's formulation of the sick role was primarily theoretical: it was not based on extensive systematic empirical investigation. Empirical analysis subjects his definition of the sick role to a number of criticisms. A few of these criticisms will be examined in the following sections.

(1) The sick person is exempt from "normal" social roles.

The extent to which a person is allowed exemption depends on the nature, severity, and longevity of the sickness, and also on the characteristics and normal social roles of the person. A short and self-limiting burn on the fingers merits only temporary, minimal exemptions from life roles. On the other hand, multiple sclerosis, a chronic, degenerative, and usually progressive disease, allows extensive exemptions.

The university student's sick role is mostly informal. Usually sick role exemption is not required. Most professors do not take attendance; students can avoid the library for weeks on end without any official notice being taken. They can stay in bed half the day and stay out half the night. These things are the student's own responsibility. It is only at the time of regularly scheduled deadlines for papers, presentations, and examinations that universities typically take any official notice of the student's actions. At these times the student may need to adopt the sick role formally by obtaining official legitimation from a physician through a note.

(2) The sick person is not responsible for her or his condition.

This belief varies depending on the nature of the condition and the circumstances through which the person is believed to have acquired the condition. The sick person may be held responsible for having a cold, for instance, if he or she stayed out overnight and walked miles in the freezing rain without a jacket. The notion of stress that is prevalent today often has an aspect of blame attached to it—that is, people who succumb to disease because they have overworked or worried may be chastised for having failed to take preventive action. One of the implications, in fact, of the recent emphasis on health promotion through lifestyle change (moderating the amount of physical exercise undertaken, and so on) is that people who do not change and become more active may be more likely to be held responsible and blamed for any diseases with which they later are diagnosed. For example, the person with AIDS may be blamed for disease because of his or her sexual habits or intravenous drug use. A number of different diseases are thought to reflect on the moral and social worth of the individual, and when an individual succumbs to these diseases he or she may be blamed according to the degree of social **stigma** (Goffman, 1963) attached to the condition.

Even though the specific causes of particular cancers are not known, the person with the disease is sometimes blamed for receiving a cancer diagnosis. For instance, the person with lung cancer may be held responsible if he or she has smoked or still smokes. Crandall and Moriarty (1995) asked people to examine case histories representing 66 illnesses and to rate the illnesses according to a number of dimensions. They found that the diseases most likely to lead to social rejection, i.e., to be stigmatized, were those (1) that were believed to be under personal onset control and (2) that were most severe. They did not find that gender, age, or ethnicity had an impact on the stigma associated with different diseases. Today, ironically, sometimes a cancer diagnosis may be associated with a positive stigma. It may seem almost a badge of honour and an opportunity for "growth" (Seale, 2001). In fact, many think that breast cancer ought to be an occasion to learn and practise "optimism" (Ehrenreich, 2009). It is used as a marketing ploy (King, 2006). Prostate cancer has spawned its own celebratory marketing through the November growth of moustaches among millions of men for the "Movember" fundraising movement. Over the last decade a number of different identities and reconfigured identities have been associated with cancer and its meaning to those diagnosed (Kerr et al., 2018). Some of these, such as pancreatic cancer, likely reflect neutrally on the person and others may reflect positively or negatively.

(3) The sick person should want to get well.

This is only true if the sick person is not diagnosed as terminal or chronically ill. People are expected to adjust to such illnesses, not to seek healing. In fact, if people continue to want to get well when they have been thus diagnosed, they are often criticized and possibly even diagnosed with a mental illness because they may be said to be denying reality. Similarly, people with a whole range of chronic illnesses are not expected to want to get well, but rather to adapt to and cope with daily limitations and challenges.

(4) The sick person should seek technically competent help and co-operate with the physician.

The dominant medical care system is that of **allopathic medicine**, which treats disease by trying to create a condition in the body that is opposite to or incompatible with the disease state. While this conventional medical care system still claims a monopoly and governmental support for the right to provide treatment and thus to legitimate sickness, there are competing medical systems with varying and possibly growing degrees of popular legitimacy. A significant proportion of Canadians use alternative health-care providers. This includes those who have used self-help and complementary and alternative medicines (CAMS), such as meditation, herbs, vitamins and minerals, music therapy, or yoga, for their health. Moreover, allopathic medical practice is the subject of growing critique by a variety of consumer interest groups (see Breggin, 2014, for ongoing opposition to the **pharmaceuticalization** of children's mental health issues). The anti-vaccine or "anti-vax"movement, which the World Health Organization has named one of the biggest global threats to health in the future, may reflect a growing popular skepticism about conventional medicine (Ryan, 2019). Near-universal social media availability can provide an additional impetus for the rapid growth of such movements. Critical evaluations of such things as unnecessary surgery, side effects from taking prescribed drugs, and unnecessary medical intervention in childbirth raise the real possibility for many critics that care from a physician may not always be the most effectual road to good health. In the case of childbirth, for instance, there seems to have been a fairly drastic shift in Canada away from dependence on medical doctors, including specialist obstetricians/gynecologists, towards the wide acceptance of midwifery for childbirth. This is evident in state funding for midwifery since 1994 (Kaufman, 1998).

Parsons was the first to note explicitly that there are ways in which medical practice, its ideology, and its associated medical institutions serve to fulfill social control functions for the society. The concept of medicalization, which will be discussed later, has been used to describe this process.

While **positivism** is the research methodology most closely associated with the structural-functional perspective, not all positivists are structural functionalists. Contemporary positivists study human health behaviours as both **independent** and **dependent variables**. An examination of the impact of a diagnosis, e.g., of cystic fibrosis, on the family of the ill person treats health behaviour related to the diagnosis as the independent variable. On the other hand, when the impact of income level on the **incidence** of disease is studied, human health behaviour becomes the dependent variable.

Today, positivists, following Durkheim, assume that the social has a constraining impact on individuals. Social-structural positions (social facts) determine individual thoughts, behaviours, feelings, and, in this case, ideas about health and illness, medical utilization, and so on. Research along these lines examines the effects of such things as gender, race, class, educational level, family type, marital status, age, rural/urban background, religious affiliation, religiosity, and political ideology on such (dependent) health-related variables as disease and death rates, prevention activities, and utilization of medical care. The **social determinants of health** perspective is a contemporary illustration of this methodology because it examines the impact of social inequities on health outcomes (see Chapters 4 and 5 for examples of this type of research).

The methodological assumptions of positivist social science are outlined in Table 1.3.

Conflict Theory

Conflict theory has had a somewhat less dominant role in the development of sociology in North America. It has provided a radical critique of the more conservative aspects of structural-functional sociology and of the economic and social arrangements found in society. In **conflict theory**, all social arrangements, all sociological theories, and all sociological methods have political and economic bases and consequences. Traditional conflict theory tends to focus on class- or economic-based power relations and dynamics. Research topics, methodological approaches, and commitment to the use of findings are all said to reflect the political and economic interests of the researcher.

The model of this paradigm is the work of Karl Marx (1818–83). Marx was directly involved in the

Table 1.3	Methodological Assumptions of Positivist Social Science
Objectivity	Social science can be as objective as physical science and should be modelled on the physical sciences.
Generalizability	One of the most important goals of social science is to generalize and thereby to describe the world in a series of "if x then y" causal laws.
Validity: Construct	It is possible to design measures that accurately and briefly describe sociological concepts.
Validity: Internal	It is possible in any social scientific research design to say with a degree of surety that "x" is the probable cause of "y."
Validity: External	It is possible to select a sample so that generalization from the sample to the total population is accurate with a known but limited amount of error.
Reliability	It is possible for the same research to be completed in different settings and by different researchers and with essentially the same findings.
Causality	It is possible to demonstrate probable causal relationships between social science variables.
Adequacy	The data collected adequately describe and explain the phenomenon under investigation.
Data Collection Strategies	The usual data collection strategy involves survey research with either a questionnaire or an interview, administered either in person or over the telephone. Experimental laboratory research is sometimes done.
Quantification	Sociological phenomena can be quantified in statistical data.
Probability	Analysis is based on assumptions of probability, not determinism, i.e., hypotheses are put forward as possibilities.

analysis of and the organization for changes in his society. The author of numerous books, he was the leader of the First Communist International in Europe during the nineteenth century, and was also a busy and effective investigative journalist. He asserted that human thought and behaviour were the result of socio-economic relations, and that both were alterable for human and social betterment. Believing that human beings could change their social order, Marx worked towards human liberation through a social and economic revolution.

Society, according to Marx, has historically been composed of a constantly varying balance of opposite forces that generate change through their ongoing struggle. The motivating force behind this continuous struggle is the way in which people interact with one another as they attempt to obtain their livelihood. Marx described the various modes of production with their corresponding types of social relations that occurred in consecutive historical periods as a struggle between classes. The class struggle is related to the means of production, e.g., the land or the factory, because members of one class own the means of production and members of the other class sell their labour for goods and services and cash. For Marx, an end to conflict was both possible and desirable and would happen in a communist state in which all citizens owned the means of production.

In doing sociology, conflict theorists use information from a variety of sources, but it tends to be historical and critical. As with structural functionalism, the level of analysis is the social system, because ultimately the system must be changed and a new one established. What is distinct about some conflict theorists is that they may also be highly political and social activists. Some see injustice everywhere, and try to alleviate it.

Conflict theory can be distinguished in the following ways: (1) the sociologist's work is to discover and document injustice (and sometimes to attempt to change it); (2) all knowledge is rooted in social, material, and historical contexts; and (3) sociological research methods must acknowledge social, economic, and historical circumstances.

When the conflict theorist is particularly influenced by Marx's analysis, the primary subject of study is social classes, because they are thought of as the most important means to effect change.

Sociology from the perspective of conflict theory involves the documentation of injustice for the purpose of understanding its origins and causes in a historical and socio-political context. Social class and social injustice are everywhere, and medical institutions and patterns of disease and death are no exception.

A long tradition of scholarship documents the ways in which health and illness are related to unequal social arrangements. Marx's collaborator, Friedrich Engels, in *The Condition of Working Class in England* (1845), showed how the working and living conditions that resulted from early capitalist production had negative health effects. Engels described how capitalism introduced mechanization on farms, resulting in a mass of unemployed rural workers who were forced to migrate to the cities to make a living. Capitalists in the city, driven to make a profit, kept their labour costs low, and thus the working classes could afford only very cheap shelter and food. The great slums that resulted were the perfect breeding grounds for the diseases endemic to such living conditions, including rickets, tuberculosis, typhoid, scrofula, and other infectious diseases. Thus, ill health was related to the living conditions of the working class and the material conditions of capitalism.

More than a century and a half later, advanced monopoly capitalism, globalization, and neo-liberalism (O'Connor, 1973; Turner, 1987; De Vogli, 2011) have generated considerably different but equally inhumane working conditions for workers and their families around the globe. Under neo-liberalism, inequality has widened in the developed world (Heisz, 2015). The share of income, beginning in the 1980s, has grown especially rapidly among the top 1 per cent of the population. By 2000, the gap between the top 1 per cent of income acquirers and the rest of the population was larger than at any time since the 1930s (Heisz, 2015). Inequity, as evident in the disparities in income, is reflected in mortality and morbidity statistics and in corresponding standards of living around the globe. Contemporary capitalism is dominated by huge international corporations such as, among the top 10, Walmart, BP (British Petroleum), Volkswagen, Exxon Mobil, Berkshire Hathaway, and China National Petroleum (see Fortune Global, 2019). These huge companies are characterized by strategies designed to provide large shareholder profits rather than to satisfy workers. Strategies include enlarging profits through increased worker productivity and new time-saving technologies, and moving from developed into less-developed countries both for cheaper wages and production costs and for new markets. As a result, a perpetual contradiction pits the needs of the workers—for a good living wage, good working conditions, adequate time for rest and relaxation, and meaningful, satisfying, and predictable work (all of which are prerequisites to ongoing good health)—against the needs or desires of the capitalists for continuous expansion and profit. This trend has also hit universities in Canada, which increasingly are relying on part-time instructors who are easily replaceable and non-tenured, and are paid considerably less. Thus, the "gig" economy has entered academe. The mental and physical health consequences of such insecure labour for the temporary labour force, including part-time university instructors, are often considerable.

Vincente Navarro (1976) has been one of the foremost conflict theorists of medical sociology in the context of the United States. He explains that there is a contradictory relationship between capitalism, which is an economic system fuelled by the profit motive, and the health needs of the population. Often, the perceived need to make a profit requires that workers labour, live, and eat in unhealthy and unsafe environments. The manufacture, sale, and tax level of cigarettes around the world illustrate how the desire for corporate profits and state tax revenues may outweigh the desire for good health for a population. For example, we are more likely to be warned about the dangers of terrorism than of cigarette smoking. Think of what you hear on the news about the threat of international terrorism as compared to cigarette smoking. The Global Terrorism Database as maintained by the US Department of Homeland Security listed the number of deaths globally due to terrorism in 2012–13 at 20,432. Cigarette smoking kills about 7 million people annually according to the World Health Organization (2018).

The tobacco industry has maintained a successful profit margin by opening up new markets in spite of anti-smoking sentiments and increasingly restrictive legislation on the marketing, sale, and packaging of tobacco products. In Canada, for example, the market has expanded into the younger age groups and women (Weeks, 2014; Begley, 2014). Though laws prohibit the sale of cigarettes to people under 18 (Abedi, 2017), they are rarely enforced, and even when they are enforced the fines for retailers are so low that they are virtually useless. Mini-cigars, flavoured as candy and lacking any warning labels, are one of the latest attempts to make inroads into the youth market (Begley, 2014). Vaping is sometimes used by smokers as a way of maintaining the smoking habit. Some states in the US have increased to 21 years old the age at which smoking is legal in an effort to diminish the number of deaths from tobacco smoking (Abedi, 2017). However, as the overall rates of cigarette smoking are declining in the developed world, until recently the rates had been rapidly increasing in developing countries around the globe. Even today, according to the World Health Organization, the rates are continuing to increase in the Mediterranean and African regions (WHO, 2018). Now almost 80 per cent of the world's smokers live in middle- and lower-income countries, according to the WHO.

There are two main goals of contemporary capitalism: the concentration and protection of capital and the deployment of the state by capitalists to ensure protection is in place. The state intervenes in the health sector in several ways to promote capitalist goals. First, the class structures of society are reproduced within the medical sector, so that the hierarchical distribution of functions and responsibilities of occupational groups within the medical care system mirrors the class, ethnic, and gender hierarchies within the other sectors of capitalist society. Second, the medical system has adopted a bourgeois ideology of medicine that regards both the cause and the cure of illness as the responsibility of the individual. Health itself has become a commodity with a certain value within the marketplace. The medical model is a politically conservative model; it directs attention away from the social-structural causes of ill health, such as gender, racialization, class, occupation, income, and environmental degradation. Third, the state supports alienation when it is costly for people to choose alternatives to conventional physicians, such as chiropractors, naturopaths, masseuses, or dieticians. The state provides full financial support for only one type of medical service—that provided by the allopathic practitioner. Today, with globalization, many would argue that states have actually given away much of their power of governance to international capital through multinational corporations such as the pharmaceutical and medical technologies industries. This has resulted in innumerable threats to health and well-being (De Vogli, 2011).

The state also uses strategies to exclude conflicting ideologies from debate and discussion. One example is the emphasis on individual and family (primarily maternal) responsibility in the causation of disease, in promoting early detection practices (such as mammograms), and in health-promoting behaviours. Such viewpoints exclude analysis of the processes through which class origins, environmental pollutants, occupational hazards, and working conditions are significant causes of ill health *Women, Health and the Family* (1984) illustrates research in the conflict perspective. Although Graham's research was carried out in Great Britain a number of decades ago, it continues to raise questions for all societies regarding the significant home health-care work that women, in particular, are expected to do for the state—with no compensation. This invisible work continues today. Policies supporting home health-care leave have not been adequately developed in Canada, and the definitions of home health work vary widely across the country (Johnson et al., 2017).

Graham demonstrates how the class position of the family is reinforced in the home health-care work done by mothers. She analyzes the impact of poverty on the availability of fundamental resources such as transportation, housing, fuel, food, and health care in the home, and notes that the relative lack of such resources has negative effects on the health status of family members.

Home health-care work is composed of four elements. First is the provision of healthy conditions in the home. This involves the maintenance of a warm and clean home with sufficient space for rest and relaxation for all family members, sufficient and adequately nutritious foods, and clean water. Home health care also involves managing social relations and meeting emotional needs for the optimal mental health of family members. The second element is nursing the sick: much of the work of caring for the sick child or adult, and for elderly or disabled people, falls on the shoulders of the women in the home. Furthermore, increasing deinstitutionalization of the mentally, chronically, and acutely ill increases the level of intra-family responsibility. Nursing the sick is often a very time-consuming and exhausting job. It involves sleepless nights, heavy lifting, preparation of complicated menus, administering medicines, coping with bandages, and the like. A third element is teaching about health, including such things as modelling good health habits and giving instruction on diet, hygiene, and exercise. The fourth and final aspect of home health-care work is mediating with outsiders such as doctors and hospitals, making visits to clinics, talking with a social or public health worker, or getting advice from an expert in a health-related area, such as nutrition. The hidden health-care work of women continues today in Canada and elsewhere. It reinforces gender inequality.

Graham also documents the existence of class differences in home health-care work and in associated mortality and morbidity rates. She notes the consistently inverse relationship between class and some of the most sensitive indicators of a nation's health: stillbirths, prenatal mortality, neonatal mortality, postnatal mortality, and infant mortality rates. These class differences in outcomes among infants are mirrored in the morbidity statistics for children and adults. Accidents, the largest single cause of childhood death, are probably one of the best indicators of an unsafe, inadequately supervised environment: the accident rate increases sharply among the lower social classes. Kronenfeld et al. (1997), using a survey research methodology with a sample of 1,247 young mothers, found that such parental resources as income and education were associated with better safety practices in respect to their children. Higher income was positively associated with safety behaviours such as not leaving a child alone in the house, not hiring babysitters younger than 13 years of age, not leaving a child alone in the bathtub, using an approved car seat, and a child's wearing a safety helmet while bicycling. Poorer families were more likely to suffer from other environmentally related causes of the death of children, such as respiratory diseases. The incidence of infections and parasitic illnesses is also class-related. There is evidence that the mortality rate for some childhood cancer is inversely related to class (de Kok et al., 2008). Traffic accidents involving children are associated with class and neighbourhood (Haynes et al., 2008). Poverty is also related to mental health in children (Strohschein & Gauthier, 2017)

Samuel S. Epstein (1998) is an epidemiologist with an expertise and a lengthy list of publications on the occupational and environmental causes of cancer. In an analysis of the policies of the National Cancer Institute (NCI) he drew our attention many years ago to conflicts of interest in medical practice and the funding of health-care organizations. He was one of the first critical analysts to document the high incidence of preventable cancer deaths and the minimal research investment of the NCI in understanding these preventable deaths. More recently, Devra Davis (2007) provided a critical historical overview of the so-called "war on cancer," which was started in the US by President Nixon in the 1970s. She documented how the "war" was plagued by ongoing conflict of interest among cancer policy-makers because of their roles as directors in other industries that were either known to or thought to cause cancer. For instance, she showed how the leaders of industry who were responsible for the manufacture, advertising, and sale of cancer-causing products such as cigarettes were also in positions of power in the supposed fight against cancer. These leaders clearly paid lip service to the eradication of cancer even while they fought to suppress the scientific evidence of many of its fundamental causes. For example, she stated: "Some of the early leaders of the American Cancer Society and the National Cancer Institute left their posts to work directly for the tobacco industry . . . they were hired to generate uncertainty about the association between tobacco and lung cancer" (Davis, 2007, p. xv). Davis also documented how the media presentations of public research and information about trendy new products obfuscate the potential threats of some contemporary commodities such as cosmetics and other personal care merchandise, pharmaceuticals such as Ritalin, the sugar-free sweetener aspartame, and cell phones. Davis has been trying to warn people that while the data are not all in yet, the idea that cell phones are bad for the brain should not be ignored. Meanwhile the National Cancer Institute continues to argue that the research on this link is inconclusive. In a situation in which there are powerful interests in support of such new technologies, caution in their endorsement is important. This stand on the careful and reluctant adoption of new technologies until they are proven safe is called the **precautionary principle**.

Cancer rates are significantly higher among poorer people because of their relative food insecurity, smoking rates, obesity, lesser physical activity, and lack of access to good medical care (O'Connor & Gross, 2018). The strongest individual causal connector is food security. There are innumerable complex social and economic causes, too. Thus, regions with the highest cancer mortality rates can have as high as seven times the cancer incidence of those with the lowest rates. However, cancer prevention itself is also heavily medicalized and biomedicalized. Prevention is widely understood to be early detection via such measures as mammograms, hormone replacements (HRT), and mandated HPV vaccinations, for example. Early detection technologies are aspects of medicine. They reflect medicalization. They are not and should not be thought of as prevention. This link conflates two processes that should be distinguished one from another. Moreover, research has found that the safety and effectiveness of such early detection interventions as mammograms and HRT are equivocal and may cause disease at times and unnecessary anxiety in the face of false positives at other times. The fact that doctors may be financially invested in these technologies is also problematic. The guidelines for some of these early detection strategies are not perfect. For instance, there are new guidelines for mammography screening from a required frequency, depending on age, to women's choice (Ubelacker, 2018). Such change in health policy reminds us again that scientific findings are always in process and that scientific truth is based on probability, not certainty. One additional example of the uncertainty of some medical interventions is the growing evidence that many medical devices implanted into Canadians have safety risks (McClean & Cribb, 2018).

In contrast to the emphasis on early detection, there is a relative lack of emphasis on research on prevention. For example, a vanishingly small amount of the money that goes to investigating cancer in either children and adolescents or adults is dedicated to prevention. Possible environmental causes of cancer, such as pesticides and herbicides, are seldom a research focus. Treatment and biology receive the greatest proportion of the financial investment in cancer research (see Table 1.4).

Samantha King (2006) has documented how popular breast cancer activism has often led to an obfuscation of the links between the economy, the environment, and breast cancer. She argues that one of the ways this happens is through products advertised as leading to the eradication or minimization of a particular problem. This type of marketing essentially obscures the responsibility of governments for caring for their citizens and intervening for prevention. It encourages people to buy products through advertising the association between the philanthropic activities of the business and the disease. Such an emphasis can disguise the disease-causing effects of the products being advertised. For example, the Look Good . . . Feel Better campaign dedicated to "makeovers" for women with cancer is used to advertise cosmetics and other products, some of which have carcinogenic properties. The dominance of such fundraising strategies supports the neo-liberalism and **privatization** that characterize the modern economy, including its valorization of the market along with individual responsibility or "responsibilization."

The methodological assumptions of conflict theory are shown in Table 1.5.

Interpretive/Social Constructionist Theory

What is the meaning of illness? Does cancer have the same meaningful impact when it happens to an 80-year-old adult as when a 10-year-old child is diagnosed? What are the processes through which the slow onset of Alzheimer's comes to be noted by family, friends, and the patient? How do families work through their changing understanding of the uncertainty and then the certainty of the death of one of their members? How does the self-identity of the person with AIDS alter once he or she has received the diagnosis? How do others alter the ways they relate to the person with AIDS? These are the sorts of questions asked by those who study health and illness issues from the perspective of **interpretive/social constructionist theory**, which is sometimes known a **symbolic interactionist theory**.

Max Weber provided a definition of sociology from this perspective: "a science which attempts the interpretive understanding of social action in order thereby to arrive at a causal explanation of its course and its effects" (Weber, 1947, p. 88). There are two crucial elements in this statement, each of which exemplifies an aspect of Weber's work. First, social action, as defined by Weber, meant action to which the individual attached subjective meaning. Second, the sociologist, while looking for what Weber calls causal explanation, was actually directed to interpret empathetically the meaning of a situation from the viewpoint of the subject.

Table 1.4   Values about Cancer Research Funding by Common Scientific Outline (CSO) Categories

No. crt	Authors	Publication Year	Region/Year	CSO categories						
				Cancer Biology (%)	Etiology (%)	Prevention (%)	Early Detection, Diagnosis, Prognosis (%)	Treatment (%)	Cancer Control (%)	Scientific Model Systems (%)
1	S. Eckhouse & R. Sullivan	2006	EU / 2002–3	41	14	4	9	20	5	6
			USA / 2002–3	25	17	9	12	25		3
2	N. Shiraze et al.	2011	Western Australia / 2008–10	40	6	6	8	23	12	5
3	Canadian Cancer Research Alliance	2014	Canada / 2005	43	11	2	10	24	8	1
			Canada / 2011	30	14	2	14	30	10	<1
4	C. Gotay	2012	Canada / 2005	43.1	11.3	1.7	10.5	24.5	8.1	0.8
			Canada / 2010	31.5	13.3	2.6	12.3	29.8	10.3	0.2
5	International Cancer Research Partnership	2012	Global level / 2005	22.1	17.9	7.9	11.9	25.9	10.5	3.8
			Global level / 2008	24.9	13.8	6.8	13.3	26.7	10.5	3.9
6	S. Eckhouse et al.	2008	Europe / fiscal year 2002–3	41	14	4	10	20	5	6
			USA / fiscal year 2002–3	25	17	9	12	25	9	3
			Canada / fiscal year 2004–5	45	10	2	8	22		1
7	Canadian Cancer Research Alliance	2012	Canada / 2005	42.9	11.4	1.7	10.5	24.5	8.1	0.9
			Canada / 2009	32.9	12.4	2.5	13.4	28.2	10.2	0.3
8	Cancer Australia	2014	Australia / 2003–5	51	7	5	8	19	9	1
			Australia / 2006–8	38	10	2	13	27	7	3
			Australia / 2009–11	32	8	2	16	28	9	4
			Australia / 2006–11	35	9	2	15	28	8	4
			Canada / 2006–11	36	12	2	13	27	10	<1
			UK / 2006–11	41	10	3	11	25	6	3
9	Institute National du Cancer	2010	France / 2009	24.29	5.34	0.09	24.3	34.72	9.25	2.01

Source: Matei et al. (2015, pp. 9–11).

Table 1.5   Methodological Assumptions of Conflict Theory Social Science

Value Commitment	Rather than seeking objectivity, the conflict theorist believes that sociologists must discover, document, and record recurrent patterns and dynamics of power/class/gendered/racialized relations both because they have no choice (members of a society are committed to the ongoing action of the society) and because they believe that this is the morally correct position.
Historical Specificity	Rather than looking for generalizations, conflict theorists assert the necessity of understanding the unique features of the particular situation in its socio-historical context as an example of these recurrent patterns of power/class/gendered/racialized relations.
Validity: Construct	Formal tests of validity are considered irrelevant. Researchers, it is assumed, of necessity and because of political commitment study what they claim they are studying.
Validity: Internal	Formal statistical tests of causal relationships are not always necessary. Rather, logical meaningfulness may be the relevant criterion of causality.
Validity: External	The conflict theorist assumes that inequities based on power/class/gender/racialization relations are ubiquitous, yet analyzes the components separately in each historical situation.
Ethical Concerns	The primary importance in the research of the conflict theorist is the commitment to such ethical and humanitarian principles as justice and equality.
Data Collection	The usual sources of data are historical documents. As well, the conflict theorist may use other data collection methods, including surveys, statistical data, and methods such as unstructured interviews and participant observation that provide subjective and descriptive data.
Objectivity	Objectivity is not possible. Knowledge cannot be separated from the power/class/gender relations of the researcher and the subjects.
Quantification	While numerical data may be used to document an argument, they are not always available.

Interpretive sociologists study how the subjective definitions of social reality are constructed and how this reality is experienced and described by the social actors. Human beings create their social worlds. As W.I. Thomas said, if a situation is defined as real, it is real in its consequences (Martindale, 1960, pp. 347–53).

The paradox here is that, just as the subjects who are being studied are busy defining reality for themselves, so, too, are the researchers. Thus, the interpretive theorist is faced with the problem, when collecting data, of intersubjectivity or reflexivity, that is, that the data are given a subjective slant both by the people being studied and by the researcher. Furthermore, the research act itself creates and changes meanings and processes. From the perspective of interpretive theorists it is impossible to gather objective data. All social reality is subjectively defined and experienced and can be studied only through the interactive subjective processes of social researchers.

Empathetic understanding, or what has sometimes come to be called, following Weber, *vestehen*, is the desirable methodological stance of the researcher. Generally, sociologists adopting this stance collect data by observing social action in close participation with the subjects or by long, unstructured interviews. The level of analysis is not of the system but rather of individual interaction with others, the mind or the self, and meaning.

This is microanalysis. The structural-functional and conflict theories, because they focus on systems, are macro analyses.

Three assumptions are characteristic of this perspective: (1) sociology is a science, the purpose of which is to understand the social meanings of human social action and interaction; (2) reflexivity or intersubjectivity, rather than objectivity or critical analysis, characterizes the relationship between the subject and the researcher; and (3) rich, carefully detailed description and analysis of unique social situations from the perspective of the subjects under investigation are typical of interpretive research.

The sociological problem to be understood and explained in the interpretive tradition is the meaning that individuals see in the actions of themselves, of others, of institutions, and so on (Weber, 1968). Analysis of society demands different methods from those used to describe and explain the natural world. It requires methods that attempt to grasp the motives and meanings of social acts. Sociology is a science that must deal with the subjective meanings of events to social actors.

A classic and historical example of work in this perspective is the study of the meaning of the diagnosis of epilepsy within the lives of a sample of people with this disease. *Having Epilepsy* (Schneider and Conrad, 1983) is based on long, semi-structured interviews with a number of people who have been diagnosed with epilepsy. The authors make the point that it is important that sociologists provide an antidote to medical research. It is crucial, they note, to distinguish between disease and illness. Disease is the pathology of the human body; illness is the meaning of the experience associated with a given pathology. In this research the subjects were selected for study because they have an epilepsy diagnosis. However, they live most of the time without the symptoms of the disorder being present. They go about their daily activities, eating, dressing, working, cooking, cleaning, visiting, enjoying leisure and social activities, unrestrained and unconstrained by an awareness of their disease.

Medicine attempts to understand the nature and cause of disease and to formulate methods for its treatment. One of the tasks of the sociologist is to describe the impact of disease and diagnosis on the individual's self and on his or her relationships with others. As Schneider and Conrad (1983, p. 205) say: "We cannot understand illness experiences by studying disease alone, for disease refers merely to the undesirable changes in the body. Illness, however, is primarily about social meanings, experiences, relationships, and conduct that exist around putative disease."

Schneider and Conrad suggest that one of the most pervasive aspects of epilepsy is a continuing sense of **uncertainty**. From the earliest stages of pre-diagnosis and throughout the illness, a sense of uncertainty is a defining quality of this and many other chronic conditions. People with epilepsy, like those with Alzheimer's disease, diabetes, or multiple sclerosis (just a few of the chronic conditions to which this analysis is relevant), at first wonder what is happening to their bodies or their minds. They wonder whether or not to take this or that small sign of change as a symptom of a disease. They wonder whether it is a symptom of a serious or a minor issue. At this stage people generally normalize their symptoms.

Once diagnosed, they wonder how severe their illness will become and whether they will live for long or only for a short time. They ask whether they will be seriously debilitated or only mildly affected. Each day is different. Planning the next day or the next week may be fraught. Relationships are altered. Others respond to this sense of uncertainty with their own confusion about the disorder and its likely course. Not only does relating to the self become tinged with ambiguity arising from dealing with constant change, but commitments to others also become difficult. The lack of easy, honest, open, and straightforward communication is frequently seen as one of the most painful aspects of the disorder. Cancer patients, for instance, have said that the difficulties of communication are frequently even more painful than the disease or its treatment (Dunkel-Schetter & Wortman, 1982). Arthur Frank (1991) has noted how we now live in a **remission society** because of the ongoing sense held by so many people who have lived through serious diagnoses that anything can happen and the disease or another just like it may (re)occur. It takes a long while for people who have survived some serious disease to feel "normal" again—if they ever do. Conceptualizing life after diagnosis and treatment in terms of the five-year survival rate adds to this continuous uncertainty for people in the remission society. As blogger BCBecky explains, "I shall never not be a cancer survivor. Breast cancer is a sickness that will always be part of my identity, regardless of how healthy I am at any given moment" (BCBecky, 2017).

Another source of uncertainty surrounding some chronic illnesses is the fact that many are poorly understood by the medical profession and by the lay public, including those diagnosed. There is a general lack of knowledge about the probable prognosis of some chronic illnesses. Some chronic diseases receive a considerable amount of press; others receive very little. Some are well recognized by the lay public; most are not. Some have been diagnosable for many, many years. Others, such as fibromyalgia and chronic fatigue syndrome, seem to be new and growing diagnoses. For some, particularly the norms of possible remissions, plateaus, and disease exacerbations have long been charted. The short history of others means few standards for what to expect.

Epilepsy is a disease with a long history. It has often been thought to reflect not just the state of the physical body, but also the moral character of the person. At times the person with epilepsy has been considered to be divine, at other times satanic. At various times and places seizures have been understood as signs both of prophetic ability and of madness.

Chronic illness requires symptom control. This is particularly necessary when the symptoms can be highly disruptive, as in diabetes, which can exhibit diabetic reaction or coma; or in colitis, which may involve unexpected evacuation; or in epilepsy, if there is a grand mal seizure. Symptom control can involve following the doctor's orders.

It can also involve non-medical procedures such as biofeedback, hypnosis, diet change, meditation, exercise, relaxation, vitamin therapy, and others. Managing medical regimens does not necessarily mean following the medical rules. Instead, people often manage their medicines according to their own values, habits, activities, relationships, and side effects.

People with epilepsy control their drug use in such a way as to moderate the number and severity of seizures to a level with which they feel comfortable. Doctors' orders are only one of several sources of information upon which people with epilepsy choose to base their use of medication. Drug-use patterns develop as an outcome of a complex of self-perceived considerations such as (1) the meaning of the seizure to the subject, (2) the personal view of the effectiveness of the drug, (3) the personal estimation of the costs of side effects, (4) the desire to test whether the epilepsy is still present, (5) the wish to avoid having others recognize that one has epilepsy, and (6) the need to protect oneself from seizures in particular situations (Schneider & Conrad, 1983). Medication use is a social process and as such is vulnerable to the social needs and experiences of users. People then tend to interpret their illness meanings and adjust their drug regimen schedule to suit themselves.

The study of the meaning of illness is extensive today. For example, a great deal of study is occurring on how masculinities may be affecting the use of health care and the management of illness and disability. In some ways the very definition of hegemonic masculinity includes strength and action. It belies sickness and incapacity. The question asked in research by Flurey et al. (2018) is how men manage their identities when they are diagnosed with a disease that is not only more common among woman but is also defined by causing weakness and loss of, or painful, mobility. Flurey and colleagues found three typologies of response to the threat to masculinity posed by the diagnosis of arthritis. The first was characterized by retaining hegemonic masculinity, for example, by trying to continue in full-time work.

The second incorporated a negotiation with the concept of masculinity by adapting work hours and responsibilities but identifying masculinity as an ability to maintain an active social life, particularly with the male friends, and engaging in male activities such as motorcycling. The third group rejected hegemonic masculinity through retirement from work along with the maintenance of a slower pace of social life. Ask yourself, how do you think men deal with their masculinity when they are diagnosed with breast cancer as compared to prostate cancer? Or how do people change or adapt as they construct their identities after receiving a diagnosis of a sexually transmitted infection?

These are the sorts of questions that have motivated research in the social constructionist/interpretive tradition, the assumptions of which are outlined in Table 1.6.

The research of Flurey et al. (2018) exemplifies the interpretive approach to understanding behaviour in health and illness. Through the presentation of meaningful comments from the subjects interspersed with sociological analysis, the authors have provided a piece with empathetic relevance to others in similar health circumstances, to their families, to health-care workers who deal with people with such diagnoses, and to the academic sociological community.

Table 1.6   Methodological Assumptions of Interpretive/Social Constructionist Social Science

Reflexivity	Social researchers interpret the sayings and behaviour of their subjects from the subject's perspectives and within the context of the researcher's perspective. The researchers are affected by the needs and expectations of their subjects and the subjects' knowledge of the data collection process, and at the same time, they change the subjects' understanding. Thus, it is impossible to measure human social behaviour objectively.
Ethical Concerns	Just as it is impossible to study human social action as if it were the action of so many atoms, molecules, neutrons, and protons, so it is impossible not to change the social situation that is the subject of the analysis.
Generalizability	While the method of analytic induction, one of the operating logics of this perspective, claims universality, most research in this paradigm is based on the specificity of human social action.
Causality	Causality is recognized in this perspective as a subject of study, e.g., "I believe I have cancer because I sinned against God," rather than the "if x . . . then y" causality of positivism.
Proof	The most stringent criterion of proof is sometimes required within this perspective—negative case analysis.
Validity	Validity is always hampered by intersubjectivity, but the depth and detail of the description of the data and their "meanings" are considered important criteria.
Reliability	This is considered less important than validity because it is assumed that different researchers would be researching different situations and would therefore have (at least somewhat) different findings.
Scope of Analysis	The interpretive or symbolic interactionist sociologist is generally content to describe the social world of a small population of people in rich complexity and detail.
Advocacy	Some researchers who follow this methodological approach view their work as advocacy through giving voice to the voiceless or the unheard. Others fervently argue for the value of knowledge for its own sake.

Feminist and Critical Anti-Racist Theories

Feminist theory and feminist methods have grown rapidly in the past half-century. A number of journals in a wide variety of academic areas are now dedicated to feminist, women's, and men's studies and they abound in many fields of scholarship. The social sciences, in particular, have been challenged and critiqued as having been "male-stream" in subject matter, research strategies, and theoretical assumptions. Following in the wake of Betty Friedan's *The Feminine Mystique* (1963), the women's health movement can be seen as a major impetus to feminist scholarship and policy. The organization of women in the late sixties and seventies for abortion and other health-care reforms and the widespread prescription of the birth control pill were crucial steps in the second wave of the women's movement in the twentieth century. The women's health movement, as exemplified by such monumental publications as *Our Bodies, Our Selves* (Boston Women's Health Collective, 2011 [1971]), led to a radical critique of the patriarchal, allopathic medical care system and practice. The book was updated continuously until 2011 and online until 2018.

A major theme in a feminist analysis of health has been a criticism of the medicalization of women's lives. Much of this analysis has focused on the dominance of the medical care system, medical practitioners, and the medical constructions of knowledge and power over women, especially in regard to reproductive issues such as birth control and childbirth (Oakley, 1984), PMS (Pirie, 1988), and menopause (McCrea, 1983; Kaufert & Gilbert, 1987; Walters, 1991). Other feminist researchers have examined gender differences in disease and death as well as reactions to disease and interactions with the health-care system. A variety of theorists and researchers have explained how women's (poor) health is a result of social-structural inequities, such as class, racialization, participation in the labour force, or familial and domestic roles (Hankivsky et al., 2011). The work by Flurey et al. (2018) discussed in the previous section is an example of a "spin-off" of gender studies, i.e., men's studies, with a particular concern to understand men's lives, including their health and illness.

Today in Western democracies including Canada, sexuality, pregnancy, birth, and child-rearing are understood within the prisms of gender, knowledge, and power. All of these aspects of women's lives are subject to the risk-based, uncertainty characteristic of the political turn to the right along with neo-liberalism and gendered public health policies. Godderis (2010) shows how women's bodies and minds are increasingly likely to be subject to medicalization in areas related to reproduction, such as the period of time immediately after childbirth. In the 1960s some few women were thought to become depressed after childbirth. By the 1980s this experience acquired a name and a specific, serious, and much more common diagnosis of PPD or postpartum depression. This condition was situated as a disease that constituted one more instance of a greater proclivity for women's passage through formerly "normal" life stages to be accompanied by mental illness. Pre-menstrual syndrome was previously considered a variable experience that included a variety of personal challenges including acne, tiredness, and tender breasts. Through expanding medicalization it became a specific diagnosis (and with it came specific treatments) of premenstrual dysphoric disorder (PMDD). Further, according to Godderis (2010), the new diagnosis of PPD was linked to a continuum of suffering said to beset up to 92 per cent of women after they had given birth, including baby blues, postpartum depression, and, in the worst-case scenario, postpartum psychosis. The spread of the discourses surrounding these issues opens up new requirements for the surveillance or monitoring of women's bodies and minds during these life transitions. Having a baby has become a risky endeavour, as have many other public health concerns involving potential illness in the "risk society" (Beck, 1992). Ironically, too, much of the concern regarding the possibility of PPD focuses on the duty of mothers to "watch themselves and get help if they need it" for the sake of their children. Another women's issue, abortion may be the most controversial women's health issue today. Shepherd and Turner argue that it is over-medicalized to the detriment of women (2018), particularly poor women. Should abortion be allowed outside of the medical care system?

Today there is a prevailing dogma that breast-feeding is best for both mother and baby. It has been linked to better physical health for babies and to emotional health for mothers. Many women in the developed world have the sense that breast-feeding is a moral imperative (Crossley, 2009) and something they must do for the health of their babies. It is described as having benefits that will last a lifetime. But Crossley argues that this may be costly for both mothers and babies (Johnson, 2016). Colen and Ramsey (2014) studied 25 years of data from the National Longitudinal Study of Youth and found that the previously documented effects of breast-feeding were largely the result of selection pressures into breast-feeding due to socio-economic status and race differences. All but one of the previously accepted benefits of breast-feeding were found to be insignificant in case-controlled studies. Courtney Jung, in a book called *Lactivism* (2008), has argued that, to their emotional peril at times, women are subject to significant pressures to breast-feed their babies. This often leads to shame and suffering for those who cannot or do not want to breast-feed for one reason or another.

Critical anti-racist theory adds another important lens for understanding the social world of health and illness. It focuses on the fundamental significance of racialization (Sefa Dei, 1999). This theoretical position asserts that all knowledge is racialized and, filtered through a racialized lens, is associated with power and wealth. Individual identities around the globe are patterned by racism, just as they are by gender, class, and sexual identities. There is no objective truth outside of that which is constructed in the context of racism and corresponding inequality. In this context, power and dominance are gained by those who possess (or claim) knowledge because of their skin tone; and this knowledge effectively determines what people think, feel, believe, and so on. Colonialism has led to the hegemonic dominance of European/Western knowledge and thought processes. As Sefa Dei says, "there exists a racialised, gendered, sexualized, and classed discursive practice." In practice this means that, for example, black immigrants are 76 per cent more likely than other immigrant groups to consider themselves to be unhealthy (Nestel, 2012). Furthermore, racial status predicts health and health-care outcomes. For example, both black and Latino people with diabetes had poorer health outcomes over time than did other "race" groups (Nicklett, 2011). Veenstra (2017) found that black Canadians had more hypertension and poorer self-rated health than white Canadians.

Differences in health and health care mirror racial and other inequitable distinctions. Furthermore, how questions are asked, topics are chosen for consideration, and definitions of health and illness are created take place in the context of racism and are therefore are not objective.

All knowledge is questionable because of potentially racist assumptions. According to **intersectionality** theory it is crucial to move beyond attention to one variable (such as race or gender) at a time to a consideration of the dynamic interplay of multiple identities in the context of shifting powers (Hankivsky et al., 2011). From this point of view, none of us is merely "gendered" or "raced"; we also can—and must, for a good understanding of our health determinants and related health policy—be described in terms of our education, age, sexual identities, gender identities, "abilities," citizenship, and so on. However, from an activist's standpoint it is often best to focus on one oppressed status at a time. We will look at the health of people of First Nations status, along with other race-based analyses, at some length in Chapter 5. Racism continues to be a major source of inequity and consequent suffering throughout the life course. For instance, and as one example only, as I write this the news of the day is reporting that the likelihood of being shot by police is 20 times higher for black Canadians living in Toronto than for other citizens of the city (Branigan, 2018).

With the death of George Floyd in Minneapolis under the cruel knee of one   policeman with three police witnesses, and a number of phones set to videograph this atrocity, a world wide movement has started and continues. There are protests in the streets against police violence and against racism in countries around the world. The demand to "Defund the Police" has become a rallying cry and a symbol of the possibilities of restructuring societies so that they become more equitable, provide social services and income to the poorest among us. This is a cry against criminalization. It is a cry for racial

Table 1.7 Methodological Assumptions of Feminist and Critical Anti-Racist Theories in Social Science

Objectivity	It is impossible to be objective in social research. Therefore, it is important to be as clear as possible about the biases brought to any research study. The necessity for continuous reflexivity in research is acknowledged.
Generalizability	Class, gender, race, and power differences between researcher and subjects limit generalizability.
Subjectivity	Often focuses on women's experiences and those of racialized people and/or other marginalized viewpoints.
Subject Matter	Gender and race and other inequalities are always an important component of the investigations.
Language	Uses gender-neutral and non-racialized language where appropriate and specifies actual gender/race etc. when relevant.
Data Collection Methods	All methods are used but a collaborative approach between researcher and subjects of research is advocated. Triangulation is suggested.
Purpose	Feminist and anti-oppression anti-racist and intersectional research usually has change as one of its goals.

justice that began in the Unites States but resonates virtually everywhere.

Table 1.7 presents some of the methodological considerations for research from the theoretical perspectives of feminism, anti-racism, and intersectionality.

Post-Structuralism

A number of theorists are associated with the field now called **post-structuralism**, but the most influential for health and medical sociology is Michel Foucault. The work of Foucault both builds on and provides a radical reconsideration of the work exemplified by the perspectives described previously in this chapter. Rather than framing power or inequalities as structural forces that exist outside of some individuals who might have been called powerless, Foucault directs our attention to the ways that power is imbricated in mutual relations and infused by socially constructed knowledges and everyday micro practices supported by state policies and circulating discourses. One of the most important of these for our purposes is biopower. Biopower is Foucault's answer to how social control and power occur in bodies in modern

democratic and capitalist states. The population is controlled, in his view, by the government categorizing, counting, and developing policies related to managing "bodies" through "public health," science, and medicine. The medical or clinical gaze is part of a new technology of power. Thus, our very notion of what constitutes a human body—anatomy, physiology, relation to the mind, and so on—is determined by circulating disciplinary knowledge such as medical science through popular discourses. What we consider to be disease, illness, wellness, and good functioning are continually recreated as we are subjected to, produce, and resist prevailing discourses via everyday conversation and the mass media and by interaction with the medical care system.

Foucault's influence in the English-speaking world was originally due to his work on mental illness: *Madness and Civilization* (1964), *The Birth of the Clinic* (1973), and the three-volume *The History of Sexuality* (1978, 1984) in which he developed the notion of biopower. His early work was consistent with the writings of the powerful anti-psychiatric movement ideas articulated by scholars such as Thomas Szasz in *The Myth of Mental Illness* (1974 [1961]) and *The Manufacture*

Komsan Loonprom/Shutterstock.com

Have you been vaccinated against HPV? Has vaccination affected how you think about other methods for preventing cervical cancer, such as Pap smears or barrier methods of protection?

of Madness (1997 [1970]) and R.D. Laing and A. Esterson in *Sanity, Madness and the Family* (1970 [1964]). It was consistent, too, with Howard Becker's labelling theory as found, for instance, in *Outsiders* (1963). Today, through his influence on the field of mental illness, medicine, and sexuality, Foucault's ideas have moved well beyond reinterpreting and contributing to our understandings of mental illness to problematize all notions of the normal and abnormal body and their links to notions of governmentality, identity, and the medical or clinical gaze. In a sense, our ideas about and practices surrounding health constitute a sort of policing to ensure the "normal" functioning of the body/mind by individuals and by many others, such as professional groups including psychiatrists and other medical doctors. Table 1.8 outlines the assumptions of post-structuralism.

One recent Canadian example of powerful governmentality is the rapid, widespread uptake of the human papillomavirus (HPV) vaccine for young girls, ostensibly to prevent cervical cancer and genital warts (Connell & Hunt, 2010). The authors of this study analyze the ways in which the speedy adoption of the vaccine across countries was publicly justified through new and particular types of power/knowledge that were linked among governments, pharmaceutical interests, biological and medical scientists, and medical organizations. In 2006 a new vaccine, Gardasil, was approved

by Health Canada. By the beginning of 2007 the National Advisory Committee on Immunization recommended that all Canadian girls between the ages of nine and 13 be immunized. The federal government assigned $300 million to this end. A number of medical groups such as the Canadian Paediatric Society, the Canadian Cancer Society, and the Federation of Medical Women of Canada supported this decision. Stories addressed both to mothers and to their daughters advocating the vaccine and emphasizing the risk to young women of not being vaccinated spread through a sudden deluge of mass media. School boards took up the call and offered schools as locations for vaccination. Notably, too, these dominating discourses raising concerns about the risks of cervical cancer and warts in young women prevailed, despite the fact that cervical cancer has the lowest incidence of all female cancers, has had a very stable rate of incidence for many years, and was already well controlled in the presence of the early detection mechanism of the Papanicolaou (Pap) test. A less expensive and less aggressive intervention might have been to ensure that marginalized populations who had not taken the Pap test would do so. As HPV expert Dr Diane Harper reports on the dangers of Gardasil:

> Pap smears have never killed anyone. Pap smears are an effective screening tool to prevent cervical cancer. Pap smears alone prevent more cervical cancers than can the vaccines alone.
>
> Gardasil is associated with serious adverse events, including death. If Gardasil is given to 11 year olds, and the vaccine does not last at least fifteen years, then there is no benefit—and only risk—for the young girl. Vaccinating will not reduce the population incidence of cervical cancer if the woman continues to get Pap screening throughout her life. (Yerman, 2011)

In addition, the long-term consequences of the vaccine, including side effects, were not known, nor was it clear how frequently the three-"shot" administration would have to be repeated and over how many years. Further, it was targeted at girls/women even though boys/men were clearly

Table 1.8   Methodological Assumptions of Post-Structuralism in Social Science

Objectivity	It is impossible to be objective as a researcher in the social world because the linkage between power and knowledge imbricates the entire social world through circulating discourses.
Generalizability	Generalization is irrelevant because of the focus on micro practices in historical social contexts.
Subjectivity	Researchers and their subjectivities are irreducibly tied to the social and the historical.
Subject Matter	Disease and wellness are understood through concepts such as biopower, the medical gaze, and governmentality.
Language	Uses gender-neutral language where appropriate and specifies actual gender when relevant. Uses non-racialized terminology.
Data Collection Methods	Historically situated practices are studied as discourses and through Foucault's genealogy and archaeology.
Purpose	To understand and critically expose circulating power/knowledge discourses.

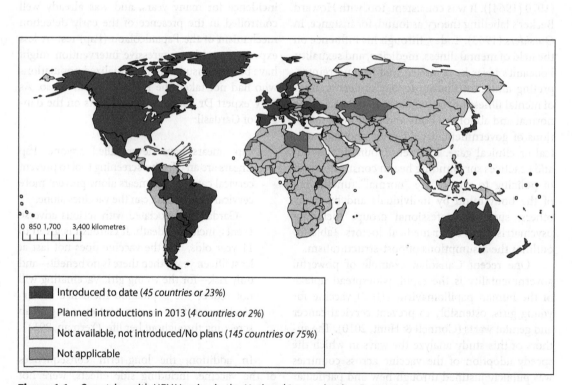

Introduced to date (*45 countries or 23%*)

Planned introductions in 2013 (*4 countries or 2%*)

Not available, not introduced/No plans (*145 countries or 75%*)

Not applicable

0 850 1,700   3,400 kilometres

Figure 1.1   Countries with HPV Vaccine in the National Immunization Program

Source: Data from: WHO/IVB Database, as at 29 May 2013. Map production: Immunization Vaccines and Biologicals (IVB), World Health Organization.

implicated in its transmission and were themselves vulnerable through the same viruses to penile, anal, and back-of-the-throat cancers as well as genital warts (see also Lippman et al., 2007). A few years later it was also approved for young men (Weiss, 2019).

The link between the HPV vaccine and a decline in cervical cancer is still debated. Some research has documented numerous side effects. Some studies suggest the rates of HPV not covered by the vaccine are increasing. Other researchers have suggested that the rate of cervical cancer may actually increase in the wake of the uptake of the vaccine, possibly because people have become less vigilant about barrier means of protection (Gartland, 2018). Nevertheless, it is important to observe that as a result of aggressive and effective marketing of the vaccine it is used in a sizable minority of 40 per cent of the countries around the world, as Figure 1.1 indicates.

Summary

1. Illness is experienced in a social context: we learn to think and talk about it with a vocabulary that others share and we learn what to do about it through interactions with family and friends, the formal medical system, and the media.

2. The sociology of health and illness describes and explains the social causes and consequences of illness, disease, disability, and death. The sociology of medicine is the study of the institutionalized medical recognition of and response to illness.

3. Sociologists use a number of perspectives to study the social world: structural-functional theory, conflict theory, interpretive/social constructionist theory, feminist and critical anti-racist approaches, and post-structuralist theory. Each of these perspectives makes different assumptions about the social world and, therefore, has different ways of understanding it.

4. Structural-functional theory was first discussed by Émile Durkheim. Its goal is to understand the social causes of social facts; it does this by studying the causal relationships among institutions. The parts of society are inextricably bound together to form a harmonious system. Human beings are constrained by the external world and they are, therefore, predictable and controllable through the knowledge of social facts.

5. The origin of the conflict perspective is attributed to Karl Marx. Conflict theorists study competing groups within societies through history. The basic competing forces are the different classes. Conflict theorists are committed to the description and documentation of injustice through the understanding of economic arrangements and their impact on other conditions of social life. In the conflict perspective, health and illness are related to the unequal social arrangements found in capitalist, patriarchal societies.

6. Interpretive/social constructionist theory is based on the definition of sociology given by Max Weber. These theorists, also called symbolic interactionists, attempt to understand the subjective meanings and causes that social actors attribute to events. The meaning social actors give to their diseases affects their self-concepts and their relationships with others.

7. The feminist and critical anti-racist perspectives provide a critique of sociology and a corrective to its narrow, neglectful, or biased representations.

8. Post-structuralism highlights the ways that power produces its effects through the bodies and minds of individuals and populations. It describes how changes in public health and medicine provide new ways of governing populations.

Key Terms

allopathic medicine
biomedicalization
conflict theory
critical anti-racist theory
dependent variables
discourses
epidemiology
feminist theory
home health-care work
incidence
independent variables
interpretive/social constructionist theory
intersectionality
medicalization

neo-liberalism
pharmaceuticalization
positivism
post-structuralism
precautionary principle
privatization
remission society
sick role
social determinants of health
stigma
structural functionalism
symbolic interactionist theory
uncertainty
verstehen

Questions for Study and Discussion

1. Many university students, particularly during the first year, are likely to drink alcohol and become drunk more often than they had done in the past. Explain this behaviour using one of the theories articulated in the chapter.

2. Several of your roommates have been taking anti-depressant drugs given to them by the health services doctors at the university health clinic. They do not appear to be taking them appropriately but rather in handfuls when they say they feel depressed or stressed. How would the theories discussed in this chapter help to explain this situation?

3. Male and female students tend to enrol in different disciplines, and they also tend to use health services at different rates and for different issues. How might the six theories presented in this chapter be used to explain this?

4. The uptake of the HPV vaccine was rapid, particularly in Canada and the US. How could you use each theoretical perspective to explain this?

5. Power is an endemic feature of human social interaction. It is implicated in decisions as to the "normal" and "abnormal," the "ill" and the "well." How do the various theories help us to understand this?

Suggested Readings

Aneshel, C.S., Phelen, J.C., & Bierman, A. (Eds). (2013). *Handbook for the sociology of mental health*. Springer. Edited collection surveying some of the most important and most recent research in the sociology of mental health and illness.

Ayo, N. (2012). Understanding health promotion in a neoliberal climate and the making of health conscious citizens. *Critical Public*

Health, 22(1), 99–105. This short, scholarly article provides an excellent and brief overview of the highlights of neo-liberalism.

Foucault, M. (1994). *The birth of the clinic: An archeology of medical perception*. Vintage Books. A complex and intriguing history of medicine.

———. (2006). *History of madness* (J. Khalfa, Ed. and Trans, J. Murphy, Trans.). Routledge.

Another of the classic works by Foucault, this time focusing on "madness."

Horwitz, A.V. (2013). *Anxiety: A short history of anxiety.* Johns Hopkins University Press. An excellent critical analysis of one of the many increasingly "popular" and inclusive mental health diagnoses.

Levy, J., Ansara, D., & Stover, A. (2013). *Racialization and health inequities in Toronto.* Toronto Public Health. http://www.toronto.ca/legdocs/mmis/2013/hl/bgrd/backgroundfile-62904.pdf. Overview of the impacts of racialization on health.

Navarro, V., & Shi, V. (2003). The political context of social inequalities and health. In R. Hofrichter (Ed.), *Health and social justice: Politics, ideology and inequality in the distribution of* desease. Jossey-Bass. An overview and analysis of health inequalities using a political economy perspective.

Pescosolido, B.A., Martin, J.K., McLeod, J.D., & Rogers, A. (Eds). (2011). *Handbook for the sociology of health, illness and healing.* Springer. An edited collection on key contemporary issues in the field.

Part II

Sociology of Health and Illness

The next six chapters of the book illustrate the theoretical perspectives we have discussed so far. They do this through the presentation of empirical research findings in theoretical context within the sociology of health and illness. Chapter 2 examines some of the changes in mortality and morbidity around the world and in Canada today and over the past century and a half. Chapter 3 describes environmental and occupational challenges to health in the context of Canadian society as a whole. Chapter 4 examines the relevance of social determinants of health—such as inequality, poverty, and racialization—to sickness and disease in Canada. Chapter 5 considers the inequities based on other social determinants of health, including social-structural positions such as gender, age, social class, immigrant and refugee status, and racialization. It considers, in particular, the situation of Indigenous peoples in Canada. Chapter 6 focuses on how the social-psychological aspects of behaviour and attitudes are linked with wellness, illness, and death. Chapter 7 is interpretive and social constructionist in its focus on the description of the meanings of illness experiences from the perspective of those who are ill as well as those who aspire to "improve themselves" through medical interventions.

Table II.1 provides an overview of many of the factors to be considered in explaining the health of a population. Notice that the context for this table is medicalization and biomedicalization. This table points to the importance of biopower or medical power in determining (1) what constitutes disease and death and (2) what is relevant to medical social constructions or discourses. Disease and death are seldom the result of isolated conditions or incidents. Death rates, and most deaths, are the result of complex social, political, economic, biological, and other causes. Causes are direct and indirect. Ultimately they are biological when viewed from a medical perspective. In the case of cancer, for instance, starvation might be the direct cause; the underlying cause might be the growth of malignancies; the bridging cause might be the malfunctioning of the stomach resulting from malignant growth so that food cannot be absorbed; contributing causes might include smoking and excess alcohol ingestion; predisposing conditions might be air pollution resulting from a certain industrial process; and generating conditions might be the economic position of the worker who had no choice but to work in an asbestos mine. However, this empirical complexity is obfuscated by the "simplification" required by death certification. Thus, the meaning and interpretation of the recorded causes of death are variable and subject to sociological, not merely medical, analyses. Statistics Canada lists a number of different groups of causes of death. Keep in mind, though, that each declared cause of death is complicated and finally is the result of a series of decisions and not an "absolute truth."

The chapters in Part II examine some of causes of morbidity and mortality in detail. Others are not dealt with because of space limitations and/or because of a lack of informative research.

Generally speaking, Chapters 2 and 3 focus on predisposing conditions ("A" in Table II.1) and, to a limited extent, social-structural position within society ("B" in Table II.1); Chapters 4 and 5 focus on social-structural inequities (B) and, to a limited extent, predisposing conditions such as historical and environmental factors (A); Chapter 6 focuses on social-psychological (C) and lifestyle (D) conditions; and Chapter 7 focuses on existential factors (E). They all are understood as contextualized within the forces of medicalization and biomedicalization within a society.

Table II.1   Conditions Affecting Life Expectancy Related to Medicalization and Biomedicalization

Predisposing Conditions	**Generating Conditions**
(A) Historical Factors	**(B) Social-Structural Position within a Society**
Global and Regional Ecological/Geographical Conditions	age
natural disasters (e.g., earthquake, tornado,	sex
tsunami, heat wave, war, famine, drought, flood,	sexual orientation
epidemic)	marital and family status
	class
	education level
Local Environmental	occupation
quality and quantity of water	rural/urban location
quality of air	religion
quality and quantity of foodstuffs (nutrition)	religiosity
safety: roads, airways, waterways, transportation	region
vehicles, workplace, home, tools, equipment	ethnicity
birth control	racialization
Medical	**(C) Socio-Psychological Conditions**
immunization	stress experience and stress management
antibiotics	type A or B behaviour
other chemotherapy	sense of coherence
surgery	gender role expectations
radiation	social support
	resilience
Societal Structure	
political-economic system	**(D) Lifestyle Conditions**
cultural values	smoking habits
	seat-belt use
	alcohol consumption rate
	sexual behaviour
	drug use and abuse
	(E) Existential Factors
	the meaning of the illness
	experience of illness
	hope for self-improvement cognitively, emotionally, or aesthetically

Just as causes of death are complex, so too are considerations of health, illness, and disease. Definitions and measurements of disease, illness, and health are multi-faceted and debatable. They vary substantially from cultural group to cultural group within a diverse society and world. In the Western medical tradition disease is measured and determined in a number of ways, including *self-reporting*, which involves asking people to describe their own state of health; *clinical records*, which include the records of physicians as well as hospital statistics, labs, and specialty clinics; and *physical measurements*, which include such things as blood pressure readings and tests of tissue pathology. Each of these methods may record health or a disease state at a different level of development or potential acknowledgement; for example, a Papanicolaou (Pap) test may indicate evidence of precancerous or cancerous tissue before either the physician or the woman would be able to notice it through a visual inspection of cells. No single method can be considered a "true" or "objective" way to determine illness. In combination, however, they may point to "true disease," the absence of disease, or an intermediary state. On the other hand, methods and tests may also contradict each other. For instance, people with chronic fatigue syndrome, fibromyalgia, and Lyme disease often have to go through many different tests, or even to consult a variety of doctors, before they are able to get a diagnosis and even then it is likely to be a "negative diagnosis" (a diagnosis in which certain other possibilities are ruled out). Most progress in allopathic medical knowledge entails *revising a misapprehension* of what had been considered to be a "good practice," one in which doctors and patients had placed their confidence. Thus, a diagnosis that is valid at one time may become invalid from a different perspective and at a different time.

In addition to understanding multiple factors in disease causation, students of the sociology of medicine are interested in questions regarding the socially and culturally specific constructions and discourses about disease—the differentiation of variable meanings among "disease," "sickness," and "illness" (Chapter 7). Finally, sociologists take a critical approach to "official" statistics regarding both disease and death, looking at social factors that may impugn the validity of those data.

Disease and Death

Canada in International and Historical Context

2

Chapter Overview

- Life expectancy has ranged widely over the years in Canada and continues to vary around the globe.
- Several explanations have been offered for these variations, including the demographic transition, social determinants, post-structuralist, and political economy perspectives.
- In a global context death, disease, and disability are related to poverty, inequality, food security, physical and social environments, safety,

security and stability, the social position of women, birth control, pregnancy and childbirth, comprehensive health care, and immunization, among others.
- In Canada, the chief causes of death are the "diseases of civilization": circulatory diseases, cancer, and accidents.
- PYLL or potential years of life lost is a particularly useful way of conceptualizing the cases of death because of its policy implications.

- The behavioural "risk factors" or prerequisites to disease, in health promotion discourse, are thought to include alcohol consumption, cigarette smoking, the amount of physical activity, weight, and sexual activity, among others.

The individualistic and medicalized aspects of these perspectives are critiqued.
- New infectious diseases of concern have surfaced in Canada and around the world.

Introduction

What are the major causes of death in Canada and around the world today? What were the major causes of death in Canada a century and more ago? What is the average life expectancy in Canada today? How long, on average, did Canadians live when your grandparents and great-grandparents were children? How important have modern medical discoveries been to the increase in life expectancy over the last century or so? You have probably heard that antibiotics are "wonder drugs." Were antibiotics or immunizations very important in the overall improvement of the health of the nation? This chapter will consider these and similar questions as it places Canadian rates of disease and death—historically and today—in an international context.

Life Expectancy

The average **life expectancy** for men and women has varied considerably over thousands of years and through many different types of social, cultural, and economic arrangements. For example, the average life expectancy of late Ice Age hunter-gatherers of about 11,000 years ago has been estimated to have been approximately 38 years (Eyer, 1984). According to available records and estimates, the average life expectancy in Europe varied between 20 and 40 years from the thirteenth to the seventeenth centuries (Goldscheider, 1971). In Canada, too, there have been wide variations in life expectancy. In 1831 the average for Canadians is estimated to have been 39 years. According to the latest available statistics from the World Health Organization (WHO), Canadian females today can expect to live for about 84.7 years while males can

expect to live for about 80.9 years (WHO, n.d. a). The life expectancy for Canadian men and women averaged together is 82.8. A significant—almost four-year—gap in life expectancy continues to exist between males and females, although the gap declined over the latter part of the last century. Life expectancy is one thing but the health quality of life lived is another. The average healthy life expectancy for Canadians overall is much less than the overall life expectancy, at 73.2 years. All of these figures, however, are considerably higher than the comparative figures for the United States. According to the World Health Organization men can expect to live 76.0 years and women 81.0 years in the US. Combining both sexes, the average life expectancy in the US is 77.5 (WHO, n.d. a).

The life expectancy of Canadians has dramatically improved over time. There were two primary causes for this improvement. The first was a decrease in infant mortality, and its effect is seen largely up until 1951. There has been a drop in infant mortality among Indigenous peoples in Canada, but their rate of death remains much higher than that of other Canadian infants. The increase in overall life expectancy was also the result of public health advancements, including immunizations among children and the development of penicillin and insulin for children and adults. After these public health breakthroughs over the first half of the twentieth century, the increases in life expectancy (in the non-Indigenous population) were largely the result of declines in circulatory disease rates (Decady & Greenberg, 2014).

The dramatic changes in life expectancy that have occurred in the past 100–150 years in Canada and elsewhere can be explained by a host of other factors. One theory of the changes in patterns of death is the epidemiological transition

(Omran, 1979), which is based on the idea of demographic change. Simply put, this idea suggests that as the economy changes from low to high per capita income, a corresponding transition occurs from high mortality and high fertility to low mortality and low fertility. Changes in the patterns of disease occur in what were considered to be three distinct stages: the Age of Pestilence and Famine, the Age of Receding Pandemics, and the Age of Degenerative and Man-Made Diseases (Omran, 1979).

The Age of Pestilence and Famine is characterized by socio-economic conditions in which communities are traditional, economically underdeveloped with a low per capita income, and generally agrarian. Women usually have low status, the family is extended, and illiteracy is high. The high mortality rate is largely attributable to famine and infectious diseases. The Age of Receding Pandemics is characterized by a decrease in epidemics and famine and a consequent decline in the mortality rate. At this point the fertility rate continues to be high, resulting in a "population explosion." The fertility rate then begins to decline as people begin to live longer and to die of emerging industrial and degenerative diseases such as cancer, stroke, and heart disease, which characterize the Age of Degenerative and Man-Made Disease.

There are several other approaches to explain the overall decline in the **mortality rate** and the increase in life expectancy in the developed world. McKeown (1976) has offered one explanation based on studies of the decline in mortality in Britain (and supported by findings for Sweden, France, Ireland, and Hungary) over the last few hundred years. First, the decline in the mortality rate was almost entirely due to a decline in infectious disease. Second, the decline in infectious disease was largely the result of three basic changes: (1) improvements in nutrition, (2) improvements in hygiene, and (3) increasing control of disease-causing microorganisms. Improvements in birth control were another factor.

Canada's infant mortality decline has been significant but the rate of decline has not kept up with that in other developed countries. Furthermore, the relative rate of improvement for infant mortality in Canada has decreased since the 1990s, as shown by the "report cards" for various countries in Figure 2.1. As recently as the 1980s our overall grade in respect to infant mortality was a "B" and now it is a "C." It should be noted that some of the reasons for this comparative decline may be the result of the differing tools and data used for the measurement of infant mortality from one country to another. Another part of the explanation is the greatly improved but still much higher infant mortality rate among Indigenous people. The infant mortality rate for Indigenous babies is about twice the rate of that for non-Indigenous babies (Sheppard et al., 2017). Similarly, and as can be seen in Figure 2.2, Indigenous men live an average of six years less than the total population of men in Canada and Indigenous women live an average five years less than the total population of women in Canada.

The **political economy perspective** considers the roles of economic and political development in comparing life expectancy and **infant mortality rates** across the globe. It takes the position that the place of workers in the global economy, in terms of occupational conditions such as employment, income, security, and safety, is the prime determinant of equality, living conditions, and, ultimately both directly and indirectly, of health and well-being. Dependency theory explains how the global economic order and globalization are fundamental factors in global inequality. It also explains how multinational expansion by the wealthy and powerful nations maintains an over-utilization of resources and a relative under-financing of labour in the rest of the world. Trade relations and political interventions also buttress the continuation of dependency.

Per person income varies widely across the globe. For instance, the average income is approximately US$82,000 in Norway. It is about

REPORT CARD

Infant Mortality

	1960s	1970s	1980s	1990s	2000s
Australia	A	B	C	C	B
Austria	C	D	D	B	B
Belgium	B	C	D	C	B
Canada	B	B	B	C	C
Denmark	A	A	B	B	B
Finland	A	A	A	A	A
France	B	B	B	B	B
Germany	C	C	C	B	B
Ireland	C	C	C	C	B
Italy	D	D	D	C	B
Japan	B	A	A	A	A
Netherlands	A	A	B	B	B
Norway	A	A	B	A	A
Sweden	A	A	A	A	A
Switzerland	A	A	B	B	B
UK	B	B	C	C	C
US	B	C	D	D	D

Figure 2.1   Has Canada Improved Its Relative Performance on Infant Mortality?

Source: Conference Board of Canada (2012). International Ranking: Canada benchmarked against 15 countries. "Infant Mortality." Retrieved from https://www.conferenceboard.ca/hcp/Details/Health/infant-mortality-rate.aspx.

US$56,000 in the US and US$280 in Burundi (Olya, 2018). World systems theory names three types of national economic actors: **core, periphery, and semi-periphy countries** (Wermuth, 2003). The core includes countries such as Canada, the UK, and Japan. These countries have diversified economies, strong and stable governance structures, and large middle classes. In brief, these are the industrial/post-industrial democracies. Civil liberties tend to be relatively strongly supported and there is little overt class conflict. Core countries exploit countries in the periphery and semi-periphery by extracting raw materials (e.g., oil, lumber, and metals), employing their residents as inexpensive labour, and using these poorer countries as consumers at the end of the process of manufacture and distribution. Periphery countries such as Cambodia, Haiti, and Ethiopia have considerably less-developed or diversified economies and limited infrastructure and technology (such as transportation and communication networks). Their economies are based on subsistence agriculture and a few simple products such as tea, fruits, coffee, metals, or lumber. They tend to have weak state organization and to be exploited

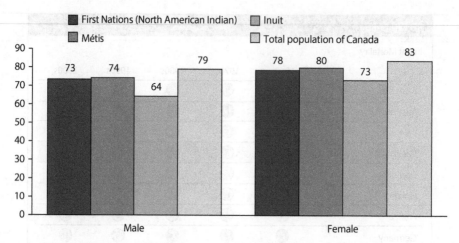

Figure 2.2   Projected Life Expectancy at Birth by Sex, by Indigenous Identity, 2017[1]

1. Estimated data.

Note: "Life expectancy" is an estimate of the number of years a person is expected to live, for a given year. Most often reported as life expectancy at birth, it can be reported at any age, for different population groups.

Source: Statistics Canada, Projections of the Aboriginal populations, Canada, provinces and territories, 2001 to 2017 (Catalogue no. 91-547-XIE).

Table 2.1   Life Expectancy, Maternal Mortality, and Under-Five Mortality in Core, Periphery, and Semi-Periphery, Selected Countries

	Total Population (000s)	Life Expectancy at Birth (years)			Healthy Life Expectancy at Birth (years)	Maternal Mortality Rate (per 100,000 live births)	Under-Five Mortality Rate (per 1,000 live births)
		Male	Female	Both Sexes			
Member State	2016	2016			2016	2015	2016
Cambodia‡	15,762	67.3	71.2	69.4	60.8	161	30.6
Canada*	36,290	80.9	84.7	82.8	73.2	7	4.9
Chile†	17,910	76.5	82.4	79.5	69.7	22	8.3
Ethiopia‡	102,403	63.7	67.3	65.5	57.5	353	58.4
Haiti‡	10,847	61.3	65.7	63.5	55.3	359	67.0
Japan*	127,749	81.1	87.1	84.2	74.8	5	2.7
Mexico†	127,540	74.0	79.2	76.6	67.7	38	14.6
Saudi Arabia†	32,276	73.5	76.5	74.8	65.7	12	12.9
United Kingdom*	65,789	79.7	83.2	81.4	71.9	9	4.3

*Core
†Semi-periphery
‡Periphery

Note: Estimates are based on comparable data among countries.

Source: Adapted from World Health Statistics 2018. Monitoring health for the SDGs, sustainable development goals. Geneva. Licence: CC BY-NC-SA 3.0 IGO Modified from ANNEX B Part 1, pp. 60–7.

by core countries for their raw materials, cheap labour, and markets. At the same time, these countries have a greater proportion of people unable to meet their basic needs. Countries on the periphery of the global economy may need foreign capital and may make agreements with international corporations to give these firms special access to raw materials, a compliant labour force, and product marketing. In the long run, neither corporate investment nor intensive "aid" have helped these countries substantially and people live, on average, on a few dollars per day (Wermuth, 2003). The semi-periphery countries fall between core and periphery countries and include, for instance, Mexico, Chile, and Saudi Arabia. Over time, the periphery and semi-periphery countries may become less likely to develop because the corporations have substantial levers of power and control in the context of global capitalism and neo-liberalism. Thus, from this perspective, the ultimate explanation for different health outcomes around the world is location in the world economy. Table 2.1 offers some comparisons of life expectancy, healthy life expectancy, maternal mortality, and under-five mortality in a few core, periphery, and semi-periphery countries.

Death, Disease, and Disability in Global Context

About 5.4 million children and infants under five years of age died in 2017, according to the World Health Organization (WHO, n.d. b). Most of these children and infants died of easily prevented or treated diseases such as pneumonia, diarrhea, birth asphyxia, malaria, and preterm birth complications. Although this figure has been decreasing over the past 20 or so years, progress has begun to slow in parts of the world and it varies considerably from country to country. For instance, children in sub-Saharan Africa are eight times more likely to die before the age of five than children from the European Union. Childhood poverty, malnutrition, and lack of clean water and adequate

sanitation are significant factors in the vast majority of these deaths. Table 2.1 indicates the mortality rates of children under five in selected core, periphery, and semi-periphery countries.

In a worldwide context, the prime determinant of health is the (absolute) ability of individuals and families to meet their basic human needs. In addition to absolute levels of material well-being, most research has found that the greater the relative inequality in societies, the higher the rates of disease and death (Wermuth, 2003; Wilkinson & Pickett, 2010). Inequality has both direct and indirect effects on health. Greater inequality is coincident both with greater proportions of a population living in poverty and also with governments that are less likely to invest in equalizing infrastructure projects such as a guaranteed annual wage, free education, public transportation, adequate and affordable housing, sufficient food production and distribution, and other goods and services that provide the fundamentals for health. Inequality also has indirect effects on health through the psychosocial issues and feelings such as shame and anger experienced particularly by the relatively poor (Wermuth, 2003; Wilkinson & Pickett, 2010). The well-off and the middle-income people may also feel this shame and anger, which can lead to the diminution of their health, but its origins are different and may lie in the sense of wrongly benefiting from the suffering of others.

To the end of equalizing development internationally, the United Nations member states signed The Millennium Declaration in 2000. The eight interrelated goals that were to be met by 2015 included: (1) the eradication of poverty and hunger; (2) the achievement of universal primary education; (3) the promotion of gender equality; (4) the reduction in child mortality; (5) the improvement of maternal health; (6) reducing HIV/AIDS, malaria, and other diseases; (7) ensuring environmental sustainability; and (8) developing global partnerships to achieve the aforementioned goals (UN, 2000, 2015) The targets have not been reached. Some argue that the very fact that there are targets and explicit goals is reason to be optimistic. Others criticize the uneven progress and the lack of explicit pathways to reaching the existing goals, as well as the paucity of financial commitments necessary for success. In a world of devastating environmental disasters, conflict, wars, and unprecedented numbers of migrants (Adams, 2015) these targets may seem elusive. Some argue that it is still a good thing to state the goals and to measure progress towards meeting them. What do you think?

Poverty and Inequality

Health is determined by social as well as biological determinants. In the following sections we look at some of the major social determinants of health and well-being in any society.

Both the average level of income and the relative income of a society have obvious impacts on health. Income level is the context for all of the other elements of daily life such as work, education, food, shelter, transportation, green space, water, hygiene, and sanitation. Poverty often is associated with political powerlessness and marginalization. While the economic growth of a whole country is not necessarily associated with better health for all, economic decline usually affects the standard of living and, consequently, the health of many, in particular those who are poorer. Furthermore, the health costs of an economic recession tend to fall most heavily on those who were least well-off.

Food Insecurity

The term **food insecurity** refers to a situation, either chronic or acute, in which people do not have access to enough safe, nutritious, and culturally acceptable food. The availability of an adequate amount of nutritious food is fundamental to the health of a population and, especially the protein component, has a larger impact on **morbidity** and mortality than any other public health or medical measure. Millions of people around the globe presently lack adequate nutrients for daily life and even more people lack essential micronutrients such as iodine, vitamin A, and iron. More than half of the deaths occurring each year in the developing world are associated with malnutrition. Inadequate nutrients limit neurological development and productivity, as well as overall health and well-being, and make people even more vulnerable to the cascading effects of disease and subsequent death. The incidence of malnourishment around the world is actually rising (Food and Agricultural Organization [FAO] et al., 2017). According to the 2017 report by the FAO and other agencies, about 10.7 per cent of people in the world in 2016 suffered from chronic malnourishment. Africa has the highest **prevalence** of chronic hunger with 23 per cent of the population chronically lacking adequate nourishment. South Asian countries such as India, Bangladesh, and Pakistan are home to the largest absolute number of malnourished people and the rate there is now 11.5 per cent. In addition, 45 per cent of the deaths of children worldwide are due to hunger. Under-nutrition exacerbates the effects of all other diseases. For instance, malaria, a significant cause of death in areas with high transmission rates such as sub-Saharan Africa, is magnified by malnutrition. Food insecurity results from war, poverty, natural disasters, epidemics, and political and economic crises as well as climate change and agricultural and food-related social policies (FAO et al., 2017).

The place of women in a society is also pivotal for children's food security. Nutrient deficiency in women is an even more prevalent and significant problem than it is for men. Because women bear and breast-feed their children, they have a greater need for calories at times. Adequate nutrition among women is crucial for the health of their offspring. In brief, underweight babies are born to women who suffer nutritional inadequacies. Underweight babies are more likely to die as infants and to suffer from any one of a number of diseases, as well as to have intellectual and physical disabilities.

The Physical and Social Environment

The availability of a sufficient amount of clean drinking water is another fundamental factor in health. According to a report by several United

Nations agencies only 71.2 per cent of drinking water supplies globally are safely managed and only 39.3 per cent of sanitation is managed safely (FAO et al., 2017). These two figures are essential to understanding morbidity and mortality around the world. Shortages of clean, potable water are often due to political and economic conditions that disable infrastructural development because of the lack of a necessary tax base and other investments. Numerous fatal and debilitating chronic illnesses are spread by unsanitary water. Two of the most prevalent are cholera and dysentery. **Diarrheal disease** is a leading cause of the death of children in the developing world (WHO, 2017a). It kills approximately 525,000 children under five every year. Its prevention depends on a clean and adequate water supply, personal and social hygiene, and sanitation. The infrastructure developments necessary for adequate improvements are extensive and urgent. They include drainage systems for the disposal of human and animal wastes, access to potable water, and water for irrigation.

The lack of available and affordable drinking water was one of the factors in the historical crisis that occurred in the developing world over the seemingly innocuous question of how best to feed infants. Starting in 1969, a new market for infant feeding formula was developed in Third World countries. Formula feeding had spread in the developed world and new markets beckoned. It was promoted as a wise and humane intervention that would extend the lives of many of the millions of children who died annually as a result of malnutrition. Advertising and promotion for infant feeding formula quickly became successful. Free samples donated by the companies manufacturing the formula were given to women who had just given birth. Feeding babies formula rather than breast milk was very quickly taken to be a symbol of mother love and responsibility, in part because formula was associated in the minds of people of the developing world with the successful middle and upper classes in the Western world. However, a number of unexpected negative consequences resulted.

1. Sometimes when women used the free samples given to them at the birth of their babies, their milk supply would dry up and breast-feeding would become impossible.
2. When women went home with their babies, they were often ill-prepared to continue with the infant feeding formula for a variety of reasons.
   (a) Formula was frequently unavailable in the small villages and communities, and as women's breast milk had dried up, the babies starved to death.
   (b) When the formula was available, there were often no instructions on how to use it, the mothers were illiterate, or the instructions were in a language the mothers could not read.
   (c) Generally, the formula was sold in powdered form, to be mixed with water. Frequently, the water source was polluted, resulting in unnecessary illnesses and death. Lacking clear instructions, many women mixed the formula with too much water, so that the nutrients in the mixture were inadequate for the baby's growth.
   (d) The bottles and nipples used for feeding the babies should have been sterilized. Many Third World mothers were unable to sterilize the bottles because they lacked clean water, a heat source, or a chemical sterilizing agent.
   (e) Aside from the problems enumerated above, one other fact stands out: breast milk is actually better for babies (*Business Week*, 1979; Zabolai-Csekme, 1983; WHO, 1981; Rabin, 2006).

When the dangers of infant formula became clear to the Western world, the companies manufacturing infant formula were boycotted, especially Nestlé, which held more than 50 per cent of the world market. A World Health Organization conference called in 1979 initiated the adoption of a code to govern infant formula sales. The infant formula companies agreed to support the code. While the extent of the problem declined, there were numerous violations of the code. Problems associated with infant formula have not disappeared and the World Health Organization is continuing its educational campaign declaring that breast-feeding is of benefit to babies for a number of reasons and for a period of at least six months (WHO, n.d. c). It can protect babies from colds, influenzas, asthma, eczema, ear infections, diarrhea, sudden infant death syndrome and obesity, among other problems. It may also be of benefit to emotional well-being and to the health of mothers in whom it lowers the risk of breast cancer, diabetes and hypertension (CDC, 2018).

Safety, Security, and Stability

Personal safety is of great concern, particularly in times of heightened national tensions. Civil war, international warfare, and violence in communities, workplaces, and the home all are threats to fundamental safety. As local and international inequities grow, so, too, do violence and war. The consequences of violence have expanded dramatically globally along with population growth. About one and a half million people lose their lives due to violence every year around the world (WHO, n.d. d). Men are at greater risk of death through violence than women. About 80 per cent of homicides are of men. However, women are at great risk of violence from their domestic partners: according to available statistics, 87,000 women were killed intentionally in 2017. Most of these women are victims of domestic violence and were killed by their intimate partners (United Nations Office on Drugs and Crime, 2018). Others at high risk of violence are more likely to be children, adolescents, old people, the homeless, the unemployed, migrants, refugees, members of visible ethnic minorities, the chronically ill, the mentally disabled, and victims of war. Around the world, 1 billion children under 18 are thought to have been victims of sexual, emotional, physical violence, or neglect last year (WHO, 2019a). The consequences of such abuse can last a lifetime. Prevention is sorely needed.

Health and Women's Place in Society

For a number of reasons the position of women in a society has a significant impact on the health of men and children. In a worldwide context women's health is considerably poorer than that of men. In no region of the world are men and women equal in legal, economic, or social rights. This is particularly true in the developing world, although there were significant improvements in the last half of the twentieth century and into the twenty-first century. In many areas of the world women are unable to own land, do business, or even travel without the approval of their husbands. Despite improvements in education of women around the globe, women continue to have fewer occupational opportunities and to earn much less than men. The share of women holding national political office worldwide had climbed to 22 per cent by 2015. This was almost double the figure for 1995 (11.3 per cent) according to statistics from the United Nations. Nevertheless, one out of every five office-holders is a far stretch from gender equality. In Canada by 2015 women held a record number of parliamentary seats federally but still that was not representative of their numbers in the population. Twenty-six per cent of office-holders were women. The prime minister, Justin Trudeau, appointed a gender-equal cabinet. The global average of women in national parliaments increased slightly from 22.6 per cent in 2015 to 24.6 per cent in 2019. Thus Canada is now slightly above average (UN Women, 2017).

Gender disparities are exacerbated by poverty. Thus, women in the poorest of circumstances are even less likely to have economic or political power. According to the World Bank Gender and Development Group the relationships between gender inequality and poverty are mutually reinforcing, and causal links move in both directions. Power is important in both the private and the public spheres. It is important that women have power in households because they are more likely than men to use the available household resources for food, education, and health-related expenditures for their children. Productivity, economic growth, health, health care, and effective governance all are increased by gender equity in the household and in politics.

Birth Control, Pregnancy, and Childbirth

Effective birth control is another important cause of the decline in the mortality rate around the globe. Too many pregnancies, or pregnancies spaced too closely together, are a threat to the health of the mother and the child for a number of reasons. First, when the pregnancy is unwanted, women may seek illegal abortions, which can be extremely dangerous. Nearly half of abortions performed worldwide are unsafe and 98 per cent of unsafe abortions occur in developing countries. Nevertheless, induced abortion worldwide is estimated as being about 56 million per year between 2010 and 2014. However, that this represents an increase in numbers is due to population increase because the rate of abortion globally for these years (among women of ages 15–44) was 35 per 1,000 as compared to 40 per 1,000 in the years 1990–4, according to the Guttmacher Institute (2018).

Second, as a result of malnutrition, women's bodies may be undernourished and small, their pelvises misshapen. They may experience fatigue during pregnancy and a difficult delivery. Third, pregnancy itself takes a toll on a woman's body because nutrients are needed for the baby as well as the mother. During pregnancy large increases in calories, vitamins, and minerals are required, including more iron, vitamin B12, and folic acid, especially during the last trimester of pregnancy. Fourth, because energy is used up during pregnancy, rest, especially in the last trimester, is important. Most women in developing nations, however, do not have the leisure to take the necessary rest. Fifth, childbirth itself, because of the lack of sanitation, prenatal care, or emergency medical services, is responsible for a much higher rate of maternal mortality and morbidity in developing nations than in developed nations. Some of the most prevalent causes of childbirth-related deaths are postpartum hemorrhage, which occurs when a woman has anemia, and sepsis (infection), which occurs because of inadequate sanitation or because of hypertensive disorders of pregnancy. Levels of maternal mortality remain high (see Table 2.1). Every day women die from preventable causes in childbirth (Index Mundi, 2018).

Fertility is another important component of the health of women. The global fertility rate has decreased from 5.0 births per woman in 1960 to 2.42 in 2016 (Index Mundi, 2018). However, many women are unable to control their pregnancies. There are still about 70–80 million unintended pregnancies each year in developing countries (UNFPA, 2011). The power to space births is a significant component of childhood deaths and women's health. Abortion for gender selection and for trivial purposes such as the zodiac sign under which the birth would occur has shifted the male-to-female proportions of the population in certain countries. Abortion as a means to select characteristics of the offspring has become a significant problem in various parts of the world. For example, there are 33 million more males than females in China because of years of gender bias in social and health policies (Mudle, 2015).

Violence against Women

Another threat to women's health worldwide is female genital mutilation or female circumcision. I use both terms here because some argue that female genital surgery is mutilation, others that so-called female circumcision is beautification. Some say it is a form of violence against women done to maintain their subordinate status, to control their reproduction and their sexuality, and for the purposes of beautification. Beautification is said to increase men's desire. There are (at least) three different types of procedures: circumcision, where the hood of the clitoris is cut; excision, where the clitoris and all or part of the labia minora are cut out; and infibulation, which includes cutting the clitoris, labia minora, and at least part of the labia majora. The two sides of the vulva are then sutured to obliterate the vaginal area except for a small opening for passage of urine and menstrual blood.

Infibulation prevents female sexual pleasure and is believed to assure the faithfulness of women to their husbands. It reinforces the male right to control and dominance, and the female's dependence. Women's imputed attractiveness to men may depend on infibulation. In some places, virtually 100 per cent of young girls of ages 4–10 years undergo infibulation. Little girls know that it is essential to their marriageability and thus may want to have it done. It is also associated with gifts for the girls. Never having seen it occur, they may be unaware of the pain involved. The procedure is not only painful, however, but may also be dangerous because the tools used and the hands that use the tools are often unhygienic and the stitching may be done with silk, catgut, or even thorns. Girls may have their legs bound together for a period of weeks to ensure the buildup of scar tissue. Sexual intercourse is forever likely to be painful and even dangerous for infibulated women. Female genital mutilation can cause severe bleeding, complications in urinating, difficult childbirths, infections, and even death. It can risk the lives of babies during birth among women who have undergone the procedure. More than 200 million women alive today have had this procedure (WHO, 2018a). The World Health Organization calls female genital mutilation a violation of the human rights of women and girls.

The issue of circumcision is not exclusive to other countries. Canada has long supported infant male circumcision through universally supported medicare. However, the rates have decreased dramatically. About 32 per cent of male infants are circumcised today. This trend seems to reflect growing knowledge regarding some of the negative side effects of the practice. Male infant circumcision is no longer taken for granted in Canada. The Canadian Paediatric Society indicates that because of the medical costs and because the benefits are mixed, the decision should be up to the parents (Sorokan et al., 2015).

The society indicates that there are no medical benefits to the procedure (Circumcision Reference Library, 2008). The side effects may include both a diminution in sexual pleasure and an increase in certain health problems as well as the risks associated with any surgical procedure. Some people argue that any circumcision is a violation of a child's rights and that, therefore, all children should be protected under the Criminal Code against this "aggravated assault." Others believe that it is a religious obligation and results in better health to have boys circumcised.

According to studies undertaken by the United Nations (UN Women, n.d.) approximately one in three women around the world will be a victim of violence, including sexual violence and rape or attempted rape, at some time in her life. Rape and domestic violence are major causes of disability and death, especially among women in their reproductive years. Sexual violence is also an important component of women's high rates of HIV/AIDS, especially in Africa. The rape of women in war or as an act of terrorism is another serious concern. In 2014, the Islamist militant Boko Haram in Nigeria kidnapped hundreds of girls from their school. Some were to be married, some to be raped, some sold in sexual or other slavery, and others kept for the other various purposes of the abductors. Boko Haram continues in its fight for an Islamic state that includes the rule that girls not be educated (*BBC News*, 2016). Dowry murder, honour killings, and sexual trafficking in female children are well institutionalized around the world. Malala Yousafzai, who was viciously attacked and seriously wounded by Taliban extremists on a school bus in Pakistan, has become renowned (and shared the Nobel Peace Prize in 2014 with Kallash Satyarthi of India, a long-time proponent of children's rights and education) throughout the world for standing up for the right of girls to be educated. Reports of one or another of myriad gender-based sexual and/or violent crimes against girls and women appear virtually daily.

The health consequences and the continuous fear of rape and sexual assault include psychological distress, socio-cultural impacts, and somatic consequences. Psychological distress—**post-traumatic stress disorder (PTSD)**—may last throughout the lifetime of the woman who has been raped, and the symptoms can be diverse, extensive, and recurring. Survivors of rape and violence are more likely to experience depression, to self-harm, to have flashbacks, to abuse alcohol and drugs, and to have sexually transmitted infections, among other potentially long-term and powerful impacts. All of these problems are also likely to be exacerbated by the silence and shame that often accompany the experience of having been raped, as if the woman is to blame somehow.

Socio-cultural effects are those that spread beyond the suffering of the individual woman and lead non-victimized women to change their behaviour and restrict their movements out of fear. Surveys done in countries around the world indicate that many women consider the fear of rape a major stress in their lives. In some countries women who have been raped may be doubly abused. For instance, in parts of Asia and the Middle East, consequences of rape may include being divorced by one's husband, ostracized by one's family, or even murdered by family members to repair family honour. Rape can lead the victim to commit suicide. In the US alone, thousands of women become pregnant every year as a result of rape (CDC, 2019a). Physical illnesses that are disproportionately diagnosed among women who have been raped include gastrointestinal disorders, migraines and other headaches, chronic pain, premenstrual symptoms, cervical cancer, and sexually transmitted infections (CDC, 2019a). Women who have been victims of rape and other assaults report more symptoms of illness across virtually all bodily systems and perceive their health and themselves less favourably than non-victimized women. Numerous health issues that may result from rape and sexual abuse including premature menarche, pregnancy, sexually transmitted diseases, high-risk sexual behaviours, and loss of self-esteem (Koss et al., 1994). The rates of sexual assault and violence reflect the inferior position of women as compared to men around the world.

Comprehensive Medical Care

Comprehensive medical care, although largely ineffective without such fundamentals as adequate food and clean water, is also an important factor in good health. Health care can be divided into three types. **Primary health care** emphasizes equitably distributed prevention through community development and education. Environmental issues may also be addressed. **Secondary health care** is directed towards disease treatment in hospital and community via various (usually Western-style) medical practitioners. **Tertiary care** especially occurs in a teaching hospital attached to a university and has a side emphasis on health promotion. Primary health care, including such interventions as oral rehydration therapy, vaccinations and antibiotics, and disease-specific initiatives (such as malaria reduction programs), has made a positive difference. The topic of global health-care systems is explored in more detail in Chapter 15.

Immunization

Immunization makes an important contribution to the health of a population, although its historical importance appears to have been overemphasized. McKinlay and McKinlay (1977), following our earlier discussions of McKeown's work on this topic, used American data since about 1900 to show that most of the decline in mortality from the infectious diseases prevalent in 1900 (about 40 per cent of the deaths in 1900 were attributable to infectious diseases) was the result of public health measures such as water purification and improvements in nutrition and birth control. Data for tuberculosis, typhoid, measles, scarlet fever, polio, whooping cough, influenza, diphtheria, and pneumonia demonstrate that the significant decline in mortality for each disease came before the introduction of the vaccine or drug to treat it. This is not to argue that vaccinations are ineffective, just that they are ultimately effective only in the context of good public health and environmental infrastructures.

In the developing world, the immunization rate is currently about 85 per cent (WHO, 2019b). This means that an additional 1.5 million deaths annually could be prevented around the world if universal coverage was in place. Immunization offers protection from a wide variety of causes of death and disability, including such illnesses as measles, tuberculosis, whooping cough, polio, tetanus, cervical cancer, and diphtheria. The WHO continues to monitor this situation with a goal of universal coverage as soon as possible.

In the midst of confusing information about the safety and efficacy of vaccination, as well as some skepticism about the "motives" of pharmaceutical companies, some Canadian parents of infants and children choose not to have their children immunized (Scheifele et al., 2014). In fact, Canada's rate of child vaccinations is very low, at 28th out of 29 countries of the OEDC (Organisation for Economic Co-operation and Development) (Scheifele et al., 2014). The overall immunization rate is 84 per cent for Canada as compared to the 96 per cent average for other OEDC countries. Thus, significant numbers of children in Canada are not receiving an adequate level of immunization for potentially fatal and disabling diseases such as polio, diphtheria, and measles even though vaccinations are widely available and free. People who choose not to vaccinate may be part of a powerful new movement sometimes called anti-vaxxers (*Guardian*, 2019). Some anti-vaccination proponents believe that autism and other diseases can result from vaccines. Celebrity spokespeople and anti-vaccination websites have been powerful influencers for some. Another reason to reject vaccines has been the suspension of some in mercury (thimerosal), although apparently mercury has been used for decades (Centers for Disease Control and Prevention [CDC], 2015) with few known problems. The efficacy of flu vaccinations for adults and children has been called into question because they are always manufactured ahead of time (flu season) and based on a hypothetical projection as to the most important next influenza virus (Osterholm et al., 2012).

Despite this level of vaccination resistance, serious infectious and bacterial diseases have all but disappeared in the developed world (with the notable exception of HIV/AIDS). However, as the "anti-vaccine" and "slow-vaccine" (one vaccine at a time and spread out over time) movements grow and with ever-increasing international travel and migration, we are seeing the re-emergence in the US, Mexico, and Canada of some diseases such as measles (Poland & Jacobson, 2012) linked to visits to popular American theme parks such as Disneyland and Disney World (Harbarger, 2019). Moreover, the developed world awaited a seemingly inevitable global pandemic of new strains of infectious and contagious disease such as the avian or the H1N1 influenza. Except for international co-operation, excellent surveillance, and interventions, SARS might have been a global pandemic, and in early 2020 just such a pandemic, first identified in China, spread across the world as a deadly coronavirus (COVID-19). This pandemic led to national and international health agencies being on alert, to newly restrictive screening at major international airports, to entire countries being placed on lockdown and shelter-in-place orders, and to the deaths of hundreds of thousands of people by 1 July 2020. The World Health Organization in co-operation with countries around the globe has ongoing monitoring and response systems in place to observe the development of such a new disease. Of course, too, the continuing threat that new diseases may be ignored too long to enable the development of prevention and treatment protocols had been worrisome. In an era characterized by constant international travel for pleasure and commerce, the rapid and uncontrolled spread of a new disease had appeared likely, if not inevitable.

Figure 2.3 presents a picture of the decline in mortality rates over the twentieth century. Notice the historical place of immunization and drug development in the overall trajectory of decline along with the impacts of social and economic changes. This historical decline in mortality could end abruptly in the face of a global pandemic of another infectious disease.

Figure 2.3   An Image of the Decline in Mortality Rates over the Twentieth Century

Source: Adapted from information in McKinlay & McKinlay (1981).

Canada in a Global Context

Box 2.1 • The Growth in Global Inequality

Global inequality has been growing over the past half-century or so (De Vogli, 2011) under neo-liberal globalization. Paralleled by increased inequity in Canada, as well as in other developed nations such as the United Kingdom, the United States, Australia, New Zealand, Russia, and Sweden, these growing in-equities are concomitant to the changing economic policies favouring the dominance of market prin-ciples in governance over principles of justice and equity. Rather than enacting policies that focus on a balance between the protection of the weak, poor, and vulnerable in society and on economic prosper-ity and growth, current policies increasingly support free markets first and foremost. There has been grow-ing evidence of declines in government involvement

in the provision of adequate and universal health and social services, coupled with decreasing taxes from corporations and the richest members of society. Societies with greater inequality tend to have higher morbidity and mortality rates. Countries with more internal equity, such as Japan, tend to have higher life expectancy. As well as the overall degree of relative societal equality and inequality, the socio-economic status of individuals within societies is negatively correlated with both morbidity and mortality. Those lower in the socio-economic hierarchy tend to have higher levels of sickness and death. Those higher in a societal socio-economic hierarchy tend to have lower levels of morbidity and mortality. If the avail-ability of material goods and services accounted

continued

for all health disparities between people located at different places in the social structure, then overall inequity in a society would not affect life expectancy or other health outcomes. However, it does. Do people feel unhappy and stressed when they live in a society where there is a great deal of disparity? Are people happier and less stressed when they feel that life circumstances and life chances are generally similar among most other people in their country? If so, how does this work to affect their health and well-being? There are a number of explanations for the fact that both poorer people and more inequitable societies tend to have higher rates of disease and death.

For some evidence and interesting illustrations, see the Global Wealth Pyramid, Figure 2.4. The large base in Figure 2.4 indicates the relatively high percentage of people, 63.9 per cent, in the world who have less wealth than US$10,000. These 63.9 per cent hold merely 1.9 per cent of the wealth in the world. At the middle, holding between $10,000 and $100,000 in wealth, are a further 26.6 per cent, holding a further 13.9 per cent of global wealth; a further 8.7 per cent of the people have between $100,000

and $1 million. They hold 39.3 per cent of the world's wealth. The final grouping of 0.8 per cent at the very top of the pyramid hold 44.85 per cent of the world's wealth. It is now widely accepted that global structural adjustment designed to enable the poor nations to pay their debts to the rich nations has led to greater inequality than existed prior to structural adjustment policies

The burden of global inequality falls most heavily on women. Many countries still lose money because they fail to take advantage of women's labour. Around the world, $160 trillion in wealth has been lost because of gender inequality (Wodon & De La Briere, 2018). Gender equity has repeatedly been shown to be associated with lower fertility and better health for women and children as well as overall economic development. Gender equity seems to be important for health both at the level of the public economy and within individual households. Within the household, characteristics of equity such as decision-making power and equity in the allocation of resources, as well as education for girls and women, are now seen as fundamental forms of human capital investment.

Figure 2.4   The Global Wealth Pyramid, and the Apex of the Pyramid

Source: Adapted from *Global Wealth Report*, https://www.credit-suisse.com/about-us/en/reports-research/global-wealth-report.html

The Impact of Specific Issues on Global Health

The World Economic Forum recently published its forecast of the top 10 threats to global health in the next 10 years (World Economic Forum, 2018). All of them have known consequences for nations, families, and individuals. They include fiscal crises in key economies, structurally determined high underemployment and unemployment, clean water availability and accessibility, income disparity, climate change, extreme weather events, failures in global governance, food crises, and political instability.

Mental illness is another of the most significant contributions to the disease burden of people around the globe and causes years of disability in the lives of millions. It has long been neglected and received a disproportionately low share of global health dollars (Wainberg et al., 2017). Mental illness is related to poverty, economic insecurity, and low levels of education (Patel & Kleinman, 2003). Hopelessness, poor physical health, rapid change in social status, and constrained opportunities resulting from educational impoverishment are related to mental illness rates. The majority of individuals who suffer from mental illness lack access to care and treatment (Wainberg et al., 2017). People with mental illnesses often experience stigmatization and isolation. Feeling as if they lack options they may end their lives through suicide. It is estimated that in 2016 about 793,000 people died by suicide. This is about one person every 40 seconds. Males are more likely to fail to cope with their problems by committing suicide, at a rate of 1.8 to 1. Suicide is the leading cause of death for young adults between 15 and 44 in many countries (WHO, n.d. e). The World Health Organization estimates that 300 million people suffer from depression, 60 million from bipolar disease, 23 million people from schizophrenia and other psychoses, and 50 million from Alzheimer's and other forms of dementia

(WHO, 2018b). Moreover, the capacity to deal with people who suffer from mental illnesses varies across the world and care is unevenly distributed so that poorer nations are less likely to have mental health policies and are less able to care for those who suffer. It is important, however, to be aware that Western medical models of care may not always be appropriate or helpful.

Refugee Health around the World

Many people do not have a permanent home. Many others do not even have a country in which to establish a home. The number of refugees around the world is at an unprecedented level. According to the United Nations High Commissioner for Refugees (UNHCR), by the end of 2018 there were 70.8 million people who had been forcibly displaced around the world: 41.3 million were internally displaced; 25.9 million were refugees located beyond their home-country borders; 3.5 million were asylum seekers. A whopping 57 per cent of the refugees under the mandate of the UNHCR (5.5 million Palestinian refugees are under the jurisdiction of an earlier UN mandate) are from three countries: Syria, (6.7 million), Afghanistan (2.7 million), and South Sudan (2.3 million). Of note, most refugees are hosted by the poorer countries of the world—84 per cent are hosted by neighbouring developing nations. While the UNHCR has data on 3.9 million stateless people who do not have access to basic human rights, it is believed that millions of others also are stateless (UNHCR, 2019). Many of these displaced people do not have access to the basics of everyday living, such as reliable shelter, food, water, recreation, health care, or, especially for those who are stateless, a legitimate identity. More than half of the people in this situation are children, many of whom are unaccompanied by family. They are fleeing conflict zones, crossing borders, and seeking food, water, and shelter wherever they can find

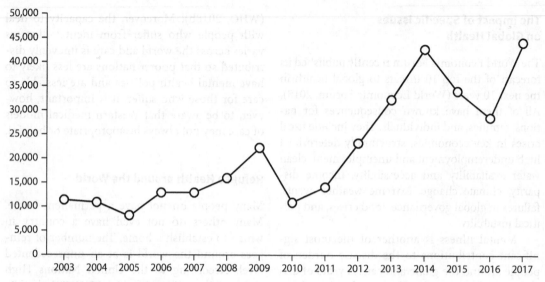

Figure 2.5   Number of People Newly Displaced per Day, 2003–17

it. Most of these many millions of people will experience challenges to their mental health. Some will experience such horrible conditions as to be diagnosable with post-traumatic stress disorder, grief disorders, anxiety, and depression (WHO, n.d. f). Figure 2.5 shows the rapid increase in refugees since 2003.

Living in a war-torn country or a country overwhelmed by a natural disaster such as a tsunami, major volcanic eruption, or earthquake, trying to survive in a land impacted by the floods, droughts, or massive fire events caused by climate change, or belonging to a stigmatized group such as the Rohingya in Myanmar is clearly not conducive to mental or physical health. Such events obviously cause death, disability, and ongoing diseases They contribute to food insecurity, lack of access to clean water, poverty, and innumerable other social, economic, and human health problems. Deforestation, flooding, and manifold other threats to the environment that take a long recovery time mean that affected people may not be able to care for themselves, their families, or

their communities for generations. Attempted genocide, a motivating factor in some conflicts and expulsions, is a threat to the very life of a whole community or country.

Death, Disease, and Disability in Canadian Society

In Canada the infant mortality rate, one of the most sensitive indicators of the health of a nation, has dropped significantly as a result of better nutrition and living standards for the mother and baby, coupled with improved prenatal and postnatal medical care. With the exception of Japan, Canada had the most significant drop in infant mortality rates over the period 1960–95. As indicated in Figure 2.1, however, our infant mortality rate decrease has stalled. A significant aspect of the comparatively higher rates of infant mortality Canada is the infant mortality rate of Indigenous peoples in Canada, as shown in Figure 2.2, with estimates of between 20 per cent and 360 per cent higher than the rate for non-Indigenous people (Webster, 2012).

Canada in a Global Context

Box 2.2 • The Horrors of War

Not only are millions of people wounded, killed, maimed, and raped as a result of wars, but the consequences of being in a war can be extremely disruptive for survivors. Western governments are now realizing the potential for returning soldiers to suffer from a variety of psychological problems, including **post-traumatic stress disorder**. Approximately 24 per cent of returning Canadian veterans experience mental health issues including anxiety, depression, and PTSD. Ninety-five per cent of these vets who had been diagnosed with a mental health issue also suffered from ongoing and chronic physical condition. In consequence, the Canadian government has established a virtual centre for veterans' mental health, the Centre of Excellence for Post-Traumatic Stress Disorder and other Related Mental Health Conditions. This is essentially an online site providing various resources for veterans and their families to peruse if they believe they need help.

At times the mental suffering of returning soldiers has led to suicide. Between 2002 and 2011, when Canada's role in the Afghanistan combat mission ended, 158 Canadian soldiers had been killed in combat. At least 54 soldiers killed themselves when they returned (Aliesio, 2017). Evidently, in this sample, being killed in action is only three times as prevalent as taking one's life after returning home. In a recent study published in the *Canadian Medical Association Journal*, 13.5 per cent of the 40,000 soldiers deployed from Canada to Afghanistan returned with a mental disorder that was said to be the result of their time in Afghanistan. Of these 5,400 military personnel, only 26 were reported to

have sought help (Boulos & Zamorski, 2013). This is possibly because of the stigma attached to mental illness (especially in a largely male, conflict-oriented environment) and possibly because they believed or recognized that psychiatric services, as presently constituted, could provide little help. Canadian psychiatrist Norman Doidge's recent book, *The Brain's Way of Healing* (2015; see also Tallman, 2011), is one of few works by a medically trained doctor who begins to appreciate how ear damage can affect an individual's behaviour and health across many measures. (Note that post-traumatic stress disorder used to be called "shell shock.")

Other returning soldiers have committed murder, possibly as a result of PTSD. It may be that these murders are one of the consequences of the experiences that soldiers undergo as they do their work. Another one of the tragic long-term effects of engaging in conflict is the heightened risk among former military personnel of homelessness upon return (Metraux et al., 2013). Canadian Forces officials have become especially sensitized to the issues facing returning soldiers because of the outspoken work of General Roméo Dallaire, who had headed a United Nations peacekeeping mission in Rwanda and was unable to halt the genocide or alert the world about the atrocities occurring. He has continued to speak openly about the drastic mental health consequences on his own life and that of his family. Clearly, the effects of war are far-reaching and profound, even in countries well removed from the ongoing conflict and after soldiers return home.

The chief causes of all death in Canada today are cancer, heart disease, and cerebrovascular diseases, followed by lower respiratory infections and accidents. This ranking reverses the historical situation when heart disease was the first and growing cause of death (Hamo & Bloom, 2015). However, since the 1950s the cardiovascular death rate in Canada has declined significantly. Then it comprised 50 per cent of the deaths and now heart disease is responsible for about 24 per cent of Canadian deaths. Today, 95 per cent of people who make it to the hospital after heart attack survive. During the 1950s, 65–79 per cent survived (Hamo & Bloom, 2015).

The chief causes of death in the 1921–5 period were heart disease followed by influenza, bronchitis, and pneumonia, diseases of infancy, tuberculosis, and cancer (Arnup, 2018, p. 6). Today, tuberculosis is virtually absent as a cause of death and pneumonia, bronchitis, and influenza are comparatively much lower. The fact that these infectious diseases were more common among young people contributed substantially to the lower life expectancies. Cancer has increased in importance as a cause of death essentially because it tends to be a disease of aging. That is not to deny the importance of childhood cancer as a cause of disease. It accounts for 1 per cent of the total cancers in Canada (Canadian Cancer Society, 2019). Moreover, because of the success of treatments about one in 530 young adults between 20 and 39 is a survivor of childhood cancer (Cure Search, n.d.).

Heart disease, cancer, and accidents are called the **diseases of civilization** or diseases of affluence, or what Omran (1979) has called "man-made" diseases. Their causes are different from those of the diseases of development. Food security and lack of clean water and birth control are no longer problems for most people in most of the "affluent" or developed world. Rather, socio-economic inequity within developed societies and lifestyle, environmental, and work-related factors are particularly important in explaining Canada's present mortality rates. Indigenous peoples in Canada are an exception to the general pattern because they experience both diseases of development and diseases of civilization. Their health status will be discussed more thoroughly in Chapter 5.

Precursors to the Major Causes of Disease and Death in Canada

The Impact of Alcohol

Alcohol ingestion appears to affect health in paradoxical ways. On the one hand, excess consumption is known to be associated with morbidity and mortality through alcoholism, cirrhosis of the liver, malnutrition, accidents, obesity, suicide, homicide, and other violent behaviour, as well as fetal alcohol syndrome when an excess of alcohol is ingested by a pregnant woman. On the other hand, moderate drinking, particularly of red wine, may have a beneficial impact on health. Drinking excess alcohol does seem to be a continuing problem for Canadians. About 19 per cent of Canadians 12 years of age and older reported in 2016 that they drank enough alcohol to be classified as heavy drinkers. Males (23.8 per cent) are more likely to be heavy drinkers than females (14.2 per cent) (Statistics Canada, 2016). The age group with the greatest proportion of heavy drinkers is 18–34. Even though it is illegal almost one-third of people younger than 18 consumed alcohol in 2016. Alcohol advertising is increasingly targeting young women (Flegel, 2013), which may foretell significant increases in routine or excessive drinking among women.

Street drugs can cause a multitude of health effects, ranging from immediate death as a result of an overdose or poisoned drug intake, to diseases and disabilities resulting from long-term addiction. Among the effects are malnutrition, emotional instability, neurological impairments including psychosis, inadequate or no housing, and decrements in all of the other social determinants of health discussed in Chapter 4. Injection drug use in particular is associated with ill health. A sizable minority of Canadians who live on the streets are at risk of contracting and spreading sexually transmitted infections (STIs) including HIV/AIDS, as well as blood-borne infections, as a result of their drug use and consequent uninhibited sexual behaviours.

The picture of drug use in Canada has changed dramatically since the previous edition of this book. First of all, cannabis is no longer an illegal drug in Canada. Cannabis stocks have been ricocheting on the stock market as legitimate corporations compete to grow, package, and distribute cannabis to eat and cannabis to smoke. Still, the long-term benefits and costs of the legalization of cannabis are unknown. One clear benefit to the state, according to a study done in Colorado (where recreational cannabis use has been legal since 2014), is the increased revenue in tax dollars (Zhang, 2018). Colorado found that the tax revenue more than compensated for the additional costs incurred for social services and law enforcement. The study also found that there did not appear to be any increase in youth use or in homelessness. On the other hand, there are long-term negative health consequences for regular use and these consequences can fall most heavily on people who begin smoking or ingesting cannabis regularly as youth. Ingesting cannabis is known to affect memory, attention, and learning abilities. Frequent use is linked to mental health concerns such as disorientation, anxiety, and even paranoid thoughts. Nevertheless, and although all the evidence is not in, cannabis use is now normalized in Canada. It is poised to increase tax dollars and stock values. It may also be poised to increase problems of various sorts.

The other dramatic change in drug use is the increasing use of opioids as street drugs, along with the tremendous costs of their rapidly growing prevalence. The use of opioids began in the late 1990s when doctors began to prescribe them for chronic pain and for pain after dental and other surgery. Opioid use is now a Canadian crisis (Belzak & Halverson, 2018) because these drugs are highly addictive and can be harmful, especially as people who can no longer get prescriptions turn to the streets to purchase it illegally. Some people who had never before used street drugs became dependent. The death rate has grown: just under 14,000 apparent opioid-related deaths occurred in Canada from January 2016 to June 2019 (Government of Canada, 2019b). Opioids have become the prime cause of death for people under 50 in the US, and while the Canadian rate is behind it mirrors that in the US (Belzak & Halverson, 2018). About 6 per cent of people who are first prescribed opioids for pain after surgery or other pain become addicted to the euphoria or pain relief and develop a tolerance and then need to increase the amount used just to prevent symptoms of withdrawal. In the late 1990s about one-third of the population of the US (about 100 million people) were using one or another opioid for chronic pain. In 2007 the pharmaceutical company Purdue was sued and fined for fraudulent marketing even after they knew that it was being used illegally on the street and to get high. Over 200,000 people in the US have died in the last two decades or so because of opioids (Meier, 2018). Other lawsuits have continued (Walters, 2018). Opioid prescribing endures. As the amount of opioid prescribed per prescription is decreasing, the number of prescriptions continues to increase, according to the Canadian Institute of Health Information (2018).

Opioid use is now viewed as a crisis in Canada. Public education campaigns and information directed towards prescribers such as doctors and dentists have changed prescribing patterns somewhat, and there have been other social and health policy innovations. Insite, located in Vancouver, was Canada's first government-sanctioned and supervised facility to aid people who are addicted to injection drugs to use them "safely." Its former director, Dr Gabor Maté, is a popular writer and lecturer on the program. There was a great deal of opposition to this facility and to the principle of "harm reduction" upon which it was based. It involved the provision of clean needles and other social and health services. The previous and popular theory of addictions treatment was "zero tolerance." This did not seem to work with many people and people were dying from such practices as sharing needles. Nevertheless, many thought that zero tolerance was the only legal and moral route for drug policy and treatment. After a Supreme Court decision in 2011, Insite was allowed to continue to operate after first being threatened by the federal government with closure. This issue continues to be very controversial. Some argue that in keeping the facility operating the government is condoning illegal drug use. Others argue that in the face of addiction the principle of least harm possible should operate (Zlotozynska et al., 2013). Meanwhile, and slowly, Health Canada has approved more safe injection sites, including another for Vancouver and others in Surrey, BC, Toronto, and Montreal (Canadian Press, 2017). Safe injection sites, listed on a Heath Canada website (Government of Canada, 2019a), are now available across the country. Do you think such sites are a good idea?

CRITICAL THINKING

Box 2.3 • Is There Too Much Pressure to Drink Alcohol on Campus?

How often do you go to the pub? How do you feel about it? Is it fun for you or is it just something you feel pressured to do with your friends? Since the late 1970s, most universities have permitted at least one pub on campus. In addition, bars and pubs have grown up around college campuses around the country. Drinking alcohol is a major social activity for young people in university and college today (Anderson, 2016). A recent survey of 43,780 students at universities and colleges across the country found that binge drinking of more than five drinks at one time was common among about one-third of the respondents, one-quarter reported that they had engaged in unprotected sex during this drinking, and 38 per cent mentioned that they regretted doing something afterwards (National Institute on Drug Abuse, 2016).

Many people are concerned about the excessive amount and the frequency of alcohol consumption on campuses. It appears to be normative to go to the pub regularly, as well as on "special" occasions as a part of celebrations such as "frosh week." Students say they drink to enhance their social activities and to "break the ice" in a new social situation (Syre & Martino-McAllister, 1997). Stress reduction and celebrating milestones in the school year (e.g., finishing a

test or a paper and exams) are among the other reasons students give to justify their drinking. As well as personal and peer-based reasons, many universities institutionalize alcohol consumption as a regular part of campus life by including it in college-sponsored activities such as orientation and residence socials. The presence of bars on campus and their centrality as meeting places for students living off campus, as well as in residences, implicitly support some degree of alcohol consumption.

Cheaper beer prices, careless checking of age and identity cards, and the linking of alcohol with other forms of entertainment such as music are ways to increase consumption of alcoholic beverages on campus and in nearby venues. This sometimes becomes a serious problem. For example, students have died from excess consumption. Police have had to be called as the result of rioting from too much St Patrick Day celebrating. Other students have become addicted and left school (Tamburri, 2012). Exams and tests have been failed and courses dropped. There are new policies and partnerships across the country among the college and university sectors and health professionals attempting to challenge the centrality of alcohol on campuses. Should anything be done? And if so, what can be done?

Impact of Cigarette Smoking

Cigarette smoking has been a major public health concern and a cause of premature mortality in the developed world. Its effects and use are declining and have been for the last quarter of a century. However, cigarette smoking is spreading rapidly in the developing world where tobacco is quickly becoming a major cause of death. Approximately 50 per cent of people who smoke die as a result of their addiction to cigarettes (WHO, n.d. g). According to the World Health Organization, about 7 million

people die annually as a result of smoking. Most of these deaths are a direct result of smoking, but almost a million are from second-hand smoke. Approximately 80 per cent of the people in the world who smoke live in middle- to lower-income countries (WHO, n.d. g). Some people have used vaping to quit cigarette smoking and some of these people have become addicted to vaping. The available evidence suggests that many possible negative effects, up to and including death, can result from this habit (Wheeler, 2016, CDC, 2019c). This may not be the best way to quit smoking cigarettes.

Cigarette smoking is considered to be the leading cause of preventable death in Canada (CDC, 2019b). People affected by smoking go well beyond those who actually smoke and include those vulnerable to the numerous health effects of second-hand smoke. More males smoke than females, by about 5 per cent. After years of obfuscating debate sponsored by tobacco companies it is now clear that smoking has harmful effects on health (Novotny, 2013). Today, although the smoking rates for youth have declined, at least in part due to the high cost, research, which involved analysis of cigarette butts in public places where school students regularly smoke during school recesses and breaks, found that 30 per cent of these discarded butts in Ontario and 45 per cent in Quebec were from contraband cigarettes. Thus, a surprising portion of teen smokers are circumventing the high price of cigarettes by purchasing illegal, untaxed tobacco products. Interestingly, this "on-the-ground" study was conducted for the Canadian Convenience Stores Association, whose members are facing declining revenues (Canadian Press, 2009).

The regulations regarding contraband (untaxed) cigarettes are poorly enforced. People who use such products tend to be heavier smokers, are more likely to perceive themselves as heavy smokers, and experience more barriers to quitting (Mecredy et al., 2013). Furthermore the Canadian government, which had been a world leader in smoking cessation efforts and had advocated for visual and textual warnings on cigarette packages, has now fallen behind. In 2000 Canada became the first country in the world to require full-colour representations of the dangers of smoking on at least 50 per cent of the package for cigarettes. In 2012, in the face of lobbying by the tobacco industry, the government resisted the call for 75 per cent warning coverage, but this finally was effected in late 2019, as well as a change to black packaging without brand logos on all brands. On the other hand, there are no warnings at all on products such as chewing tobacco, cigars, and cigarillos. The World Health Organization has advocated regulating e-cigarettes, which use battery-charged cartridges to produce nicotine to be inhaled in vapour. The industry says that they are safe because they lack the tars and other toxins of nicotine cigarettes. On the other hand, health advocates, backed by research, insist that they still contain carcinogens and other particulates that are bad for the lungs (Begley, 2014). The current outbreak of lung disease and even death as the result of vaping is a reminder of the lack of the precautionary principle in the uptake of e-cigarettes (CDC, 2019c).

Physical Activity

More than half of all Canadians over 12 years of age engage in physical activity in their leisure time (57.4 per cent). This percentage is slightly higher among males (60.4 per cent) than among females (54.6 per cent), according to physical activity data for 2017 (Statistics Canada, 2018). The level of physical activity declines as men and women age. Physical activity is negatively related to socio-economic status, and the types of physical activity are related to family income (Wiltshire et al., 2019). For example, some recreational activities such as golf or skiing can be very expensive. Fitness clubs may be costly and unaffordable yet necessary in some seasons of the year in Canada. Leisure time itself may be scarcer for those who work shifts or more than one job. Clothing and equipment may be other constraints. Do you have other insights into the socio-economic correlations with physical activity?

The Impact of Weight, Body Image, and Eating Disorders

The number of overweight Canadians has increased. Between 1985 and 2011 the prevalence of obesity in adults tripled, growing from 6.1 per cent to 18.3 per cent (Twells et al., 2014). Obesity has nearly tripled around the world since 1975 according to the World Health Organization (WHO, 2018c). Currently Canada stands near the top with respect to percentages of overweight people (Ferreras, 2017). Sixty-four per cent of Canadians are overweight or obese according to the government of Canada (Government of Canada, 2018).

This is up from 49 per cent in 1978–9 and 59 per cent in 2004. Men are more likely to be overweight and obese than women, but women are more likely to be underweight. Despite women's tendency to underweight (especially when young), a sizable proportion of Canadian women with normal weights believe they weigh too much. Now considered an epidemic, obesity is a significant risk factor for a variety of diseases, including cardio-vascular disease, non-insulin-dependent diabetes mellitus (NIDDM), cancer of the breast, colon, and prostate, musculoskeletal problems, and gall bladder disease (WHO, 2018c). Obesity can also lead to declines in the quality of life and in self-esteem. It can lead to mental disabilities such as depression. Extreme obesity may mean exclusions and requirements for many things others take for granted, such as having to purchase two seats to fly on an airplane.

There may be an irony to the fact that the incidence of both overweight and obesity is growing in spite of the proliferation of a wide range of products and services designed to help people lose weight. Fat-free, low-fat, and sugar-free products now control major market shares of every conceivable foodstuff and beverage category. The ownership of personal exercise machines continues to accelerate and health and fitness clubs have become popular locations for social interaction. Obesity in children is a particular problem as they may be more likely to face a number of health problems, including hypertension, glucose intolerance, and orthopaedic problems as well as interpersonal and socio-psychological issues related to self-acceptance, bullying, and body image.

Think for a minute about the causes of eating and of food choice. When do you eat? Are you always hungry before you eat? Are you hungry after you eat? When you are hungry, how often do you stop to make a fresh salad or to eat a piece of fruit? How often do you stop at a fast-food outlet? What do you know about nutrients in various foods? What social changes do you think have led to the "obesity epidemic"?

Of course, as sociologists we are concerned, too, about the ways in which the social construction of obesity as an epidemic serves the interests of those who profit from it, such as pharmaceutical firms, food and drink companies, "health" clubs, the diet industry, the manufacturers of exercise equipment, and even, as this book's editor suggests, medical sociologists(!). One study found a link between the body mass indexes (BMI) of a population and the density and proximity of fast-food restaurants (Reitzel et al., 2014). Another experimental study found that children preferred food wrapped in decorative and colourful wrapping to other food, despite the actual equivalence of the food being tasted (Elliott et al., 2013). There is no doubt that advertising can be highly effective and lead to craving high-fat and high-sugar foods. Some innovative ways are being developed to help people change their eating and exercise behaviour. New apps on cell phones have been successful at times in increasing physical activity and in helping people to lose weight (Schoeppe et al., 2016)

Sexual Assault and Rape

Self-reported sexual assault of Canadian women numbered 635,000 in 2014 (Young, 2017). However, only a fraction of sexual assaults are ever reported. This may reflect the way that reporting experiences with law enforcement and with others can lead to more suffering. These interactions may violate the women who report the assault (Makin, 2018). This lack of valid statistical counts is undoubtedly similar or even more problematic in other parts of the world. Sexual assault is one of the most under-reported of crimes (Benoit et al., 2015). It is estimated that one in 17 women is raped during her lifetime and a woman is sexually assaulted every 17 minutes in Canada.

Change in reporting frequency may be on the horizon in Canada. The "#MeToo" movement, which started as a way to bring sexual assaults in Hollywood and in the entertainment industry more generally to light and to make the perpetrators take responsibility for their actions, spread rapidly across the US in 2016. In the process some of the most trusted news reporters on television and others in industry management lost their jobs amid accusations of sexual assaults. This movement may result in widespread changes both in reporting and in prosecuting sexual assaults in the US and in Canada.

Sexual predation also occurs in the medical care system. Assaults by physicians on their female patients have been reported (McDonald, 2018). Recently, a medical student from the University of Toronto was found guilty of rape after his victim was provided with extra support from new policies in the criminal justice system (Grant, 2018). Further, rape, sexual assault, and gender-based harassment of women in the military and in policing, particularly the RCMP, are critical issues that have come to light in the news recently (Boutilier & Campion Smith, 2015). Rape on college campuses has become a particular problem in recent years. Some even argue that there is a "culture of rape" on college campuses in Canada. What do you think? Some women have responded by organizing and protesting in some creative and novel ways, including the Take Back the Night and Slut Walks.

Sexuality and AIDS

Sexual activity is considered to be another aspect of the public health of Canadians. It is monitored regularly as an indication of the effectiveness of public health policy, especially in regards to STIs. About 30 per cent of teenagers between 15 and 17 have had sex at least once. Sixty-eight per cent of those 18–19 years old have had sexual intercourse at least once (Rotermann, 2012). Clearly, premarital sex is now normative. Beginning sexual activity early is more likely to result in engaging in sex with several or numerous partners over time. Only a fraction of teenagers use condoms always. In the absence of consistent condom use it is no wonder that sexually transmitted infections (STIs) in Canada have increased. These figures reflect a need for continuing concern about unwanted pregnancies and the spread of AIDS and other sexually transmitted diseases among Canadian young people. We will focus on HIV/AIDS in the subsequent discussion.

AIDS is a highly infectious and contagious disease. One important means of transmission is unprotected sex with someone carrying the virus. Discovered in the late 1970s in the US, its presence was not officially noted until 1981. The first case recorded in Canada was in 1982 (Frank, 1996). By 1991 an estimated 50,000 Canadians were infected with the HIV virus, the precursor of AIDS and, by 1995, 9,133 Canadians had died due to AIDS-related conditions (Frank, 1996). As of 2001, 55,000 Canadians were living with an HIV diagnosis and there had been 62,247 reported cases of HIV/AIDS in Canada (Ghosh, 2002). Estimates for 2016 indicate that between 2014 and 2016 HIV infections increased by 5 per cent (CATIE, 2018). Approximately 63,110 Canadians were living with HIV in 2016, according to CATIE, the organization supported by Health Canada that monitors HIV/AIDS in Canada and is a source for information about the infection. A further estimate is that about 14 per cent of those who have been diagnosed, or an additional 9,090, were living with HIV but had not been diagnosed. Any lack of diagnosis in an infected person can be a serious problem for others because infection is spread from person to person via bodily fluids.

Transmission rates by various social groupings or categories follow: about 51.9 per cent of those living with HIV are men who have sex with men (MSM). About 17.4 per cent are injection drug users. About 32.6 per cent of transmission appears to be through heterosexual sex. A small minority of 601 people have HIV due to other means of transmission, most likely blood transfusions, needle-stick injuries at work, and mother-to-child transmission (CATIE, 2018). The incidence of HIV/AIDS among women is increasing in Canada. In 1986, 2 per cent of the HIV-positive population was female; by 1993, 15 per cent of the cases were female; and by 2001, 25 per cent of newly reported cases were female (Ghosh, 2002). Women accounted for approximately 23 per cent of all positive test results in the most recent statistics provided by CATIE, and almost 10 per cent (9.6 per cent) of people with AIDS were Indigenous. This represents a rate of infection approximately twice that of non-Indigenous people because Indigenous people make up somewhat less than 5 per cent of the total population of Canadians (CATIE, 2018).

The presence of HIV/AIDS raises a very important legal/public health issue. Should people be required to divulge their HIV/AIDS status prior to engaging in sexual activity? The Supreme Court of Canada has said yes, if there is a "significant risk" or "realistic risk" of HIV transmission. However, significant/realistic risk is difficult to determine. Further, some argue that this requirement may inhibit the willingness of people to be tested and might therefore be the more dangerous option ultimately. Others think of this as a matter of individual rights versus public health. What do you think?

There is another significant issue for us to discuss in this consideration of sexuality in Canadian society. For many years Canadian women have depended on the annual "Pap smear" to extract cells from the cervix and to detect changes that might mean the beginning of cervical cancer. This screening, which occurred in doctor's offices, was very effective and the rate of cervical cancer remained very low. About 15 years ago, in 2006 (WHO, 2017b), a vaccine against some strains of the virus that causes cervical cancer was introduced and soon spread around the globe. There were a number of public policy debates about its introduction in Canada at the time. For one thing, it was to be administered only to young women and not men. Many people argued that was a bad decision because it targeted only half of the possible vectors of the virus. One feminist position was that it was wrong because it reinforced the idea that the responsibility for safe sex was that of women and girls. Others raised vaccine safety concerns and questioned whether or not it had been tested adequately before marketing. Still others were concerned that it might diminish the success of the annual "Pap smear" if women and girls did not understand that the vaccine offered only limited protection and the annual physical exam was still necessary.

Now, however, the human papillomavirus vaccine is widely accepted and legitimated by the state via the provinces (Government of Canada, 2017). It is administered in schools to girls, and to (fewer) boys, beginning at age nine. It is designed to prevent several strains of the human papillomavirus, which cause some cervical, anal, and penile cancers. The vaccine is not mandatory in Canada, but because it is frequently administered in schools it is offered with an image of substantial legitimacy, without cost, and likely with some felt pressure; consequently, it is widely taken up. About 75 per cent of girls in the relevant age groups have been vaccinated, according to a 2013 survey (Government of Canada, 2016). Figures regarding the uptake among boys are not yet available.

At the same time, a great deal of ongoing controversy has been associated with the administration of the vaccine. Some parents and others have continued to resist the vaccination of youngsters with a relatively newly developed and tested vaccine. There may also be some resistance due to the link between HIV and sexual activity, particularly as it is administered to girls as young as nine years old. There are researchers and advocates who claim that the manufacturing pharmaceutical companies may be obfuscating the many side effects, ranging from minor transient symptoms such as headaches to death. Gartland (2018) reviewed a number of different studies and ultimately claimed that there was insufficient evidence that the Gardasil vaccine, in particular, reduced the incidence of cervical cancer. In fact, in some jurisdictions, she argued, its use might be associated with increasing rates of some cervical cancers due to strains of the virus not prevented by the vaccine coupled with a tendency to ignore the need for Pap smears. Gartland also reports that about 500 people have died from the vaccine itself and that there are 85,000 reports of adverse events around the world. As Gartland notes, the fact that the arbiter of good medical science or evidence-based medicine, the Cochrane Collaboration, is immersed in a controversy about the safety and efficacy of the vaccine may be particularly troubling. Despite the debates and reported side effects the vaccine is still being administered widely around the globe. In fact, it is recommended as a part of routine vaccinations to countries around the world by the World Health Organization (2017b). Have you had the vaccine? If so, do you remember how it was explained to you? Are you comfortable with the amount of research that has been done on its safety and efficacy?

Summary

1. Over the past 150 years there have been dramatic changes in life expectancy in Canada and other developed nations. Many explanations have been suggested for this change, such as improvements in public health, immunization, improved nutrition, improvements in hygiene, and improvements in birth control.

2. Among the major issues affecting health are poverty and inequality, safety, security and stability, the social position of women, birth control, pregnancy and childbirth supports, comprehensive health care, and immunization.

3. Three problems with health consequences are of particular concern in a worldwide context—HIV/AIDS, mental disorders, and conflicts and natural disasters as with the socio-economic inequities revealed by the pandemic of 2020 and beyond, called COVID-19.

4. The chief causes of disease and death in Canada today are cancer, heart disease, cerebrovascular disease, and accidents. These can be referred to as "diseases of civilization and affluence" and are typical of developed nations. Causes of death are related to lifestyle, environmental, and work-related factors. "Self-imposed" contributions to mortality include smoking, drug abuse, excessive alcohol consumption, nutritional inadequacies, lack of exercise or recreation, overwork, reckless driving, and sexual carelessness, all of which are also tightly tied to social status and social class.

5. Physical activity and obesity levels are related to health.

6. AIDS is a devastating new disease that is still spreading in populations around the world. At present, the greatest incidence of AIDS is in sub-Saharan Africa.

Key Terms

core, periphery, and semi-periphery countries
diarrheal disease
diseases of civilization
food insecurity
infant mortality rates
life expectancy
morbidity

mortality rate
political economy perspective
post-traumatic stress disorder (PTSD)
prevalence
primary health care
secondary health care
tertiary care

Questions for Study and Discussion

1. What is the relevance of medical treatment to the overall extension of life expectancy in Canada today?

2. Why do women tend to live longer than men?

3. What are the major causes of global disparities in health and death rates?

4. Why is the position of women central to social and economic development in a worldwide context?

5. Explain the changing gender ratio with respect to HIV/AIDS.

Suggested Readings

Boulos, D., & Zamorski, M.A. (2013). Deployment-related mental disorders among Canadian Forces personnel deployed in support of the mission in Afghanistan 2001–2008. *Canadian Medical Association Journal, 185*(11), 545–52. One study of the after-effects of the global and national issue of war.

Flegel, K. (2013). Big Alcohol catches up with adolescent girls. *Canadian Medical Association Journal, 185*(10), 859. A critical analysis of gendered advertising to increase alcohol consumption among young women.

Lewis, S. (2005). *Race against time.* House of Anansi Press. An impassioned plea for the world to care about the AIDS crisis in Africa by Stephen Lewis, the former United Nations AIDS ambassador to Africa and former Ontario NDP leader.

McKenna, M. (2017). *Big chicken: The incredible story of how antibiotics created modern agriculture and changed the way the world eats.* National Geographic Books. An excellent book on the use of antibiotics in industrial farming.

Moore, S., Teixeira, A., & Shiell, A. (2006). The health of nations in a global context: Trade, global stratification, and infant mortality rates. *Social Science and Medicine, 63,* 165–78. An article linking the big economic picture to health.

Osterholm, M.T., & Olshaker, M. (2017). *Deadliest enemy: Our war against killer germs.* Little, Brown and Company. A description and analysis of the challenges of keeping ahead of new germs.

Palmer, L. (2017). *Hot, hungry planet.* St Martin's Press. An important study linking climate change, starvation, and chronic undernourishment as food excesses exist in parts of the world, and calling for an immediate global response to this crisis.

Environmental and Occupational Health and Illness

3

Chapter Overview

- Water, air, and land are three fundamental parts of the environment upon which we depend for health.
- Environmental threats to all three are ubiquitous and increasing in their potential for destructiveness.
- Among the important environmental threats are climate change, chemicals, air pollution, second-hand smoke, medical pollution, land pollution, e-waste, loss of biodiversity, and lack of food safety and security.

- Occupational health and safety are significant causes of morbidity and mortality in Canada and around the world. Major issues are shift work, time-loss injuries, stress, the health-care industry, and agricultural work.
- Work can be dangerous in Canada. Significant differences according to occupational group, age, and gender occur in accidents related to the workplace.
- Traffic, sports, and other accidents and violence pose important challenges to health and life in Canada, especially for younger Canadians.

Introduction

Our shared physical environment is the bedrock of our own health and well-being and that of other people in the communities in which we live. Researchers are continuing to study the positive mental and other health benefits of various aspects of our environments. For example, researchers have been investigating the effects of living near trees. Kardan and colleagues (2015) found that living on a street with more trees provided marked self-reported benefits both in respect to mental health and in cardio-metabolic health. They claim that living on such a street is comparable, in epidemiological terms, to having an income of $10,000 higher and being seven years younger. Importantly, this finding controlled for both income and other socio-demographic factors. Living near a body of water is also associated with better health (Crouse et al., 2018). However, as the world becomes more dense and urban the health benefits of trees and water may be obscured and their health benefits diminished. The purpose of this chapter is to provide an overview of some of the major environmental and occupational health hazards, their effects on health, and possible sociological explanations for environmental conditions. Do you know anyone diagnosed with allergies or asthma? Are occupational hazards greater for people working in the labour force or for those working at home? Is environmental degradation a threat to health? What are the specific relationships between environments, occupations, and health? What has been the significance, for health, of the following disasters: the nuclear accident at Chernobyl in 1986; the Bhopal, India, gas accident of 1984; PCBs in the Great Lakes; the 2011 tsunami in Japan; the depletion of the Newfoundland cod fishery; the 2000 Walkerton, Ontario, water crisis; and the 1992 Westray mine disaster in Nova Scotia?

The Major Environmental Issues

There are three fundamental components of the environment: air, water, and land. They affect our health both directly (e.g., through the air we breathe and water we drink) and indirectly (e.g., through the food we eat). Environmental hazards in the air and water and on land have increased tremendously over the last century. It has been estimated, although widely disputed and difficult to prove or disprove, that from 60 to 90 per cent of all cancers are in some way environmentally or occupationally caused. The link between particular environmental issues and health is challenging to substantiate. This is partly because environmental hazards may affect our health in ways that are unseen in the short term and only evident in the long term in the health of people as they age or in future generations. Separating specific effects from an infinitely complex environmental "soup" is difficult. Only by accumulating different types of studies—epidemiological, animal, genetic, and others—all of which address the same environmental issue, will it be possible to begin to demonstrate adequately the effects of specific aspects of the environment on health. The studies of trees and water discussed above are just a beginning look at some of the positive effects of environmental factors on health.

It is urgent that we understand the negative effects of the environment on human health. Many diseases of major organ systems—lungs, heart, liver, and kidneys—as well as reproductive problems, birth defects, and behavioural disorders, have been associated with environmental factors. An estimated 50,000 to 70,000 chemical substances are used commercially in farming, manufacturing, and forestry. Every year new chemicals are introduced in North America and worldwide, many of which have not been tested for potential ill effects or for their interactions with chemicals already available. Many new products are used in the home for cleaning or in makeup, shampoo, conditioners, toothpaste, and other personal care items. Radioactive waste, with a half-life of 250 centuries, uranium mine tailings, and low-level radiation leakage from routinely functioning nuclear power plants and weapons facilities are taken for granted as an inevitable part of the environment. For example, just outside of Toronto is the Pickering Nuclear

Generating Station. It is one of the oldest of such facilities in the world. According to the website of this generating station, experts think it can, despite its age, be operated safely until 2024. Maintaining operation until then is explained as saving taxpayers more than $600 million and avoiding eight million tonnes of greenhouse gases. It is said to be saving 4,500 jobs. However, more than two million people face possible devastation if these estimates are faulty. These people live within its fallout zone. But it has a few more years before it will have to be decommissioned. In the meantime, other experts warn that it may be unsafe and that it has been patched together so many times that its longevity is not really guaranteed. Despite the fact that the Pickering facility is meeting all of its government-required safety checks there is always the possibility of error. Thus, there may be some potential for a nuclear disaster posed by this facility just 30 kilometres east of Toronto.

No one expected the Fukushima nuclear disaster. It occurred after a confluence of events, which led to the meltdown at the Fukushima nuclear generating station on 11 March 2011 (see Box 3.1). The first event in the unique chain of events was an earthquake. This led to a tsunami. The tsunami caused a power outage. And the power outage led to the cooling of the nuclear reactors and the meltdown. This was followed by the escape of radiation into the air, water, and soil in this northern area of Japan. Thousands of people died as a result of the disaster, and 100,000 people were evacuated in the aftermath of this catastrophe. Most of the possible health effects are not yet known.

Other countries have become extremely concerned about nuclear accidents. The German moratorium on further nuclear development as a reaction to the Japanese disaster is a case in point. In many ways nuclear accidents are taken for granted by some as the cost of "doing business" and providing energy for modern societies. Nuclear facilities provide a relatively cheap and "clean" source of energy. Yet, they have the ongoing potential for destruction, death, and disease. The prevailing sense of uncertainty that results from living in a society where accidents are normalized, coupled with the certainty that things will go wrong sometime, lies at the heart of the so-called **risk society**.

Environmental risks are now ubiquitous—and growing in potential destructiveness. The whole world is a **global ecosystem**. Changes in one nation-state's environmental policies and procedures, in the amounts of air, water, and land pollution, for example, have the capacity to affect aspects of the ecology of the rest of the world. Even the snows of the remote, virtually uninhabited Antarctic contain residues of PCBs, DDT, and lead, which have emanated directly from industries and combustion in developed and developing nations. Water, air, soil, ice, and snow have been infiltrated with various types and degrees of toxic chemicals. Like other health threats, environmental hazards are unequally distributed. Poorer people in both the developed and developing worlds are less likely to be able to move away from a toxic waste dump, to drink bottled water, which, ironically, may itself be a significant health hazard because of the leaching of chemicals from the plastic into the water, not to mention the pollution generated by the dumping of plastics into the world's oceans, waterways, landfills, and roadside ditches. Poorer people are more threatened by various environmental hazards and are more likely to live on and near contaminated land, and water, and near industrial sites with poor air quality. In addition, decisions about locating noxious facilities are less likely to affect the well-off than the poorer in the population. Figure 3.1 models the impacts of a degraded environment on human health.

The poorer, less-developed countries are unequally subject to the destructive effects of environmental degradation when they, for instance, allow the destruction of precious rainforests for agribusiness, such as cattle ranching, and to provide timber for furniture, housing, or other purposes for the developed world. Moreover, cash-strapped economies of the developing world, lacking alternatives, are more likely to allow the dumping of wastes within their borders in return for cash payments. Thus, the environment of the

Figure 3.1   A Model for the Impact of the Environment on Human Health

Source: WHO (2015). Climate change and human health: Global environmental change. http://www.who.int/globalchange/environment/en/

underdeveloped South, in spite of a relative lack of industrialization, is more vulnerable in some ways than that of the developed North.

Climate Change

A number of environmental issues threaten the everyday health and safety of all people on the planet. The most critical is **climate change**, sometimes referred to as global warming. This is chiefly the result of the production of carbon dioxide by the burning of fossil fuels to provide home heating and power for industry, automobiles, and other vehicles, and of methane produced through livestock emissions. Planes produce more carbon dioxide and thus contribute even more to global warming than other modes of travel, particularly because of their altitude (Clark, 2010). Some calculate that the methane from animal waste (because of its particular properties) is responsible for as much global warming as all of the other gases added

together (Mohr, 2005). An implication of this argument is that one of the most effective ways of combatting global warming is through adopting a vegetarian or vegan diet.

The problem is that carbon dioxide and other air pollutants, including methane and nitrous oxide, reflect the sun's radiant energy back to earth, causing a warming trend that affects, among many things, crop growth and the probability of flooding from the melting of glaciers. As glaciers retreat and shrink and snow cover decreases, the earth absorbs more heat from the sun rather than reflecting this radiant heat back into space (the albedo effect). According to recent estimates the average global temperature on earth has grown about 0.8 degrees Celsius since the end of the nineteenth century, or about 1880. Two-thirds of this warming has occurred since 1975 (NASA Earth Observatory, n.d.). In northern Canada the temperature increase has been and may continue to be greater than average. The evidence indicates that the average temperature of the surface of the globe will continue to increase over the next century if changes are not made quickly. This could result in a continuation of severe weather patterns and drought, greater flooding, more devastating hurricanes and tornadoes, and increasing wildfires, along with a rise in sea levels that could displace coastal and island people.

Global warming has both direct and indirect effects on human health. The indirect effects operate through the many changes in the physical environment in Canada, such as drought on the Prairies, decline of water supplies in southern Canada, soil degradation, erosion, and flooding of coastal regions, more extreme and longer-lasting wildfires (Hausfather, 2018), and extreme weather events. In Canada's North, sea ice is already declining dramatically and is expected to decline further. Wildlife and fish have been affected and wildlife hunting and fishing patterns have altered. These changes will continue to result in fundamental degradations in the quality and availability of primary requisites for human life—food and water for people in the North. Temperature increases may also directly cause certain health problems, especially affecting the cardiovascular, cerebrovascular, and respiratory systems. As

A firefighting helicopter approaches a wildfire in British Columbia. As climate change is allowed to worsen, extreme weather events such as wildfires will have a greater impact on the physical and mental health of Canadians.

well, the northward migration of tropical and subtropical health risks such as malaria and Lyme disease will likely continue. As carbon dioxide concentrations in the atmosphere increase, the number of deaths can be expected to grow. For example, during summer heat waves in Los Angeles, when temperatures averaged about 41°C, the peak mortality was between 172 per cent and 445 per cent higher than would have been expected (at all ages) at lower temperatures. Among people over 85 the peak mortality was considerably higher. It ranged from 257 per cent to 810 per cent more

Figure 3.2 Global Temperature, 1880–2017

Source: Climate Atlas of Canada (2018). Climate change: The basics. https://climateatlas.ca/climate-change-basics

than the expected mortality levels. The 2003 heat wave in Paris is said to have resulted in 14,802 deaths and across Europe claimed more 35,000 lives (*USA Today*, 2003; Bhattacharya, 2003). More than 700 people reportedly died in the Chicago heat wave in 1995 (Semenza et al., 1996). In Canada, work-related illnesses linked to excessive heat exposure are increasing and are expected to continue to be a growing problem (Government of Canada, 2019a).

Canada's global role in climate change is significant. Canadians emitted an estimated 704 million tonnes of **greenhouse gases (GHGs)** into the atmosphere in 2016 (Environmental Defense Fund, 2019), a decrease from 2007 emissions of 761 megatonnes. But is this a case of too little, too late? In fact, our rate of production of GHGs has surpassed even the rate of population growth. When Canada ratified the **Kyoto Accord** in December 2002, it made a commitment to reduce emissions to 6 per cent below the 1990 levels by 2008–12. This goal was subject to the whims of politics and the pressures by industry on the political party in power. In Canada, these pressures are complicated by our federal system of government whereby industry, through lobbying tactics, can

pressure provinces, or the federal government in Ottawa, with the threat of lost revenues and jobs if more stringent environmental regulations are enacted. Similar scenarios play out around the world, and much depends on the will of political leaders, corporations, and the people. US President Donald Trump, for example, did not believe in climate change and opted out of global agreements and targets for reducing greenhouse gases, loosened regulations within the United States, and opened up vast areas of protected lands to exploitation. In Canada there has never been a clear and irrevocable plan for implementing GHG reductions. By 2008, Canada's GHG emissions, driven primarily by energy-intensive projects in Alberta's oil sands, were 24 per cent above 1990 emissions and 31 per cent higher than the Kyoto target (Commissioner of the Environment and Sustainable Development, 2011, p. 47). Canada formally reneged on its commitment at the United Nations Climate Change Conference in Durban, South Africa, in December 2011, where countries of the world, after much dispute, agreed to try to reach a new agreement by 2015, which became known as the Paris Agreement. Regardless of any significant international agreements in the foreseeable future,

Figure 3.3   Carbon Dioxide Concentration, 1958–2018

Source: Climate Atlas of Canada (2018). Climate change: The basics. https://climateatlas.ca/climate-change-basics

the likelihood is negligible of Canada meeting any firm targets, especially since the hugely polluting oil sands projects and related pipeline developments in Alberta, British Columbia, and elsewhere across the country are supported by the federal government. Meanwhile, the federal government's policies for mitigating these polluting economic drivers have not garnered widespread support, despite the stalwart resistance of some First Nations communities and their supporters, as well as environmentalists and some provincial governments.

Chemicals and Health

The World Health Organization has summarized research on the major threats to health caused by a few select and well-researched chemicals that are part of the everyday life of people around the globe. These substances include arsenic, asbestos, benzene, cadmium, dioxin or dioxin-like substances, fluoride, lead, methyl mercury, and highly hazardous pesticides. They are especially problematic for the most biologically vulnerable, including children, infants, fetuses, and the elderly (WHO, n.d. a). Arsenic is a concern because chronic exposure can lead to severe health problems including cancer and heart disease and, with enough exposure, death. Asbestos has been linked to lung diseases of many kinds, including lung cancer. Benzene's domestic exposure is through petrochemical products and solvents. It is associated with a number of different diseases including cancer. Cadmium mostly comes from cigarette smoke and contaminated foods. It is a carcinogen. Lead is problematic as it is associated with neurotoxic effects such as neuro-developmental impairment, learning disabilities, attention deficit, poor motor co-ordination, poor language development, and anemia. Children are especially susceptible because of their frequent hand/mouth activity and their tendency to eat chalk (some but not all of which has been found to contain lead), sand, and dirt. Lead and other harmful toxins are found in some antique toys and in toys imported from countries with different standards of production. Pencils, however, are made of non-toxic graphite,

not lead; the term "lead pencil" is a misnomer. People, including children, are exposed to lead through emissions from automobiles, water from lead-lined pipes, old paint, and so on.

Methyl mercury, derived mainly from combustion in incinerators and coal plants, as well as from the decomposition of vegetation when land is flooded by dams built for hydroelectric projects, is deposited into water systems where fish take it up. Eating such fish (particularly freshwater fish such as trout, pike, and bass; and saltwater shark and swordfish) inserts mercury into the human system. Mercury is a neurotoxin associated with seizures, blindness, deafness, cerebral palsy, and developmental delays. It can be passed through breast milk. Dioxins, dibenzofurans, and PCBs result from industrial processes and incineration. Human exposure is mostly from food, including breast milk. Among the health consequences are neuron-developmental and reproductive problems.

Pesticides (including fungicides, herbicides, and insecticides) are used extensively in agriculture and for other, sometimes cosmetic, purposes (e.g., lawn care). Exposure is through food, water, inhalation, and skin absorption. Some pesticides can cause cancer and damage to the nervous, reproductive, and immune systems. Nitrates can be reduced to nitrites in the body, which are associated with changes in the blood as well as stomach and esophageal cancers. Pesticides have also been linked to attention deficit hyperactivity disorder (ADHD) through an epidemiological study of 1,139 children. Pesticides were found in 94 per cent of all of the children in this study, but those with higher levels of pesticides in their blood were more likely to have been diagnosed with ADHD. Children living on and near farms are especially susceptible to pesticide ingestion but all children (and adults) who eat non-organic food regularly absorb pesticides (Johnson, 2010).

An estimated 21,000 premature deaths are attributable to air pollution in Canada every year. This figure is nine times that of the number of people who die in traffic accidents annually (Brauer et al., 2013). Several studies have found a

Remembering Our History

Box 3.1 • Bhopal and Fukushima

One historical example of the effects of the political economy on the environment and the health of peoples in the developing world brings to light a number of issues. In 1984, in one of the worst industrial disasters ever, an explosion in a Union Carbide plant in Bhopal, India, spewed more than 40 tons of lethal methyl isocyanate gas into the slums immediately surrounding the plant. More than 6,000 people were killed. Many thousands of others were blinded, disabled, and made ill as a result of the "accident."

This tragedy was absolutely avoidable; that it happened is the result of a number of important factors common in industries imported from the developed to the developing world. First, the Union Carbide plant in Bhopal was relatively unprofitable as compared to other divisions of Union Carbide elsewhere in the world. At the time of the accident, the Bhopal plant was for sale. It lacked top-level interest or support within the corporation. A number of divisions within the plant had been closed down. Personnel had been let go and not replaced. Thus, it was operating with only a partial complement of workers and with equipment in poor repair. It was also, however, involved in the manufacture of dangerous chemicals such as methyl isocyanate. In spite of the objections of the municipal authorities, the central and state governments allowed it to continue operating without adequate safety precautions and regulations. There were no adequate plans for dealing

with a major accident, and the company personnel did not really understand the potentially lethal effects of the methyl isocyanate gas. The external regulation was extremely weak. In the interest of fostering the importation and investment of capital to their countries, governments in developing countries frequently ignore or are unaware of even minimal health and safety standards. The "accident" at Bhopal is just one example of the potential for widespread industrial-based devastation in the developing world.

More recently, Canadians indirectly witnessed the effects of the March 2011 earthquake followed by the tsunami in Japan, one of the most successfully developed and populated countries in the world. These ecological catastrophes led to the nuclear meltdowns at Fukushima nuclear plant and the nearly immediate deaths from drowning and other environmental destruction of about 20,000 people. The most serious nuclear crisis since Chernobyl in Russia, the consequences of the Fukushima disaster threatened the ocean waters near Japan and the land upon which millions depend for food and a place to live. Debris washed ashore as far away as the west coast of Canada. The long-term effects of the radiation exposure resulting from the meltdown are still not completely understood. A nuclear plume reached Canada's Pacific coast in 2014 but it had apparently become so diffused by the current that it did not pose any threat to human health (Smith et al., 2015).

link between living near a busy road and a 50 per cent increase in leukemia in children, possibly because of the higher concentrations of benzene, a product of gas combustion. One study (Rundell et al., 2006) has raised another concern about the vehicular air pollution that occurs when children's playgrounds, school playgrounds, and athletic

fields are located near busy traffic roadways. The study found a strong relationship between distance from high-traffic roads and levels of particulate matter in the air. Numerous potential policy options have been put forward. Our continued dependence on the car for transportation ensures that this is an ongoing source of major pollutants. It is

CRITICAL THINKING

Box 3.2 • Environmental Illness

An increasing number of North Americans are suffering from what they consider the results of low-level exposures to synthetic chemicals and what has been called by a variety of names, including multiple chemical sensitivity (MCS), chemically induced hyper-susceptibility, immune system dysregulation, **environmental illness (EI)**, and **twentieth-century disease**. These diseases are characterized by multiple, complex symptomatology in which both the symptoms and the causes are subjectively defined by the patient. They usually involve indications across a variety of organs. The sufferer is often subject to a range of signs and indications, of varying severity, some of which change considerably from day to day. Among the various symptoms often reported are headaches, rashes, depression, shortness of breath, muscle pains, and irritability. Equally troubling is the fact that symptoms often cannot be detected by standard methods. Nor can their intermediary effects on such things as the immune system be measured. They are not caused by known pathogens. Thus, sufferers are sometimes thought to be malingering or mentally ill.

In 1965 a small group of physicians, scientists, and health professionals founded the Society for Clinical Ecology to address the issues being brought forward by such sufferers. Today, in Canada, this organization has been combined with occupational medicine and renamed the Occupational and Environmental Medical Association of Canada. It has become a well-established medical association with physicians from across the country and annual research meetings.

However, a great deal of research needs to be undertaken to define, diagnose, and begin to treat such multi-system diseases as those mentioned above.

People with environmental sensitivities have to be careful about where they live, where they go to school and play, what they eat, drink, and smell. Their whole lives may be affected by their sensitivities. Because of the many biological systems possibly involved in EI or MCS, the multitude of ever-changing symptoms, and the time lag there may be between exposure and the development of health problems, this, like fibromyalgia, chronic Lyme disease, and chronic fatigue syndrome, may the patient to search from doctor to doctor to find one who believes the patient, accepts that there is a biologically based problem, and is willing to offer a diagnosis. These are examples of illnesses for which one has to "fight to get a diagnosis" (Dumit, 2006).

Varieties of perfumes and fragrant after-shave products that used to be pervasive in the air are virtually absent now. They have often been banned because so many people have developed responses ranging from severe health reactions to nausea and discomfort. Peanut allergies have become so common that many Canadian parents just assume they cannot send peanut butter to school on their children's sandwiches. The gradual spread of food sensitivities, such as to gluten, is another reflection of creeping but largely invisible changes in the environment. We have come to accept these sensitivities or allergies as inevitable side effects of modern life and life in a risk society.

essential to the healthy future of the country and of Canadians that we support the use of alternative means of transportation such as electric cars, bicycle lanes, scooters, and forms of public mass transportation that do not rely on gas and oil and are less polluting or not at all polluting.

Air Pollution and Human Health

Both indoor and outdoor air contribute at least low levels of pollutants, including ozone, sulphur oxides, nitrogen oxides, carbon monoxide, and other particulates that may irritate eyes and inflame the respiratory tract. Long-term exposure may have a negative effect on the immune system and be implicated in chronic respiratory problems such as emphysema and chronic bronchitis, cancer, asthma, cardiovascular disease, chronic obstructive pulmonary disease, and various respiratory infections (Raven et al., 1993, p. 435). Ground-level ozone has been linked to health impacts ranging from minor respiratory problems to cardiovascular disease, hospitalizations, and premature death. It also has associated economic effects, including lower labour force participation and increased health-care costs.

Air pollution is already known to kill men and women across the globe. The World Health Organization estimates that nine out of ten people in the world breathe polluted air. They estimate that it kills seven million people a year. Approximately one-third of the deaths from lung cancer, stroke, and heart disease are estimated to be the result of air pollution. Furthermore, these problems are bound to get worse as the world heats up (WHO, n.d. b). Air pollution also affects general human health, principally through the respiratory and the cardiovascular systems. Among the other illnesses most likely linked to or exacerbated by air pollution are minor lung illnesses, such as the common cold, as well as lung infections such as pneumonia, asthma, chronic obstructive pulmonary disease (COPD), and coronary artery disease (WHO, n.d. b). Burnett, Cakmak, and Brook (1998) examined daily deaths in 11 Canadian cities from 1980 to 1991 and evaluated the association of these deaths to concentrations of ambient gaseous air pollutants. They found that nitrogen dioxide had the largest effect on mortality, a 14.1 per cent increased risk, followed by ozone (1.8 per cent), sulphur dioxide (1.4 per cent), and carbon monoxide (0.9 per cent). The five cities (Montreal, Toronto, Winnipeg, Edmonton, and Vancouver) that were able to reduce sulphur content in gas to 30 ppm were able to show a risk reduction. This study was published 20 years ago. During those years cities have grown, the climate has changed, the world has gotten hotter, there are more automobiles and

other vehicles, and air travel has increased dramatically. The levels of pollutants can only have increased. The Canadian government's response has "individualized" the problem, another example of our being expected to learn to live with risk under a neo-liberal order. It offers the Air Quality Health Index (AQHI), a measure of how polluted the air is on any given day in specific locations, and advises what level of activity is safe given the risk level (Government of Canada, 2019b). Air pollution also gets inside buildings. An extreme case of indoor air pollution is the "sick-building syndrome" in which the presence of air pollution inside tightly sealed buildings can lead to a variety of illnesses. Total environmental sensitivity, in which a person is allergic to myriad components in the modern environment, including indoor and outdoor air pollution, has forced some people to live in totally sterile environments.

The chief source of air pollutants is industrial manufacturing and the second is transportation. Since the proportion of the Canadian economy dependent on manufacturing is decreasing, that portion of the cause of the problems should also decrease. If there is a reduction in transportation dependent on fossil fuels there should be a diminution in air pollution in the long run. But all air pollution does not originate in cities. The countryside contributes a share of greenhouse gases, largely via methane gas. About 9 per cent is from natural processes such as wetlands, animal manure, and the like. Methane is a serious problem that traps CO_2 and thus magnifies the effect of global warming.

An important harmful indoor pollutant may be radon, a tasteless, odourless gas that forms naturally during the radioactive decay of uranium in the earth's crust. Radon seeps through the earth and into basements. It greatly increases the deleterious effects of smoking on the lungs of smokers. Recently published research has linked high radon levels in the home to lung cancer. One geographic study positively documented the association between levels of radon across the country of Canada and levels of lung cancer

CRITICAL THINKING

Box 3.3 • Last Gasp

Asthma is a confusing disease. Although it tends to run in families, it also develops in those who have no history of asthma among their kin. It may strike at any age, but children, with their small breathing tubes, are particularly vulnerable. It is chronic and thus continues for a lifetime. Asthma is especially prevalent among people in certain occupational groups such as hairdressers (Albin et al., 2002). About 15 per cent of asthma is caused by occupational exposure. Today, 3.8 million Canadians, or approximately 10.8 per cent of the total population, have been diagnosed with asthma (Government of Canada, 2018a).

Asthma involves a sometimes lethal inflammation of the airways to the lungs. In asthma sufferers, the bronchial tubes or airways are extremely sensitive to a variety of triggers unique to each patient. These triggers include those in modern office buildings, such as the hundreds of chemicals and biological agents in the air, including chromium dust, acrylates,

and epoxy resins. In factories and shops, there are more unseen dangers like fluorocarbon propellants breathed in by beauticians, sulphur dioxide fumes inhaled by brewery workers, and chlorine gas encountered by petrochemical workers.

Other triggers are common in homes. Central heating, mattresses and upholstering, curtains and wall-to-wall carpeting are breeding grounds for microscopic dust mites that produce a potent allergen in their dung. Common household products such as vapours from cleaning solvents and paint thinners and the fumes from such personal products as spray deodorants and scented cosmetics can also set off an asthmatic attack. Some individuals display fewer and milder symptoms while others face life-threatening spasms. While the most popular instant treatment, the puffer or inhaler, may at times save lives, it also is associated with iatrogenic diseases. Thus, frequent, long-time use may prove dangerous to the health of the user.

(Hystad et al., 2014). Another indoor pollutant with serious health costs is asbestos. Often used as insulation because it does not conduct heat or electricity, asbestos can break down into almost invisible fibres that can be inhaled. When inhaled, asbestos irritates the lungs. It is related to lung cancer and mesothelioma, a rare and almost always fatal cancer. Many millions of workers in Canada and around the world have been exposed to asbestos in mining, textile industries, and construction industries (Firth et al., 1997).

In the last several decades various levels of government have acknowledged the dangers of asbestos, which have been known since the 1920s, and have introduced laws to remove asbestos insulation from public buildings such as schools and

offices and to eliminate its use in new buildings. Unfortunately, some research has shown that removing asbestos can release fibres that would otherwise remain stable; thus, it is sometimes safer to seal asbestos in place. For a number of years, however, the Canadian government continued to reject the idea of a ban on asbestos, which had been supported by developed countries around the world, including Japan, Sweden, Britain, and Australia (Galloway, 2014). This is surprising because more than 1,200 successful claims for fatality benefits were made in Canada by workers between 2007 and 2012. Canada continued to mine asbestos until 2011, long after its destructive effects were widely known. It was not fully banned until 2018 (Nelson, 2017).

Thirteen per cent of Canadians smoke cigarettes. This varies by province: the percentage is 18.5 in Newfoundland and Labrador and 10.2 in British Columbia (Statistics Canada, 2015). This means that there is still a substantial burden of second-hand smoke in the atmosphere. Second-hand smoke is both an environmental and an occupational health issue. It is an environmental issue because smoking may affect others in homes, apartment buildings, on the streets, in public buildings, on public transportation, and in restaurants and stores. It is a workplace issue because workers may be involuntarily exposed to the second-hand smoke of their colleagues. All provinces in Canada have banned indoor smoking in all public buildings. Further, most Canadian provinces have banned smoking in cars when children under 16 are present and many households have decided to voluntarily ban smoking within their homes. Second-hand smoke contains over 100 chemical agents, including carcinogens and toxins (Ontario Campaign for Action on Tobacco, 2003). Substantial documentation now shows that second-hand smoke is associated with higher risks of various other diseases. There are two sources of second-hand smoke: sidestream smoke (given off by the burning tip of a cigarette, pipe, or cigar) and exhaled smoke (puffed out by the smoker). Among the toxic chemicals released into the air in these ways are nicotine, tar, carbon monoxide, formaldehyde, hydrogen cyanide, ammonia, and nitrogen oxide. The health effects include lung cancer, nasal sinus cancer, bronchitis, emphysema, asthma, hay fever, cystic fibrosis, headaches, coughs, throat irritation, heart and circulatory diseases, pregnancy complications, sudden infant death syndrome (SIDS), and low-birth-weight babies.

Automobiles and other motor vehicles continue to be a major source of air pollution, although emissions per vehicle have been reduced since the Clean Air Act of 1971. However, the number of vehicles has grown as the population has increased and the total number of kilometres driven per car has increased. There were 33.8 million registered vehicles in Canada in 2016. This was an increase of 1.8 per cent over the previous year, according to Statistics Canada (*The Daily*, 2016). Three of the top-selling automobiles in 2017 were "gas-guzzling" pickup trucks (Driving.ca, 2018). Pickup trucks and sports utility vehicles (SUVs) are relatively popular and make up a significant part of the market. In overall terms there has been a shift in the types of vehicles used for personal transportation from automobiles to mini-vans, SUVs, and light-duty gasoline-powered trucks. Not only do these vehicles consume more petroleum products but they also release more emissions. Four common air contaminants from automobiles are carbon monoxide, nitrogen oxides, hydrocarbon, and ground-level ozone. In high concentrations, these substances can affect pulmonary function, suppress immune responses, and result in toxic and carcinogenic effects and even, in high enough concentrations, death. They also contribute to acid rain, depletion of the ozone layer, and global warming or climate change.

Another significant source of pollution comes from household cleaners, **pharmaceutical and personal care products (PPCPs)** such as cosmetics and shampoos, and prescribed and over-the-counter medicines. Any of these may contain chemicals that are bad for your health. Although the amounts may be very small or "trace," the fact that we may rub them into our skin and use them daily has potential ill health effects. Many people are intolerant of or allergic to some scents and chemicals, even when used by others, because they circulate in the air, much like second-hand smoke (Weeks, 2010). Researchers have been finding chemicals in the water supply from cosmetics, toiletries, food additives, veterinary drugs, and pharmaceuticals for humans (Batt, 2004, 2010). PPCPs are growing in use and in consequence they are building up in the water. People frequently flush PPCPs down the toilet or drains, although the recommendation is to return unused products to a pharmacy. Eventually, those chemicals reappear in the consumable water supply, as they are not all eliminated from drinking water. We each carry a personal plume of chemicals from the personal care products that we use. This can be tracked and this plume is an important contributor to air pollution (Jamal, 2018).

Farm animals are another significant source of pollution from pharmaceuticals, particularly of hormones and antibiotics. These chemicals are excreted onto the land and then absorbed by humans who eat animal products and then, in turn, excrete a portion of the chemicals. Even cemeteries are a source of PPCPs, as they are emitted after death. This is especially problematic because of the substantial ingestion of highly toxic chemicals as pharmaceuticals, a routine part of end-of-life health care. Routinely, as we use PPCPs our bodies absorb only a portion and the rest are expelled in the short term. In the long term PPCPs are building up in the air, water, and earth and have the potential to increase pollution. Growing antibiotic resistance, a significant health concern, can be attributed to the widespread and routine use of antibiotics in animals as well as in human health care.

Water Pollution and Human Health

The World Health Organization reports that water and sanitation are the major focuses of public health interventions worldwide. Unclean water is linked to many different diseases, including but not limited to diarrhea, malaria, schistosomiasis, Japanese encephalitis, hepatitis A, cholera, and typhoid. The WHO (2017) estimates that about 2 billion people depend on water contaminated by feces. Such contaminated water can cause diarrhea, cholera, dysentery, typhoid, and polio. It is estimated to cause 502,000 deaths every year from diarrhea alone (WHO, 2017). On the positive side, about 71 per cent of the world's population has access to well-managed water (US Environmental Protection Agency, n.d.). The Great Lakes comprise about 21 per cent of the world's fresh water and 84 per cent of the fresh surface water for North America. However, 25 per cent of Canadian agriculture and 7 per cent of US agriculture is located around the Great Lakes Basin. The continuing pollution and destruction of the Great Lakes could be a disaster because they are a source of drinking water for millions people on both sides of the border. Still, the health of the Great Lakes is threatened by farming and industries on both sides of the borders. There is also some good news in this story. The Canadian and US governments have dedicated substantial funds to rehabilitate fish stocks and wildlife, improve the sediment and the overall quality of the water in the lakes, and improve wastewater treatment plants. The continuity of policies designed to keep the water clean are always vulnerable to political change and may be particularly fraught because any policies and programs have to be negotiated with the US, bordering as it does on these same bodies of water.

The overuse of water is another environmental threat, and Canada is among the top water consumers in the world. Canadians consume more water daily on a per capita basis than any other country, although this statistic declined 35 per cent from 1991 to 2013 (McKenzie, 2016). Free trade agreements and pressure from the US to divert some of Canada's water south of the border potentially comprise a great hazard to the Canadian water supply and health. Domestically and industrially, Canada is a major consumer of water. The selling of Canadian water to for-profit water bottling companies also stands as an ongoing threat to water adequacy for Canadians into the future.

While oil spills, pollutants released into water from pulp mills, chemical companies, and other industries, and hydroelectric dams have caused serious water pollution, killed fish, and irrevocably damaged health in particular areas, human exploitation of freshwater and ocean resources has been even more devastating. Overfishing and bottom dredging by foreign and Canadian trawlers exhausted the cod stocks off Newfoundland. In response, the Canadian government declared a moratorium on the cod fishery in 1992. This chain of events has been a disaster for Newfoundland and Labrador, as cod had been the basis for the economy for hundreds of years. The World Wildlife Foundation has posted a notice that the cod fishery is in the process of being partly restored with new guidelines to govern fishing policies. In fact, cod fishing was restored to the south coast of the island in March 2014. As guidelines and policies for fishing going forward will involve conditions for international fishers to meet, their oversight may very well be "tricky" (World Wildlife Fund, 2014). On Canada's west coast, beginning early in the twentieth century, hydroelectric dams cut off salmon from their spawning grounds in some rivers. Overfishing, Canada–US disputes regarding fishing quotas, and the continued pollution of salmon rivers have significantly reduced the wild salmon fishery. At the same time, salmon farms pollute coastal estuaries and foster viral diseases. Furthermore, the demand for fish pellets as feed in aqua farming places food chains and fisheries in other parts of the world under severe stress. On both sides of Canada and around the world the health of the oceans is threatened.

Waste, Land Pollution, and Human Health

One of the most contested of contemporary issues is what to do with solid waste—domestic, manufacturing, hospital, radioactive, e-waste, or waste from any other source. Literature on hazardous waste disposal in Canada and the United States points to a problem with fewer and fewer solutions as land masses on both sides of the border and, indeed, around the world become populated. Debates about such waste disposal have spawned a popular acronym, NIMBY (not in my

backyard). Without doubt, this environmental problem concerns the effect on humankind of the thousands of by-products and wastes of our industrial society, ranging from slightly annoying products to deadly toxins and chemicals. Canada is both an importer and exporter of hazardous wastes for disposal. Some of the hazardous materials Canada accepts are arsenic, phenols, acid, and lead (Environment Canada, 2017). As the deleterious effects of hazardous waste disposal become more widely known, dumping wastes becomes a complicated legal and political issue. Chapter 14 discusses drug dumping in the less-developed world. Hazardous waste dumping in countries of the Global South is a similar problem. When some industries in the richer developed world have needed to get rid of hazardous wastes, they have shipped them to countries in the developing world. Some nations around the world have tentatively committed to some controls on international shipments of wastes, such as those from hospitals and pharmaceutical companies, PCBs, mercury, lead, and other chemicals that are known to be harmful. Such commitments are almost impossible to monitor effectively.

E-Waste

E-waste refers to all waste that comes from or is caused by electronics. It contains materials such as lead, mercury, arsenic, and chromium—all known or suspected agents of harm to wildlife and human health. E-waste is a major concern because of our heavy and growing reliance on electronics. This includes electronic technologies such as cell phones and computers and the many new devices that regularly enter the marketplace because such items are readily discarded as they quickly become obsolete. E-waste is the fastest-growing hazardous waste in Canada and around the world (Schroeder & Schroeder, 2018). In 2000, Ontario was home to four companies in the business of e-waste recycling; by 2004, there were 14 companies (*Canada Year Book*, 2006). This number continues to grow as entrepreneurs develop markets for the various valuable components of computers, televisions, and other electronic devices. Still the problem

Box 3.4 • Plastics

Plastic bags take between 500 and 1,000 years to decompose (Hague, 2019). Yet we in Canada use about 3 billion single-use plastic bags every year. It is not that we don't worry about it. Even by 2012, 59 per cent of Canadians felt that stores should not hand out plastic bags to customers (Cross, 2012). Another poll, in 2019, found that 90 per cent of Canadians worried about the effects of plastics on the environment (Hague, 2019). However, eliminating plastics completely from our lives is virtually impossible. While moving to carrying our own cloth bags for grocery and other shopping is a step in the right direction, supermarkets, in particular, are filled with items surrounded by plastic. Meat and fish that have been cut and prepared, for example, typically are presented in a Styrofoam platter covered in plastic. Fruits and vegetables often come packaged in plastic. Further, how would we be able to dispose of garbage without plastic bags? Plastic is not only ubiquitous in our everyday lives, it is also hard to imagine a life without it. And yet plastics are a serious threat to land (through landfill sites), air through incineration, and water through choking waterways and the fish and animals of the sea.

It is estimated that by 2050 there will be more plastic in the oceans of the world than fish (Hague, 2019).

continues to surge even as small companies are trying to manage it. Most provinces have introduced e-waste diversion programs for some products that transfer the cost of removal from the municipalities to the companies that produce the products (Schroeder & Schroeder, 2018). This has usually involved charging the consumer the fee for disposal of the device up-front at the time of purchase. Although 90 per cent of computer parts can be recycled only about 40 per cent of the population recycles. About half of those who do not recycle say it is because they do not know where to do so. Fifty-two per cent of Canadians with unwanted computers sent them to a drop-off centre for recycling (Paul, 2014). Clearly, we have far to go in ensuring that all e-waste makes it to recycling centres.

Biodiversity

All of these threats to the air, water, and land have another profound implication for the future of life on the planet—the decline in biodiversity. For instance, although the rainforests comprise only 7 per cent of the earth's surface, they are home to almost half of the living species on the planet. While it is impossible to know exactly how many species exist at present, some scientific estimates suggest that the total number of species is in the range of 30 million. For example, researchers have identified more than 1,000 species of ant (Wilson, 1991). The impact of the decline in biodiversity on the health of human populations is not entirely known. However, the enormous interdependence in this complex ecosystem implies that the extinction of some species may indirectly lead to the extinction of others and ultimately may lead to the destruction of species that serve to protect human life. You may be aware of the serious concerns raised by the collapse of some honeybee colonies (colony collapse disorder). This is not just a problem of the decline of available honey but has the possibility of widespread, catastrophic ramifications on other natural phenomena, such as the pollination of a wide variety of plants—including many nut trees, berries, vegetables, and fruits. But there is good news to report here, too. The incidence of colony collapse disorder seems to have been decreasing (Bjerga, 2017).

Canada in a Global Context

Box 3.5 • Dumps around the World

All around the world are places where people live on the proceeds of the materials left by those richer than they are. They live on and off dumps. Delhi's dumps are just one example and have been called "public health time bombs" (Glauser, 2013). The Okhla landfill is one of three major dumps in New Delhi. It receives about 8,000 tons of waste on a daily basis. New Delhi is planning to incinerate the waste to produce energy. The dumpsite workers ("rag pickers") are unhappy about this possibility. The introduction of the first incinerator for garbage in New Delhi has resulted in the elimination of hundreds of jobs. As

sickening as the dumpsite work is (with bacterial infections, biological hazards, and other unwanted and unsafe and polluting materials), it has provided a squalid but basic income for thousands of children and families. Some people argue that the government, instead of throwing these people out of work, should equip them with safety gear and pay them for the recyclable and reusable things they find. Others support incineration because of the multitude of dangerous contaminants faced by the "rag pickers." What side would you take on this issue in a debate? Why?

Highlighted Issues

Box 3.6 • Wildfires and Suicide

Environmental catastrophes can and often do have serious impacts on the mental health of those who have been in their midst. We understand how these disasters have a catastrophic bearing on the physical body and can even lead to death. However, the psychological consequences are often equally traumatic. Whether a tsunami, a hurricane, a tornado, an earthquake, a wildfire, or something else, such catastrophe can disrupt one's ongoing sense of security. The day-to-day routine disappears. The coping mechanisms that we all develop to manage our everyday lives are overturned. Perhaps you rely on coffee in the morning, or a particular type of pillow for sleeping, organic foods, vegetables only, or another special diet, working out at the gym, reading, watching television, or something else entirely. Routines in eating and exercising, sleeping, and so on can become totally disrupted. More than that, victims may lose contact with the people who are close to them—family and friends. They may not be able to locate significant others for a period of some time, and likely will be temporarily homeless. Indeed,

depending on the disaster, it may be a very long time, if ever, before they are able to return home, that is, if there even is a home to return to.

It is in this context that a recent study of the consequences of the May 2016 Fort McMurray wildfire on students between Grades 7 and 12 was undertaken (Brown et al., 2019). Many people lost their homes. The town was evacuated. The researchers who studied the students 18 months after the disaster found that 31 per cent of the students who had experienced the wildfire had symptoms characteristic of a diagnosis of depression. Of these, 17 per cent had symptoms of moderate to severe depression and 16 per cent had contemplated suicide. The researchers contrasted these results with a control group of students from Red Deer (a town of approximately the same size, 100,000 and also in Alberta) who had not gone through such a disaster and found that the rates of depression were almost twice as high in Fort McMurray and four times higher for suicidal ideation.

Food Safety

In August of 2014 a California slaughterhouse was indicted for selling beef infected with cancer. The owners faced up to 20 years in jail and hundreds of thousands of dollars in fines for trying to avoid detection, misbranding the meat, and placing it in the market (Weller, 2014). Alberta, in 2012, witnessed the largest meat recall in Canadian history. In September 2006, Canadians were warned not to eat spinach packaged in the US after the US Food and Drug Administration linked an outbreak of E. coli to raw spinach. Spinach was found to be contaminated and recalled in 2019. In October 2006 two Toronto residents became paralyzed after drinking organic carrot juice infected with botulism. Three brands of organic carrot juice produced in the US were taken from the market (*CBC News*, 2006). Food safety has emerged as an important environmental and public health issue in the last three decades or so. Frequent outbreaks of food-borne diseases have caught the attention of the media and, thus, the public, including but not limited to bovine spongiform encephalitis (BSE). Each year, about one in eight Canadians or 4 million people are affected by a food-related illness, including salmonella, norovirus, and listeria. This results in about 240 deaths and 11,600 hospitalizations annually (Government of Canada, 2018b). Some of these cases are the result of home preparation methods; others result from contaminated food from the grocery store (e.g., the Listeria outbreak in 2008 that caused the deaths of 22 people and serious illness among 57 is a case in point). Another source for contaminated food is restaurants. Often the exact location of the contamination is not known. These numbers may also under-report the actual incidence. Tips for food handling at home can be easily found online but are not universally taught in schools and homes. Restaurants and foodstuffs for market are subject to inspection, but, of course, inspection is not universal and thus contaminated food gets into the grocery stores and restaurants. Careful food handling in restaurants may be lacking at times. Proactive policies to prevent this suffering are, as well, limited by the prevailing ideologies supporting neo-liberalism, with its greater reliance on arm's-length monitoring of regulation compliance, that is, of industry monitoring itself.

Contamination of food occurs through air, water, and soil pollution by such toxins as toxic metals, PCBs, and dioxins. In addition, some intermittent poisoning occurs via pesticides. Poorly prepared, cleaned, and cooked food is also a health hazard. Clearly, work needs to be done in cleaning the food supply and developing higher levels of kitchen hygiene and cooking and storing food so that it is safe to consume. The use of antibiotics in animal husbandry has also been associated with the growing problem of antibiotic resistance in humans.

Many people have turned to organic foods in the past few decades as a way to avoid the pesticides and fertilizer and other contaminants that may be found in food grown in the standard way. This trend continues to grow (Organic Trade Association [OTA], 2019). In 2001 the retail sales of organic foods in the US, Canada, Japan, Europe, and Oceania were said to be about $19 billion. In 2016 the sales amounted to $65.8 billion (OTA, 2019). In the US alone in 2017 organic food sales totalled $49.4 billion. Fruits and vegetables comprise the majority of this market, beverages are second, and breads and grains third. In 2016, 1.7 per cent of agricultural land in Canada was used for organic farming, and in the same year the Canadian market share of organics comprised $5.4 billion. In some locales this reflects a growth rate in the organic sector that has outstripped that of the market for regular foods, and about 82 per cent of consumers purchase some organically grown products on a regular basis (Statista, 2019). The demand is apparently greater than the production capacities and this keeps the costs relatively high and, thus, the market limited to those who can afford to purchase organic. The reasons people buy organic food include a belief that it is healthier, that it lacks pesticides, that it is not genetically modified, and to prevent allergic reactions. However, and perhaps ironically, organic foods are not necessarily safer than non-organic foods because of potential contamination by E. coli, for instance.

Highlighted Issues

Box 3.7 • Why Is It Difficult to Demonstrate Effects of the Environment on Health?

It is extremely difficult to assess the effects of the environment on health. Among the challenges are the following:

- The environment is exceedingly complex: differentiating among different parts of the environment and their independent effects is practically impossible.
- Since new chemicals are released into the environment almost daily, noting and then measuring the particular amount and proportion of the chemical in the changing environment is exceedingly difficult.
- The ratio of the potential contaminant to the total environment is usually so extremely small that instruments capable of measuring such minuscule amounts are not readily available.
- Double-blind studies of the effects of potentially noxious substances using human subjects are unethical, although they do occur in some populations such as prisons and mental hospitals. The exception is patients deemed terminal who may wish to participate in limited trials in an experiment.
- The amount of a contaminant necessary to account for time lag (experiments with non-human animals cannot be longitudinal to match the human life span) and for the low weight of the typical laboratory mammal (rat) is relatively enormous. Drawing conclusions applicable to humans from such a situation is perilous.
- Synergistic relationships are inevitable in the environment, yet because all of the elements in the synergistic relationship are not known, the effects of the environment cannot be duplicated in the laboratory.

- There is a variable latency period between exposure and the onset of disease. This variability in latency and its length make identifying causal connections between toxic substance and illness difficult.
- Few physicians are trained in environmental and occupational health.
- A cause-effect demonstration is required as proof of the deleterious effect of a substance on humans.

The causes of only a small number of environmentally based illnesses have yet been proven and only a fraction of occupationally caused illnesses has arguably been compensated. The ideological/financial issues include the following:

- Frequently, sponsors of research of the illnesses with potential environmental causes are pharmaceutical and medical device companies with a vested interest in research that involves their products and proves them and their manufacture safe.
- When research is funded by interest groups, objective research is difficult, at best.
- Scholarly research, including in medical journals, the major legitimate purveyors of new scientific findings, is often funded by major pharmaceutical and other "interested" companies, compromising their objectivity.
- Certain types of basic research have dominated medical research and, because of the peer-review system (an "old boys' network," some say), basic research using small samples and experimental designs (the so-called gold standard of medical research) has a greater likelihood of garnering support than other types of research.

Another important issue affecting the quality of food both in the short term and in the long run is genetic modification. There are those who argue that it enables the reduction in pesticide use and is therefore of great promise and future value. However, others are seriously opposed to genetically modified foods because of the potential unknown dangers. The Canadian government does attempt to regulate GMOs (genetically modified organisms). Still, genetically modified crops have already been widely introduced in Canada and the US (but not in Europe) despite these attempts—as well as the lack of perfect evidence as to their safety. The European Union may have the strictest limits to GMOs in the world (GMO-free Europe, 2018). We still do not know whether GMOs constitute a serious problem for the quality of foodstuffs in the long run and the precautionary principle may, again, be advisable.

Occupational Health and Safety

Some Canadians face a relatively high degree of danger when they go to work. Statistics on workplace accidents and work-related injuries likely underestimate the number of injuries that occur because many injured people do not receive or request compensation. Some people may be unaware of their labour rights or may be unwilling to pursue claims for any of a variety of reasons, such as the necessity of making a living even while working through severe pain and disability. Some workers may fear job loss if they report injury or disability or may lack belief in the fairness of the Workplace Safety and Insurance Board (WSIB). Others may be transferred to lighter jobs during the time of recuperation so that reporting compensation is unnecessary. The three largest industrial sectors from which claims emanate are the service industry, manufacturing, and chemical processing. In 2012 there were 977 reported workplace-related fatalities in Canada, which was just above the average of 972 fatalities for the years 2000–12 (Schwartz, 2014).

The highest incidence of death was found in manufacturing, construction, transportation, and mining. There were 240,682 lost time claims in Canada in 2016 and 904 fatalities (Association of Workers Compensation Boards of Canada, n.d.). Some have argued that the very counting of lives lost and injuries suffered reflects a commodification of human beings, their health, and their labour (this topic is discussed at greater length in the next chapter). Debates continue about the extent to which the subjective experiences of suffering reported can be considered as legitimate for claiming compensation. Clearly, the interests of those who must pay compensation may be pitted against the needs of the workers.

In addition to workplace accidents, workers face a number of hazards on the job. These can be classified as physical (e.g., noise, heat or cold, postural, radiation), chemical (e.g., solvents, heavy metals, pesticides, pharmaceuticals), biological (e.g., HIV, hepatitis B and C), and psychological (e.g., **occupational stress** and violence). Workplace hazards, like accidents and death on the job, are likely to continue to increase under globalization and free trade. To attract multinational companies, poor countries will compete with one another by lowering labour costs, banning workers' unionization, reducing environmental standards, and creating free-trade industrial zones such as the maquiladoras along the US border in Mexico. Lower labour costs and the lack of unionization result in, among other things, fewer health and safety precautions for workers as well as an absence of workers' compensation for job-related injuries. In 2013, for example, a fire in a clothing factory in Bangladesh, where a portion of the clothes being constructed at very low cost were for the popular Canadian label "Joe Fresh," several hundred people were killed and many others were burned and maimed as a result (*Toronto Star*, 2013). We all support similarly unsafe working conditions around the world when we shop for cheaper brands.

Women, Work, and Stress

Occupational health and safety are major concerns for all working women, for those who work in the paid labour force and those who do not. Less publicized than the hazards associated with men's blue-collar work are the places where most Canadian women work, including in clerical and administrative jobs in places such as banks, retail stores, child-care institutions, schools, and health clinics and hospitals. Each of these occupations has its own peculiar health risks. Clerical workers may be subject to poor lighting and ventilation, excessive noise, and toxic substances such as emissions from computer terminals. They may spend long hours sitting on uncomfortable and poorly designed furniture, which may lead to back and neck pain, and working at keyboards can cause repetitive strain injuries, such as carpal tunnel syndrome. Working at relatively tedious jobs in which they may lack personal control may lead to stress, boredom, anxiety, and other related psychological harms. Retail and service workers may be vulnerable to health hazards from bending, lifting, and carrying. They may experience varicose veins and foot, neck, and back problems. Dealing with varieties of customers offers its own special challenges. Hochschild (1983, 2012) calls one of the most important aspects of service work or labour "emotion work" and suggests that the health-threatening consequences of selling feelings or the "commodification of feeling" are manifold. Being paid to be inauthentic can lead to alienation and frustration. Hairdressers, who usually stand all day, suffer neck, back, foot, and leg problems along with the dangers of exposure to toxic chemicals such as hair permanents, dyes, and aerosol sprays. Respiratory difficulties and skin reactions may occur. Teachers and child-care workers are continually exposed to a variety of contagious and infectious diseases. Health-care workers may be exposed to radiation, toxic chemicals, and contagious diseases, and may have to cope as well with excessive lifting, bending, and standing as well as the aggression of patients. In this regard the health-care work of nurses is among the most vulnerable to violence at the hands of their patients. Fifty-four per cent of nurses in an Ontario survey reported that they experienced physical violence at work; 85 per cent indicated that they had been verbally abused; and 19 per cent reported sexual violence or abuse (Ontario Nurses Association, 2018).

If this were not enough, women who work at home may be subject to dangers from all sorts of household cleaning substances, including abrasives, astringents, soaps, and detergents, as well as to the possibility of injury due to falls, burns, and the like. Home-based work can lead to loneliness and isolation and mental health issues, including depression and anxiety.

Occupational stress has been recognized as a significant problem associated with a number of poor health outcomes. Workplace stress can arise from the content of work, workload and pace, working hours, and lack of control over the working environment. It also results from the work context, including such things as the value placed on the work in the society at large, the position in the hierarchy of workplaces, pay and other compensation such as holidays and benefits, work–life balance, organizational culture, and bullying by colleagues. Persistent stress can cause all manner of physical and mental health symptoms such as depression, increased blood pressure, increased blood serum cholesterol, increased risk of coronary disease, migraine headaches, and increased drug and alcohol consumption as well as sleep deprivation, depression, anxiety, and so on. The topic of stress is developed in Chapter 6.

Many women work in female-dominated job ghettos at jobs that are different from the work men do. For example, 56.1 per cent of women and 17.1 per cent of men work in teaching. Men hold 75 per cent of the jobs in professional science (Israel, 2017). Gender parity has almost been reached in the public service. However, men are much more likely to be in positions of higher income and power in the private sector and business world. Many of the jobs in which women dominate are characterized by lower pay, less power, and, often, little independence, autonomy, or control. Despite an acceptance of the principle of equality of opportunity as a basic tenet of human development and well-being, according to Statistics Canada, in 2015 women earned 87 cents on the dollar as compared to men (Israel, 2017). When the gender comparison is within the same field the disparity is greater and women earn about 72 cents for every dollar, according to research by the Canadian Centre for Policy Alternatives and Oxfam (Evans & McInturff,

2016). The Conference Board of Canada (2020) has found that the wage disparity between men and women varies by age, by occupational group, and by level of education. Overall, using 2013 data, Canada received a C in gender wage equity when compared to 16 relatively comparable countries. Belgium, France, and Denmark were among the countries that received an A.

Frequently, women are the last hired and the first fired. To the extent that women's jobs are considered less important than men's jobs, women have less power to demand safe, clean, and healthy working standards. Women's occupational health and safety issues are thus both different from and potentially more problematic than those of men. Even if the risks women face tend not to be as dramatic and acute—that is, they are not as likely to result in immediate or almost-immediate death—the long-term chronic health problems that result are serious. Women workers are exposed to a broad range of occupationally related health hazards. In addition, the work life of women is problematic because of their multiple roles. Observations made about the relative poverty and lack of control in the female-dominated parts of the labour force are exacerbated among women of minority status who may be likely to work in even more marginalized settings such as domestic work, office cleaning, agriculture, cottage industries, and prostitution. Women with disabilities are also more likely to be underemployed, unemployed, and relatively invisible in our society (Council of Canadians with Disabilities, 2019).

Estimating the actual prevalence of occupationally related disease is complex. The issues are similar in many ways to those discussed above with regard to the assessment of environmental health issues. Most importantly, there may be a long period of latency between exposure to the damaging substance or activity and a resultant disease. Second, there may be a lack of information about work-related health and safety concerns. For example, owners may equivocate about which chemicals are being used in ways that could harm workers, and about which chemicals or activities have damaging long-term effects. Even when information is available about the negative consequences of a substance, that information may be withheld. Workers may be reluctant to complain about work-related problems for fear of losing their jobs. One additional set of problems has to do with the fact that physicians usually are poorly trained in recognizing occupationally related diseases.

Shift Work

About one-quarter of employed Canadians work shifts (Institute for Work & Health, 2010). Canada has long needed 24-hour service from the medical, elder care, police and fire protection, and transportation sectors, but "24/7" has also become a catchword for commercial, financial, and industrial services in the neo-liberal economy. Health costs associated with shift work, however, include cardiovascular disease, hypertension, gastrointestinal disorders, reproductive problems, and breast cancer among women, and a greater likelihood among teens who work shifts to later develop multiple sclerosis, according to a Swedish report (Dallas, 2011). In addition, shift work may exacerbate such chronic conditions as asthma, diabetes, and epilepsy (Shields, 2003). Some research has found that people who work shifts also tend to have an increased propensity for heavy drinking, poor eating habits, and weight problems. Although the precise reasons for the links between shift work and health challenges are not known, evidence suggests that the association may be due to the disruption of the circadian rhythms, which can lead to stress and to the adoption of unhealthy habits. Various psychosocial problems are more likely to result from shift work, including those related to mental health issues such as depression and family problems (Shields, 2003). Following is a list of some of the effects of shift work on health.

1. Persistent fatigue is common. Sleep problems are frequent.
2. Possibly because long-term shift work disrupts the circadian rhythms, it is associated with breast and colorectal cancers, mental health problems, gastrointestinal disorders, and pre-term childbirth.

3. Shift workers are more vulnerable to heart disease and heart attacks. In general, shift workers have lifestyles associated with ill health, including smoking, obesity, little recreation or regular exercise, and poor diets.

4. Medication may affect the person on shift work in an unpredictable way.

5. Shift work has negative effects on family activities and relationships, which can lead to depression, isolation, broken relationships, and loneliness. The lack of daycare associated with most shift work may mean that children sometimes are left unattended. Participation in "normal" parent–child, husband–wife, and family socializing is severely restricted because of the unpredictability of scheduling.

6. Some evidence indicates that more work-related accidents occur among shift workers.

7. Working conditions can be substandard (lighting, ventilation, cafeteria services) and opportunities for socializing may be restricted.

8. The rates of psychological stress are high.

9. There are increased odds of being diagnosed with a chronic condition

Agricultural Work

Agriculture has long been associated with a pastoral, idyllic, and healthy style of life. However, after mining and construction, agricultural work can be one of the most health-threatening of occupations. Not only do agricultural workers suffer a high rate of accidents and associated fatalities but the working conditions in all kinds of variable weather, including working with and repairing farm machinery, the intensification of the farm labour process, poor housing and sanitation, and low wages and long hours of hard labour, constitute a heavy burden. There are times, too, when it is impossible to take a break or a holiday because of the relentless demands of farming. In addition, as the ozone layer thins, the rate of skin cancer is bound to increase among farm labourers.

Pesticides are major threats to human health, as a result of direct ingestion via pesticide-coated fruits and vegetables and indirect ingestion via long-term accumulation in soil, water, and air. Pesticides are known to have a tendency to break down or to combine with other compounds over time, which may be even more dangerous to human health. Short-term effects of mild pesticide poisoning include nausea, vomiting, and headaches, as well as more serious permanent damage to the nervous system, miscarriage, birth defects, sterility, and reproductive disorders. Long-term pesticide exposure has been found to be associated with various cancers of the lungs, brain, and testicles (the herbicide 2,4-D, for example, has been found to be associated with a type of lymphoma, birth defects, hormone disruption, and soft-tissue sarcoma). Pesticide use—whether insecticide, herbicide, fungicide, or rodenticide—constitutes a potentially catastrophic experiment with human life (Raven et al., 1993).

Compounding the problems resulting from agricultural work is the fact that much of the hired labour force is composed of vulnerable and often temporary, immigrant, illegal, or undocumented workers (Stastna, 2012). The tenuous nature of a stay in Canada for such immigrants and refugees has meant that many have had to take whatever job was offered and to accept these working conditions without complaint. Racism, a lack of language facility, and, in some instances, a lack of skills or training render these people particularly vulnerable. Our immigration and temporary worker laws, the lack of employment options once in Canada, poverty and lack of jobs in the country from which workers emigrate, and the lack of unionization in the temporary work sector place many foreign workers in a weak position in relation to their employers. In 2011, as a terrible highlight of the vulnerable situation of temporary migrant farm workers in Ontario, 11 migrant farm workers were killed in a van accident as they returned from a long day at work. This accident raised awareness again about the questionable health and safety conditions experienced by migrant farm (and other industry) workers (Paperny & Bascaramurty, 2018).

Other Accidents and Violence

Each year about 5 million people around the world die from accidents. These deaths comprise about 9 per cent of all deaths (WHO, 2014).

Among these, automobile and other vehicle accidents are the most prevalent. They also cause significant injury around the globe and are a major cause of injury and death among all age groups. In 2017 in Canada, 1,841 people were killed in motor vehicle accidents. To some extent accidents result from human error—driving while under the influence of alcohol and drugs or driving at excessive speed, for example, can be avoided. Sometimes, road design, weather, or traffic conditions and speed limits are implicated in traffic accidents.

A new source of traffic accidents is associated with the use of cell phones (Min & Redelmeier, 1998). In consequence, growing numbers of jurisdictions have laws that prevent the use of a cell phone while driving. A recent news report indicated that almost 50 per cent of teenagers had texted while driving. One investigation of 167 crashes and 518 near-crashes of inexperienced drivers noted the increased odds of about 8 to 1 if dialing a cell phone, 7 to 1 if reaching for a cell phone, 4 to 1 for texting, and about 3 to 1 for eating while driving. The odds ratios regarding dialing a cell phone were lower among experienced drivers (2.49 to 1) but still significant (Klauer et al., 2014). Texting while driving increases the probability of an accident about 23 times according to a consortium of insurance companies (ThinkInsure.ca, 2020). Traffic accidents are predicted to be the fifth leading cause of death by 2030 around the globe. Current yearly losses in life come to about 1.2 million people worldwide. Twenty million people are said to survive with disabilities. Some argue that medical policy has ignored these huge causes of death and suffering (Redelmeier & McLellan, 2013). The training of professional drivers is also lacking. The traffic accident in April 2018 involving the Humboldt Broncos hockey team, when a truck plowed into their bus at an intersection in rural Saskatchewan, killing 16 and injuring 13 others, was partly the result of the truck driver's lack of training.

In 2016–17 several hundred thousand Canadians suffered an injury severe enough to limit their usual activities. The largest cause of injuries was falls. There were 152,504 falls that led to hospitalization; the second and third major causes of injury leading to hospitalization were vehicle accidents (23,174) and attempted suicide (21,162). These were followed by accidental poisoning (10,168) and intentionally inflicted injury (7,241) (Statista, 2018).

Sports-related accidents comprise a significant proportion of all accidents—approximately 64 per cent of accidents leading to emergency room visits among adolescents. Thirty nine per cent of these young people were diagnosed with concussion and 24 per cent with possible concussion. Participation in sports has many psychological and physical health benefits. It can, however, be dangerous. From 2004 to 2014, head injuries increased by 40 per cent in football, soccer, and hockey (Government of Canada, 2018c). Another significant cause of sports-related impairment relates to the widespread abuse of performance-enhancing drugs in both amateur and professional sports.

Violence against women and children is an important factor in ill health and death, a factor that has long been under-reported. The World Health Organization has documented that about one-quarter of Canadian women have experienced domestic violence or sexual violence in their lifetimes (McInturff, 2013). However, the actual rate of violence against women is likely to be much higher than has been recorded because the vast majority of women do not report their experiences (Sinha, 2013). About one-quarter of women have experienced violence in the last five years. Seventy per cent of the women who have experienced spousal violence were working women and one-third were from households with an income of $100,000 or greater (McInturff, 2013). Women who leave home because of violence are 20 times as likely to use food banks within the first three years. The health consequences are not entirely clear, but some evidence suggests that they are serious and last a long time. Aside from long-term health consequences, women who have been assaulted are more likely to be afraid in various situations, such as taking public transportation, entering or leaving a car alone, or staying alone in their home. Violence reflects prevalent socialization patterns and culturally based value systems. It is extolled as glamorous and exciting. It is featured in popular television shows, films, and video games, with the brutality of mixed martial arts becoming a staple of sports television in recent years. Young boys are given toy guns and military equipment to play with, while macho superheroes are provided as role models. The few cases of mass shootings at Canadian schools and the numerous shootings at US schools in recent years are not entirely shocking when we consider, among other things, the prevalence of this culture of "macho" violence on television and in the movies along with the availability of guns. On the other hand, it should be noted that domestic violence against men also has serious consequences, including depression, anxiety, loss of self-esteem, drug and alcohol abuse, and fear of losing one's children (Mayo Clinic, 2017), as well as inability to work, the injuries caused by the abuse, suppressed anger, isolating behaviour, and reduced libido.

Men are more likely than women to die by violence at the hands of strangers and friends or acquaintances. Women are more likely to die by violence as a result of altercations with intimate partners and family members. Overall, though, men are more likely to die by violence than women (Sinha, 2013).

Medical error is another important cause of accidental death in Canada. It is also a frequent cause of death, illness, and suffering around the world. Yet for most of modern history medical error has been largely invisible and considered to be entirely anomalous. Its measurement was never considered a part of official statistics. In Canada, the US, and elsewhere in the developed world, causes of death are registered using the 10th revision of the World Health Organization's International Statistical Classification of Disease and Related Health Problems (ICD-10).

Recently, a number of organizations have worked to develop ways of estimating various error rates. A British Medical Journal article assessing different methods for measuring rates of medical error in the US found that error is the third leading cause of death in hospital (Makary & Daniel, 2016). The three most common causes of death in the US overall were heart disease, cancer, and accidents. This finding has been fairly consistent across developed countries. These accident figures only include deaths that occur in hospital. They do not include deaths in outpatient offices, clinics, and communities or even in long-term care institutions. Official statistics in Canada do not record hospital-based deaths by medical error (Statistics Canada, 2018), so the overall medical error rate for Canada is impossible to estimate accurately and is under-estimated. However, rates similar to those in the US of inadvertent hospital-based deaths are likely (Finlay, 2015).

Summary

1. Water, air, and land are the three fundamental parts of the environment on which we depend for health.
2. The major environmental issues facing Canadians today include: climate change, chemicals, air pollution, second-hand smoke, medical pollution, land pollution, e-waste, decreasing biodiversity, and food safety.
3. Pollution of water in the Great Lakes continues to be a serious concern.
4. With respect to land, the issue of waste disposal is critical.
5. Occupational health and safety issues are a major concern, even in today's post-technological era. It has been estimated that a significant proportion of all cancers are related to work and the environment.

6. The health and safety issues of working women in female job ghettos, while less dramatic (and less studied) than those of predominantly male occupations, are nevertheless myriad and consequential.
7. Particular health and safety issues are related to work in agriculture, the health-care industry, and shift work.
8. Traffic and sports accidents are a significant cause of morbidity and mortality, especially among young people.
9. Accidents and violence have a considerable impact on the morbidity and mortality rates of Canadians.

Key Terms

climate change
environmental illness
e-waste
global ecosystem
greenhouse gases (GHGs)
Kyoto Accord

medical error
occupational stress
pharmaceutical and personal care products (PPCPs)
risk society
twentieth-century disease

Questions for Study and Discussion

1. Why is it difficult to demonstrate the effects of the environment on human health? Scientifically? Politically?
2. Could the industrial accident in Fukushima have been prevented? How? Explain.
3. What are the most significant threats to the sustainability of the globe? Explain.
4. Why is cancer prevention under-emphasized by the Canadian cancer establishment?
5. What problems do pesticides cause? Should they be banned?

Suggested Readings

Beck, U. (1994). *Ecological politics in an age of risk*. Polity Press. A classic text for the new modernity.

Bloomberg, M., & Pope, C. (2017). *Climate of hope*. St Martin's Press. Discussion of practical solutions to help save the planet.

Brauer, M., Reynolds, C., & Hystad, P. (2013). Traffic-related air pollution and health in Canada. *Canadian Medical Association Journal*, *185*(18), 1557–8. This article brings to light an under-recognized health concern with a growing level of impact.

Fortune, M.K., Mustard, C., & Etches, J.J.C. (2013). Work-attributed illness arising from excess heat exposure in Ontario, 2004–2010. *Canadian Review of Public Health*, *104*(5), 420–6. A paper pointing to the problem of excessive heat in the workplace.

Galloway, G. (2014, 18 June). Government mum on asbestos policy. *Globe and Mail*. A critical note on the Canadian policy on asbestos.

Hystad, P., Brauer, M., Demers, P.A., Johnson, K.C., Setton, E., Cervantes-Larios, A., Poplawski, K., McFarlane, A., Whitehead, A., & Nichol, A.M. (2014). Geographic variation in radon and associated lung cancer risk in Canada. *Canadian Journal of Public Health*, (1), 4–10. A recently documented environmental issue that requires ongoing monitoring.

Kiec-Swierczynska, M., Chomiczewska-Skora, D., Swierczyriska-Machura, D., & Krecisz, B. (2013). Manicurists and pedicurists—occupation group at high risk of dermatoses. *Medycyna Prasy [Medical Practice* (Warsaw)], 64(4), 579–91. This draws our attention to the costs of working in the "aesthetics industry."

Marra, P., & Santella, C. (2016). Cat wars. *The devastating consequences of a cuddly killer.* Princeton University Press. An examination of the threats to global biodiversity, the environment, and public health posed by free-ranging cats.

Thunberg, G. (2019). *No one is too small to make a difference.* Penguin Books. A collection of the speeches of Greta Thunberg, the now 17-year-old Swedish girl who decided not to go to school one day in protest of government inaction on the climate crisis, leading to a global movement for action.

Wallace-Wells, D. (2019). *The uninhabitable earth: Life after warming.* Tim Duggan Books. The author describes some of the consequences of unchecked climate change, such as food shortages, refugee emergencies, and other crises that will reshape the globe.

Neo-liberalism, Social Inequity, Disease, and Death

The Social Determinants of Health

Chapter Overview

- Health, illness, and death are not randomly distributed across society.
- Morbidity and mortality rates are linked to inequalities.
- The "social determinants of health" approach is essential for understanding the reasons for health inequalities in the population.
- Three explanations for the social determinants approach to understanding disease and mortality outcomes are the materialist, the neo-materialist, and the life course approaches.
- Social inclusion/exclusion and social capital are important contributors to health outcomes.

- Politics and economics are major determinants of health outcomes.
- Ideology affects health outcomes.
- Inequality, employment, unemployment, food security, housing, poverty, and education are among the significant social determinants of health.
- Social theory, including the commodification of health, helps to explain the findings presented in this chapter.
- Inequality is growing in Canada and around the world.

Introduction

The next two chapters will focus on one of the most important conceptual frameworks for understanding the health of people in Canada and in nations around the world. This is the causes and consequences of numerous inequities in social structure and how they are linked to the distribution of death, illness, disease, and disabilities. The notion of social structure is used here as a metaphor and a tool for thinking about the ways that people in society differ from one another, in the sense that some people have more than others of various benefits and resources necessary to, or valued in, social and material life. The social structure can be thought of as hierarchical, as a ladder. Hierarchy, or placement up and down an invisible ladder, can be observed along a number of different dimensions. Placement of the individual and of particular communities can be by economic, educational, gender, and/or social status variations, among other social conditions. For example, it is possible to consider that society is structured so that those with more money are at the top and those with less money are at the bottom. It is also structured so that those with more education, or those who hold more prestige because of their families or jobs, for example, can be seen as being located at or near the top of an invisible hierarchy and those lacking in these ways, along the bottom. Cross-cutting indicators of inequity can both reinforce one another and/or contradict one another. The relationship between gender and income provides an example of how inequities can be reinforcing. The well-documented fact that women are more likely to be poor than men illustrates two "variables" (gender and socio-economic status) or conditions working together or reinforcing one another. If we add Indigenous status to the equation, we can think about how the gender differences in levels of income are exacerbated by Indigeneity. Thus, Indigenous women are likely to be poorer than Indigenous men and non-Indigenous women. This reflects a situation in which cross-cutting sources of inequity (in this case, the addition of Indigenous status) can complicate a simple two-variable relationship such as that between gender and income. This dynamic interaction of many variables is an example of intersectionality. Often, systems of inequality and inequity are linked together so that, for example, the elderly are more likely to be female, and the elderly also are more likely to be poor. From the perspective of social justice, hierarchical structure is indicative of inequality. Inequality becomes inequity when we judge the inequality as morally wrong.

How Do Inequity and Health Relate?

How does inequity relate to health and illness? There is a consistent and positive relationship between good health and location further up the social-structural hierarchy. This means that in a society such as Canada, people who have more wealth tend also to be healthier and to live longer and people who have less wealth tend to have poorer health and to live shorter lives. Thus, the individual level of well-being tends to correspond to the location of the individual in the social structure. In addition, there is general agreement that the overall degree of equity or inequity within society affects the well-being of everyone within the society, including those at the top and those at the bottom of the income hierarchy. Societies in which the differences between levels of the hierarchy are smaller tend to have better overall health among all of the people in the population than those that are more differentiated. As the degree of overall inequality declines or increases, so, too, will the level of health be likely to vary (Figures 4.1 and 4.2).

How do these processes work? First, why would relative economic equality in a society be associated with health while a lower position in the economic structure is associated with illness? A number of different mechanisms and answers have been proposed. Dennis Raphael (e.g., 2002a, 2002b, 2004; Mikkonen & Raphael, 2010), especially, has helped to explain the consequences of inequality and health consequences for Canadians. The most obvious one is that health is linked to

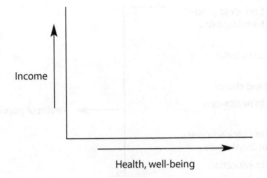

Income

Health, well-being

**Hypothetical Explanations for Health Differences
among People of Different SES Backgrounds**

Material Resources

Housing

Food

Clean water

Clean air

Access to necessary
immunization, drugs, and
health care

Lifestyle

Smoking

Drinking

Exercise

Sexual safety

Risk-taking

Family/Community

Stability/integration into family
and community

Supportive mutual aid
relationships

Decision-making authority

Privacy

Social-Psychological Resources

Stable, secure employment

Supportive work relationships

Education

Coping abilities

Sense of coherence

Social readjustment

Emotional stability

Sense of efficacy

Figure 4.1 A Hypothetical Model of the Relationship between Socio-economic Status and Health for an Individual

the provision of basic material goods and services. This has been called the **materialist approach** to the social determinants of health. From this perspective human health depends fundamentally on available, accessible, and good-quality nutritious food; clean, accessible, and available water; good transportation systems and infrastructure, including public transit; stable, safe, adequately compensated, interesting, fulfilling employment; safe,

available, appropriate, and affordable housing; and other essential components of life. Without these, health is compromised and challenged. Income is central to health in the materialist view. At least two aspects of income are relevant: income sufficiency or adequacy for such things as the purchase of food, shelter, transportation, and recreational or leisure activities; and income stability so that the money is available consistently and predictably

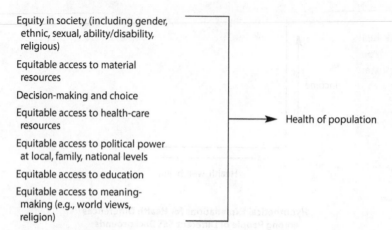

Figure 4.2   A Hypothetical Model of the Contributions of Equity to the Health of a Population

from month to month and from year to year. Access to material goods is absolutely necessary for the health of the individual and the family. Moreover, there are ways that income inequality perpetuates itself and leads to poorer health status for disadvantaged families through the generations and tends to grow through the life course of an impoverished individual. Similarly, the children born of those further up the income hierarchy tend to experience health benefits throughout their lives and these benefits tend to accumulate over time.

Material circumstances can influence health directly through assaults to the physical body, for example, from the spread of infections among homeless and poorly or densely housed people. Nutritional inadequacies due to insufficient funds for healthy foods are linked to a variety of illnesses such as the potentially serious and even fatal adult-onset diabetes. Once a person is ill, relative poverty leads to a diminished capacity to cope and to earn income because of a dependence on an hourly or daily wage or unemployment rather than a salary with sick leave and other benefits. This problem of having to rely on an unstable income exacerbated when a person suffers from one of the growing numbers of chronic illnesses requiring complex personal management. Violence and accidents also occur more often in situations lacking material adequacy. Children may be more likely to be left alone

or to become the victims of domestic violence and child abuse. In addition, material insufficiencies are associated with challenges to mental health and well-being. Poorer people are more likely to suffer from such difficulties as depression, stress, and challenges to self-esteem. They may be less resilient. All of these are directly linked to human physical as well as mental health. For instance, the stress response may be a chronic reaction to continuous relative impoverishment or sudden loss of a job, among other things. The stress response, described in more detail in Chapter 6, weakens the immune system and may lead to the onset of disease.

Poorer people are also more likely to cope by engaging in behaviours that may have health-threatening results, such as diets high in carbohydrates, sugar, and trans fats and low in protein, along with a paucity of fresh fruits and vegetables (Darmon & Drewnoski, 2008). A correlation is known to exist between a person's position in the invisible social-structural hierarchy and other specific behaviours known to be associated with particular disease processes. Cigarette smoking, for example, is irrefutably linked to lung cancer both for the smoker and for those who inhale the second-hand smoke. Cigarette smoking is also negatively associated with income and education. Thus, poorer and less-educated people are more likely to smoke cigarettes.

A second explanation for the link between inequality and health has been called the **neo-materialist approach**. This perspective acknowledges the importance of a basic level of material adequacy but then centres its attention on the significance of the relative distribution of material and social goods in societies. The argument here is that once a certain degree of absolute material adequacy has been reached, certainly enough for living above the poverty line, then equity in the society and perceived equity become essential to the overall health of a population. This argument has substantial empirical support (see, for instance, Wilkinson & Pickett, 2010, for a wide-ranging treatise on this topic). Societies with progressive redistribution and equalization policies designed to ensure the basic material and social welfare of their whole populations, such as a basic guaranteed annual income, unemployment insurance, generous leave policies for sickness, compassionate care, disability insurance and income, early childhood education and care programs, universal education, and adequate pension policies, are more likely to have a population with lower infant mortality, longer life expectancy, and longer disability-free life expectancy.

A third explanation for the links between social determinants and health shows how the materialist and neo-materialist theories might work empirically at the level of individual social-psychological functioning. It focuses attention on the personal impacts of inequity and highlights the importance of **social inclusion** or exclusion to the ongoing daily social processes of life for individual people as social beings in a community. **Social capital** is said to enhance inclusion. Social capital can be defined and measured in a variety of ways. Access to, as well as the presence of, certain social benefits is one way of defining social capital. We are familiar with the idea that capital is an economic resource that provides access to material benefits. Aday (2005) builds on the work of Bourdieu (1986), who distinguishes among social, cultural, and economic capital and theorizes about how they work together in providing resources to people in societies, through social networks and community inclusion. Aday expands this notion in reference to the types of capital or resources that are necessary for health. She includes natural capital (parks and environmental conditions of various sorts, e.g., access to green spaces); human capital (education type, amount, and quality, e.g., universal early education or child-care programs); material capital (occupation, income, and employment); and social and cultural capital (including social support, absence of discrimination, and freedom from stereotyping). We could add the component of psychological capital (a personality with a sense of well-being, optimism, and self-esteem) and bodily capital (a genetic background leading to strength and health, and aspects of body shape, size, and functioning). Those with adequate social capital are less likely to be marginalized and more likely to be included in social life (Spitzer, 2005). Social capital also has implications for health globally (Erickson, 2011).

Social inclusion is related to social capital and is evident in characteristics of communities, such as civic engagement, voter turnout, and the representation of people of diverse backgrounds in positions of power in local governments, community organizations, and distant governments. The presence of a well-functioning infrastructure, including availability of and access to green spaces, public transportation, free or inexpensive libraries, sports arenas, and community centres, is thought to contribute to a high level of social inclusion. On the other hand, private education, health clubs, and sports complexes and the lack of publicly accessible services for transportation, the arts, recreation, and so on marginalize and may even polarize people. The lack of such universally available infrastructure, a lack that excludes some members of the community, leads to negative social comparisons, lowered self-esteem, and, finally, poorer health. This explanation highlights the integral nature of the body–mind connection that is further explored in Chapter 6.

The **life course approach** to health outcomes overlaps with the previous perspectives but draws attention to the fact that the harms caused by impoverishment, inequity, a lack of

Highlighted Issues

Box 4.1 • The Social and Personal Costs of Alzheimer's Disease

Have you ever forgotten the name of a person or the word for a thing? Among the most troubling and important of the disorders facing elderly Canadians are the various types of dementia, and memory loss is one of the most noticeable early symptoms of dementia. Dementia is a condition that increases sharply as people age, although only a minority of people over 65 have dementia.

Alzheimer's disease, the most common form of dementia, is characterized by a progressive deterioration and destruction of cells in the brain and leads to increasingly severe declines in memory, thinking, and reasoning. People suffering from Alzheimer's often begin with an inability to remember information, words, or names. Over unpredictable periods of time, these memory difficulties result in greater and greater problems with reasoning, judgement, and emotional and personality stability. Denial that anything is wrong by the Alzheimer's patient can be one of the most difficult stages of the disease, both for the patient and for those close to him or her. Eventually, people with the disease may become unable to care for their own basic needs or to engage in the activities of daily living on their own. Alzheimer's is a fatal disease, though many sufferers die from other causes linked to old age. It is estimated that 44.4 million people suffer from dementia globally and this number is expected to increase, as people live longer lives, to 135.5 million by 2050.

It is still impossible to diagnose Alzheimer's with certainty until biopsy, but, according to the Alzheimer Society's widely accepted practice criteria, the accuracy rate of live diagnosis is now about 90 per cent (Alzheimer's Society, 2019a). Numerous different hypotheses regarding disease causation have been examined, but there are still no definitive conclusions. While no medical treatments are available for the cure of the disease, several drugs now work to delay and temporarily moderate the worsening of symptoms. Numerous experimental treatments and preventative strategies are being developed and tested in various places around the world.

In the context of an aging population and lack of clear or certain methods of prevention, the disease is likely to grow in the next 30 years or so as the population turns 75, 85, and 95. In the absence of effective treatments, knowledge about prevention, or adequate financing and support for home or institutional care, the burden of this disease for the sufferers and their friends and families is bound to increase. Approximately 747,000 people are living with various dementias including Alzheimer's in Canada (Chang et al., 2015). This means that about one in 13 people over 65 is estimated to have Alzheimer's or another related dementia. It is also noteworthy that most older people do not suffer from dementia. Nonetheless, about 110,000 new cases of dementia were diagnosed in 2010. Women, possibly because of their longer lives, account for approximately 72 per cent of those diagnosed with Alzheimer's and 62 per cent of those diagnosed with other dementia (Alzheimer's Society, 2019b).

Somewhat less than one-half of those diagnosed with dementia live in institutions such as nursing homes, homes for the aged, and retirement homes (Chang et al., 2015). About 55 per cent typically live at home or in the residence of their caregivers. They are cared for by family members—spouses, daughters, daughters-in-law, sons, or grandchildren—with only a small amount of voluntary or paid assistance. Apparently, a mere 3.4 per cent of family caregivers use respite care (designed to give caregivers a brief break). Partly because of inadequate levels of home care and support services for people with dementia and partly due to the financial cost of respite care, informal caregivers seem to have more chronic health problems than others in their age cohort. A significant number of those caring for a person with severe or moderate Alzheimer's, report symptoms of depression. Caregiving can be likened to living with chronic stress (Schulz & Sherwood, 2009).

redistributive policies, social exclusion, and negative social comparisons are compounded when they occur to and among children because, in a multitude of ways, they persist and accumulate over time and throughout life. The health costs of early childhood poverty are heightened and their consequences increased through three different mechanisms, pathway, latency, and cumulative effects. Some have called these the **fundamental causes** of health and illness (Chang & Lauderdale, 2009) and the **cumulative advantage theory** (Willson et al., 2007). This theory seeks to explain how advantage and disadvantage build up over time. Like a snowball that gets bigger as it rolls, so, too, do social and health benefits grow over time. **Pathway effects** set children on a direction, a road, or a course resulting either from unhelpful or from helpful early experiences through compounding effects. For example, a child who begins school already counting and familiar with books, crayons, pencils, and paper is likely to fare much better in kindergarten. Doing well in kindergarten sets the child on the path to higher marks and a better educational and social life in elementary school and high school. This, in turn, preconditions the child, now an adolescent, for success in post-secondary training, apprenticeship, college, or university. And success in post-secondary education leads the young adult into a better-paying job and greater life chances. **Latency effects** occur in the early developmental stages and also influence later life. Premature birth, for instance, is a strong predictor of a variety of developmental delays in cognitive and physical functioning. It is associated with a number of different disease (and pre-disease) states later on. Underweight and overweight infants are more likely than those born at normal weight to suffer from overweight and obesity later on. Overweight and obesity are linked to diabetes and various cardiovascular diseases, among other things. **Cumulative effects** are the repeated additions of disadvantage or advantage over a lifetime and include combinations of both latency and pathway effects that lead to health and/or disease in the adult. This is not to say that people cannot take control over aspects of

their difficult start in life, but they may have more challenges doing so.

Cumulative effects of inequity can be assessed through generational and life course approaches. One example may be seen through an examination of class-associated premarital or teenage pregnancy (Penman-Aquilar et al., 2013). Working-class and lower-class teenage girls are more likely to become pregnant out of wedlock. Teenage and unmarried women tend not to have adequate economic, emotional, and social support to take good care of themselves. Thus, if they become pregnant, this lack of support may affect the growth of their fetuses and babies. Compared to those whose pregnancies are planned, they may have access only to insufficient or non-nutritious diets and may be less able to engage in prenatal care and healthy prenatal behaviours. Lacking social acceptance, they may try to hide their pregnancies and maintain their (non-pregnant) body image. Stress may lead them to consume alcohol and other potentially harmful substances. Low-birth-weight babies are more likely to be born to women in these circumstances. Low birth weight is a significant problem that tends to result in all manner of difficulties for the child, including a greater likelihood of death, disability, and disease. Low-birth-weight babies, as they reach school age, tend to be poorer students and to have learning difficulties and various chronic illnesses. Thus, the results of this one behaviour associated with income may lead to complex and extensive health- and income-related threats to the newborn and to the growing child.

Political Explanations for Inequality and Poor Health

Health inequities result from forces and decisions at the global and national levels. Navarro and Shi (2003) have compared four different types of politically organized nation-states with respect to inequities and to health outcomes. They divided countries in the Organisation for Economic Co-operation and Development (OECD) into the following political categories: social democratic, Christian democratic, "liberal" (i.e., "neo-liberal" in the taxonomy that we have described above), and ex-fascist. Then, they compared them over the period 1945–80, "the golden years of capitalism" (Navarro & Shi, 2003, p. 195). The comparison focused on the degree of inequality, public expenditures and health-care benefits, public support for families, and the overall health, disease, and death in a population. All of these countries are developed Western nations and among the richest countries in the world. The social democratic countries included Sweden, Denmark, Norway, Finland, and Austria. Those categorized as Christian democratic were Belgium, the Netherlands, Germany, France, Italy, and Switzerland. The liberal (neo-liberal) countries included Canada, the United Kingdom, the United States, and Ireland. The ex-fascist countries were Spain, Greece, and Portugal. The social democratic countries, which were more "committed to redistributive policies (both economic and social) and full-employment policies, . . . were generally more successful in improving the health of populations" (Navarro & Shi, 2003, p. 195). The social democratic countries also had relatively high levels of union involvement, full-employment policies, high levels of expenditures on the social "safety net," high levels of taxation (as a percentage of the GDP), and a relatively high percentage of employment in health, education, and welfare. Social democratic countries were characterized by high rates of female engagement in the labour market. The infant mortality rates in the social democratic countries ranged from 4.0 to 5.1 in 1996, from 3.0 to 5.0 in 2011, and from 1.9 to 3.1 in 2016. By comparison, the infant mortality rates in the liberal countries ranged from 5.5 (Ireland) to 7.8 (US) in 1996, and from 4.0 (Ireland) to 8.0 (US) in 2011 and averaged at 4.1 in 2016 (OECD, 2019). In 2016 the average infant mortality rate was highest in the (neo-)liberal countries and lowest in the social democratic countries (see Table 4.1). Canada's infant mortality rate was fairly high at 6.0 in 1996, remained at 6.0 in 2011, decreased to 4.7 in 2016. Although the study by Navarro and Shi cannot be taken as conclusive, it supports the theories regarding the importance of social determinants to the health of populations. The infant mortality rate, while only one indicator of social health, is a highly sensitive measure of the overall health of a nation. Table 4.1 shows estimates of infant mortality rates for the countries in this study.

Inequality and inequity have been growing since 1980. The explanation for this is rooted in the ideology of neo-liberalism. This ideology is the one most students reading this book grew up under. According to the Canadian sociologist David Coburn, the chief assumptions of neo-liberalism are: (1) "that markets are the best and most efficient allocators of resources in production and distribution"; (2) "that societies are composed of autonomous individuals (producers and consumers) motivated chiefly or entirely by material or economic considerations"; and (3) "that competition is the major market vehicle for innovation" (Coburn, 2003, p. 340). He argues that this ideology undergirds development and has spread around the globe since 1980 at varying rates, from the time of deregulation of markets and the push for free (or freer) trade by the Thatcher Conservatives in the UK, the Reagan and now Trump Republicans in the US, and, in Canada, the Progressive Conservatives under Brian Mulroney, continued by Stephen Harper. This continues under the Liberal government of Justin Trudeau. It is this fundamental and dominant ideological belief that drives the globalization of capital.

Neo-liberalism is antithetical to redistribution of goods and services because any interference with the freewheeling powers of the market is believed to fetter economic growth, and economic growth, above all else, is thought to be the "good" that societies produce. Thus, taxing corporations limits their freedom to take risks and respond creatively to the needs (or create needs through advertising and so on) of the populace for new consumer products such as pharmaceuticals or the next generation of electronic widgets. Rather than policies designed explicitly by the state to ensure, for instance, that unemployed people have access to training, unemployment insurance, and government-sponsored assistance in locating a new job, the ideology of neo-liberalism advances the proposition that everyone in society will do

Table 4.1 Infant Mortality, Selected OECD Countries, 1970–2016

	Deaths per 1,000 Live Births					
	1970	**1980**	**1990**	**1996**	**2011**	**2016**
Social Democratic Political Economies						
Austria	25.9	14.3	7.8	5.1	5.0	3.1
Sweden	11.0	6.9	6.0	4.0	3.0	2.5
Denmark	14.2	8.4	7.5	5.2	4.0	3.1
Norway	12.7	9.1	7.0	4.0	4.0	2.2
Finland	13.2	7.6	5.6	4.0	3.0	1.9
Mean	15.4	9.1	6.8	4.5	3.8	2.6
Christian Democratic Political Economies						
Belgium	21.1	12.1	8.0	6.0	5.0	3.2
Germany	23.6	12.6	7.0	5.0	4.0	3.4
Netherlands	12.7	8.6	7.1	5.2	5.0	3.5
France	18.2	10.1	7.3	4.9	4.0	3.7
Italy	29.6	14.6	8.2	5.8	4.0	2.8
Switzerland	15.1	9.1	6.8	4.7	4.0	3.6
Mean	20.1	11.2	7.4	5.3	4.3	3.4
Liberal Anglo-Saxon Political Economies						
United Kingdom	18.5	12.1	7.9	6.1	5.0	3.8
Ireland	19.5	11.1	8.2	5.5	4.0	3.0
United States	20.0	12.6	9.2	7.8	8.0	5.9
Canada	18.8	10.4	6.8	6.0	6.0	4.7
Mean	19.2	11.6	8.0	6.4	5.8	4.3
Former Fascist Dictatorships						
Spain	26.3	12.3	7.6	5.0	4.0	2.7
Portugal	55.1	24.3	11.0	6.9	4.0	3.2
Greece	29.6	17.9	9.7	7.3	4.0	4.2
Mean	37.0	18.2	9.4	6.4	4.0	3.4

Sources: Navarro and Shi (2003, p. 210). Source for updated 2011 data: WHO, 2. Under-five mortality rate (probability of dying by age 5 per 1000 live births), World Health Statistics 2011, p. 24. Source for updated 2016 data: https://stats.oecd.org/index.aspx?queryid=30116

better if the market is allowed to generate jobs as it creates wealth. This is said to happen through what has been called the "trickle-down" effect. The market will generate wealth and consumer goods and will automatically, in this perspective, provide work and income for all (if not in the short run, then certainly in the middle and long run).

Coburn also makes the point that the ideology of neo-liberalism, both theoretically and in practice, is able to tolerate a high degree of inequality within and between states because of its fundamental assertion that the markets will ultimately prevail and lead to wealth for all. The neo-liberal position is consistent with a low degree of social cohesion, based as it is on a philosophy that cherishes individual rights and freedoms over collective integration or societal well-being.

In effect, then, the prevailing economic doctrine of the late twentieth century and the early years of the twenty-first century produces and justifies high levels of inequality within and between nations and high levels of social exclusion. As has been argued, both social exclusion and inequality are linked to poor health among the peoples of the world.

An Operating Model for the Social Determinants of Health

Thus, as we have argued, health, illness, and death are not randomly distributed in a society. Rather, their incidence and prevalence are inextricably linked to the social organization of the society. One aspect of this social organization, as noted above, is the extent of inequity or inequality in the social structure. Inequity causes different life chances and experiences, as well as unequal access to fundamental social resources such as food, recreation, satisfying work, and adequate shelter. Because of unequal access, people who differ in age, sex, income, occupation, race, ethnicity, marital status, rural or urban location, and religiosity differ in their rates of sickness and death. As a first step to this analysis, however, it is essential to put the relationship between illness and death and the social structure into a broad, comprehensive context. Table 4.2 is a model of the major social variables and their possible connection with rates of illness and death.

On the broadest level, (1) the globalization of capital—i.e., trade rules and regulations, as well as the ease and quickness with which capital and business decisions can move around the globe via electronic media—and (2) the neo-liberal ideologies at the level of nation-states have encouraged the dominance of free markets and free-flowing capital. The spread of this political-economic regime has affected the disease burdens of peoples around the world. In addition, numerous cultural, ecological, and historical differences between societies manifest themselves through such things as varying definitions of health and illness and varying views regarding appropriate types of medical treatment. For example, some societies are more "medicalized" (or characterized by modern or conventional medical treatments) than others. Developing societies are increasingly influenced by the discourses and practices of allopathic medical explanations and treatments, which often are pharmaceutical, for what might be seen as social or educational problems. An example is hyperactivity, which used to be regarded as naughtiness but is now widely treated with a drug such as Ritalin, and another is depression for the "normal" sadness of bereavement, which is often treated with antidepressants. These are two of the diagnoses that are spreading around the world, along with the conventional pharmaceutical treatment when possible. (Medicalization will be discussed further, in more detail and more critically, in Chapters 8 and 9.)

Table 4.2   A Model for Analysis of Morbidity and Mortality Rates at the Societal Level

Culture	Political-Economic System	Ecological System	Social Structure	Social Psychology	Micro Meaning
the degree of medicalization/ biomedicalization	capitalism/ neo-liberalism socialism communism	environmental and condition (water, air) quality of agricultural land and foods transportation and communication systems	gender age ethnicity education religious affiliation	stress type A behaviour* sense of coherence* perceived social support	the definition and meaning of health, disease, and death

*These will be defined fully in Chapter 6.

Differences in mortality and morbidity are related to political-economic systems at the level of the nation-state, as well as to national cultural differences. The level and distribution of numerous resources, such as food, shelter, access to meaningful work, environment quality, and satisfying social relations, vary within societies. As long as the political-economic system causes differences in people's access to resources, there will be structured inequities in rates of death and illness.

Social policies at the national and sub-national levels also have a significant impact on the health of populations. Such policy measures as a guaranteed annual wage, early childhood education and care, laws against discrimination and promoting special status for those who are disadvantaged, pension availability, and the provision of unemployment, sickness, and compassionate-care insurance help to redistribute income within a society and to improve the health of everyone. Health depends, as well, on the availability of regulations and monitoring to ensure safe consumer products such as foods, drugs, sterile needles, and condoms; safe physical structures such as bridges, well-lit streets, and buildings constructed to satisfy adequate safety criteria; and public service advertisements and other cultural messages promoting health-related behaviours. Our health-care system and many social and medical policies still, however, support a **downstream model** rather than an **upstream model** of health. The metaphor used in these concepts points to the fact that our health-care policies focus on providing diagnosis and treatment once a problem has been detected (downstream) rather than preventing the development of health problems in the first place (upstream). Note the following visual representation of upstream and downstream thinking. This policy preference for downstream medical intervention tends to allow stressors from the social determinants of health such as poverty, racism, unhealthy or insufficient food, violence, poor neighbourhood conditions, lack of easily accessible health care, and so on to accumulate over time so that disease finally occurs. The focus then is on treatment and the financial support of the conventional allopathic medical

care system. This may sometimes be at the expense of investing in other options. For example, one consequence of the lack of sufficient numbers of long-term beds for people with serious disabilities and people who are aging is that emergency rooms at hospitals across the country are frequently overcrowded. This is because the elderly (and some of the seriously disabled) who have been hospitalized may have nowhere to go when they have recovered but cannot go home alone or without someone at home who is able to take care of them and ensure their safety and well-being. They may still need a rehabilitative or residential level of care. The lack of long-term beds leads to long waiting times and increased suffering and disease for those who have to wait unattended. It may also lead to bedsores, confusion, and other problems among people who are hospitalized over a period of time while they await residential care.

The notion that all social policies potentially have health consequences is exemplified by the phrase **health in all policies** (HiAP). Attention to the impact of social policy on health has been recently acknowledged in parts of the world where there is a consequent concerted effort to minimize the stresses and strains of problems arising from inadequacies in the social determinants of health (Peña, 2013). In practical terms this idea points to the necessity of considering the health outcomes of all social interventions. This can also include an evaluation of the financial costs to the health-care system of neglecting a consideration of the health consequences of policy. For example, the introduction of mass transit is often thought of in terms of its costs and benefits to enabling access to employment and economic innovation. In addition, HiAP argues it is also important to measure the benefits of new transit lines to accessing the health benefits of parks, a river or a lake, or a recreation centre (see Figure 4.3). This is just one small example of many.

Cultures differ in the interpretation of symptoms and behaviours associated with health and illness. This means that social and health policies and practices need to be culturally sensitive. They need to respect and accommodate differences.

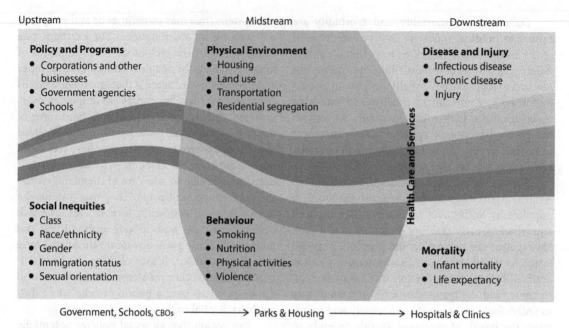

Figure 4.3   The Health in All Policies Approach

Source: Health in all policies: Richmond adopts a health in all policies (HiAP) strategy and ordinance, City of Richmond (2014).

For example, for Indigenous people, health always includes spirituality. This means that feeling or being disconnected from community, history, and Mother Earth may be seen as signs of a lack of wellness by Indigenous peoples. Relatively stable and unchangeable social-structural positions such as gender, age, racialization, ethnicity, sexual orientation, dis/abilities, and so on are related to health outcomes—but in distinct ways. People who are in different positions in an invisible but effective hierarchical social structure are more or less likely to suffer from mental and/or physical illness. For example, women are more likely to be diagnosed with depression and men, possibly in the face of the same feelings and circumstances, are more likely to engage in excessive alcohol consumption.

The social determinants of health operate through the social structure and such things as the availability, accessibility, and quality of food, water, housing, income, education and literacy, and early childhood education and care. In addition, education and ongoing choices in education through the life course are significant determinants of the health of a society.

Individual behaviours and coping responses, including smoking, alcohol consumption, seatbelt use, stress, self-esteem, sense of coherence, social and instrumental support, resilience, and religiosity, are implicated in health outcomes. The socio-psychological and phenomenological strategies people use in their everyday lives contribute to illness rates and ultimately even to death rates.

Health outcomes from all of these factors are seen in mortality and morbidity rates, disability rates, subjective assessments of health and well-being, and clinical health measures.

The Social Determinants of Health: Evidence from Canada

Inequality and relative poverty become translated into ill health through specific mechanisms. These determinants have been conceptualized in

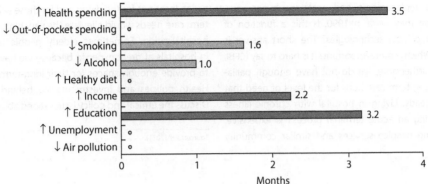

Analysis based on 35 OECD countries for the time period 1995–2015

Figure 4.4   Life Expectancy Gains Associated with a 10% Change in the Main Determinants of Health

Source: OECE (2017).

a variety of ways historically and geographically. We will consider the social and economic reasons for differences in inequality and in rates of morbidity and mortality in Canada today. In the next section we will examine some of the social determinants of health or differences in social capital among people in Canada. It is important to note regional and other geographic differences in the distribution of social determinants and the health

of Canadians across the country (Gore & Kothari, 2012). The social determinants of health play an important role in all aspects of health and well-being in Canada and around the world. Figure 4.4, based on data from OECD countries, demonstrates the effects of health-care spending as compared to decreases in smoking rates, alcohol consumption, income, and education. Together, two social determinants (income and education) contribute

CRITICAL THINKING

Box 4.2 • Are the Elderly Responsible for Increases in Health Costs?

You have probably heard the concern voiced that as the population ages as a result of the aging of the baby-boom generation that the costs to health care will skyrocket. In fact, people over 65 are more likely to be ill than adults at other ages. Moreover, they are also more likely to use the health-care system when they are ill. Interestingly, however, evidence suggests that healthy seniors, not sick seniors, are responsible for a significant part of the increase in utilization and, therefore, costs. Thus, "well-person check-ups" and early detection measures among the well aging population drive up expenses. Further, although the costs of health care

are expected to rise as the whole population ages, the impact of aging itself is only a small part of the overall increase. Other, more significant cost-drivers include inflation and technological innovations, especially in the field of pharmaceuticals. Aging, itself, is expected to contribute about 1 per cent per year of the increase in health-care costs between 2010 and 2036.

The picture is complex, because aging, inflation, and innovation are difficult to separate as the standards change for what can and should be done as people age and approach death. For instance, older people are now much more likely to have knee

(continued)

and hip replacements and coronary bypass surgery than they were in 1990. Is this a function of aging or of new technologies? The short answer is "both." Which is more important? It is hard to say (CFHI, 2011). Furthermore, we do not have enough palliative or long-term care beds for the level of need that exists already. Living in hospital with chronic illness and during an acute terminal process is expensive. Expanding hospice services and similar community

caring locations for the dying and for those with long-term care needs would alleviate the very high costs of hospitalization. Sometimes elderly people languish in hospitals at great expense because we have failed to provide enough spaces for their long-term needs. Health policies and investments lag behind needs. Discuss the ethical and policy issues raised above.

Source: CFHI (2011).

5.4 years to life expectancy. Declines in smoking and alcohol consumption contribute 2.6 years. Health-care spending contributes 3.5 years.

Inequality

Inequality in a society is a significant predictor of the health of its population. Further, income inequality among the OECD countries is at record levels (OECD, 2016), as Figure 4.5 shows, and has continued to rise over recent decades (Figure 4.6). Inequality has increased in terms of market inequality, gross income inequality, and disposable income inequality. To understand this further, let us compare the degree of

inequality and the health outcomes of three different developed societies—Japan, the US, and Canada. Japan in 2016 had the highest life expectancy at 80.8 for males and 87.1 for females, as compared to 79.6 for males and 83.8 for females in Canada and 76.3 for males and 81.2 for females in the US (OECD, 2017). The relative longevity of people in Japan has been a long-standing phenomenon. Japan's success in health terms arguably is related to the tradition of relative equity within the country. After World War II, Japan began to emphasize the pursuit of income equality and to redistribute income throughout the whole society. The redistribution of income resulted in a greater degree of

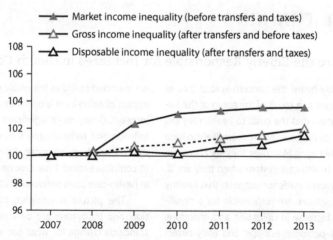

Figure 4.5 Inequality before and after Redistribution through Transfers and Taxes, Working-Age Population, OECD Average, 2007–13

Note: The year 2007 = 100.

Source: OECD (2016).

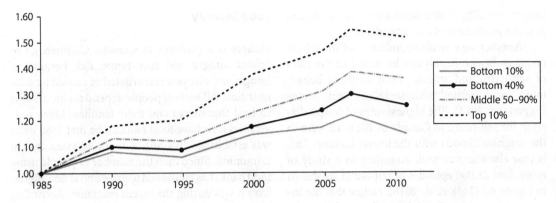

Figure 4.6 Trends in Household Incomes at the Bottom, the Middle, and the Top, OECD Average

Note: The year 1985 = 1.

Source: OECD (2015).

equality among Japanese people. This would have enhanced their equal ability to take up the social determinants of health that are within their control, such as quality housing, increased education, and a greater possibility of fulfilling, stable, safe, and interesting work. These advantages in the various social determinants of health undoubtedly have resulted in greater well-being. Furthermore, Japanese corporations traditionally put the welfare of their workers ahead of profits. For instance, in an economic crisis, some top Japanese executives and managers took pay cuts rather than lay off workers. This action was considered the honourable thing to do. Japan is a cohesive society in which income equity has been a chief value. In comparison, Mikkonen and Raphael (2010, p. 4) estimated that Canadians lose a significant portion—approximately one-quarter—of their lives prematurely because of income differences. Today Japan and Canada experience almost the same degree of inequality and their values under globalization are melding (OECD, 2016). Japan's redistribution policies have decreased in the recent past and life expectancies of the two countries have grown closer together.

In the US, the differences between the richest and the poorest citizens have been growing. The US is characterized by relatively high rates of mortality and by a high degree of income inequality. According to a study by Piketty (2014), the top 10 per cent of the US population controls 71 per cent

of the country's wealth and takes home 48 per cent of the income. Further, under the current political economy, wealth and inequality continue to grow. In tandem, the poorest Americans are getting poorer and this trend will continue if the current neo-liberal processes continue. As is the case in the US, racialization and racism are important contributors to the income gaps in Canada. For example, in Toronto in 2016 the poorest neighbourhoods were 31 per cent white, middle-income neighbourhoods were 61 per cent white, and the wealthiest neighbourhoods were 73 per cent white (Hulchanski, 2018). The growing disparity between rich and poor around the world, including in the developed countries, is linked in part to globalization. That health is affected is evident in many indicators. Three of the most important are life expectancy at birth, child injury, and infant mortality. The US had an infant mortality rate of 5.9 per 1,000 births as compared to India with 37.9 deaths per 1,000 live births, according to the latest data available (OECD, 2017). Canada was just slightly better than the US rate at 4.7 deaths per 1,000 whereas Iceland ranked first, with an infant mortality rate of 0.7 deaths per 1,000. Despite spending considerably more on health care than any other OECD nation, the US compares poorly on outcomes. Canada, too, has a relatively poor showing (OECD, 2017). The political explanation offered by Navarro and Shi (2003) in regard to income equality, as described above, is significant, as is the prevalence of neo-liberalism.

Another very sensitive indicator of the effects of inequality on health can be found in the rates of self-harm and suicide. Both of these behaviours are correlated with socio-economic status (Eggertson, 2013). The highest rates of hospitalization for self-harm in Canada in 2011–12 were in the neighbourhoods with the lowest income. This is true elsewhere as well, according to a study of more than 21,000 episodes of self-harm, as shown in Figure 4.7 (Mok et al., 2018). Notice that the incidence rate ratios for violent offences follow the same pattern as those for self-harm. Moreover, people who live in northern Canada have had exceptionally high rates of hospitalization due to self-harm (almost six times the national rate) for causes such as attempted hanging, drug overdoses, and cutting. The rate of self-harm resulting in suicide was 10 times higher than the national average among Inuit people.

Food Security

Hunger is a problem in Canada. Children go to school hungry and stay home sick because of hunger and diseases exacerbated or caused by malnutrition. All sorts of people depend on food banks to feed themselves and their families. Many universities now have food banks. The first food bank was established in Canada about 40 years ago, in Edmonton. Since then the number of people using food banks has continued to grow and is now higher than it was during the recent recession. According to Food Banks Canada, 13 per cent of Canadians live with food insecurity, which means they cannot rely on consistent access to good-quality nutritious food. In March of 2016 alone almost 900,000 people used a food bank in Canada. About one-third of these were children. This number of users represents the results of a growing trend in this service. The growth has been 28 per cent since 2008. Almost 4 million people were served a meal

Figure 4.7   Incidence Rate Ratios among 15-Year-Olds for Self-Harm and Violent Offending by Parental Income Quintiles

Source: Mok et al. (2018).

by a meal program in 2016 (Food Banks Canada, 2016). A disproportionate 14.2 per cent of food bank users are Indigenous and another 12.5 per cent are immigrants and refugees to Canada. These figures reflect racism in employment, housing, and government and industry policies regarding training equivalencies between place of origin and Canada. They also reflect the lack of an adequate living wage in some cases. Approximately 11 per cent of food bank users are currently employed. The use of food banks represents an ongoing inequity in Canada. Food bank use also perpetuates inequity through indirectly contributing to both mental and physical illness because of the lack or limited supply of healthy foods such as fresh fruits and vegetables available in food banks. Children's feelings of worry, sadness, and unhappiness are associated with the quality of their diet (Martin et al., 2013). Relying on a food bank because of the relatively poor nutritional value of the canned and dried foods available and the lack of fresh fruits and vegetables contributes not only to poorer physical health among the children who depend on food banks but also to their poorer mental health. This outcome is in addition to the complex and difficult feelings of embarrassment, anger, and shame related to having to depend on a food bank.

Among those who are most vulnerable to food insecurity in Canada are the elderly (Payette & Shatenstein, 2005). Approximately 34 per cent of those 65 and over (4.1 million people) are on the brink of malnutrition in Canada according to the Community Health Survey—Healthy Aging (Chenier, 2013). This malnourishment is partly due to diminishing appetites and decline in sensitivity to smell and taste as people age. However, it is due, also, to the inability of the elderly to get to the store to purchase healthy food and to their mobility limitations in daily life. Depression, loneliness, and the grief of loss may also affect and be affected by the nutritional level of the elderly through a lack of energy to maintain mealtime routines, shop for food, cook, bake, and so on.

Food insecurity is a serious problem in Canada. A question to consider is: Are we committing a type of economic abuse when, as a society, we fail to provide sufficient money for adequate nutrition? Clearly, an economic gradient is evident in the reliance on food banks and thus access to nutritious food, which is shown in the earlier research of Power (2005), who found a link between socio-economic status and the levels of consumption of nutritious food. One study examined the cost of food in 43 randomly selected grocery stores and estimated the cost of a nutritious diet for people living on a minimum-wage income (Williams et al., 2006). According to the authors of this study, such people could not afford to purchase an adequately nutritious diet. Moreover, cost estimates suggested that Canadians living at this level of poverty could not afford other routinely required products such as those needed for cleaning, personal hygiene, or unusual and unexpected needs such as medication.

An examination of the links between obesity and income demonstrates that excess food as well as insufficient quantities can be problematic. This is true especially if the food is manufactured, boxed, and/or encased in plastic. So far this is more common in rich countries and is linked to higher rates of obesity. Figures 4.8 and 4.9 illustrate the link between obesity in children and young people aged 5–19 and the relative wealth of a country, as measured by body mass index (BMI).

Ironically, food insecurity and, most likely, food bank use are associated with both obesity and hunger. This is because foods that are higher in caloric content and often full of sugar and carbohydrates tend to be cheaper than the much more nutritious foods, such as fresh fruits and vegetables and proteins such as meat, cheese, and nuts. Obesity, or excess body fat, is a growing problem in richer countries such as Canada (Government of Canada, 2011). However, the relationship between socio-economic status and obesity is complicated and nuanced and it does seem to vary by gender. There is a negative relationship between socio-economic status and obesity among women, but the opposite appears to be true among men. However, neighbourhoods with lower levels of socio-economic status tend to have more overweight and obese people (Government of Canada,

Figure 4.8   Average BMI by Education Category

Note: for men (n = 26,334) and women (n = 22,918) age 25–64 (unadjusted associations). For men: the following groups differ from <HS at P < 0.05: complete postsecondary +. For women: the following groups differ from <HS at P < 0.05: HS graduate, some postsecondary, complete postsecondary +

Source: Social Class and BMI Among Canadian Adults: A Focus on Occupational Prestige by Lindsay McLaren and Jenny Godley Obesity (2008) 17, 290–299. Reproduced with permission of Wiley.

2011). Obesity has been linked to hypertension, type 2 diabetes, heart disease, osteoporosis, and mental health problems in various studies.

It must be noted that parallel to the increasing concerns about obesity is an equally vocal oppositional position that thinks the problem of the obesity epidemic in overdrawn and even manufactured. The idea of "fat fabrications" is a concept that points to this debate (Monaghan et al., 2013). The stigmatization of people who are overweight and obese is certainly another problem with consequences for health and health-care utilization (Fruh et al., 2016).

Poverty

The definition of poverty is a political matter. What counts as "poverty" for the purposes of state interventions is different from what counts as poverty in the perspective of poverty activists or those living in impoverished situations. However defined, "poverty" refers to the economic position and stability of people who have a difficult time or who fail to meet their own and their family's basic needs for food, shelter, water, clothing, transportation, and access to education, community facilities and services, and health care. In Canada "poverty" is often defined as the low-income cut-off point. Currently (although the definition changes from one year to the next), those people who spend at least 20 per cent more of their income on food, shelter, and clothing than the average Canadian spends on those essentials are considered to be below this "poverty line." This definition is hotly debated. Perhaps the most useful approach is to compare, using consistent definitions, Canada's poverty line with that of other similar countries. In this regard Canada's poverty level is now above the average of our comparator countries in the OECD. In the mid-1990s we were substantially below the mean

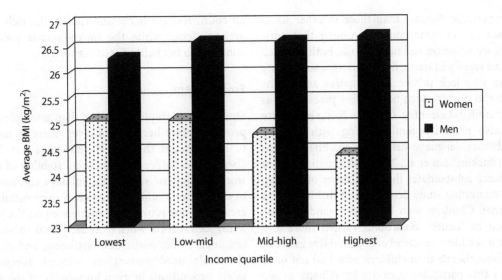

Figure 4.9 Average BMI by Income Category

Note: for men (n = 26,334) and women (n = 22,918) age 25–64 (unadjusted associations. For men: the following groups differ from lowest quartile at P < 0.05: low-mid, mid-high, highest. For women: the following groups differ from lowest quartile at P < 0.05: mid-high, highest. HS, high school.

Source: Social Class and BMI Among Canadian Adults: A Focus on Occupational Prestige by Lindsay McLaren and Jenny Godley Obesity (2008) 17, 290–299. Reproduced with permission of Wiley.

of the OECD countries. More recently, Canada was 22nd out of 38 countries in respect to the poverty rate. At the same time, the US had a rate almost twice as high as Canada's.

In 1989, the federal Canadian Parliament unanimously proclaimed its intent to eradicate child poverty by the year 2000. Whether this was merely a grand gesture on the part of Canada's parliamentarians or they failed to realize how intractable poverty is and what would be required to meet such a goal is not known. More than 30 years since that aspirational goal was set, child poverty in Canada certainly has not been eradicated. Indeed, it has increased consistently each year since the mid-1990s. Children living in poverty are more likely to experience developmental delays, and such delays often lead to a lifetime of underachievement and, consequently, the continuance of poverty from one generation to the next. They are also more likely to experience various childhood illnesses, some of which

are directly related to their probable lower birth weights. One in seven children in Canada is living below the poverty line. Canada, according to the Conference Board of Canada (2019), ranked 15th out of 17 developed countries and received a C grade for our level of child poverty.

As noted, definitions of poverty are political and contested. Progressive political parties and societies governed by them are more likely to be generous in their definitions of poverty—that is, they are likely to think that more people are poor and in need—and conservative political parties are more likely to think that a greater proportion of people are above the poverty line. For the purposes of this book, although there are differences in the presumed poverty rates, they all indicate that a substantial number of children today live in families where their basic needs are not being met. Furthermore, and to the point of this book, those living in poverty, even in advanced industrial and post-industrial societies, are more likely to experience diseases than those in other social classes in the same country. Among these diseases are influenza and tuberculosis, both of which spread rapidly in dense living quarters and among those who lack private living spaces and/or the ability to practise such basic safety precautions as frequent hand-cleaning. Children living in poverty are also more frequently dealing with learning disabilities, language delay, and reading challenges (Buckingham et al., 2013). Although plenty of evidence substantiates these outcomes of poverty, one interesting study demonstrates this in a novel manner. Children who have been randomly assigned to "better" classrooms earned more and were more likely to attend college and live in better neighbourhoods than children who had not been given this particular opportunity (Chetty et al., 2011).

In addition, impoverishment may be associated with various mental health problems, chronic diseases, distress, and low self-esteem (WHO, n.d.). An impoverished child with a disease such as childhood cancer is disadvantaged because the treatment carries on for a long time and because one parent (usually) has to provide continual home (and in-hospital) health-care work, taking the child back and forth to medical care and testing. Further, because the treatments often involve assaults to the immune system through chemotherapy, children may become very vulnerable to infectious diseases and frequently have to stay home from school or any other public gathering. Parents have lost homes and jobs as a result of having to stay home to care for their children when they are ill with a chronic or terminal illness such as cancer. While we do not have good research on the social class correlates of childhood cancer, it is clear that a family can become impoverished as a result of caring for a child with a life-threatening, serious, or chronic disease. The absence of good parental and other caregiving policies to financially support people who need to stay home to take care of loved ones exacerbates this problem. We also know that under neo-liberalism the richer countries in the OECD (and the richer people within

all countries) are becoming richer. The rich are getting richer while the lower-income groups continue to fall behind (see Figure 4.6).

Employment

Simply being employed rather than unemployed provides some benefit. However, there is more to employment that merely having a job. We also must consider the safety and stability of the work, the pay or salary, the holidays and hours of employment, and the degree of responsibility, creativity, and autonomy experienced on the job. Many jobs involve work with dangerous substances, such as the pesticides, fertilizers, and other chemicals used sometimes without adequate safety precautions or even knowledge of the necessity for such precautions. Other work is dangerous because of susceptibility to new diseases, including health-care work, as the SARS crisis demonstrated and as the spread of the novel coronavirus in 2020 emphasized, or because of violence at work where, ironically, health-care workers are among the most vulnerable, along with correctional officers, social service workers, and teachers. Aside from safety at work, employment stability and good wages are crucial to adequate employment. The minimum wage across the country, as of late 2019, ranged from $11.32 in Saskatchewan and $11.40 in Newfoundland and Labrador to $14 in Ontario and $15 in Alberta (MacIntosh, 2020). Consider, for example, how much one has to pay for a one-bedroom apartment in your community and calculate how much of the income of a person collecting minimum wage must go to housing. Or think about the number of students you know who have more than one job in order to make ends meet as they continue their education.

Barbara Ehrenreich, a noted author and social critic with a PhD in biology, in *Nickel and Dimed: On (Not) Getting By in America*, documents her experiences in trying to get, and then live on, minimum-wage jobs in several different states in the United States. She points out that having to live on minimum wage can happen to anyone, and most students know this very well. She also shows how difficult it was for her to get a job and then how impossible it was to distinguish herself and her unique abilities and training no matter where she found work. As she says, "Several times since completing this project I have been asked by acquaintances whether the people I worked with couldn't, uh, tell—the supposition being that an educated person is ineradicably different, and in a superior direction from your workday drones. I wish I could say that some supervisor or coworker told me even once that I was special in some enviable way—more intelligent, for example, or clearly better educated than most. But this never happened" (Ehrenreich, 2001, p. 8). This research might be taken to suggest that good jobs often depend on being hired in a position commensurate with one's education, skills, and training. By contrast, it also emphasizes the difficulties of moving up in the occupational ladder without additional qualifications. What experiences do you have in trying to find work based on your level of education? How might you expect these experiences to possibly change once you have your degree?

Work and its absence are significant determinants of health and illness. Occupation is also an important predictor of health through the mechanism of income because the most important determinant of income is employment, although there are those who live on investment income or pension income and are not dependent, or not entirely dependent, on the paid labour force. So, what is a good and healthy job aside from one that is stable and provides an adequate income? The quality of work life is important and yet under-studied. A good job offers a manageable workload, and flexibility and autonomy in the execution of the workload. Being able to decide what to do and when in order to accomplish goals, which the worker takes a part in setting, is important. Having to work to persistent deadlines established by others, particularly urgent deadlines, is often experienced as problematic. Creativity, self-expression, and self-development, possibly rare aspects of work in the paid labour force, are also important to

the quality of human work life. Satisfying social relations are another aspect of what might be described as "good" work. Important as these qualities appear to be to health and well-being, very little research actually addresses such questions with respect to work in Canada (Jackson, 2009). Polanyi (2004), in reviewing research in this area, notes that topics studied include "job control" (which includes "pace, participation and control, and opportunities for personal development"), effort–reward balance, and job strain, work hours, work–life conflict, and job insecurity. All of these have been found to have links to health outcomes. Good work, according to Polanyi, is available, adequate (as to income, benefits, and rights), appropriate to training and life circumstances, and meaningful to workers. Good work is also acknowledged and appreciated. However, in the economy of the day many people are just grateful to get any job.

Unemployment

As difficult, dangerous, unstable, and poorly paid as some work is, at least it provides a degree of involvement in the economy and a minimal sense of being able to contribute to one's own or one's family's well-being. As of December 2018, the unemployment rate in Canada was 5.6 per cent (Trading Economics, 2019). This figure is considered to be relatively low in a global context today, but it had been declining over the past decade and a half until the market meltdown of 2008, when it rose rapidly for a time. This is the lowest rate of unemployment since 1974. The rate still means that more than a million people in Canada are actively looking for work. In addition, a sizable proportion of Canadian workers, such as fishers, loggers, roofers, and other outdoor workers, are intermittently or seasonally unemployed. Further, untold thousands of other people out of work are not factored into unemployment statistics because they are not actively seeking employment. Unemployment and underemployment are also differentially and inequitably distributed across such socio-demographic categories as gender, education level and type, ethnic background, immigrant status, age, and rural/urban location. Regional variations persist, with unemployment rates highest in Atlantic Canada and lowest in the western provinces. Today, as often, the youth unemployment rate is particularly high.

Education/Literacy

Education is an important resource in Canadian society. It opens doors to certain (and often better) occupations; it increases the chances of promotion to more satisfying occupations. Education often increases financial stability and security, job satisfaction, and choice, and may help people cope with problems of living, including those related to healthy living. People with higher levels of education are also more likely to have good or excellent health (Centers for Disease Control and Prevention, 2012).

Education is related to types of employment, the prestige of a person's occupation, and the level of individual income, as well as to health-related behaviours, such as eating nutritious food and driving safely, and to awareness of and access to health information. People with more formal education are more likely to work in jobs in which they have control and self-sufficiency. Jobs requiring more education are more likely to be those that are predictable from season to season and year to year and have higher social status and prestige. Such jobs are associated with self-esteem, respect, health, and well-being. Education is a powerful predictor of income and health.

The importance of early childhood education and care cannot be overemphasized (Friendly, 2009; American Public Health Association, 2017). It can set the stage for later successes in school and all other aspects of life. It is particularly important that early childhood education be available to the children of single-parent families and of poor mothers and families as a way of levelling the playing field for later educational achievement. Literacy is also a powerful predictor of income and health status (Ronson & Rootman, 2009). It is also

likely that illiteracy limits the ability of a person to know about how to engage in healthy behaviours and to understand all sorts of health-related messages regarding exercise, disease prevention, early detection guidelines, and the like. Imagine, for a moment, how your life would be altered if you could not read.

Housing

The number of homeless people in Canada has grown in recent decades. Current estimates of the total number of those experiencing homelessness in Canada vary because of the difficulties of actually measuring the phenomenon—after all, not having a fixed address makes one difficult to locate and contact. Measuring this is and will be always subject to error of an unknown size. However, the Canadian Observatory on Homelessness (2016) suggests that about 35,000 people are homeless in Canada on a given night and about 235,000 people in a year. One partial measure of housing inadequacy is how many people are staying overnight in shelters across the country because they cannot afford their own apartments, rooms, or homes. Shelter counts provide a snapshot of only one night at a time. Shelter use varies seasonally, and cannot account for those on the streets or in other conditions of homelessness. In addition to **absolute homelessness** or being unsheltered, some people are sheltered on an emergency basis only. There are also people who can be classified as **provisionally accommodated** (those who live in a car, the "couch surfers" who live with friends or family, and those in long-term institutions). In addition, many other people, in substandard housing or on the verge of losing their shelter, are said to be at risk for homelessness. Housing insecurity is particularly problematic among certain vulnerable groups of people, including the working poor, youth and the elderly, those who are unemployed or mentally ill, lone-parent families, recent immigrants, and Indigenous people, both on reserves and in urban areas. Veterans, who comprise 2.2 per cent of the homeless, are also over-represented.

Spotlight on Ethics

Box 4.3 • Bioethical Dilemmas

Many Indigenous reserves lack reliable access to clean, potable water and sewage disposal. Do you think that we as a society are ethically bound to correct this situation immediately? This is not a question of research ethics but of policy. If we understand that health is in all policies, do we have an obligation to ensure that the human right to water is honoured? You might want to co-ordinate your answer with the Universal Declaration of Human Rights.

Neighbourhood

Some research has found that neighbourhood characteristics, such as the degree of stability and affluence, have a powerful and independent effect on health status and may, at times, be more important to health than individual social and economic status, health behaviours, and insurance coverage (Browning & Cagney, 2003). According to Browning and Cagney, neighbourhood explains a large portion of the health gap by "race" in the US. Other research has documented that poorer neighbourhoods, assessed through both quantitative and qualitative measures, may be highly stressful and linked to both physical and mental illness (Latkin & Curry, 2003). Among the contributing factors existing within disadvantaged neighbourhoods are the relative lack of social support and social integration, vandalism, litter and trash, vacant housing, teenagers hanging out with nothing to do, burglary, drug-dealing, and robbery. Such findings underscore the significance of social cohesion and the neo-materialist explanation for the link between inequalities and health outcomes. Neighbourhood deprivation is correlated with health inequities (Bell & Hayes, 2012).

The chief cause of death and disease in Canada today is cardiovascular disease (CVD). The following map (Figure 4.10) shows how the incidence of both mortality and morbidity are patterned by neighbourhood in Toronto. Essentially what this map demonstrates is the powerful association between neighbourhood characteristics and the death rates from CVD. CVD is caused by a combination of factors including stress, diet, smoking, and exercise. People living in the poorest neighbourhoods are more likely to receive a diagnosis of CVD and to die as a result. Income, employment, and household data on the neighbourhoods shown in this map and study of CVD demonstrate clearly the significance of inequities in neighbourhood characteristics for death from CVD.

Social Theory, Economics, and Health

While we have discussed each of these social conditions as if it were a singular and separable condition, in reality they operate together through individual bodies and lives and through social policies and practices. It is only possible theoretically, or in the abstract, to characterize any one individual or any one policy by only one social characteristic, such as "degree of poverty." All such social categories intersect. In other words, people are gendered, racialized, employed/unemployed/poor (or not) all at the same time. Moreover, any single characteristic can exacerbate or mitigate the effects of any other characteristic.

Why are there pervasive correlations between death, disability, disease, and inequalities? Marxist analysis attempts to integrate all discrete and superficially unique explanations into a unified explanation. A substantial body of scholarship documents the relationship between the economy and health

Figure 4.10   Crude Cardiac Arrest Rate per 100,000, by Neighbourhood

Source: K. Taylor, Where you live in Toronto can increase your risk for cardiac arrest: Study. St. Michael's College. 6 January 2012. http://www.stmichaelshospital.com/media/detail.php?source=hospital_news/2012/20120106_hn

status. Beginning with the work of Friedrich Engels in The Condition of the Working Class in England (1985 [1845]), analysis has focused on the state and on the economy as they affect health outcomes. Engels noticed in the earliest industrialist economies the contradictions between the workers' need to sell their labour power and the capitalist factory owners' need and desire for profit. Because industrial profit was necessary to maintain factory-based production, the wages of workers were kept low and their working conditions poor. Shelter for the poor was frequently inadequate, crowded, unheated, and unsanitary. Poor hygiene and inadequate nutrition

resulted in widespread contagious diseases such as tuberculosis and typhoid.

The first principle of capitalism or neo-liberalism is that business requires profit. Profit is the bottom line. According to Marxist analysis, all capitalist states are arranged in such a way as to maximize profits. Furthermore, competition forces capitalists to maximize outputs while minimizing the costs of production. The growth of profits results in the accumulation of capital. Excess capital is invested in new or more efficient production units. New and greater profits are then realized. Increased production invokes a need to find and create new markets. When domestic markets are saturated, new foreign markets must be opened up. Profits from these markets are reinvested, and the cycle of profit, competition, accumulation of capital, investment, and expanded markets repeats itself. All the while, the owners of capital—the capitalists—take some of the profits to live luxuriant lives, usually bolstered by substantial savings and investments. The Christian Science Monitor's list of the 10 companies with the largest gap between the average salary of the worker and that of the CEO, published in December 2013, is enlightening. The average wage of the Walmart worker was $8.86 and the hourly wage of the CEO calculated to $6,898, or 779 times that of the average worker. The hourly wage of the McDonald's worker was $7.73 whereas the average hourly wage of the McDonald's CEO was $9,247, or 1,196 times that of the average worker, the largest difference among these 10 companies (Velasco, 2013). Walmart was seventh on the list of the wage gaps between CEOs and workers.

When the state economy is based on capitalism (or neo-liberalism), state decisions are guided by the apparent necessity of supporting the most successful profit-making initiatives. Usually, when a choice between profitability and human need is confronted, profitability comes first. The argument is that the good of the whole—the freedom and well-being of individuals—is advanced when economic productivity and profitability prevail. Consequently, when the need for profit is the determining principle, the health needs of the population assume secondary importance. The worth of individuals in a capitalist economy is measured by their relationship to the means of production. Because of upturns and downturns in the economy, a reserve labour force is required. The reserve labour force is made up of people who are peripheral to the paid labour force and can be brought into it or dismissed from it depending on market demands.

The more marginal the worker is in this economic system, the more easily he or she can be replaced. Maintaining occupational health and safety standards may be expensive to the capitalist owner. To the extent that the cost of implementing such standards threatens the level of profit, and in the

absence of state legislative requirements, health and safety standards will be minimal. Indeed, less stringent health, safety, and environmental regulation is one reason why so much industrial production has shifted to developing countries in recent decades. Accidents, job-related sickness, and alienation will be most prevalent among those workers who are most marginal and most replaceable. One overriding reason for income, gender, age, and ethnic differences in health is the variation in access to safe, satisfying, adequately remunerated work. Marxist analysis provides an important explanation for inequities in health outcomes.

To conclude: good health is the outcome of access to fundamental resources. Poverty, poor nutrition, inadequate housing and transportation, and the lack of effective birth control all contribute in known ways to ill health. In a capitalist economy with a neo-liberal ideology there are significant differences in access to these life-giving resources depending on differences in age, gender, income, and ethnic group.

Commodification

One other contribution of Marxist analysis to understanding inequities in death, disease, and disability is through the concept of commodities or **commodification**. Commodities are objects or activities that have an "exchange value." They can be bought and sold in the marketplace and can be used to acquire other things. Their value is determined by market factors such as supply and demand. Health can be seen as a commodity. Health no longer is simply the individual experience of well-being but, in a capitalist profit-driven economy, is subject to supply and demand. The buying and selling of organs for transplantation into unhealthy bodies is perhaps the most blatant example of commodification. Poorer people can sell organs to richer persons in return for cash. Poorer women can carry babies for richer women who are unable or unwilling to go through pregnancy. Health (and even a baby) is purchasable for those with the money, even at the expense of the health of others. There is also a way in which health itself is an object that reflects value and worth back on the individual. In this case, health is used to indicate the productive value of the person to the society. Healthy people are sometimes thought to be "good" people. Health implies the embodiment of a certain level of conspicuous consumption. It can also be thought to reflect a degree of much valued self-control.

Whenever a government or a corporation decides to allow the continuance of a practice that is destructive to the health of a population in the interests of financial benefits, such as taxes or profits, health is being commodified. Cigarette manufacturing is a case in point. There is absolutely no doubt that cigarette smoking is a significant cause of disability and death in Canadian society. Yet neither the cigarette industry nor the government has been willing to pull cigarettes from the market

or to limit their production to low-tar cigarettes. The compromise is the high level of taxation on cigarettes. Cigarettes are a fundamental and crucial aspect of contemporary economies. According to Doyal (1979), the state made a deliberate decision to allow the tobacco industry to continue. The British Department of Health showed that a reduction in cigarette smoking would be costly to the state. Not only would the tax on cigarettes be lost, but the additional financial costs of caring for people longer into their old age would be the inevitable result of increased life expectancy. Do you think this hypothesis has credence? Should taxes on cigarettes and alcohol be higher than they are in order to pay for the additional health costs that may result from these behaviours? How has the legalization of cannabis been in the interests of state taxes?

Summary

1. Health and illness in societies are linked to social inequities.
2. One way of conceptualizing the various inequities is through the social determinants of health.
3. The social determinants of health work through materialist processes and include the neo-materialist, socio-psychological, and life course approaches.
4. Other theorists use a different conceptual framework and have focused on social capital and its role in health outcomes. These

perspectives are largely consistent with one another.
5. Morbidity and mortality are linked to political and economic systems and to particular ideologies such as neo-liberalism.
6. Among the social determinants of health discussed in this chapter are: inequality, food security, employment, unemployment, housing, and neighbourhood.
7. Social theory, economics, and health are linked. Health is sometimes treated as a commodity.

Key Terms

absolute homelessness
commodification
cumulative advantage theory
cumulative effects
downstream model
fundamental cause
health in all policies (HiAP)
latency effects

life course approach
materialist approach
neo-materialist approach
pathway effects
provisionally accommodated
social capital
social inclusion
upstream model

Questions for Study and Discussion

1. How can we explain the different life expectancies of racialized people, those with different sexual orientations and identities, and those from higher and lower social classes?
2. What is the relevance to health outcomes of the increase in inequality in Canada over the last several decades?
3. Compare a magazine that is written for an African-American audience (e.g., Ebony, Jet, or Essence) and one that is written for a mainstream audience (e.g., Maclean's, Reader's Digest, or Cosmopolitan) with respect to advertisements for health- and body-related products, such as anti-depressants, hair colouring chemicals, diet pills, and the like). Theorize your findings.
4. Critically examine your personal social determinants of health.
5. Should your university or college develop policies to encourage social inclusion? Why or why not?

Suggested Readings

Hanauer, N. (2014, July–Aug.). The pitchforks are coming . . . for us plutocrats. *Politico*. http://www.politico.com/magazine/story/2014/06/the-pitchforks-are-coming-for-us-plutocrats-108014.html#. An interesting alternative economic proposal by an Internet entrepreneur who labels himself a "zillionaire" and warns others of the wealthiest class that unless they provide more than barely adequate wages to narrow the income gap, they won't have time to escape in their private jets when revolution occurs.

Martin, M.C., Seanna, E., Willows, N.D., Colman, I., & Ohinma. A. (2013). Diet quality and feelings of worry, sadness or unhappiness in Canadian children. *Canadian Journal of Public Health*, 104(4), 322–6. This article raises the question of whether some of the increase in the diagnoses of children's mental health issues relates to the quality of food.

Mikkonen, J., & Raphael, D. (2010). *Social determinants of health: The Canadian facts*. York University School of Health Policy and Management. A brief overview of the health impacts of the major social determinants of health in Canada.

Raphael, D. (Ed.). (2008). *The social determinants of health*, 2nd edn. Canadian Scholar's Press. Important research on the social determinants of health and interventions by policy-makers that can improve the health inequities in Canadian society.

Wilkinson, R., & Pickett, K. (2010). *The spirit level: Why equality is better for everyone*. Penguin UK. This book offers analysis and statistics on the impact of inequality on health and social issues.

Diversities and Health

Age, Gender, Sexualities, Racialization, and Indigenous Peoples

5

Chapter Overview

- Inequity in a society impacts health at the level of the individual and of the population as a whole. It affects people of diverse socially constructed identities and social statuses differently.
- The social determinants of health discussed in the previous chapter operate through cross-cutting or intersectional social identities and statuses such as age, life stage, gender, sexual identities, and marital status, as well as ethnic and racialized identity membership.
- The most significant change in life expectancy over the last century and a half has been in infant and child mortality. This factor has been important

in the overall aging of the population. Age and age identity are linked to morbidity and mortality.
- Gender identity, marital status, sexual identity, and "race" are associated with wellness, sickness, and death in predictable ways.
- Indigenous peoples in Canada—including First Nations, Métis, and Inuit—face particular health hazards linked to the history of colonialism, the "Sixties Scoop," the residential school system, the lack of autonomous governance on reserves, and so on. These issues have created ongoing inequity along all of the social determinants of health, among other factors.

Introduction: Social-Structural Positions and Health

Socio-economic status is a fundamental cause of health disparities. This is because of the higher rates of illness and earlier death among those lower on the socio-economic status hierarchy or living in more unequal societies. It is also because of the inequitable and uneven access to care and treatments. All of the socio-economic (social) determinants of health discussed in the previous chapter impact people with varying social identities, cultures, and social-structural positions differently. We will look in more depth in this chapter at gender and sexual identities, age and stage-of-life identities, and racialized and ethnic identities and their relationships to morbidity and mortality. The second half of the chapter focuses on the particular situation of Indigenous peoples in Canada.

In discussing diversities, identities, and health, we will examine one variable at a time and the interaction of several variables at once. An intersectional approach is fundamental to understanding the effects of multiple variables at one time. For example, the social determinant of health, occupational insecurity (an aspect of one's social-structural position), will likely affect income levels and this may operate differently among those identified as male and those identified as female. Occupational insecurity may also affect those with LGBTQ identities differently than it does heterosexually identified people. Notice the use of the term "identities" here. This idea reflects the notion that the taken-for-granted **essentialized** social statuses such as male and female, as biologically given and unquestionable, need to be critiqued. Whether a person is seen by himself/herself as a male or female and in turn whether others see individuals as belonging to the gender they would like to be seen as is sometimes a very complicated issue. Until recently we, in our society, and we, as sociologists, have failed to carefully examine the complexities of various identities such as gender. Now, however, we are coming to understand more fully the pervasiveness of the social in the construction of the ways that persons act, think, feel as cis- or transgendered

men or women. Sexualities, sexual preferences, age or life course stage, racialized and other identities are also being deconstructed and their health impacts studied with more nuance and depth. We will review some of the literature on the health effects of various diverse identities in this chapter.

Underlying the following analysis is the argument that the social determinants (as discussed in the previous chapter) affect those with different identities differently. The social determinants and different identities interact and this leads to an increase or a decrease in impacts. This means that poverty, for example, can have a different effect on an elderly person who is less able to get a job, retraining, or an education than on a younger person who may have more freedom to make a change. Furthermore, we must underscore the idea that the effects of identities such as gender, sexualities, life course, age, **racialization**, and Indigenous group status are not applied to individuals and groups within society one variable at a time. Every woman, for example, as well as having a gender identity also has an age, a sexuality identity, and is racialized (or has a racial identity) both by herself and by others within the society. She will also have a certain level of income, a particular type and level of education, and so on. Therefore, it should be emphasized that we are simplifying the picture of the causes of health and illness for purposes of discussion. Readers must recognize that, empirically and theoretically, the situation is more complex in any given case. It is also important to note that there are other cross-cutting sources of identity, inequality and status such as religious group membership, neighbourhood, language preference, occupational status, and country of origin. Think of yourself for a moment. What do you consider to be your primary social identities? Do you think that your ideas correspond to those of others?

Among other questions, this chapter considers the following: Are women more often sick than men? Do men and women suffer from different illnesses? Why are children in the first years of life particularly fragile with respect to illnesses? Does old age bring increasing infirmity and illness? Are the elderly over-prescribed medicines by their doctors? Do the elderly feel that their health is poor? Are racialized groups more likely to be sick and/or to die early? What is the health profile of various Indigenous peoples in Canada?

Age, Gender, and Life Expectancy

Age is associated with morbidity rates and life expectancy in both predictable and surprising ways. You have probably heard of "the grey tsunami" or "the greying of the nation." These terms point to the most obvious projected change in the Canadian population over time, as shown in Figure 5.1. This shows the overall aging of the population and the corresponding decrease in the younger proportion of the population. This **population pyramid** is the most basic graphic method used to describe the age distribution of a population. Figure 5.2, which includes population pyramids for Canada from 1925 to 2050, illustrates the demographic shift in the population over more than a century. The rapid growth of the older population is especially evident among women (the right side of the pyramids). The last two graphs, for 2025 and 2050, show the flattening of the middle ages and the gradual increase in the

older ages. There is an especially dramatic increase by 2050 in the age group over 80 years.

A number of explanations have been offered for these complex and changing phenomena. The most important factor in population aging is the overall decline in the **birth rate**. As people have fewer babies, there are correspondingly fewer young people. The presence of fewer young people in the population results in a greater proportion of elderly. A second and somewhat less important factor is the increase in life expectancy in Canada.

Life expectancy increases are the result of a number of changes. As we discussed in Chapter 2, first and most important is the rapid decline in the infant mortality rate. The average life expectancy for Canadians over the last 160 years or so has grown substantially. Women's life expectancy has increased more than that of men. Significantly, men, in all of the years recorded, have lived shorter lives than women. Women's mortality rate has declined so that it is almost half the rate it was in 1921. The drop is not so dramatic for men. The most significant decline for both sexes is in the early years of life. An important part of women's increasing longevity in particular is improved nutrition and other public health measures linked to pregnancy and childbirth.

Figure 5.1 Population Projections for Canada, Percentage of the Population Aged 60 and over, 2001–51

Source: Commission on the Future of Health Care (2002, p. 22).

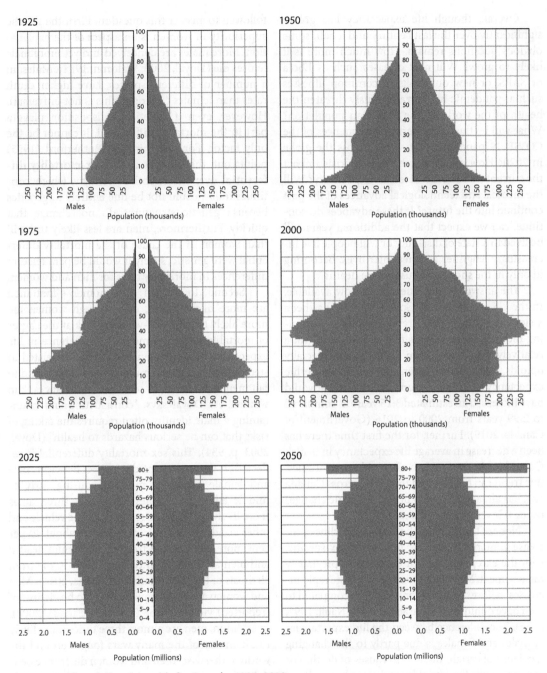

Figure 5.2 Population Pyramids for Canada, 1925–2050

Source: For 1925–2000: Statistics Canada, Age pyramid of population of Canada, July 1, 1901–2001, www12.statcan/english/cencus01; for 2025–2050: US Census Bureau, International Data Base, Population pyramid survey for Canada, www.census.gov/cgi-bin/ipc/idbpyrs.pl?cty=CA&out=s&ymax=25

Overall, though life expectancy has grown significantly over the last century and a half, some obvious questions remain. How much more is it likely to grow? Will new diseases such as Ebola or SARS, or new outbreaks of common illnesses such as pandemic influenza seriously threaten the health of the world or the Canadian population? What will be the longer-term consequences of the COVID-19 pandemic that swept across the globe in 2020? How much will the opioid crisis impact the current trend in increased life expectancy? Will the medical and technological advances of the past continue into the future? If these advances do continue, can we expect that the additional years will be lived in a state of disability or will people live increasingly lengthier and healthier lives, becoming ill only in the short term just before death?

The answer to one question is now available. In the US and in British Columbia there has been a slowing of the overall trend towards a continuing increase in life expectancy due to deaths (at a relatively young age) from drugs, most especially opioids. Without the recent opioid crisis the life expectancy in Canada from 2000 to 2016 would have increased an estimated 3.15 years as compared to 2.99 years from 2000 to 2016 (Government of Canada, 2019). Further, for the first time there has been a decrease in average life expectancy in British Columbia. As the problem of opioid use continues, this trend can be expected to spread across Canada as it has already in the US unless dramatic changes occur (Government of Canada, 2018).

None of the causes of the dramatic decline or increase in mortality rates are necessarily sex-specific, with the exception of birth control and pregnancy management. Moreover, the early and more rapid increases in life expectancy for women as compared to men have diminished since about 1978 (Nault, 1997, p. 36). The difference between the life expectancies of males and females is due partly to the changing incidence of certain diseases as causes of death. For instance, while the rate of heart disease has declined for both men and women, the absolute decline has been faster among men than women. Still, men are more likely to die from a variety of causes.

Why, then, do men today live shorter lives than women? Several lines of inquiry might be followed to answer this question. First, the genetic superiority of women is an aspect of the explanation. More males are conceived and yet more male fetuses die (Doyal, 2003; Waldron, 1981). Males, in a number of different species, have higher death rates than females (although this is not universal). However, even if genetic predisposition plays a part in the mortality differential, it cannot be the only factor. For one thing, as Rutherford (1975) points out, the changes in the **sex-mortality differential** over the twentieth century, which continues today, could not be due entirely to genetics because genetic structures do not change that quickly. Furthermore, men are less likely to be ill than women. If the cause of the mortality differential were genetic, surely it would be paralleled in differences in morbidity rates for men and women.

Second, to explain this anomaly—that men are more likely to die, even though women are more likely to get sick—we must look at the causes of mortality by sex. Some of this difference in life expectancy between men and women is related to stereotyped machismo masculinities, which tend to put men more at risk in certain circumstances than women. As Doyal says, "constructing and maintaining a male identity often requires the taking of risks that can be serious hazards to health" (Doyal, 2003, p. 934). This sex-mortality differential is reflected in the important distinction between male and female causes of mortality during early to middle adulthood: males are almost three times more likely to die as the result of motor vehicle and other accidents and suicide; men are about 40 per cent more likely to die from all accidental deaths; and men are more than twice as likely to die from cirrhosis of the liver (Statistics Canada, 2011). Men and women are about equally likely to be victims of (reported) violent crime (Statistics Canada, 2008). In addition, men are almost three times more likely to die in any of the many wars fought around the world. Otherwise, men and women die from essentially the same causes, although at different rates and ages: cancer in general and lung cancer in particular, cardiovascular disease and stroke, accidents and adverse effects associated with motor vehicle accidents, chronic obstructive pulmonary disease, influenza and pneumonia, and Alzheimer's disease are the top causes of death (Statistics Canada, 2016) (see Table 5.1).

The most important contributions to higher male mortality may be related to causes associated with the performance of masculinities. The higher rate of cigarette smoking among men has had a significant and long-term impact on the sex differential for lung cancer, cardiovascular disease, and respiratory diseases. This sex differential is narrowing as women have taken up smoking and the smoking rates of men have declined. Another important contribution to the respiratory and lung

cancer differential is likely linked to the higher risks of breathing toxins at men's employment venues. Men are more prevalent in the workforces of industries involving work with carcinogenic substances. It is worth noting, however, that some cleaning, hygiene, and beauty products used primarily by women in the home and on their bodies have been found to be carcinogenic and of significant potential danger to women's health. Risk factors for heart disease include smoking, high-fat diet, overweight, and stress resulting, in part, from the performance of hegemonic masculinities.

Table 5.1 Leading Causes of Death, All Ages, Both Sexes, Canada

Leading Causes of Death	Characteristics	2013	2014	2015	2016	2017
Malignant neoplasms	Rank of leading causes of death	1	1	1	1	1
	Number of deaths	75,112	77,059	77,054	79,084	79,844
Diabetes mellitus	Rank of leading causes of death	6	6	7	6	7
	Number of deaths	7,045	7,071	7,172	6,838	6,882
Alzheimer's disease	Rank of leading causes of death	8	8	8	7	8
	Number of deaths	6,345	6,410	6,587	6,521	6,675
Cardiovascular diseases	Rank of leading causes of death	2	2	2	2	2
	Number of deaths	49,891	51,014	51,534	51,396	53,029
Cerebrovascular diseases	Rank of leading causes of death	3	3	3	3	4
	Number of deaths	13,400	13,573	13,795	13,551	13,893
Influenza and pneumonia	Rank of leading causes of death	7	7	6	8	6
	Number of deaths	6,551	6,597	7,630	6,235	7,396
Chronic lower respiratory diseases	Rank of leading causes of death	4	4	4	5	5
	Number of deaths	11,976	11,876	12,573	12,293	12,847
Chronic liver disease and cirrhosis	Rank of leading causes of death	11	10	10	10	10
	Number of deaths	2,961	3,126	3,176	3,385	3,425
Nephritis, nephrotic syndrome, and nephrosis	Rank of leading causes of death	10	11	11	11	11
	Number of deaths	2,978	3,098	3,129	3,054	3,270
Accidents (unintentional injuries)	Rank of leading causes of death	5	5	5	4	3
	Number of deaths	11,452	11,724	11,833	12,524	13,894
Intentional self-harm (suicide)	Rank of leading causes of death	9	9	9	9	9
	Number of deaths	4,054	4,254	4,405	3,978	4,157
Assault (homicide)	Rank of leading causes of death	24	23	23	25	22
	Number of deaths	446	439	456	396	459

Source: Statistics Canada, Table 13-10-0394-01: Leading causes of death, total population, by age group, https://doi.org/10.25318/1310039401-eng

These risk factors are more prevalent among men than women (Rosenfeld & Faircloth, 2006). Higher alcohol consumption among men is implicated in several causes of mortality—but chiefly accidents and suicide. Men drive more than women and less safely. Almost one-third of automobile accidents are associated with alcohol consumption (US Department of Transportation, 2017). The probability of other accidents, assaults, homicides, and suicides is increased by alcohol consumption. Liver diseases associated with alcohol ingestion are more than twice as common as causes of death among men.

Thus, while there may be gender-based genetic differences, male lifestyles—including a higher rate of cigarette smoking, industrial employment, excess alcohol consumption, and high-fat diet—clearly contribute to male mortality. In addition, the male proclivity to engage in violent, aggressive, and high-risk sports and other activities cannot be overlooked in gender-specific mortality rates. Such gendered behaviours are also implicated in the much higher suicide rate among men. Women are more likely to attempt suicide, but men, in part because they tend to choose more violent means, are more likely to succeed at dying by suicide.

It is also worth noting that the health issues faced by transgendered people are much less understood, although it is evident that the stigma, discrimination, and stereotyping that are both internalized and experienced by transgendered people would tend to lead to exacerbated vulnerabilities to all manner of diseases. A heightened vulnerability among trans people would inevitably result, too, from medical interventions that many will have chosen, including hormonal, surgical, and other pharmaceutical treatments. Research on the long-term effects of such treatments is in its early stages and a great deal remains unknown (Boghani, 2016).

Age

Infancy and Youth

Age is paradoxically related to morbidity and mortality. Everyone dies, and as people live to old age they will get sick and inevitably die. That statement is obvious. What is less obvious is that infants, children, and youth are particularly susceptible to sickness and death, especially when they also are poor, have darker skin and resultant racialized status, belong to families headed by lone mothers, and experience other negative social determinants of health. Rates of infant and childhood mortality, accidents, and sickness are correlated with social class. Poorer mothers are more likely to give birth to undersized babies. Despite various types of preventive strategies, such as prenatal programs for pregnant women at high risk, the rate of low-birth-weight babies is still problematic. Mothers who smoke and experience various forms of social disadvantage during pregnancy are more likely to have low-birth-weight babies (Dennis & Mollborn, 2014). Indigenous babies have poorer outcomes across a number of variables including being born with lower birth weight on average (Smylie et al., 2010).

The weight of newborn babies is a "key predictor of their survival chances" (Millar et al., 1993, p. 26). Low birth weight, said to be less than 2,500 grams or about 5.5 pounds, is associated with physical and mental disabilities and infant death. Low birth weight is linked to various types of intellectual and cognitive delays that impede success in learning and in school. Low birth weight is associated with a number of poor physical health outcomes, including (perhaps ironically) overweight and obesity in later years. These conditions, in turn, are linked to diabetes and cardiovascular disease. Mental health challenges are also associated with low birth weight (American Psychological Association, 2017). The first three years of life are also significant to subsequent health. During this time children's brains and nervous systems are growing and developing, and they are acquiring language and other essential skills.

The social status of women has significant consequences for the health of their children. This is true around the globe, and is especially the case with respect to women in developing nations with less access to reliable birthing and maternity infrastructure. Women's status is also important for the health and nutrition of their children (Abuya et al., 2012). Investment in women's education has been shown to significantly reduce mortality rates among children. Many studies confirm this finding, for instance, Koenen and colleagues (2006) examined this relationship in the US. They defined women's status through four complex, composite indices, including women's political participation, economic autonomy, employment and earnings, and reproductive rights in 50 states. The well-being of children was measured according to the percentage of low-birth-weight babies, infant mortality rate, teen mortality, high school dropout rate, and teen birth rate. The health and well-being of children was found to be positively associated with women's political, economic, and social status. Other research, using a similar model of women's status, found that the health of adult men and women is better in states where women have higher status (Kawachi et al., 1999). This is also true around the world where women with higher education experience fewer maternal and child deaths, tend to have fewer children, use contraception, and marry later and are likely to be better informed about nutrition and other needs of their children (Population Reference Bureau, 2011). Today in Canada approximately 21 per cent of single mothers and 7 per cent of single fathers are raising their children in poverty (Canada Without Poverty, 2016).

Youth, too, are particularly vulnerable to health challenges. Young men, for instance, tend to take more risks and to be more aggressive and more stoic in the face of pain and distress (Spitzer, 2005). Male youth are more likely to suffer various injuries associated with binge drinking and to take greater risks in regard to frequent and multi-partnered sexual activity. The majority of traffic fatalities among youth in Canada are young men and many of these deaths involve alcohol or drugs or both (MADD, 2019).

Older Adults

Health problems affecting those over 65 years of age are of growing concern as the population ages. Older adults go to the doctor more frequently than young people and are more likely to be hospitalized and to be prescribed medications. In addition, evidence indicates that older people are more likely to

be given prescriptions inappropriately (Ferguson, 1990; Shorr et al., 1990; Brook et al., 1989). In fact, approximately 9 per cent of hospital admissions result from inadequate or inappropriate drug prescriptions or utilization (Oscanoa et al., 2017). Some of the problems associated with pharmaceutical use among the older population result from the fact that the drugs have been tested on much younger people. Metabolic and other changes due to aging affect the absorption rates of drugs. Moreover, side effects from multi-drug use associated with the simultaneous treatment of several problems are particularly problematic among the elderly, not only because of the rate of drug absorption but also because of the increasing numbers of memory, visual, or motor problems, which may make taking medications, particularly multiple medications, more challenging (Tamblyn et al., 1994). Medications may be prescribed to be taken with or *not* with meals, before or after meals, with or without water or milk, at different times of the day, and so on. Managing a multi-drug regime is difficult at the best of times for the most alert persons. Managing complicated scheduling is even more difficult for the elderly (especially those whose literacy is compromised) and for the elderly sick. Thus, the elderly may inadvertently use their prescribed drugs inappropriately, causing additional health problems. Falls are also a major cause of suffering and hospitalization among the elderly and their probability is often increased as a side effect of medication.

Approximately three-quarters of a million Canadians suffer dementia of various kinds, including vascular dementia and Alzheimer's disease. By 2031 it is estimated by the Canadian Institutes for Health Research that 1.4 million Canadians will suffer dementia.

Canadian elderly people have more chronic conditions, are more likely to be hospitalized and medicated, and yet are still likely to self-report excellent or good health and health satisfaction. Perhaps surprisingly, seniors continue to report greater life satisfaction than other age groups and women report more life satisfaction than men at these ages (Uppal & Barayandama, 2018). This may be because they see and evaluate themselves

Highlighted Issues

Box 5.1 • Viagra

Women's health has been and continues to be an important issue. However, men's health should not be ignored. There was a near-epidemic of desire unleashed with the marketing of Viagra, a drug designed for the treatment of angina but that, instead, was found to produce an erection in men. This discovery soon led to a multitude of diagnoses of erectile dysfunction. This is just one indication of how little is known about the ways that men may be suffering in their bodily functions. Until Viagra was introduced into the market in 1998 (soon to be followed by similar drugs, such as Cialis and Levitra), few knew of the extent of erectile dysfunction among men. Perhaps men weren't talking about it with their doctors and were thus not getting counted in morbidity figures. Perhaps this is best seen as a case of a drug in search of a problem, disease-mongering, or the medicalization of masculinity (Moynihan et al., 2002; Rosenfeld

and Faircloth, 2006). Sometimes it appears to be used in the absence of problems. One of the most dramatic examples of the voluntary or discretional use of Viagra is among some men who have sex with men and use it (sometimes along with other drugs such as amyl nitrate, a "popper" that gives a burst of dizzying energy) to enhance their sexual pleasure. One community-based study in San Francisco found that the rate of Viagra use among men who have sex with men was 32 per cent (Chu et al., 2003). Thus, Viagra and its counterparts are now used to enhance sexual pleasure as well as for erectile dysfunction. The success of the medicalization of sexual dysfunction among men has led to a new focus on the existence and biology of female sexual dysfunction along with the marketing, called the "pinking" of Viagra, and use of pharmaceutical interventions to enhance female sexual pleasure (Moynihan, 2003; Hartley, 2006).

in relative terms in comparison with others of the same age. Psychosocial factors among the elderly, such as a sense of purpose in life, a sense of control, social participation, and life satisfaction (Anstey et al., 2001; Pinquart, 2001; Ranzijn, 2001), as well as socio-economic factors, are positively related to quality of life and longevity. The elderly who live in long term care institutions have proven to be especially vulnerable as demonstrated by the fact that the vast majority of deaths (between 82 and 86 per cent) from COVID-19 occurred in long term care facilities. People in for-profit facilities were especially susceptible.

Gender, Poverty, and Mortality/Morbidity

Women and female children are particularly likely to be ill, to die, or to be killed when they live in impoverished circumstances. Women are more likely, within their own domestic spheres, to become ill and die because they tend to take responsibility for ensuring

that others are provided for ahead of themselves when there is a relative absence of necessary foodstuffs, water, or other necessities of life. When poorer women are pregnant they are less likely to have access to the essential nutrients, social support, and prenatal care. They are more likely to live with chronic hunger and lowered resistance to various chronic and infectious diseases. This situation is true around the world (Wermuth, 2003; UN Women 2019). Women usually have the responsibility of feeding their children. Inequalities in the valuation of men and women in all classes, but particularly among the poorest people, lead to higher esteem or value being placed on boy babies in many cultures. Sometimes this results in the intentional death of female babies or the abortion of female fetuses. There is no evidence of this occurring in Canada, but a survey of women in Madras, India, found that more than half reported having killed a female child (Wermuth, 2003). China, for many years, limited couples to only one child per family. This, in effect, led to the deaths of baby girls because females were less desired. In some cultures, women who are unable to produce male heirs are sometimes killed, maimed, or sent away from their families. Poor families sometimes sell their girl children into sexual slavery because they cannot support them or because they are told that their daughters will then be able to send money home to support the rest of the family. Rape is more common among poor women (Wermuth, 2003). Female genital circumcision or mutilation, depending on cultural beliefs, may be considered another type of violence against women or a sign of female beauty and desirability. It causes pain, infection, disability, and sometimes death, and interferes in the possibility of women experiencing sexual pleasure when they do engage in sexual relations. This practice affects female children not only in the countries in which such practices originate but also in countries such as Canada because of the numbers of immigrants and refugees from areas of the world where this practice is accepted and where women are thought not to be marriageable unless this is done. In the absence of **female circumcision**, their genitals are considered "ugly." The social policy and ethical issues raised by the desire of some newcomers to continue this practice in Canada are worthy of serious thought and discussion, not least under a nationally funded and supported medical care system.

The conclusion that must be drawn from our research on gender differences in health is that women are more likely to suffer from a variety of illnesses than are men and that men at every age are more likely to die than are women. Which is the better measure of parity: to live longer and be chronically ill or disabled or to die earlier? What will the future bring? Are women actually "dying to be equal," as evidenced by their rates of cigarette smoking, alcohol consumption, cannabis consumption, opioid use, high-risk lifestyles, and increased involvement in high-stress careers?

Transitions and the Life Course

Life course transitions offer additional opportunities for increased health as well as additional potential for stress and illnesses of all sorts. All transitions include the potential for health changes and stresses but especially transitions that occur out of the typical order or at a non-normative time. The transition that has garnered the most research is that of single teenage women embarking on a pregnancy and then on to child-rearing. The consequences of this trend are significant both for the mother and for her offspring. Similarly, young men who drop out of school before completion usually face greater economic and social challenges as they age. Young widowhood, early retirement, late childbearing, job loss, and educational interruptions all offer additional challenges to those that are inevitably already a part of any transition. It is also important to note that while transitions may create stress and thus a greater likelihood of illness, there is always room for individuals to cope exceptionally well.

Marriage

Marriage is a social status and identity with important links to health and illness. Married people tend to be healthier and to live longer lives. Single and divorced or separated people are more likely to become ill and to die. Nevertheless, the rates of (heterosexual) marriage are decreasing, from 70.5 per cent of Canadian families in 2001 to 65.8 per cent in 2016. However, the rate of same-sex marriage has increased: 16.5 per cent of same-sex couples married 2001 and 33.4 per cent did so in 2016. At the same time, in 2016 there were more single-person households than there were those with married couples (Eichler & Pederson, 2018). Marriage appears to offer men particular protection from illness (Robards et al., 2012). This outcome may be related to the higher social status of married men, as illness is associated with being in a subordinate position in the social structure (Thoits, 2011). It may also be linked to the fact that they are living with someone who is expected to care for them. Whether this overall positive association between marriage and health for men is a result of healthier lifestyles among the married (such as healthier eating, more controlled alcohol consumption, routine exercise) or because healthier people are selected into marriage is another issue under investigation. Loneliness has been linked to ill health (Hawkley & Cacioppo, 2010). Certainly, too, the periods of transition into and out of marriage are times of heightened vulnerability to illness.

Furthermore, particular types of caring, for instance, for gravely ill or disabled partners, can have negative health consequences for the carer and at times these can mitigate the benefits of marriage. Longitudinal research is needed on the impact on health of changes resulting from divorce and of the single people living alone. Also, nearly all research to date has focused on heterosexual couples and, thus, research on same-sex couples is needed. In addition, more research is needed on the impact of unhappy marriages on the health of the partners. Negative emotions, characteristic of unhappy marriages, are linked to elevated blood pressure and heart rate and increased levels of stress hormones (Robles & Kiecolt-Glaser, 2003), among other deleterious effects.

Lesbian, Gay, Bisexual, Transgender, and Queer Identities and Health

In the past couple of decades, a significant increase has occurred in research and policy development for people with non-heterosexual sexual identities and ambiguities in sex and gender identities. The rapid spread of the legalization of same-sex marriage is among the most important social forces enabling the growing public acknowledgement of sexual diversity. The openness of some prominent celebrities of diverse sexual identities, such as the television host Ellen Degeneres, has also played an important role in the "mainstreaming" of various differences. However, acceptance is not universal and LGBTQ people continue to experience significant amounts of stigma and discrimination in Canada and elsewhere in the world. "Coming out" to parents and to peers continues to be fraught for many Canadian young people. Research has shown that LGBTQ people have higher rates of some types of illnesses. For instance, some LGBTQ people struggle with mental health challenges such as depression, anxiety, and trauma (Zwiers, 2009). It is no wonder because protective factors for these conditions include a sense of social inclusion, freedom from discrimination and violence, and other social determinants (Canadian Mental Health Association [CMHA], 2019). Bisexual and trans people are more likely to be of poorer socio-economic status (CMHA, 2019). Hate crimes are a problem in Canada and one of the groups most likely to suffer from hate crimes is LGBTQ people (CMHA, 2019). Gay men and lesbian women are more vulnerable to certain types of cancers, excess alcohol consumption, and cigarette smoking. Gay men are more susceptible to various sexually transmitted infections and lesbian women have a greater likelihood of certain problems associated with reproduction (for instance, the side effects and after-effects of hormone ingestion sometimes used to enable artificial insemination). Health care itself may be more challenging for those with diverse sexual identities because of stigma and discrimination in the health-care system (Colpitt & Gahagan, 2016). Internalized shame and lowered self-esteem can also threaten the health and well-being of those whose identities do not adhere to heteronormativity. Compounding all of these problems is the lack of adequate education and training for health-care providers about sexual diversity and the possible homophobia, heterosexism, and other stereotyped and discriminatory practices to which the LGBTQ community is subject. Further, LGBTQ people may be less likely to seek health care because of their own fear and discomfort resulting from anticipated discrimination.

Racialization, Ethnicity, and Minority Status

"**Race**," **ethnicity**, culture, and **minority status** are important factors affecting health in Canadian society and around the world. They should be defined and distinguished. Furthermore, it is essential to acknowledge that their implications have arisen out of a context of white supremacy and reflect the actions of the white population to define race, in part, to keep racialized people in an unequal position as compared to white people. "Race" is a social and political construct that has been used to distinguish people on the basis of physical characteristics such as skin colour, hair colour and texture, bone density, blood types, and facial structure. Historically, there were thought to be three broad categories of race: Caucasian, Mongoloid, and Negroid. In fact, there are no pure races and the concept is outdated. However, the false beliefs about race continue and

CRITICAL THINKING

Box 5.2 • Movember

In 2003 a couple of men in Australia asked themselves what had happened to moustaches. In response, they decided to grow them and asked a bunch of their friends and acquaintances to join them. Each person was charged $10. They decided to use this adventure into face hair to raise money for charity and, inspired by the breast cancer movement, they chose men's health and prostate cancer as their charity of choice. The movement grew from 30 in 2003 to 4 million in 2013.

The Movember movement continues. In 2018–19 the movement raised $102.9 million and had 321,975 participants around the world (Movember, 2019). The Movember campaign is held every November in the involved countries. It essentially includes men supporting one another and raising funds through growing moustaches. It has become a major funder for research and programs for men's health in general and prostate cancer and depression more specifically.

While the Movember movement was founded by non-medical people and is lay-based, it has grown to be a global foundation with the goal of tackling a broad range of men's health issues beyond prostate cancer. It now includes fundraising for prostate and testicular cancer, suicide, and mental health issues. The organization has supported thousands of creative projects in these areas.

Us TOO, another movement, in this case for prostate cancer in particular, primarily focuses on providing education and support to those diagnosed with this disease and is now heavily funded, including by pharmaceutical companies. Us TOO was started soon after the early days of the breast cancer movement. It was initially instigated by men who were tired of all of the attention going to breast cancer, a mostly women's disease. They wanted their disease of prostate cancer included in large fundraising and research efforts.

These examples of gendered, disease-based fundraising lead us to ask a number of questions. Should medical research, and associated programming, be determined by lay people? Should research direction be determined by the efficacy of a social movement? Should "gender wars" enter into funding allocations? Should disease funding be determined by its incidence, age of the diagnosed, probability of a cure or prevention in the near future, severity of impact of the disease, or something else? Should pharmaceutical companies be allowed to contribute to lay organizations or does this inevitably lead to a conflict of interest?

These are just a few of the ethical issues and questions raised by health-related social movements. What do you think?

---

produce racialization and the prejudice called **racism.** "Ethnicity" refers to a common cultural background. Culture is a fundamental category for understanding similarities and differences in peoples around the world and within diversified countries such as Canada. There are numerous definitions of the concept of culture. Broadly speaking, "culture" refers to the total way of life of a group or aggregate of people. It often includes a unique language or "accent" and a world of everyday living based on a distinct language. "Minority status" refers to the numerical distribution of different ethnic categories

of people within a total population. Those with minority status are statistically or numerically less than one-half of the population under discussion. Of particular relevance to the topic of health is the idea that health is socially and culturally constructed, as are signs and symptoms of ill health, attitudes to those who are well and those who are ill, and different types of health care.

The relevance of race to health is primarily due to the pervasive and systemic realities of racism experienced by racial minorities. This racism is evident in interactions with major institutions such

CRITICAL THINKING

Box 5.3 • Functional Health

It is one thing to talk about the incidence of cancer, heart disease, diabetes, and other chronic and acute conditions. It is quite another to consider the question of functional health. This refers to the ability of individuals to engage in everyday life and to enjoy the simple things. Functional health includes things such as the ability to hear, see, and be mobile. It involves being able to care for oneself and one's daily needs. It also includes basic memory functioning. A Canadian Community Health Survey from 2017 found that 18.1 per cent of Canadians over 18 years had some memory or concentration challenges, 14.3 per cent had some challenges with their vision, and 15 per cent had some challenges walking. Females were more likely to have certain of these difficulties and males others. As well as gender the survey looked

at age differences and found that the percentage of Canadians with challenges increased as people aged. Thus, 59.8 per cent of Canadians over 65 had at least one area of difficulty in functional health. Functional health is also related to socio-psychological conditions such as life satisfaction and a sense of being a member of a community. Those with functional limitations also experienced poorer socio-economic status. They are more likely to be unemployed and are likely to have a lower level of education. Such socio-economic and socio-psychological challenges often restrict the overall quality of life of people and make change in these social determinants of health even more intractable than they usually are.

Source: Community Health Survey (2018).

as the educational, criminal justice, and health-care sectors. The constant and often invisible structural and systemic racism also accumulates in the day-to-day experiences of racialized people through **microaggressions** such as casual and seemingly minor slurs, slights, and interpersonal assumptions endemic in white privilege (Sue, 2011). These microaggressions happen so commonly that they are often outside of the conscious awareness of perpetrators and possibly even the recipients. Yet, they build up and are internalized and can lead to both mental and physical health problems through processes that will be described further in the next chapter. Microaggressions are a fundamental part of racism and the suffering it causes.

At the same time as Canadians extol our diversity and Americans articulate the value of their melting-pot society, violence against racial minorities continues in both places and under both political philosophies. Recently, for example, a resurgence of attention has been paid to racially based police brutality and racial profiling, especially after the death of George Floyd in Minneapolis set off protests around

the world and a resurgence and expansion of support for the Black Lives Matter movement. There are many examples of this in each country. Other forms of racism include systemic violence, racially based hate crimes, and so on. All sorts of racism and even anticipated racism can be linked to poorer physical and mental health among racialized minorities.

The term used most frequently in relation to racial discrimination is racism. It is a part of other "isms," including ableism, ageism, sexism, and phobias such as homophobia and transphobia with their constant companions of stigma, discrimination, and prejudice. We need to understand that racism wearies and hurts those who are insulted and distanced and can lead to higher rates of disease. Although less investigated, the perpetrators of racist acts likely also are hurt and made sick by engaging in this behaviour.

For all of these reasons associated with racism, a close and persistent relationship exists among racialization, ethnicity, and class. Significant economic inequality can be attributed to differences in ethnic background. Racialized groups are more likely to be poor, homeless, or inadequately housed and to experience discrimination and barriers in access to health care (Access Alliance, 2005; Colour of Justice Network, 2007; Nestel, 2012). One in five racialized families live in poverty in Canada, while one in 20 non-racialized families live in poverty (Canada Without Poverty, n.d.).

Ethno-racial minorities in urban centres have lower levels of income as a result of historical and continuing discrimination in the labour market (Galabuzi, 2001; McGibbon & Etowa, 2009). Racialized groups tend to live in different and poorer neighbourhoods in Toronto (Contenta, 2018). Poverty is especially endemic among immigrant and refugee groups from Africa, South Asia, and Southeast Asia. Among racialized groups, unemployment rates are higher and they are over-represented in low-wage sectors of the economy as well as in unregulated and temporary work. This may even be a more prominent issue today given the increases in racialized minority immigrant and refugee populations in Canada and particularly in the largest Canadian cities. However, heartening news in this regard indicates that despite the recent increase in the number of refugees admitted to Canada in response to civil war in Syria, the attitudes of Canadians remain positive (Perreaux, 2018). This is important because how others view an individual has important consequences for self-esteem, stress, mental health, and well-being. Today, 40 per cent of Canadian children are foreign-born (Statistics Canada, 2019). Their well-being and integration are fundamental to the future of Canada.

To the extent that ethnicity is related to occupational status, income, education, and other social determinants of health, people of different ethnic groups will differ in their morbidity and mortality rates. Furthermore, according to the 2016 census, racialized people are twice as likely to be poor in Toronto, the most ethnically diverse city in Canada (Joshi, 2017).

Immigrant Health

There were 5.4 million immigrants enumerated in the census of Canada in 2001 (Ng et al., 2005). Each year since 2001 an average of about 250,000 immigrants came to Canada until 2016, when, in response to the Syrian crisis, new policies were developed that included admitting about 323,000 immigrants and refugees to Canada in 2016, 272,000 in 2017, and 303,000 in 2018 (Statista, 2018). Immigration is a significant component of the growth in the population and labour force. Because of low fertility rates among native-born Canadians, immigration protects Canada from population decline as it maintains at least a slow population growth and contributes to economic prosperity. At times the population increase from immigration is much greater than that from native-born increase. In fact, Canada's growth is determined largely by immigration (Canada Population, 2018) and the argument can be and has been made by the Conference Board of Canada that Canada would benefit from increasing immigration levels (Keung, 2017).

People of colour made up about 22.3 per cent of Canada's population in 2016 (Grenier, 2017). However, gathering statistics about this sensitive topic is not easy, nor are the results as valid as would be ideal. That said, by 2030 both Vancouver and Toronto are predicted to have almost or above 60 per cent of their populations representing visible minority groups (Statistics Canada, 2010). Obviously, the term "minority" will take on a new meaning in this situation.

Considerable research in Canada, the United States, the United Kingdom, and Australia documents the relatively good health of new immigrants, partly as a result of selection (Kennedy et al., 2015; Vang et al., 2015). The notion of selection suggests that individuals who are healthier will be more likely to face the myriad challenges involved in immigrating to a new country. It also reflects the fact that new immigrants must pass a medical test and Canada is more likely to accept/select those people who are in good health. This phenomenon has been called the **healthy immigrant effect** (Beiser, 2005). The process of planning for, organizing, and executing the move for immigration demands a high level of intelligence, skill, energy, money, and overall well-being. Moreover, Canada's immigration policies (and those of other receiving countries) favour the educated, occupationally skilled, and young. In addition, immigrants are screened for various diseases prior to being accepted to Canada and may be denied admissibility solely on medical grounds. Even after they arrive in Canada in generally better health than the average Canadian, as immigrants adjust to life in Canada their health tends to deteriorate.

The situation is similar in many ways among refugees, even though, by virtue of their status as refugees, they have experienced highly stressful living conditions prior to coming to Canada. Nevertheless, the health of refugees is likely poorer than that of other immigrants and they are, for example, more susceptible to infections and parasitic diseases. Tuberculosis is a case in point. This highly contagious disease has incidence levels among refugees of approximately three times that for those born in Canada (Caring for Kids New to Canada, 2019). Canada continues to screen refugees for physical and mental illnesses so that they can be immediately treated. One study, for instance, found that new refugees to Toronto had higher rates of various infectious diseases such as HIV (2 per cent) and Hepatitis C (<1 per cent), along with several other less familiar diseases (Caring for Kids New to Canada, 2019).

Another way to consider the issue of the relative health of immigrants is through a comparison of their subjective reports with those of other Canadians. Ironically, perhaps, immigrants report that they perceive themselves to be healthy to a greater extent than do other Canadians, regardless of socio-economic and demographic characteristics when they arrive. However, the longer they remain in Canada the closer their self-reported health status comes to the rest of the population. Indeed, their overall health in general moves towards the Canadian average over time.

A Brief Overview of Indigenous Peoples in Canada

The one minority "group" for which current and historical data are becoming available now is Indigenous peoples in Canada: First Nations,

Inuit, and Métis. The variety of terms, including the older "Indians" and "Eskimos," reflects the struggle to find a name that best reflects the history and identity of peoples whose cultures were colonized by people of European origin over the past hundreds of years. Designations such as "savage," "redskin," "half-breed," "squaw," "buck," "brave," and "papoose" reflect something of the racist history to which Indigenous people have been subject by various generations of Euro-Canadians (Vowel, 2016). Some debate whether Indigenous peoples in Canada ought to be considered an ethnic group or not. Canada's Indigenous peoples are not considered "visible minorities" by the Canadian government. Those who favour the "ethnic group" designation argue that there are significant similarities among all Indigenous peoples despite their 70 or so different languages and the more than 600 registered "Indian" bands. In 2012 there were 3,169 reserves across the country, although some lacked inhabitants (Sawchuk et al., 2018). The chief similarity among all of the First Peoples in

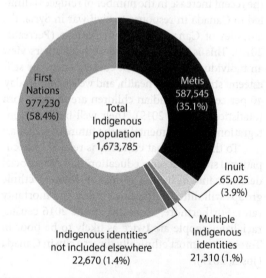

Figure 5.3   The Indigenous Population in Canada

Source: Canadian Press (2017). The Aboriginal population in Canada. http://thecanadianpress-a.akamaihd.net/graphics/2017/static/cp-census-aboriginal-pop.png

Remembering Our History

Box 5.4 • The Great Dying

The numbers have been debated and are difficult to be sure of, but the most reliable recent estimate is that the New World (First Nations) peoples likely numbered between 90 and 112 million before they were devastated by the diseases and warfare that Europeans brought with them to North and South America. Not only were the Amerindians numerous, they also enjoyed good health. Before contact they may have been in better health, in some ways, than Europeans. They did not have measles, smallpox, leprosy, influenza, malaria, or yellow fever. For most, staying healthy and living well were essential tenets of their religion. Hygiene included regular bathing and the peoples of the New World kept themselves very clean. The Europeans could not help noticing the "good smells" emanating from the healthy, robust people. Apparently, they especially admired their even white teeth and clear complexions, "something most pockmarked Spaniards, Portuguese and French had lost at an early age"

(Nikiforuk, 1991, p. 80). At this time, the average life expectancy of Europeans was about 20 years less than that of the Amerindians. It is suggested that their good health was the result of the origins of these people, who had crossed the land bridge that spanned the Bering Strait to the New World at a time of lower sea levels. Because of the harsh cold, the diseased immigrants and their germs were killed. Only the fittest survived.

Into this context of good health the new disease smallpox entered—an unknown yet dangerous predator that spread as an epidemic until it and other diseases such as the plague and tuberculosis killed upwards of 12 million people in North America. This "great dying" occurred over the course of about one century. Some historians rank this as the greatest demographic disaster in the history of the world. It is estimated that between 1492 and 1600, 56 million people died as a result of the arrival of the European settlers (Koch et al., 2019).

present-day Canada, who totalled just under 1.7 million in 2016, is that they share the powerful effects of subjugation through having been colonized (Sawchuk et al., 2018; Statistics Canada, 2018). This is a reason to consider them an ethnic group. Others, however, argue that, because the cultural diversity of the Indigenous peoples at colonization was seriously compromised by the dominance of the state, they should not be considered one cultural or ethnic group. Many different languages, cultures, and geographies distinguish them. Indeed, the majority (56 per cent) of all Indigenous people live in urban areas today (Sawchuk, 2018), and only 44 per cent of registered First Nations people live on reserves. Like First Nations and Métis people, the Inuit are also migrating south to the cities, with 27.2 per cent of Inuit, who in 2016 totalled over 65,000,

residing outside of Inuit Nunangat (i.e., Arctic Canada) (Statistics Canada, 2020). Overall, wherever they live, Indigenous people continue to face much poorer life chances, more disease, higher infant mortality, and lower life expectancy rates than non-Indigenous people in Canada.

Numerous explanations can be found for the compromised life chances and relatively poorer **health indicators** of Indigenous peoples residing in Canada. The Truth and Reconciliation Commission of Canada, under the leadership of Justice Murray Sinclair, pointed to several of these causes in its 2015 report:

> For over a century, the central goals of Canada's Aboriginal policy were to eliminate Aboriginal governments; ignore Aboriginal rights; terminate the Treaties; and, through

a process of assimilation, cause Aboriginal peoples to cease to exist as distinct legal, social, cultural, religious and racial entities in Canada. The establishment and operation of residential schools were a central element of this policy, which can be described as "cultural genocide." (Truth and Reconciliation Commission of Canada [TRC], 2015, p. 10)

Before colonization, Indigenous peoples were largely dependent on fishing, hunting, and foraging (First Nations Health Authority, n.d.). There was some manufacturing of such items as tools, chiefly for personal use. Many had very complex and sophisticated methods of harvesting and preserving foodstuffs over the seasons. People tended to be well because they had to be active to maintain life and because they usually had a varied and nutritious diet. According to oral history, during pre-contact time Indigenous people had very good health and longevity. Moreover, what they considered health was much more than merely biological functioning. It encompassed spiritual, social, and ceremonial elements of life, whereby the individual needed to be in good relations not only with other humans but with the land and with the animals and plants that shared the environment. Various types of healers incorporated some of the different components of health, and these healers included midwives, shamans, and herbalists. There was no diabetes or dental caries at this time, although there is evidence of arthritis and of abscess in the jaws of some. Spiritual wellness, which was the domain of the shaman, was considered to be essential to well-being. The people thrived with the combination of healthy foods and lifestyles and holistic health care.

After contact, widespread epidemics of smallpox, influenza, measles, and whooping cough occurred. Populations were decimated. In some villages the mortality rate was as high as 90 per cent. Chronic diseases such as tuberculosis and venereal disease arrived. The work of the traditional healer and the shaman was relatively ineffective in dealing with these new diseases. The immune systems of the remaining people were compromised. With the

population losses, many aspects of the oral culture and the histories of healing also were lost.

Treaties were signed that outlined nation-to-nation relationships and friendship agreements between the British Crown and Indigenous groups (Sawchuk, 2018). Then, in 1876, the Indian Act, which pulled together and enlarged on earlier colonial policy, was enacted. This legislation, which has undergone small and major revisions over the past century and a half, provided that the government would be responsible for funding social services and programs to the First Nations people who registered as Indians with the federal government. Treaties stipulated landownership and responsibilities. The funding was under the control of band administrators, that is, white Indian agents employed by the federal government.

Before we consider the health and medical care of Indigenous people in Canada today, we need to look at four significant factors that affect the mental and physical health of Indigenous peoples in Canada and are unique to their circumstance: (1) the experience of residential schools; (2) the "Sixties Scoop"; (3) continuing questions regarding autonomy and authority in governance structures and landownership; and (4) the quality of the physical environments upon which people who live on reserves depend.

Residential Schools

From a very early date there were some **residential schools** for Indigenous children in New France. But beginning in 1874 the Canadian state, with the help of various churches, established residential schools across the country. The aim was the education of Indigenous young people to enable their assimilation to the majority society. More than 100,000 Indigenous children were taken from their homes and educated in more than 100 residential schools across Canada over the next century. This practice reflected the government's desire to incorporate Indigenous people into the mainstream culture and was supported by the desire of Christian churches and their missionaries to Christianize the Indigenous peoples. The strategy was to remove young people from their families and cultural roots. The residential school era caused immense suffering for the children, their families, and their communities. Not only did the residential school experience disrupt the family life of these children, it also diminished their ability to parent when they grew to be adults (Barton et al., 2005; TRC, 2015). The children lost their culture, language, and identity. Their education was severely hampered by their physical mistreatment and by the racist limitations and assumptions upon which the school administrators based the curriculum. Indeed, for older children, especially, these schools often were less institutions of education than forced labour camps. Many of the children were expected to put in long days of labour tilling the soil, growing crops, and making repairs for the school.

The government and the churches designed specific training programs to manage the Indigenous children. The prime minister of the time, Sir John A. Macdonald, made the rationale very clear when he spoke to the House of Commons in 1883:

When the school is on the reserve the child lives with its parents, who are savages: he is surrounded by savages, and though he may learn to read and write his habits, and training and mode of thought are Indian. He is simply a savage who can read and write. It has been strongly pressed upon myself, as head of the Department, that Indian children should be withdrawn as much as possible from parental influences, and the only way to do that would be to put them in central training industrial schools where they will acquire the habits and modes of thought of white men. (TRC, 2015, p. 2)

The children and their families were virtually powerless to resist. Many children were sexually and physically abused. They were unable to speak their own languages and were forced to always communicate in English. They could not communicate with the family they had been forced to leave behind. Their own cultures and languages were denigrated and their previous way of life

despised and vilified by those in power, the teachers and administrators. They were fed inferior food. Sugar and starch were added to their diets. In some cases, deleterious and even dangerous experiments in nutrition were carried out with the children as the subjects. Many young people died in the residential schools, and sometimes the parents were not informed of the deaths of their children. Some children ran away from the schools, and some of these died trying to reach their homes. The Indian Act, buttressed by the state, assumed the right to force compulsory hospitalization and treatment and to intervene with the imposition of modern medicine. This power was rationalized as a way to prevent the spread of epidemic disease. The legacy of this brutalization continues today.

In order to survive and psychologically avoid the pain, many children experienced dissociation (TRC, 2015). Today, many residential school survivors suffer symptoms of post-traumatic stress disorder (PTSD), such as recurrent and intrusive memories, nightmares, flashbacks, sleep difficulties, anger management problems, a tendency to abuse drugs and/or alcohol, and difficulties in relationships. PTSD is associated with marital instability, educational failure, and unemployment (Barton et al., 2005; TRC, 2015). Some children who died at the schools were interred in unmarked graves. Tuberculosis was a leading cause of death. In one community, the Nuxalk Nation, 52 per cent of all deaths between 1917 and 1983 involved people under the age of 25. Most likely, many of these deaths were among children in residential schools.

The government of Canada, as part of the 2006 settlement for the individual, family, and community harms caused by the residential schools, established a $350 million Aboriginal Healing Fund and the Truth and Reconciliation Commission, which began hearing the stories of survivors in 2009. The government has paid damages of about $2 billion to individuals taken from their families as children, deprived of their cultures, languages, and values, and sometimes sexually or otherwise abused. The churches that ran these government schools—Anglican, Roman Catholic, United Church, and Presbyterian—worked out their degree of responsibility with the federal government (the Anglican Church, for example, paid reparations of $25 million) and, except for the Catholic Church, all of the churches made formal apologies in the 1990s (Frideres, 2020, pp. 69–72). In 2009 Pope Benedict expressed "sorrow" and "regret" for the harm caused, but the Catholic Church has refused to make a formal, official apology. According to the Canadian Conference of Catholic Bishops, this is because neither the church as a universal whole nor the entire Canadian church made the decisions to be involved in the schools. This, they state, is because the church in Canada has a decentralized structure and only 16 out of 70 dioceses in Canada were implicated (Canadian Conference of Catholic Bishops, n.d.).

With many residential school survivors in attendance, then Prime Minister Stephen Harper formally apologized in a special sitting of Parliament in June 2008, stating in part: "The Government of Canada sincerely apologizes and asks the forgiveness of the Indigenous peoples of this country for failing them so profoundly. We are sorry" (AMMSA, 2008). Leaders of the other federal parties also presented statements of apology, and the leaders of the five major national Indigenous organizations spoke in response. The response of Beverley Jacobs, at that time the president of the Native Women's Association of Canada, cut to the heart of this significant issue in Canadian health and society:

> Prior to the residential schools system, prior to colonization, the women in our communities were very well respected and honoured for the role that they have in our communities as being the life givers, being the care takers of the spirit that we bring to mother earth. We have been given those responsibilities to look after our children and to bring that spirit into this physical world. . . .
>
> I want to say that I come here speaking from my heart, because two generations ago, my grandmother, being a Mohawk woman, was beaten, sexually beaten and physically beaten, for being a Mohawk woman. She did not pass

that on. She did not pass it on to my mother and her siblings, and so that matriarchal system that we have was directly affected. Luckily, I was raised in a community where it has been revitalized by all of our mothers.

> I want to say that as mothers, we teach our boys and our girls, our men and our women equally. . . . It is not just about women's issues, it is about making sure that we have strong nations again. That is what I am here to say. (Hansard, 11 June 2008)

The long-term effects continue in the generations being born and raised now.

The "Sixties Scoop"

Another disaster followed the calamitous effects of residential schools. The **"Sixties Scoop"** or the "lost generation" refers to the policy begun in the 1960s and ended in the 1980s that had similar goals to those of the residential school system (Vowel, 2016). It was initiated by an agreement between the federal and provincial governments to take over the responsibility for child welfare of First Nations children across the country. Rather than taking children forcibly from their homes and depositing them in schools miles away, this policy involved taking children from their homes on the presumption that their parents, their extended communities, and the homes they provided for their children were not good enough. In this case the children were seized by the child welfare agencies mandated to ensure that the needs of Indigenous children were being met. If the agencies decided that their needs were not satisfied, children were removed from their families and communities and adopted out or fostered to "homes across Canada, in the United States, and even overseas" (TRC, 2015, p. 138). The idea was to provide the children with homes that reflected the values of the social workers who were judging the suitability of Indigenous parenting. On a lesser scale, this policy continues. In 2011 Statistics Canada reported that 3.6 per cent of Indigenous children were in foster care as compared to 0.3 per cent of non-Indigenous children.

The United Nations Committee on the Rights of Children has stated its concern about the removal of Indigenous children from their homes as a first response "in cases of neglect, financial hardship or disability" (TRC, 2015, p. 138). The care of children of Indigenous parents is also more likely to be investigated than that of those from other families. One study found that there were 140.6 investigations of child maltreatment per 1,000 Indigenous children versus 33.5 investigations per 1,000 non-Indigenous children (TRC, 2015, p. 139).

At the same time as child welfare authorities have taken a disproportionate number of Indigenous children into care, they also have failed to protect them adequately in their foster and adoptive homes. Some foster parents have been found to physically and sexually abuse their charges. Fostered Indigenous children were significantly more likely to die in care than non-Indigenous children. In one study 78 per cent of the children who died in care were Indigenous (TRC, 2015, p. 141). There is a lack of adequate funding for supervision and child placement, and jurisdictional disputes between the federal and provincial and territorial governments about who ought to pay for various services only complicate matters. A bill called Jordan's Principle was introduced into and passed by the House of Commons in reaction to one such dispute. Jordan was an infant born with complex medical needs. He spent his short life until he died in hospital in the midst of jurisdictional arguments regarding which level of government was responsible for his medical care (TRC, 2015, p. 142).

That the Sixties Scoop was a significant movement and had a large impact is illustrated by the fact that in one province alone, British Columbia, the numbers of First Nations children removed from their homes went from almost none to about one-third over the course of a decade. Approximately 11,132 status Indian children were removed from their homes between 1960 and 1990 (TRC, 2015). This is very likely an underestimate: knowledgeable commentators put the number, including Métis and non-status children, at 20,000. "Being from an Indigenous family was often enough to have a child declared in need of intervention" (TRC, 2015,

p. 182). Furthermore, by 2002, 22,500 Indigenous children were in foster care across the country. Indigenous children were six to eight times more likely to be placed in foster care than other children. For 46 per cent of Indigenous children taken from their homes and placed in care the explanation has been "neglect." This is quite a bit higher than the 29 per cent of non-Indigenous children who are taken from their homes because of neglect. On the other hand, non-Indigenous children are more likely to be removed from their homes because of physical abuse (23 per cent versus 9 per cent) or because they have witnessed parental violence (36 per cent versus 33 per cent). "Neglect" is an ambiguous term, but what it generally means is poverty, poor housing, and substance abuse within the household. Clearly, poverty and poor housing are both subjectively determined and caused by government policies.

Governance Structures for Indigenous Peoples

Continuing conflicts exist between the Canadian government and different Indigenous peoples regarding a number of issues, including broken treaties, a lack of respectful consultation on a nation-to-nation basis, and the expropriation of land for resource extraction and development. Such disputes have been accompanied by changing terminology. One response, through a new federal Act in 2017, has been to divide the former Department of Indian and Northern Affairs into two separate portfolios: Crown–Indigenous Relations and Northern Affairs Canada, and Indigenous Services Canada. The mandate of the former is to oversee the "big-picture" issues concerning relations between Ottawa and Indigenous peoples, including self-government and treaty agreements and economic growth in Canada's North. The Indigenous Services ministry, on the other hand, aims to give the right to self-determination and management back to Indigenous communities both by improving health and social services and by supporting and empowering them to independently deliver services and address the socio-economic conditions in their communities (Sawchuk et al., 2018). The legacy of the Indian Act and the Department of Indian Affairs is long, though, and it will take time for the potentially positive aspects of these changes to be manifest.

The Physical Environments of Traditional Lands

One of the other effects of racism is the environmental destruction of the lands of Indigenous peoples. Various threats to the environment have been documented, including flooding as the result of the construction of dams and hydroelectric projects, water contamination, and depletion of fisheries. Corporations from southern Canada and other parts of the world, with the blessing of governments, seek profits from resource extraction and hydroelectric development in northern Canada without due consideration of what such megaprojects as the Alberta tar sands, diamond mining in the Northwest Territories and northern Ontario, nickel and gold mining throughout the provincial and territorial North, and the damming and diverting of water courses such as in Labrador, northern Quebec, and Manitoba will do to environments and to the long-term sustainability of livelihoods.

These various risks are linked not only to the immediate health of the people living on reserves but also to the generational degradation of the environment. As Beverley Jacobs noted in her response to the residential schools apology, we must ask what effects our actions and decisions today will have "seven generations from now." The ongoing environmental deterioration threatens the entire natural world, including animals, birds, plants, and people. The soils in some communities are infused with toxic heavy metals such as mercury and lead, a result of previous mining and other resource extraction activities. On at least one reserve, Aamjiwnaang, just south of Sarnia, Ontario, the sex ratios have been changing—the number of girl babies born is significantly higher than the number

of boys. This shift is related to a number of nearby industries that produce endocrine-disrupting chemicals linked to the functioning of the immune system, organ and tissue growth, metabolism, behaviour, and sexuality, among other things (Shingler, 2013). There are ongoing problems with the physical and geographic conditions on reserves that have impacts on the health and well-being of First Nations people.

Demography and Health of Indigenous Communities

The Indigenous population is the fastest-growing population in Canada (First Nations Health Authority, n.d.). The 2006 census indicated that close to 1.2 million Canadians were of Indigenous identity, a 45 per cent increase over the previous 10 years. Ten years later, in 2016, there were 1,673,785 self-identified Indigenous people in Canada comprising 4.9 per cent of the total Canadian population (Statistics Canada, 2018). Of these, 977,230 reported being of First Nations ancestry, 587,545 were Métis, and 65,025 were Inuit.

Some of the recent growth in the Indigenous population can be attributed to more people acknowledging their Indigenous ancestry and to the change in the laws regarding women who have left the reserve being able to keep or resume their status. However, natural increase is the principal factor in population growth. The birth rate is increasing, as is life expectancy (Statistics Canada, 2018). However, Indigenous people in Canada live shorter lives than other Canadians (Figure 5.4) and experience a considerably higher birth rate. The average age of Indigenous people in Canada is 28 years old, about a decade younger than the rest of the population (TD Economics, 2015). This speaks to the relatively high birth rate. These factors are reflected in the fact that Indigenous communities tend to have a much greater proportion of people under 30 years old than other communities. This difference is shown in Figure 5.5, which compares the average age by province of First Nations and the total Canadian

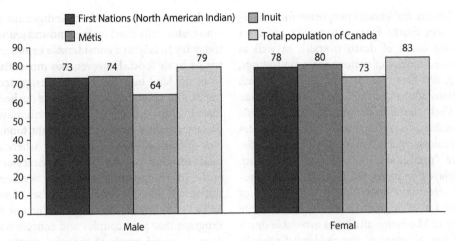

Figure 5.4 Projected Life Expectancy at Birth by Sex, Indigenous Identity, 2017

Note: Estimated data. "Life expectancy" is an estimate of the number of years a person is expected to live, for a given year. Most often reported as life expectancy at birth, it can be reported at any age, for different population groups.

Source: Statistics Canada (2015, Chart 13).

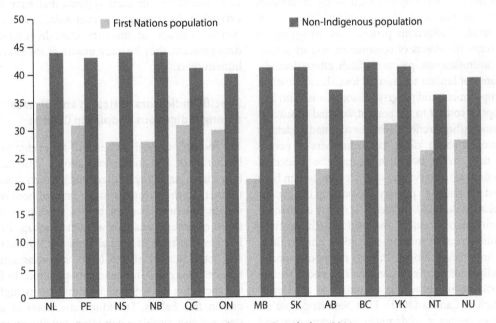

Figure 5.5 Median Age, First Nations and Non-Indigenous Population, 2011

Source: TD Economics (2013).

populations for 2011. About 61 per cent of the members of Indigenous communities are under 30 as compared to 38.8 per cent in the total population. The relative youth of the communities also reflects that the average life expectancy is shorter among Indigenous people: 64 for males and 73 for females according to Statistics Canada's estimate for 2017 (Statistics Canada, 2015).

In addition, Indigenous people are more likely to die violent deaths from automobile accidents (the leading cause of death overall), as well as from suicide, injuries of various sorts, poisonings, drowning, and fires (Fantus et al., 2009). Overall, First Nations adults under 75 years are more than twice as likely to die from what Statistics Canada calls avoidable causes (CBC, 2015). Three examples are tuberculosis, pneumonia, and breast cancer. These are "preventable" diseases in that death can be delayed or prevented through early detection and screening. Josée Lavoie, the director of the Centre for Aboriginal Health Research at the University of Manitoba, attributes avoidable death to the historical legacy of the residential schools, racism, lack of clean water, and food insecurity, as well as poor access to health care for those residing off-reserve (CBC, 2015).

These premature or avoidable deaths result from difficult and impoverished living conditions. As McCormick et al. (1997) explain, "Everywhere in Canada [Indigenous peoples] are struggling to overcome the effects of colonialism and its associated assimilationist practices. Such effects include, but are not limited to, cultural loss, discrimination, unemployment, and poverty." Colonialism, from first European contact to the present, has had broad and devastating health effects, with the repeated epidemics mentioned above killing large numbers of people over time. In the twentieth century the residential school system, reserve life, and extensive racism have played a part in high poverty rates among Indigenous peoples (Shah, 2004). Indigenous poverty is mirrored in high rates of morbidity and mortality. The continuing differences in income, education, employment, and housing are fundamental to the poorer health of Indigenous people in Canada. Indigenous seniors are particularly vulnerable, according to the Health Council of Canada (2013). First Nations people on reserves are not receiving adequate home care and long-term care in their communities and thus many must leave their communities and live far from home in culturally foreign environments. The situation for Inuit who live in remote northern communities is often especially dire as they age.

A lack of adequate and accessible food continues to pose a significant threat to the health of the Inuit and other northern Indigenous peoples, who historically lived on the land and sea and even today try to rely to a considerable extent on country or bush food. However, the movement away from the land into government-designated settlements and changing environments pushed by climate change, especially in the North, have led to dietary changes, costly store-bought foods, and a lack of fresh vegetables and fruits, where country foods formerly provided all of the necessary nutrients. To counter the sedentary, welfare-reliant settlement life, Quebec for a number of years has had a Cree Hunters and Trappers Income Security Program that paid couples and couples with children to spend much of the year on the land to acquire country food for themselves and their communities (Bone, 2016, ch. 7). Yet, as game, fish, and sea mammal populations dwindle, or as these animals at the top of food chains accumulate toxic substances in their systems that have been carried in the atmosphere from Asia, Europe, and North America, or mercury from hydroelectric dam projects, they become unsafe as the basis for human diets.

Specific Indicators of Health and Disease among Indigenous Peoples in Canada

The Indigenous birth rate is four times that of the birth rate of non-Indigenous people. Also, about four times as many Indigenous women become mothers in their teens, and the rates of both overweight and underweight babies are higher than those of other Canadian women (Kirkup, 2017). Further, the rates of fetal alcohol syndrome (FAS) and fetal alcohol effects (FAE) are substantially higher among the Indigenous population. In fact, the incidence of FAS and FAE may be as high as one in five babies. Smoking rates, rates of substance abuse, problem gambling, nutritional inadequacy, physical inactivity levels, overweight and obesity, and rates of unsafe sexual practices tend to be higher in Indigenous communities (Shah, 2004). In addition, the incidence of various communicable diseases is considerably higher among Indigenous people than in the general population. For example, whereas the Indigenous population

Remembering Our History

Box 5.5 • Nutrition Experiments and Indigenous Health

Is there any ethical justification for the nutritional experiments with Indigenous people in the 1940s?

A doctor working for what was then called the Department of Indian Affairs was concerned because there was an epidemic of tuberculosis and blindness among the 300 or so Indigenous people who lived in Norway House in northern Manitoba in the 1940s. He decided, with the approval of the House of Commons, to capitalize on this situation and to undertake experiments with nutritional vitamin supplements to see if they would improve the health of the suffering people. He chose 125 of the 300 members of the community for treatment. He followed their health over two years and noted that vitamin supplements seemed to be associated with health improvements. This nutritional experimentation then spread to British Columbia, Alberta, Ontario, and Nova Scotia and encompassed about 1,300 Indigenous people. Included among the study's protocols were keeping people on very-low-calorie diets, withholding vitamins and minerals, and denying dental care in order to observe the impacts of these strategies on the health of the people. At one residential school some children were given one-half the ration of milk to observe the influence of this on their health. Ian Mosby, a University of Guelph professor who researches the history of food policy in Canada, discovered and publicized these studies in 2014. Could this same sort of unethical research be carried out today? Or would the research ethics boards established across the country and governing research in Canada prevent such destructive research?

is about 4.3 per cent of the whole Canadian population it is burdened with 16 per cent of the cases of tuberculosis. Inuit receive 270 times the rate of new diagnoses of tuberculosis as other Canadians (Andermann, 2017).

Indigenous people, generally, are slightly less satisfied with their lives than other Canadians. The picture of Inuit health, however, is somewhat different. They are less likely than all other groups to report a chronic condition, for instance, have a much greater sense of community belonging, and their level of life satisfaction is equivalent to that of non-Indigenous people.

Sexually Transmitted Diseases

Sexually transmitted diseases are also prevalent in Indigenous communities. The incidence of chlamydia, for example, is almost seven times higher than the rate among other Canadians. HIV/AIDS occurrence has risen dramatically; from 1 per cent of the Indigenous population in 1990 to 5–8 per cent in 2012, and 6–12 per cent of the new infections in Canada in 2016 were of Indigenous people. Although they constitute about 4.3 per cent of the Canadian population, Indigenous persons living with HIV/AIDS comprise about 11.3 per cent of the total Canadian cases (PHAC, 2018). As Frideres (2020, p. 141) notes, "while the overall rate of HIV in Canada is stabilizing, in First Nation communities the incidence continues to grow." This is particularly significant and considered of epidemic proportions because of the small size of the communities and the amount of intermingling regarding both drug use and sex. Indigenous women are especially susceptible because of the higher rates of other sexually transmitted disease, inequitable gender relations, and high-risk sexual practices (Shah, 2004). The proportion of Indigenous people with an HIV diagnosis as the result of injection drug use is much higher than among other Canadians. Homosexual relations, according to these data, are a much less important cause of transfer of the virus in First Nations communities, although that may reflect a greater need in some communities to be "closeted."

Spotlight on Ethics

Box 5.6 • The Case of Makayla Sault

Should the courts have taken Makayla Sault from her First Nation parents and community and forced her to have chemotherapy?

Makayla Sault, a 10-year-old Mohawk girl from the New Credit First Nation near Brantford, Ontario, was diagnosed with leukemia (acute lymphoblastic leukemia) in 2014 by the doctors at McMaster Hospital in Hamilton, Ontario. She was given a 75 per cent chance of survival and full recovery if she completed the chemotherapy treatments prescribed to take place over several years. Makayla was hospitalized for the first stage of the treatment and experienced very severe side effects in hospital. During this time in hospital Makayla thought she received a message from Jesus telling her that her body was healed. She told her parents, both of whom were pastors, and they agreed to remove Makayla from the hospital and to pursue other types of treatments that they felt were spiritually and culturally appropriate. In response, the doctors at McMaster argued that she would die without allopathic treatment and asked the Children's Aid Society of Brant County to take Makayla into their custody so that she could receive the prescribed conventional medical treatment. The Indigenous community rallied behind the Sault family and supported their right to care for their daughter using "natural" treatments. The community remembered the spectre of children who had been taken away from their parents and forced into residential schools or gathered up in the detested "Sixties Scoop" and equated these incidents to forcing chemotherapy on Makayla. This case went to court to determine if Makayla's parents had the right to care for their child as they saw fit or whether Makayla should be removed and hospitalized so that she would receive the scientifically well-documented medical treatment.

In what was an unusual decision, the judge rejected the claim by McMaster that the child should be removed in favour of the idea that Makayla's parents had the right to choose what they considered to be appropriate care for their daughter. Makayla died less than a year later, in January 2015.

Was this a victory for Indigenous rights or a failure to protect a child?

Other Social Issues and Inequalities in Indigenous Communities

The health of Indigenous people is also related to gender, class, age, and area of residence (Wotherspoon, 1994; Shah, 2004). The same factors that explain health differences among other Canadians affect the health of the Indigenous people. Thus, those who are higher on the various social-structural indicators are more likely to have good health and, on average, the health of Indigenous people is poorer because, on average, they have lower incomes, have less education, and are more likely to be unemployed or underemployed than other Canadians. Indigenous people are also more likely to be incarcerated—22.8 per cent of all federal inmates are Indigenous. Of these Indigenous inmates, 96 per cent misused various substances (drugs, alcohol), 73 per cent noted a family history of residential school experience, and 88 per cent "had a family member struggling with alcohol or drug addiction issues" (Office of the Correctional Investigator, 2014).

The median income of $25,526 for Indigenous persons is considerably lower than that for non-Indigenous people ($34,604), and almost one-quarter live below the poverty line (Kirkup, 2017). Indigenous people are also more likely to be homeless and to be dependent on welfare, and they are disproportionately affected by housing considered inadequate. According to the National Collaborating Centre for Indigenous Health

(2020), there has been no substantial improvement in Indigenous on-reserve housing. Twenty per cent of Indigenous people, a rate more than three times higher than that for non-Indigenous people in Canada, live in homes that need significant repairs. Among First Nations and Inuit, the rate of inadequate housing is closer to 25 per cent (Kirkup, 2017). Clean water for drinking and cleaning is still missing on a significant number of reserves. In consequence a group of Indigenous leaders have sued the federal government for their failure to provide clean drinking water. Between 2004 and 2014 about 66 per cent (400/618) of First Nations reserves were under at least one water advisory, which means that their water is unsafe to drink or use for washing. One reserve had not had clean water for 20 years (Levasseur, 2015). This sorry situation has been changing under the current Liberal government: as of February 2020, 60 long-term boil-water advisories continued to be in effect, with the federal government aspiring to have all such advisories lifted by March 2021. In the fall of 2019 there were 441 infrastructure projects underway to build, repair, and upgrade on-reserve water supplies (Government of Canada, 2020).

Canada as a whole stands in good stead in educational achievement and conditions globally. The situation is different for Indigenous people in Canada (Parkin, 2015), who are less likely to have achieved all levels of education from grade school to university. The gap between Indigenous people and other Canadians is widening over time. In 1996 there was a 12-percentage-point difference in educational achievement. In 2011 that gap had grown to 17 percentage points. However, Indigenous children are staying in school longer than in the past. As of 2011, almost half of the Indigenous population had some post-secondary education, as compared to 65 per cent among the non-Indigenous population (Indigenous and Northern Affairs Canada, 2011). There has been increased funding for band-operated elementary and high schools. In addition, Indigenous programs in universities have grown, including programs for training Indigenous people in the professions (e.g., medicine, law, and, especially, social work), in part so that they can work in the Indigenous community and provide services to their people. Also, the First Nations University of Canada, in Regina, was established explicitly for First Nations people. Still, substantially higher rates of unemployment remain. Unemployment, underemployment, and low incomes all contribute to the poverty of Indigenous people, as well as to their poorer health status. As Adelson explains, "It is the complex interplay of job market discrimination, lack of education, cultural genocide, and loss of land and sovereignty that affect employment status and, ultimately, the degree of poverty faced by those who are caught in a circle of disadvantage" (Adelson, 2005, p. S53; see also Indigenous and Northern Affairs Canada, 2011).

Self-Perceived Health and Reported Social Problems

Indigenous people tend to define health as comprised of balance, harmony, holism, and spirituality. Individual pain, suffering, and disease, per se, do not necessarily alter this inner sense of well-being (Shah, 2004; First Nations Health Authority, n.d.). For some Indigenous groups, health is thought of as a "medicine wheel," which includes physical, mental, emotional, and spiritual aspects (Shah, 2004). All are important to a truly healthy person. From the perspective of the Indigenous Corporate Training group, eight main social concerns need addressing: poorer health than the general population, unemployment, education, housing, income, suicide, harm to children from unintentional injuries, and higher levels of incarceration (Indigenous Corporate Training [ICT], 2019) as major social concerns, as follows. All of these issues, directly or indirectly, relate back to the first concern, poorer health.

Suicide rates, for example, are between five and seven times higher among First Nations youth than among others in Canada, and the suicide rate among Inuit youth is among the highest in the world. It is 11 times that of other Canadian youth. Suicide and self-inflicted injuries are the chief cause of death among Indigenous people until they reach the age of 45. Deaths from self-inflicted

Remembering Our History

Box 5.7 • The Ojibway of Grassy Narrows

The experience of the Ojibway of Grassy Narrows First Nation provides a poignant and trenchant critique of the disastrous impact the Canadian state and Canadian industry have had on a people and their way of life. It is just one example of a continuing problem. Until 1963, the Grassy Narrows Ojibwa lived a settled, traditional life, hunting and fishing on and around the English–Wabigoon River system in northern Ontario. Then, in 1963, they were relocated by the Department of Indian Affairs, so the reserve would be nearer to a road, thus, nearer to a number of services and amenities in modern life, such as schools, various social services, and electricity. Uprooting and moving the people had a tumultuous impact on their health and lifestyle. Before the Ojibway had time to adjust to this crisis, another hit. This time it was the discovery that the English–Wabigoon River system, which had been their main source of livelihood for many years, was poisoned by methyl mercury, the source of which was a paper mill at Dryden, Ontario, 170 kilometres upstream (Dickason, 2002, p. 394).

Before 1963, over 90 per cent of all deaths among the Ojibway were attributed to natural causes. By the mid-1970s, only 24 per cent of the deaths resulted from natural causes. By 1978, 75 per cent of the deaths were due to alcohol-induced violence directed against the self and others. Homicide, suicide, and accidental death rates soared. Child neglect and abuse grew rapidly, and numerous children were taken into the care of the Children's Aid Society and placed in foster homes. As Shkilnyk (1985, p. 3) wrote 35 years ago: "Today the bonds of the Indian family have been shattered. The deterioration in family life has taken place with extraordinary swiftness." Despite the good intentions of the Canadian government in relocating the people, their socio-economic conditions deteriorated. "All the indications of material poverty were there—substandard housing, the absence of running water and sewage connections, poor health, mass unemployment, low income, and welfare dependency" (Shkilnyk, 1985, p. 3).

and unintentional injuries are three to four times higher than those of other Canadians death among Indigenous children (ICT, 2019). Indeed, the crisis of youth suicide is so grave that emergency measures have been called for and provided. In 2016, for example, Attawapiskat First Nation in northern Ontario called a state of emergency after 11 youth tried to kill themselves. These higher rates occur for both male and female youth, although the rate is somewhat higher for males. Figure 5.6 portrays the risk factors for suicide and thus suggests some of the changes that need to occur for its prevention.

Indigenous adults are much more likely to be incarcerated. Twenty-six per cent of those incarcerated are Indigenous, and the over-representation of Indigenous youth in the criminal justice system is even higher than that of adults. Violence is a significant problem in Indigenous communities. Teenage mothers and their children are particularly vulnerable (ICT, 2019). As Adelson explains,

citing a submission to the Royal Commission on Aboriginal Peoples, "up to 75 per cent of the victims of sex crimes in Indigenous communities are women and girls under the age of 18 (50 per cent of those are under age 14 and almost 25 per cent are under the age of 7)." Adelson also notes, "Racism coupled with sexism leaves Aboriginal women in a highly vulnerable position" (Adelson, 2005, p. S55). Indigenous people are more likely to live with spousal abuse and substance abuse, and they are more likely to be victims of homicide. As pointed out by the Royal Canadian Mounted Police, Indigenous women are more likely to be murdered due to their greater vulnerability, i.e., they are more likely to be unemployed, to have a criminal record, to work in the sex trade, to have consumed alcohol before the incident, and to made some of their money from illegal activities. The report of the National Inquiry into Murdered and Missing Indigenous Women and Girls (2019) documents

The Grassy Narrows Ojibway experienced too much change, too quickly. Their autonomy and cultural traditions were destroyed. Because of mercury pollution, they were robbed of their health and their means of livelihood. Difficulties continue in Grassy Narrows as a result of these historical incidents, along with newer challenges such as logging by private commercial companies. Logging is a threat to the livelihood of the people who rely on hunting in the forests for their food, health, and well-being.

In 2014, the Supreme Court reaffirmed the right of the province of Ontario to use this land for industrial logging (Rennie, 2014). Perhaps most telling of government attitudes, however, is the extent of inaction in regard to the mercury pollution. No remediation of the river system has ever been carried out by the federal or provincial government, although mercury levels are still rising and the earlier claim that natural processes would clean up the contamination has proven to be false (Porter, 2015). No explicit government recognition of the negative health impacts of mercury poisoning on the people of Grassy Narrows (e.g., central nervous system and brain damage, with weakness and tingling

in the limbs, difficulty swallowing and speaking, and loss of motor function) has been made. There is no ongoing Canadian research on the problem, nor had there been support for the people from government—yet Japanese researchers, from 1975 to 2014, visited the community on five separate occasions to examine the people and chronicle the consequences of mercury to the people and other life forms. They found that over 90 per cent of the people suffered the effects of mercury poisoning (Porter, 2017). Forty years ago a Japanese researcher identified numerous instances of Minamata disease, a neurological disorder caused by mercury poisoning, among the people of Grassy Narrows (Crowe, 2014). Finally, in 2017 the Ontario government announced funding to clean the English–Wabigoon system of mercury (Porter, 2017). In April 2020 the Grassy Narrows chief, Randy Turtle, signed a framework agreement with federal Indigenous Services Minister Marc Miller whereby Ottawa is committed to fund a new $19.5 million Mercury Care Home on the reserve, plus pay for operating costs for the next 30 years, to deal with a crisis that began some 60 years earlier (Bruser, 2020).

how the excess of suffering and violence against Indigenous women and girls is the logical result of centuries of colonialism with the intention of assimilation or elimination of Indigenous people. The report calls the deaths of the murdered and missing women as well as of two-spirited (2S) and LGBTQ+ people illustrative of genocide.

Canadian Indigenous peoples on reserves often suffer from isolation and limited power in the control of their own housing, location, education, and

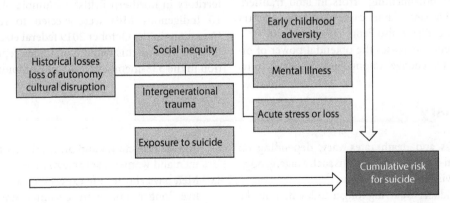

Figure 5.6 Suicide Risk Factors

Source: Crawford (2016).

StaceyL/Shutterstock.com

An installation of the Red Dress Awareness Campaign in Courtney, BC. The REDress Project, started by Métis artist Jamie Black in 2010, uses installations of red dresses to raise awareness about missing and murdered Indigenous women and girls in Canada.

occupation. The negotiations over the ownership of land and the governance of reserves continue (slowly) with the Canadian government. The consequences of this lack of autonomy and authority are problematic for the total way of life and well-being of people who live with such uncertainty and with experiences of racism that lead to low expectations of others and for themselves. Self-rule is an important factor in the health and well-being of any people, just as autonomy (or freedom) in decision-making is a value held by individuals. Indigenous people argue that their land was taken away from them through trickery in the treaty agreements and that, in any case, governments over the years have repeatedly failed to honour their treaty obligations. Thus, numerous First Nations are seeking reinterpretation of treaties, documenting errors in land transfers, and arguing land claims cases across the country (Frideres, 2020; see also Fenge & Penikett, 2014).

Evidence increases the potential power of organizing for change among First Nations, Inuit, and Métis, along with their supporters across the country. In response to the Conservative government's omnibus budget bills of 2012, which severely weakened environmental protection and limited the requirements of the assessment of resource development projects, a new movement, Idle No More, was born in November 2012. The movement was bolstered by the hunger strike of the chief of the Attawapiskat First Nation, Theresa Spence, who protested the ongoing violation of treaty rights by Prime Minister Harper and the government of Canada, and by a rapidly spreading social media campaign. Idle No More has included non-Indigenous people in Canada and, to an extent, has spread internationally. Many have great hopes for change coming from this inclusive and widespread movement, especially in the context of the power of social media. In reaction to the significant over-representation of Indigenous women among those who have disappeared and/or who have been murdered, the call for a national inquiry was met with the establishment of the National Inquiry into Missing and Murdered Indigenous Women and Girls. Along with the 2015 final report of the Truth and Reconciliation Commission, we may be witnessing the beginnings of positive change for the health and well-being of Indigenous peoples in Canada, but real change, as is so often the case, will come from grassroots organizations like Idle No More, Free Grassy, and the 2020 nationwide protests against a natural gas pipeline project that would cross unceded Wet'suwet'en territory in northern British Columbia. Although 10 Indigenous MPs were elected to represent Canadians in the October 2019 federal election, by total population this remains an under-representation in the 338-member House of Commons.

Summary

1. Illness and death rates vary, depending on social-structural conditions such as age, gender, and visible minority status.
2. Canadians are living longer today than in the past.
3. The life expectancy and the morbidity rates for men and women continue to differ.
4. Men have shorter life expectancy and women live longer but with chronic illness and disability.

5. Relative poverty is an important explanation for gender differences in health.
6. Immigrants tend to arrive in Canada in an excellent state of health, but, over time, immigrant health tends to deteriorate to match the health of native-born Canadians.
7. Indigenous health is poorer than that of other Canadians in many different ways.
8. Schooling in residential schools, environments on reserves, and continuing governance and land-ownership issues with the Canadian and provincial governments have had negative health impacts.

Key Terms

birth rate
essentialized
ethnicity
female circumcision
healthy immigrant effect
health indicators
life course transitions
microaggressions

minority status
population pyramid
"race"
racialization
racism
residential schools
sex-mortality differential
"Sixties Scoop"

Questions for Study and Discussion

1. How do age, gender, and racialization affect the health of individuals?
2. How does the overall degree of inequity in society affect the health of people at the top of the invisible social status hierarchy of the population?
3. Why and how is education related to morbidity and mortality?
4. How and why are prevention-related behaviours associated with socio-economic status?
5. What are the major challenges to the health of Indigenous peoples? What social and health policies do you advocate with respect to this issue?

Suggested Readings

Adelson, N. (2005). The embodiment of inequity: Health disparities in Aboriginal Canada. *Canadian Journal of Public Health, 96,* S45–S61. A report on inequalities in health among Indigenous Canadians.

Barker, K. (2005). *The fibromyalgia story: Medical authority and women's worlds of pain.* Temple University Press. This book investigates the sociological story of the experience of fibromyalgia among women today.

Barton, S.S., Thommasen, H.V., Tallio, B., Zhang, W., & Michalos, A.C. (2005). Health and quality of life of Aboriginal residential school survivors. *Social Indications Research, 73*(2), 295–312. An evaluation of the impacts of residential schools on the health of survivors.

Fenge, T., & Penikett, T. (2014, July–Aug.). Paper promises. *Literary Review of Canada.* http://reviewcanada.ca/magazine/2014/07/paper-promises. This article covers some of the ways in which modern treaties between Indigenous peoples in Canada and the Canadian government are not being properly implemented or enforced.

Lett, D. (2010). Police launch criminal investigation into actions of emergency department.

Canadian Medical Association Journal, 182(18), 817. This brief article highlights some of the critical issues that led to the death of an Indigenous man, Brian Sinclair, who died in an emergency room waiting for help.

McInturff, K. (2013). The gap in the gender gap: Violence against women in Canada. *Canadian Centre for Policy Alternatives Report.* www. policyalternatives.com. A contemporary picture of violence against women in Canada.

McPherson, K., Kerr, S., McGee, E., Cheater, F., & Morgan, A. (2013). *The role and impact of social capital on the health and well-being of children and adolescents: A systematic review.* Glasgow Centre for Population Health. A discussion of the impacts of social capital on children and youth.

Metraux, S., Clegg, L.X., Daigh, J.D., Culhane, D.P., & Kane, V. (2013). Risk factors for becoming homeless among a cohort of veterans who served in the era of the Iraq and Afghanistan conflicts. *American Journal of Public Health, 103*, S255–S261. An article that documents the role of serving in combat on later homelessness.

Shuster, S.M. (2016). Uncertain expertise and the limitations of clinical guidelines in transgender healthcare. *Journal of Health and Social Behavior, 57*(3), 319–32. www.jstor.org/ stable/44001212. This article raises an important public health issue relating to offering service to transgender individuals.

Tamburri, Rosanna. (2012, 29 Aug.). Heavy drinking a problem at most Canadian universities: Report. *University Affairs.* http://www. universityaffairs.ca/news/news-account/ heavy-drinking-a-problem-at-most-canadian-campuses-report. An article describing the problem of alcohol on university campuses.

Zlotozynska, M., Wood, E., Montaner, J.S., & Kerr, T. (2013). Supervised injection sites: Prejudice should not trump evidence of benefit. *Canadian Medical Association Journal, 185*(15), 1303–4. Whether it is ethical to support illegal drug users through supervised injection sites is a hotly debated topic across Canada.

Some Social-Psychological Explanations for Illness

6

Chapter Overview

- Socio-psychological factors are related to physically defined morbidity and mortality. They are also linked to mental illnesses.
- Stress, social support, social cohesion and social capital, sense of coherence, resilience, prayer, and religiosity are related to wellness, sickness, and death.
- Psychoneuroimmunology is a field of study that focuses on mind/body interactions.
- Stress was first defined and studied by Cannon and Selye and has been developed into a complex area of ongoing research.
- There are a variety of newer ways to observe and measure stress, including the frequently used and

- critiqued Social Readjustment Rating Scale (SRRS), trauma, daily hassles, discrimination, and out-of-sync life transitions.
- Social support is integrally related to health outcomes.
- The sense of coherence and resilience reflect psychological strengths in dealing with life's challenges.
- Religion and religiosity have an impact on health.
- People go to the doctor for a variety of social, psychological, and economic reasons and not simply because they feel ill.

Introduction

Interpersonal relationships play a role in illness. People can die of a "broken heart." Some believe that the repression of feelings, particularly anger, causes cancer at times. Is there any science to support this idea? Aside from the explicit act of actively and even rationally choosing suicide, can a person choose to live or die? What does it mean to say that the body and the mind are one? What is stress? Is stress sometimes good for health? Does prayer help when a person is sick? What is the scientific evidence? Is religion of any benefit to well-being? Why do people go to the doctor? When do people choose to visit a physician rather than carry on or take an aspirin and go to bed? The symptoms of a head cold, backache, digestive difficulties, or influenza will send one person to bed, another to the doctor, and others to the drugstore, acupuncturist, nurse practitioner, or neighbour. What socio-psychological processes determine the personal actions that people take when they are feeling ill? These are the sorts of issues this chapter addresses. It is always important to remember that socio-psychological processes occur inside the human mind and body but are affected and channelled by the invisible and inequitable social structure, the economy, and the person's historical and cultural context.

Evidence from a wide range of studies indicates that the mind and the body are related so that the brain affects the rest of the body and the rest of the body affects the brain, in turn. What we think, feel, and do is the complex product of our place in society, culture, and history along with our individual body/mind. Perceptions, feelings, expectations, and thoughts, for example, affect many aspects of bodily functioning such as heart rate and blood pressure as well as cognition and moods. At times psychosocial difficulties become physical illnesses through biological processes. At other times they may mimic physical illness and be considered **psychosomatic** illness. Physical illness, at times, leads to additional stress, anxiety, depression, and other mental suffering or illnesses. Many people visit doctors for psychosocial reasons such as stress, emotional distress (grief, unhappiness, depression), social isolation, or information rather than for strictly disease-related reasons. People also sometimes choose medical answers to large existential questions about the meaning of their experience and even to small aesthetic concerns such as breasts that they consider too small or too large, skin that is considered too wrinkly, the size of the nose or the shape of the eyes, or bodies that are considered too fat. They choose medicine to transform their lives, sometimes in the context of the myriad new technologies that are a part of biomedicalization of the person (Clarke et al., 2003). Perhaps the most dramatic example of such discretionary use of medicine would be parents having their genes edited in an embryo for especially desired but fundamentally aesthetic traits (e.g., height) in their offspring (Cyranowski, 2016).

This chapter is divided into two parts. The first part deals with just a few of the many socio-psychological factors associated with illness and health, including stress, social support, social capital, sense of coherence, and resilience. It also considers the relevance of religion and prayer to health. The second part will discuss the processes through which people come to define themselves as ill and as needing care, and the actions they take in regard to their health when deciding to seek help from an allopathic practitioner.

Stress

Stress occurs when an organism must deal with demands much greater than, or much less than, the usual level of activity or perceived activity. As such, stress is ubiquitous. All of us are stressed to some degree. The presence of at least some stress in life is beneficial. Early stressful experiences can fit us for positive and flexible adaptations to increased stress and sometimes more complex and intransigent stress later on. Or stress can be so overwhelming that it leads to serious illness or death. Too much change in too short a time can overtax the resources of the body.

Two prominent scientists, Cannon (1932) and Selye (1956), were involved in the early articulation and measurement of stress. Cannon suggested that health is ultimately defined not by the absence of disease but rather as the ability of the human being to function satisfactorily in the particular environment in which he or she is operating. People must constantly adapt to changes and perceptions of changes—to alterations in weather, conflicts at work, traumatic events, failure in school, great success on the hockey team, winning an important prize, flu germs, and so on. The body adapts to such changes by maintaining a relatively constant condition. For example, when the body becomes overheated, it evaporates moisture to help keep it cool; when confronted with bacteria, it produces antibodies. The process of maintaining a desirable bodily state (the constant condition) is called "homeostasis." The body is prepared to meet threats by adapting in ways that will attempt to continuously return it to the homeostatic state.

Cannon described the typical bodily reaction to stress as "fight or flight," and detailed the accompanying physiological changes. Somewhat later, Selye defined stress as a general reaction that occurs in response to any number of different stimuli. It included numerous specific changes within the biological system of the organism. Both positive and negative events can cause stress. It does not matter whether the event is the happy decision to become engaged or to be married or the disappointing failure in a course in university—each requires adaptation.

Building on several decades of research on the pituitary-cortical axis, Selye proposed the General Adaptation Syndrome (GAS) as the body's reaction to all stressful events. The "syndrome" has three stages: (1) an alarm reaction; (2) resistance or adaption; and (3) exhaustion. During the first stage, the body recognizes the stressor and the pituitary-adrenal cortical system responds by producing the arousal hormones necessary for either flight or fight. Increased activity by the heart and lungs, elevated blood-sugar levels, increased perspiration, dilated pupils, and a slowing of the rate of digestion are among the physiological responses to this initial stage of the syndrome. During the adaptive stage the body begins to repair the damage caused by arousal and most of the initial stress symptoms diminish or vanish. But if the stress continues, adaptation to it is lost as the body tries to maintain its defences. Eventually, the body runs out of energy with which to respond to the stress and exhaustion sets in. The prolongation of the stress response can result in a physiological state known as "allostasis." The allostatic load, an excess of which can lead to allostasis, refers to the "wear and tear" on the body that can lead to disease (Lantz et al., 2005).

During this final stage, bodily functions are slowed down abnormally or stopped altogether. The theory that ties the mind and body together in modern biological science is called **psychoneuroimmunology** (PNI). It is the study of the interrelations of the central nervous system, the immune system, and psychological processes. The immune system is chiefly located in the bone marrow, thymus, lymph nodes, spleen, tonsils, appendix, and Peyre's patches (clumps of immune tissue in the small intestine). The central nervous system functions in the communications between the brain and the spinal cord and psychological processes include perception, sensation, attention, learning, and memory.

Continued exposure to stress during the exhaustion stage can lead to what Selye calls the "diseases of adaptation." These include various diseases with emotional, mental, and/or physical symptoms. People are not always aware that they are living under stressful circumstances. Sometimes bodily and emotional symptoms are the first sign that something is amiss. There are many different scales available, including scales to measure the more serious manifestation of stress: post-traumatic stress disorder (PTSD). I expect you know, if you stop to think about it, when you are stressed. I imagine you also know what sorts of symptoms you are most susceptible to when you are stressed. What might surprise you is that as well as the symptoms, the suffering, and the onset of various diseases, stress can also, at times, lead to death (Lane et al., 2018).

As human beings, we have some capacity to define things as stressful or not depending on our understandings of the meanings that these things have for us (Pearlin et al., 2005). Gender is just one of the social determinants of health that plays a role in the socio-psychological definition and response to stress. What women define as most stressful, men may not (American Psychological Association, 2011). For example, in general women are more likely to say they are stressed than men, although that may be changing. Consider your male and female friends. What do you think causes each one stress, acknowledging that this is an unreliable, small, and skewed sample?

Stress is not only ubiquitous but it can be of short, medium, or long duration. Briefly, short-term stressors arise from small inconveniences, for example, traffic jams, delayed buses or subways, lost keys, or waiting for the doctor. Such things usually result in a temporary sense of anxiety, frustration, or unease. These have been called "daily hassles" (Lazarus & Delongis, 1983). Medium-term stressors develop from such things as long, cold, dark winters, a layoff from work, a difficult relationship, or an acute sickness in the family. Long-term or chronic stressors result from such events as the loss of a spouse or the loss of a job, as well as from living in poverty or, for example, in a neighbourhood characterized by vandalism, litter, burglaries, drug deals, and vacant housing (Latkin & Curry, 2003; Kravitz-Wirtz, 2016). Chronic strains can accumulate over a lifetime through "stress proliferation" and lead to an earlier onset of morbidity and to mortality (Pearlin et al., 2005). Life transitions "out of sequence," such as becoming pregnant or fathering a child prior to marriage or in the teenage years, can also lead to stress (Pearlin et al., 2005).

We have discussed the early research on stress. It is important to note, however, that this is still a very fruitful concept and an ongoing subject of some empirical research. There is, for example, recent work on the deleterious impact of the stress of racial discrimination on parenting (Nomaguchi & House, 2013). This work focuses on the ways that people who are discriminated against because of their racial status respond by feeling stressed and expressing concerns about parenting their children. Parenting a black child, for instance, is full of particular challenges such as those of explaining discrimination, racism, or police surveillance and the like (Patton, 2014).

One way of thinking about stress is that it results from too much change. The classic empirical manifestation of this is the life events scale of Holmes and Rahe (1967), which systematized the stress value attached to a list of life events. Called the **Social Readjustment Rating Scale** (SRRS), it was a gateway to thinking of how social life itself was linked to ill health and therefore was within the purview of health promotion and prevention strategies that are now so very common.

Using extensive interviews with people of varying ages and socio-economic statuses, Holmes and Rahe developed average scale values representing the relative risks of a number of specific life events. Marriage was assigned an arbitrary value of 50. The adjustment value of other items was estimated in comparison to marriage. The resulting scale itemizes 43 changes and quantifies their hypothetical impact (see Table 6.1). The higher the score in a given 12-month period, the greater is the likelihood of illness. It is important to note that, while some of the events are considered negative or undesirable and others might be considered positive or desirable, they all require psychosocial adjustment and are, thus, potentially stressful.

As the scale and other related research indicate, stressors can be the result of changes in any area of life. They can occur at a variety of levels, such as: (1) the individual biological level (e.g., bacterial or viral infections); (2) interpersonal situations (e.g., loss of a spouse or good friend); (3) social-structural positions (e.g., unemployment, promotion at work); (4) cultural systems (e.g., immigration); (5) ecological systems (e.g., earthquake; tsunami, flood, or wildfire); or (6) political/state systems (e.g., wars, political upheaval). The greater the number of stressors, and we might hypothesize the greater the number of levels of stressors, the more vulnerable a person is to the possibility of disease and emotional and bodily dysfunction.

It should be reiterated that stressors are not to be thought of as objective things that affect an unthinking organism in a consistent and objective manner (Pearlin et al., 2005). A person's evaluation

Table 6.1   The Stress of Adjusting to Change

Events	Scale of impact	Events	Scale of impact
Death of spouse	100	Son or daughter leaving home	29
Divorce	73	Trouble with in-laws	29
Marital separation	65	Outstanding personal achievement	28
Jail term	63	Wife begins or stops work	28
Death of close family member	63	Begin or end school	26
Personal injury or illness	53	Change in living conditions	25
Marriage	50	Revision of personal habits	24
Fired at work	47	Trouble with boss	23
Marital reconciliation	45	Change in work hours or conditions	20
Retirement	45	Change in residence	20
Change in health of family member	41	Change in schools	20
Pregnancy	40	Change in recreation	19
Sex difficulties	39	Change in church activities	19
Gain of new family member	39	Change in social activities	18
Business readjustment	39	Mortgage or loan less than $10,000	17
Change in financial state	38	Change in sleeping habits	16
Death of close friend	37	Change in number of family get-togethers	15
Change to different line of work	36	Change in eating habits	15
Change in number of arguments with spouse	35	Vacation	13
Mortgage over $10,000	31	Christmas	12
Foreclosure of mortgage or loan	30	Minor violations of the law	11
Change in responsibilities at work	29		

Source: Based on Neidhardt, Weinstein, and Coury (1985). *No-Gimmick Guide to Managing Stress*. Vancouver: Self-Counsel Press.

of the stressful situation, the strategies available for coping, the degree of control felt, and the amount of social support experienced all mediate the impact that the stressor ultimately has on that person. As Viktor Frankl (1965) has pointed out, some people, even in the most atrocious of circumstances such as a concentration camp, have been able to find meaning for living and have thus diminished their sense of stress somewhat. Sometimes, then, people ultimately may become stronger and healthier as a result of the most extreme of stress-filled situations. Frankl's work

has been used to develop a school of vibrant, contemporary psychotherapy called logotherapy, which focuses on helping people to find meaning in their lives, wherever and whenever they are lived.

The SRRS has been used to predict illness among a wide variety of different people in North America. It has also been used in a number of cross-cultural studies that have included Swiss, Belgian, and Dutch peoples (Bieliauskas, 1982). Overall, researchers have found significant similarities among different cultural groups in their evaluation of the impact of various events. Such studies have shown the SRRS to be a remarkably stable or reliable instrument. It has also been used to "predict" illness and symptoms of distress. Holmes and Masuda's 1974 study concluded "that life-change events . . . lower bodily resistance and enhance the probability of disease occurrence." Several researchers have correlated high SRRS scores with symptoms and with illness, including major illnesses such as heart disease (Theorell & Rahe, 1971; Rahe & Paasikivi, 1971). High SRRS scores have also been found to be associated with psychological distress in a number of studies (Bieliauskas, 1982). Several researchers have used SRRS successfully to predict the onset of illness. One interesting example is the study that examined the SRRS of 2,600 navy personnel prior to their departure on voyages of 6–8 months. The researchers found significant correlations between the levels of stress before the start of the voyage and the subsequent levels of disease during the voyage (Rahe et al., 1970). Thoits's (2011) review paper discusses a number of studies using the SRRS and contextualizes the importance of this measure historically. Another study focuses on one group of people—the incarcerated—who have experienced significant life change, and notes the increased death rate that resulted from the many stresses and strains of imprisonment (Pridemore, 2014). Consider, for a moment, the myriad life changes necessitated by incarceration—not being able to see the stars at night or to walk on the grass or to choose one's food or to enter a store or restaurant or see a friend, as well as so many worse deprivations. The lack of stimulation in a limited and threatening environment affects the brain, causes stress and provides reasons for subsequent ill health and even death. If you add to that solitary confinement the stressors multiply.

Valuable though this concept has been, the SRRS can be critiqued for the following reasons.

1. It ignores differences in the meaning people place on the various events. There is evidence that the impact of the death of a spouse, for instance, varies depending on whether the death was sudden or occurred after a protracted period of illness.

2. Some of the events listed may be signs either of illness or the results of illness, such as changes in eating habits, sleeping habits, personal habits, or sex difficulties. Thus the scale is, in part, **tautological**.

3. Some, but not all, research has found that distinguishing between the desirable and undesirable events enhances the predictive value of the scale. Marriage is generally taken as a reason for celebration, death as an occasion for mourning. It has been argued that the stress-related effects of death are, therefore, more pronounced than those of marriage.

4. The ability to control events has been shown, in a number of studies, to be an important factor in determining the degree of stress experienced.

5. Whether stress affects the incidence of disease or merely affects behaviour during illness has been questioned. It may be that life events affect the likelihood of people reporting illness rather than affecting the disease process.

6. The SRRS asks about events that have occurred during a specified period of time. Some research has shown that the association between stress and subsequent illness or disease cannot be studied separately from the previous stress level and the history of past illnesses. Thus, experiences of the years before the time period referred to in the SRRS may also have a powerful effect on the level of stress experienced. A car accident followed by the loss of a driver's licence and a household move in the years before the designated SRRS time period might exacerbate whatever level of stress is experienced during the year of the SRRS measurements.

Large and significant life events such as marriage, divorce, and imprisonment contribute to the stress response but, as noted earlier, so do daily hassles such as a fight with a friend, having to study for a test, or even a long wait for a bus (Serido et al., 2004). Stress has also been found to be linked to the experiences that arise from political differences among people who work in the same establishment, perhaps especially in the heated, polarized situation of current politics (He et al., 2018). In fact, there is some possibility that the accumulation of daily hassles can be more problematic for the individual organism than specific large and dramatic life events, either within the previous 12-month period as suggested by Holmes and Rahe (1967) or occurring at any time of life. Serido and colleagues, for example, compared the effects of daily hassles with those of chronic stressors. They argue that chronic stressors offer an "ever-present potential to erupt in ways both large and small in an individual's life" (Serido et al., 2004, p. 30). Daily hassles, on the other hand, actually constitute ongoing stressors that require an individual to respond frequently. Further, research indicates that daily hassles and chronic stressors interact so that together they cause greater stress than the simple addition of one to the other might suggest. This means that if you are already experiencing a medium- or long-term stress, daily hassles can be even more problematic and lead to a tipping point.

The notion of stress is now so widely accepted that popular magazines often include their own stress tests and cures. As an example, the conservative and popular international service club, Kiwanis, has a lengthy and detailed explanation of stress available online for its members and others (*Kiwanis Magazine*, 2018)

Pearlin and his colleagues (2005) have shown how the stress response is exacerbated by repeated hardships over a life course. These include those resulting from the major social determinants of health, including discrimination on the basis of such socially structured issues as racialization, gender, sexual orientation, and disability. In fact, they suggest that ascribed statuses originating at birth and co-extensive throughout life, such as race and gender, usually offer the potential for repeated discriminatory and stressful experiences. These become the bedrock upon which other stresses build. Furthermore, such ascribed statuses are often enacted in a multitude of varied contexts, such as work, school, housing, the justice system, medical care, and commercial transactions (Pearlin et al., 2005, p. 209). The ubiquity of the stress experience in these cases, based as it is in inescapable life circumstances, likely enhances its impact. Moreover, the experience of discrimination

at one point in time or in one life realm may prepare the person to anticipate further discrimination and lead to a constant state of vigilance. The ongoing stress—and the potential for ongoing stress—in central areas of life may lead to "stress proliferation" in that chronic strain in a pivotal social role (e.g., work or school) can lead relentlessly to other hardships or stressors. Thus, stress at work or school can spill over into stress at home with family or roommates, which can then affect family relationships and one's actual and perceived well-being. This stress can then circle back and impact negatively on school or work.

Pearlin et al. also articulated the potential stress impact of one-time-only trauma such as rape or other sudden, violent, negative, or otherwise onerous events. Such events not only tend to accumulate in some people, especially those nearer the bottom of the socio-economic ladder, but they may, like chronic discrimination, lead to the "creation" of associated stressors. Consider the case of rape. The person who has been raped may have to interact with the medical system, the legal system, the educational system (if he or she is a student), family, and friends in regard to this singular traumatic event. Any, indeed all, of these interactions may add to the stress load of the already victimized person. Moreover, some sorts of stressful events seem to repeat themselves over time. It may be, for example, that adults who were abused as children are more likely to abuse others as adults.

Pearlin and colleagues also point to the stressful effects of transitional and other life events occurring at a non-normative time in a person's life. Two that occur early in life and can have ongoing implications for the rest of life are dropping out of school and becoming pregnant while a youth. In addition, people who make "disorderly transitions" are more likely to be from economically disadvantaged families. Pearlin et al. also point out that life disruptions or events can occur on top of all of the other sources of stress, such as discrimination, out-of-sequence transition, and trauma, and then may have exacerbated consequences. Table 6.2 lists some behavioural indicators of excess stress that over time may correlate with serious illness, such as the incidence of cardiovascular disease (Roy et al., 2018)

Table 6.2   Some Examples of Indicators of Excess Stress

Physical	Psychological	Behavioural
Rapid pulse	Inability to concentrate	Smoking
Increased perspiration	Difficulty making decisions	Medication use
Pounding heart	Loss of self-confidence	Nervous tics
Tightened stomach	Cravings	Absent-mindedness
Tense arm, leg muscles	Worry or anxiety	Accident-proneness
Shortness of breath	Irrational fear or panic	Hair-pulling, nail-biting,
Tensed teeth and jaw	Feelings of sadness	foot-tapping
Inability to sit still	Frustration	Sleep disturbance
Sore back and shoulders		Increased use of alcohol
		Addictive eating

Source: Adapted from Neidhardt, J., Weinstein, M., & Conry, R. (1985). *No-gimmick guide to managing stress*, pp. 5–6. Self-Counsel Press. © 1985, 1990 International Self-Counsel Press Ltd.

CRITICAL THINKING

Box 6.1 • Moderate Wine Drinking Is Good for You

It's good for you! No, it's not! Yes, it is! There has been a lot of debate over the years about the benefits of moderate drinking. One study, which tracked 4,500 graduates of the University of North Carolina from 1964 to early 2000, found that wine consumption seems to be associated with good health (see Picard, 2002). This finding was not thought to be primarily because of the biochemistry of wine but rather because of the lifestyles associated with those who drink wine. According to this study, those who drink wine also tend to eat less saturated fat and cholesterol, eat more fibre, smoke less, and exercise more frequently. They tend to be less likely to be overweight than those who drink beer or spirits. They tend to drink alcohol in moderation as compared to those who regularly choose other types of alcohol. As compared to abstainers, they tend to eat less red meat and more fruit and vegetables. These findings are consistent across social status categories. Thus, wine drinkers from lower-income backgrounds had good health outcomes, while high-income abstainers had poorer health outcomes. In other studies moderate drinking has been found to be associated with a variety of other better health outcomes, including lower rates of heart attacks and strokes, hypertension, Alzheimer's disease, diabetes,

kidney stones, digestive ailments, Parkinson's disease, and macular degeneration.

This controversy continues with another study and another contradictory set of findings. A more recent study in the *British Medical Journal* has found that minimizing the amount of (any) alcohol consumed is beneficial and lowers the risk of heart disease and blood pressure (Spencer, 2014). An even more recent study published in *The Lancet* (another premier British medical journal), based on a considerable amount of international data, found that alcohol was the seventh highest risk factor for illness and death globally. Furthermore, this study stated that there was really no safe amount of alcohol to consume (Griswold et al., 2018).

These debates represent science in action. Depending on research design, research question, sample size and type, and a whole range of variables, different findings may emerge. There is no perfect research study. Together, though, research will build to an answer regarding the correct amount of what type of alcoholic beverage is safe or unsafe, health-giving or health-challenging. In the meantime it seems we have to be more aware of the potential harms associated with imbibing alcohol.

Social Support

Almost all people think they understand **social support**, intuitively if not on a cognitive level. If you were to ask your friends whether they know the meaning of social support, you would probably find unanimous affirmation. If you were then to ask each to define its meaning, you would likely hear as many definitions as there are people. For some, social support would be defined as "a feeling that you have or don't have." For others, it would be defined as friends with whom to party. Another would define it as someone with whom to do things. Still another might see social support as having someone on side in case of an argument. Material and practical aid might be necessary components of social support for others. While living alone does not necessarily mean living without support, at times it may be so. The number of households inhabited by one person continues to grow. In 2016, 28.5 per cent of households were single-person households; only 26 per cent of all households were couples with children (Galloway, 2017). Some people who live alone are aging, having raised families and become widowed or divorced. As they age in place (at home) they may become isolated and unable to care adequately for themselves. Social support policies such as friendly visitors may alleviate some of the loneliness. However, some people choose to live alone in the interests of individualism and freedom. Solitude can also be beneficial to well-being.

When sociologists attempt to measure social support, the varieties and idiosyncrasies of what "social support" means become apparent. One definition comes from the work of Cobb (1976), who thought of social support as information that would lead a person to believe (1) that he or she is cared for and loved, (2) that he or she is esteemed and valued, and (3) that he or she belongs to a network of communication and mutual obligation. A group of researchers used this definition as the basis for a scale that was later revised and subjected to a number of uses (see Turner & Noh, 1983). The scale asks people to describe themselves in comparison to others with respect to the amount of social support they feel they have. It is an essentially subjective measure based on each person assessing his or her felt degree of social support. It includes both social support in the sense of a person's feeling of being loved and esteemed by others, and social support as an experience of being part of a "network" of people. This definition of social support emphasizes the subjective perception of the respondent.

Others have considered social support as something that can be objectively measured—social support exists to the extent that a person can count on others to offer specific services such as cooking, cleaning, snow shovelling, or transportation when the need arises. Social support is still a complex socio-psychological and interpretive process. Among the mechanisms through which Thoits (2011) deems support exerts social influence are control, comparison, purpose, meaning, self-esteem, belonging, sense of control, and companionship. The degree of social support is demonstrated in the reliability and extensiveness of the actual aid supplied. The degree of social support perceived may also reflect the subjective feelings of the individual. In a further refinement, others have pointed out that different kinds of "support" are desired and expected from different "kinds" of others. That is, people may expect different things from their friends than from their spouses or kin. Whether or not the network is made up of people who know each other may also affect the experience of social support. Even socializing itself can be linked to better health (Troyer, 2016). Having someone to say hello to everyday, even if it is just a doorman or barista, can have positive health benefits.

A number of studies have examined the impact of social support on health outcomes (Thoits, 2011). The *Journal of Health and Social Behaviour*, a major American journal in the field of the sociology of health and illness, has published numerous articles concerning social support in a variety of situations. In recent years such articles have addressed all of the following pertinent to the issue at hand: the health consequences of being unemployed; self-assessments of the elderly; occupational stress;

mental health; psychological well-being; primary deviance among mental patients; life stress; psychotropic drug use; psychological distress and self-rejection in young adults; adolescent cigarette smoking; health in widowhood in later life; teenage pregnancy; social support among men with AIDS; and depressed patients. Race, too, seems to make a difference in the effects of social support on health.

Others have focused on social networks, a parallel concept, and found links to health (Martire & Franks, 2014). Some researchers have emphasized that social support has a direct relationship to health so that the person who has support is less likely to become ill. Others have noted that adequate social support can be indirect when it serves to minimize the harmful effects of stress on a person's mental or physical health. These two notions are compatible with one another: social support may have both direct and indirect effects on health (Thoits, 2011).

Many social policies might affect social support, including the design of housing, inexpensive or free access to public spaces such as parks, pools, and gyms, and allowances for people who want to offer home care to their significant others. University classrooms and campuses could be better designed with a view to enhancing opportunities for communication about shared interests and values. Additional tax breaks and other supports for all sorts of marriages, including those based on same sex, are other ways to enhance the possibilities of social support. Analysis of the dates of death of famous people (Phillips & Feldman, 1973) showed that death rates declined just before a significant occasion, such as a birthday, wedding, or Christmas celebration—an occasion on which these people would have the opportunity to reaffirm social ties with the group of significant others. Thus, encouraging holidays and festivals as regular breaks from the routines of work may be of help. Such research needs to be repeated.

Recent research continues to investigate the links between social support and illness and death. For example, a study by Yang et al. (2013) notes that one biological mechanism for the association is inflammation, which is said to operate differently in males and females. While studies neither establish a causal connection nor explain all of the variance, there seem to be sufficient grounds to pursue further research on the potential association between social connections and longevity as well as different disease states (Cornwell & Waite, 2012). Perhaps surprisingly, the provision of social assistance, although ostensibly supportive, does not necessarily enhance health (Shahidi et al., 2019). This reminds us that not all actions intended to offer support have benefits, but that further research is justified by the many examples of tantalizing and sometimes contradictory findings.

Professor David Spiegel, a psychiatrist and researcher at Stanford University Medical School, set out to refute the notion that the mind could be used to affect the outcome of disease. He observed 86 women with breast cancer for 10 years. To his surprise, he found that women who took part in group therapy and who had been taught self-hypnosis lived twice as long as those who had not (Spiegel et al., 1989). Subsequent research has repeated this finding, although not consistently. The promise of such research has proven to be so great that a new field, psycho-oncology, examines the psychological aspects of getting and surviving cancer and includes a now classic text, *Handbook of Psychooncology* (Holland & Rowland, 1989; see also Lerner, 1994, p. 139). According to Lerner (1994, p. 14), "Social support is . . . one of the most important and interesting categories which psycho-oncologists address." A literature review of studies of the role of social support in cancer longevity found sufficient evidence of the association in the case of breast cancer (there was an adequate number of valid studies) and less support for the link with other cancers. The authors note that considerations such as the extensiveness of the disease at diagnosis, the treatments offered, and the site of metastasis were important intervening variables (Nausheen et al., 2009).

Disease-based support groups are now commonplace. There are support groups for a wide variety of types of cancer, for end-stage diseases, for cardiovascular conditions, cystic fibrosis, diabetes, and so on. In fact, while many of these support groups take place in person many also are conducted online through social media and video conferencing. As new communications technologies are developed, the numbers of health- and disease-based support groups explode. Clearly, there is room for a great deal of additional research on the role of different types of support groups in healing.

A number of questions remain. What are the biological mechanisms through which support operates? How does social support affect biology and then health? Does support influence the interpretation of stressful life events? Are people who feel supported likely to feel that they can manage to cope with the sudden death of a spouse because they believe that others will listen and continue to care? Does social support have different meanings among people of different social categories, such as the elderly, minority populations, or the poor? Can stress lead to the destruction of potentially supportive relationships at times? Do those lower on the social ladder, lacking relative power, also experience a daily lack of social support in their interactions with mainstream and powerful social institutions such as churches, schools, and health clinics? The mechanisms through which social support affects health need to be further studied and clarified.

Recently, social support has also been studied through the related concept of "social capital" (see Chapter 4). In regard to experience at the level of the individual, however, "social support" still seems to be a very useful concept. However, when we consider the ways in which societies, neighbourhoods, towns, work groups, sports teams, and so on are organized (or not) to offer support, the alternative terms—"social capital" and "social cohesion"—are most relevant (McPherson et al., 2013; Vyncke et al., 2013). This has been a very important new direction in research. Indeed, a substantial body of empirical literature documents a link between social capital and health. According to Poortinga, there are three complementary ways of thinking of social capital; *bonding*, *bridging*, and *linking*. Bonding refers to horizontal ties among similar people in a social grouping. Bridging involves links across different social groups who are not necessarily similar. It also incorporates perceived levels of social justice, solidarity, and mutual respect. Linking refers to vertical interactions across formal and institutionalized power structures in a community. All three are thought to be important in health outcomes (Szreter & Woolcock, 2004). Another useful distinction is between objective and subjective components of social capital. This refers to the fact that social capital is both perceived and structural. The former refers to feelings of support, connection, trust, and the like and the latter to actual links observed, for instance, in membership or leadership in an organization (Poortinga, 2006). Such structural forces and the various social determinants of health play a significant role in health and can even threaten, at times, the potential beneficial effects of social relations, cohesion, and support (Rocha et al., 2017). **Social cohesion** can be defined in terms of the amount of trust, participation and democratic attitudes prevailing in a social context (Chuang et al., 2013). Social cohesion reflects the ways that people are tied together in sports teams, families, neighbourhoods, and the like. Can you think of ways that inequity can threaten social cohesion and engender isolation? Does your university, or do your classes, encourage social cohesion? Does group work lead to social cohesion? Think for a moment about the presence of social cohesion in your life at present.

CRITICAL THINKING

Box 6.2 • Bullying and Cyberbullying

Not all close social and human interactions are supportive. One particularly problematic type of interaction, according to studies of schoolyards and workplaces, is increasingly prevalent. Bullying has been known to cause stress, illness, and even, in some cases, death, including by suicide. Since

continued

bullying has been defined as a problem there have been a number of studies of its incidence and discussions of social policies that may limit it. A new kind of bullying, called "cyberbullying," is a particularly pernicious development, as hateful and hurtful taunts through social media such as Facebook can spread quickly and extend far beyond a small group of young people in a schoolyard. There are several recent Canadian examples of young people committing suicide as a result of their online experience of being bullied. In the world of cyberbullying, bullies can come from anywhere and be of any age or gender. They can live near one another or continents away. They can hide certain important facts about themselves such as age and gender. Amanda Todd, a teenager from British Columbia, for instance, apparently committed suicide as the result of being bullied by a man from Holland (Burgmann, 2016). Evidently,

the video of Todd's torment has been seen at least 30 million times around the world. More recently, 13 young men who were students in dental school at Dalhousie University were suspended from clinical practice because they had developed a Facebook page on which they made sexually explicit comments and threats of sexual assault and otherwise sexually harassed some of their female student colleagues. There was a strong outcry across the country and within Dalhousie University over this incident of men bullying female classmates (see, e.g., Rush, 2014).

Bullying among young people is rampant around the world (Tsitsika et al., 2014). Its effects can last for a long time. What can be done? What are some of the links between health and bullying? Do you have a bullying story to tell—one in which you were the bully or the bullied? Are bystanders ethically responsible for bullying, too?

CRITICAL THINKING

Box 6.3 • How Does Racism Work to Hurt People?

A great deal of research documents the many ways that discrimination hurts adults. It has been shown to cause psychological distress, depression, low self-esteem, anxiety, and declines in physical health. Are these effects the same in adolescents and children who experience racism? What are the consequences of growing up as a person who is a member of a stigmatized and stereotyped ethnic minority? Racism can lead to bullying in children. It can also lead to depression (Nittle, 2018). It can accumulate over a lifetime. Indeed, it makes sense to suggest that the impact of racism is even greater on children than on adults because young people are at the stage of developing their identities and understandings of what it means to be a member of an ethnic group. Perceived discrimination may interfere with the ongoing internalization processes of personality development because of the difficulties of identifying with a group one sees being rejected and hated.

Whitbeck and his colleagues (2001) studied 195 Indigenous children in Grades 5–8 on three different reservations in the Upper Midwest of the United States. Although this study is based in the US there is no compelling reason to believe that the processes differ in Canada. They found that the experience of prejudice and discrimination had significant consequences for the development of Indigenous adolescents. They discovered that being perceived as different from others and being rejected by the majority groups during early adolescence sometimes leads to self-hatred, anger, delinquency, and substance abuse. Those who began substance abuse behaviours early were less able to change and experienced serious impediments in later life chances. Children who use substances are more likely to drop out of or fail at school and to have problems getting along with other people, including peers and family members. These are among the adaptations to discrimination that can accumulate and severely limit opportunities later in life. Other research has documented links between perceived racial discrimination and hypertension, birth weight, sick days, respiratory illnesses, anxiety, depression, and psychosis (McKenzie, 2003). Panko (2017) reported on a number of different studies that together documented links between racism and various aspects of the health of children, including the incidence of ADHD, anxiety, depression, and decrements in expressed feelings of well-being. One of the biological links seemed to be found in increased levels of the stress hormone cortisol.

What can be done? Do you have any experiences with discrimination and prejudice? Have you felt critical or disparaging of people because of their ethnicity or visible minority status? Can you remember where and how that feeling started? What, do you think, maintains your feelings of ethnic superiority, ethnic confidence, ethnic insecurity, or ethnic inferiority?

Sense of Coherence

Antonovsky reversed the usual questions we have been asking about what sorts of psychosocial factors cause illness. Instead, he asked: How do people stay healthy? Rather than look at the deleterious effects of such things as the lack of social support and the consequences of stress, Antonovsky focused on the positive and beneficial. Citing evidence from many studies, he argued that a **sense of coherence** or a belief that things are under control and will work out in the long run is a crucial component of the state of mind that leads to health. People who have good or excellent health, all things being equal, are likely to have a strong sense of coherence, which is defined as follows:

> . . . A global orientation that expresses the extent to which one has a pervasive, enduring though dynamic feeling of confidence that (1) the stimuli deriving from one's internal and external environments in the course of living are structured, predictable, and explicable; (2) the resources are available to one to meet the demands posed by these stimuli; and (3) these demands are challenges, worthy of investment and engagement. (Antonovsky, 1979, p. 19)

The "sense of coherence" concept draws attention to the fact that the extent to which a person feels that he or she can manage whatever life has in store is an essential factor in health (see Richardson & Ratner, 2005). It is important to note that a lack of this socio-psychological factor is also associated with compromised mental health and various physical illnesses. Furthermore, it is a robust concept that a number of studies have found it to be an important mediator of good health (Ericksson & Lindstrom, 2006).

There are three components to a sense of coherence. The first is *comprehensibility*—the basic belief that the world is fundamentally understandable and predictable. Such a belief in the comprehensibility of the self and of human relationships is absolutely essential for coping. People with a high sense of coherence feel that the information they receive from the internal and external environment is orderly, consistent, and clear. People with a lower sense of coherence tend to feel that the world is chaotic, random, and inexplicable. A person with a high sense of coherence feels that his or her actions in the past have had the expected consequences, and they will continue to do so in the future. The student who knows how hard to study or how many drafts of a paper to do in order to get the desired A or B (or, heaven forbid, C) grade is someone with a high sense of comprehensibility.

The second component of the sense of coherence is *being able to cope*. The person with a sense of coherence understands what the world expects and feels that he or she has the ability and the resources necessary to meet whatever is demanded and to cope with obstacles along the way. Not only does the student know what is necessary to get an

A, B, or C grade, he or she feels able to obtain the desired grade.

The third component of a sense of coherence—*meaningfulness*—refers to the motivation to achieve a desired outcome. This component depends on the extent to which life makes sense, has a purpose, and is worth the effort. The student values learning, and the grade achieved is important because

grades and education have a purpose to play in life's satisfactions and goals.

The student with a high sense of coherence, when confronted with an unexpected (and seemingly undeserved) failure, does not give up in bitterness and disgust but rises to the challenge: he or she questions the mark, takes the course again, or takes a different course. In other words, the

---

Canada in a Global Context

Box 6.4 • World Happiness Report

There have been seven World Happiness Reports published in the last seven years, since 2012 (Helliwell & Aknin, 2019). This annual report ranks 156 countries according to the happiness of the citizens and tries to explain the rankings. The 2019 report focused on the relationship between happiness and various aspects of community structure and functioning. There are several chapters on the role of governments, pro-social behaviours, and changes in information technology. Figure 6.1 focuses on pro-social behaviours and their

consequences for happiness. This international survey notes that the happier countries are those in which a greater number of people are involved in volunteer work, are altruistic in their spending, and give charitably.

How do you think this process works? You may not have much discretionary income or even time at this point in your lives but thinking about your future social contributions to the well-being of others is an important ingredient of a healthy future.

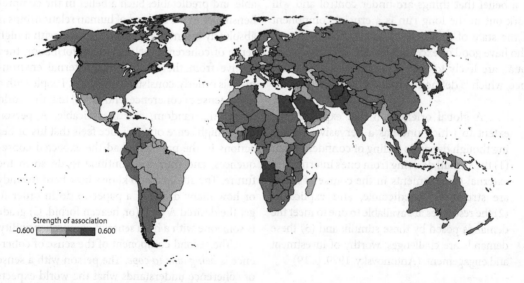

Strength of association
−0.600   0.600

Figure 6.1   World Happiness Map: Volunteerism

student with a high sense of coherence would be able to explain the failure to himself or herself, and would be willing and able to take action to improve the grade, believing that such action would have the desired outcome and that the whole process of learning and being examined is meaningful. Not surprisingly, an aspect of the sense of coherence—perceived control—is associated with socio-demographic variables so that those further up the invisible hierarchy of social status tend to have more. The sense of coherence or salutogenesis has been studied widely and inspired thinking, planning, and even design. The World Happiness Report discussed in Box 6.4 is an international study ranking countries by happiness.

Resilience

Resilience is another important concept that helps us to understand variations in illness that arise from differences in individuals at the psychosocial level (Windle, 2011). Similar to a sense of coherence, resilience is a positive trait that aids individual adaptation. People with a high degree of resiliency are able to respond to challenges in ways that are helpful to their own well-being. Resiliency can mean the difference between responding to a life event (for example, car accident, loss of a loved one, serious diagnosis) in ways that enable the person to carry on, feel well (enough) eventually, maintain overall good health, and set and achieve goals. Resilience can be seen as an asset or a resource to assist with readjustment after a difficult event. "Those who thrive under adversity (e.g., poverty, maltreatment, loss of a parent) exhibit engagement in processes described as resilience" (Liebenberg et al., 2013, p. 131). Following is a questionnaire based on studies of resiliency among young people. It includes 12 factors found to be valid measures of resiliency in youth. How resilient are you? Note that resiliency is measured in part by social relations and depends on social cohesion, connection, and the presence of social determinants of health.

1. I know where to go in the community to get help.

2. Getting an education is important to me.
3. I try to finish what I start.
4. I have people to look up to.
5. My parents/caregivers know a lot about me.
6. My family stands by me during difficult times.
7. My friends stand by me in difficult times.
8. I have opportunities to develop skills that will be useful in later life.
9. I am treated fairly by my community.
10. I feel I belong at my school.
11. I enjoy my cultural and family traditions.
12. I am able to solve problems without hurting myself or others.

All of these aforementioned socio-psychological issues—stress, social support, social capital, social cohesion, sense of coherence, and resilience—appear to operate on the body through the immune system. For an overview of the research in psychoneuroimmunology that is accessible to social scientific understanding, see Kaplan (1991) and Lerner (1994). Research in this area is ongoing and some of the results of studies can be found in the journal *Brain, Behavior, and Immunity*. One recent example investigated the positive role of the enjoyment of music in well-being (Fancourt et al., 2014) through an examination of 63 published studies. Others have documented the benefits to health and well-being of other arts such as dance, painting, creative writing, journaling, and drawing. The socio-psychological impacts on health are myriad and much remains to be studied.

Religion and Health

Theoretical Views

About 90 per cent of the peoples of the world are involved in some sort of spiritual practice (Koenig, 2009). Religion and religiosity, which are central features of culture and cultural difference, are associated with both physical and mental health. Durkheim's studies of suicide were the first to investigate sociological aspects of this relationship. His concern was with the degree of integration into a social group as well as the regulation of behaviour provided by religious affiliation. Those whose integration was poorer were, he argued, more likely to die by suicide. It would not be much of a stretch to add to this the argument that looser ties lead to mental and even physical health issues.

There are 108 different religious groups (including atheists, agnostics, and non-affiliated) in Canada (Statistics Canada, 2011). Christians are the largest group, followed by the unaffiliated. Other major belief systems include Muslim, Hindu, Sikh, Buddhist, Jewish, and Indigenous spirituality. The following discussion is relevant for consideration to all different religious groups. Today, building on Durkheim, researchers have investigated the ways that a variety of components of religious affiliation may affect health. According to Ellison's (1991) review, religion has been theorized to enhance well-being in four ways: (1) social integration and support; (2) personal relationship with a divine "other"; (3) provision of systems of meaning; (4) promotion of specific patterns of religious organization and personal lifestyle. First, religion may increase social integration through friendship and social ties entered into on a voluntary basis through a shared world view. It can provide a social support network available in a crisis, regular community celebration of ritual events, normative social control regarding behaviour associated with good health (such as dietary and drinking norms), and interpersonal and business ethics and norms. Second, a personal relationship with a divine other may involve frequent prayer and meditation, as well as identification with a supreme being or with various benevolent figures from religious texts or stories. Third, the personal system of meaning is an explanatory framework through which believers can understand and explain themselves, their personal relationships, their work, and personal crises, tragedies, and joys, indeed, the whole "round of life," including birth, life, death, and life after death. The fourth component refers to ways in which church membership may provide direction and support for patterns of behaviour such as what to do on a Sabbath, church, synagogue, or temple attendance, and family mores, as well as other patterns having to do with such health-related activities as dietary restrictions.

Religion is also a type of coping behaviour, according to Koenig (2009), that helps people make sense of reality. It can help people understand suffering, provide a feeling of control over things that seem out of control, and enhance communal relations and mutual support. As a part of the evidence he points to studies indicating that 90 per cent of Americans managed or attempted to manage the stress of 9/11 (Koenig et al., 2001) by turning to religion. Bible sales increased by 27 per cent within one week after the incidents of 9/11. Sixty per cent of Americans attended a religious memorial service in the immediate aftermath of the disaster. Religious involvement has also been linked to better mental health, enhanced ability to cope with stress, and less depression, anxiety, and substance abuse (Koenig, 2009).

It should be mentioned that religious experiences are not always beneficial to mental health: the tragic histories of groups such as Jonestown, Heaven's Gate, and NXIVM demonstrate the devastating effects that cults can have on individuals and communities. The joining of religious ideals to rationalizations for warfare is inevitably deadly. Those who kill themselves and others in the name of God or Allah or any other religious symbol use religious beliefs for destruction and suffering. Those who are anti-Semitic can cause evils such as the recent synagogue massacre in Pittsburgh (Paul, 2019). The recent attacks on the mosques in Quebec and in Christchurch, New Zealand, were done in specific opposition to those of Muslim faith (Haig, 2017) and in the interests of white supremacy. These were followed by the Easter 2019 attacks on Christians in Indonesia—allegedly a response to the terrorism in New Zealand—and the further anti-Muslim violence that followed (Slater & Perera, 2019). Clearly religious convictions and beliefs about others because of their beliefs can lead to considerable suffering.

Some medical care providers have begun to include discussions of spirituality in treatments for people with both physical and mental health issues. Some psychiatric researchers, for instance, are exploring the possible benefits of training people in religious concepts such as forgiveness, gratitude, and altruism—characteristics of personalities considered to exhibit excellent mental health—to improve health outcomes (Baetz & Toews, 2009). There is even a new field of "positive psychology" based on such principles. So seriously are some medical care personnel taking the links between health and religion or religion's common underlying values that they are proposing all Canadian physicians should receive required training in spiritual health care as a part of medical school (Miller, 2013). A number of medical schools in the US have already integrated courses on spirituality into their curricula. However, most doctors still appear to be uncomfortable discussing spirituality or religion even during a terminal phase of illness (Best et al., 2016). Many doctors appear to prefer a referral to a chaplain rather than addressing issues related to spirituality or religion.

In *Suicide*, Durkheim explained the protective and destructive effects of various forms of integration and regulation with respect to the suicide rate. In particular, he examined the results of too little integration or too much integration into the social group of which the individual was a part and the corresponding rates of egoistic and altruistic suicide. He also examined too little regulation and too much (normative) regulation and the corresponding tendency for anomic or fatalistic suicide. In *Elementary Forms of Religious Life*, Durkheim moved beyond the focus on the integrative and regulative functions of religion in society and examined such other topics as the division of time and space into the sacred and the profane and the impacts of ritual and group worship on the collective. These ideas need further study for their impacts on physical and mental health.

The Empirical Study of Religion and Health

It has been nearly 150 years since Benjamin Travers remarked that he had never seen a case of cancer of the penis in a Jew, and almost that long since Regoni-Stern first observed that Catholic nuns in Verona, Italy, were at significant risk for breast cancer yet significantly protected against uterine cancer (Levin & Schiller, 1987, p. 9). The history of the empirical study of the relationship between religion and health is a long, circuitous, and complex one. Religion and religiosity have a wide variety of components, such as denominational adherence and interaction with the divine. Health outcomes, too, have been investigated in a variety of ways, such as the increase or decrease in specific diagnosis (e.g., heart attack), overall morbidity and mortality, and uptake of health risk factors such as smoking. Among the control and intervening variables considered are ethnicity, class, and religious density in a specified geographical area. But what aspect of religion contributes to health? What pathways relate these two to one another? Levin (1993, p. 5) has reviewed over 250 studies. Regardless of the definitions of the independent variables (various religious factors) or the dependent variables (e.g., specific diagnoses or overall morbidity and mortality), the results across all of the studies found that the greater the intensity or degree of religious involvement of the individual, the better the health. Levin's review of this literature concluded that nine hypotheses have been investigated.

1. *Behaviour.* The relationship between religion and health results from health-relevant behavioural prescriptions, including limiting alcohol consumption, dietary patterns of abstinence and fasting, and not smoking.
2. *Heredity.* The genetic pools of certain religious groups, particularly the most conservative and the smallest, tend to be concentrated. This may lead to greater or lesser health. For instance, Tay-Sachs disease seems to be more frequent among Eastern European Jews. Sickle-cell anemia is more prevalent among members of the predominately black National Baptist Convention in the US than among those of the predominately white Southern Baptist Convention. In this case the difference is likely attributable to the genetic inheritance of the two groups.
3. *Psychosocial effects.* Involvement in a congregation of religious adherents provides a sense of belonging and of receiving and giving

social support. This type of investigation corresponds to the tradition of research that has independently demonstrated the benefits of good and supportive social relationships, perhaps through buffering the negative effects of stress and anger through psychoneuroimmunological pathways.

4. *Psychodynamics of belief.* The beliefs of adherents to particular denominations may engender a sense of hope, purpose, peace, and self-confidence, on the one hand, or guilt and self-doubt, on the other. Such beliefs may be associated with health benefits or decrements. For example, the Protestant ethic, which involves hard work for the glory of God, could provide the epistemological and theological foundation for the internal locus of control. So-called type A individuals are competitive, achievement-oriented, easily annoyed, and time-urgent, in contrast to easy-going type B people.

5. *Psychodynamics of religious rites.* The practice of regular, recurrent public and private rituals, such as church attendance, daily scripture reading, and prayer, moderate anxiety, dread, and loneliness and establish a sense of being loved and accepted.

6. *Psychodynamics of faith.* It is possible that belief in a God and an ordered universe may operate as a placebo. For example, "various scriptures promise victory or survival to the faithful. The physiological effects of expectancy beliefs such as these are now being documented by mind–body researchers" (Levin, 1993, p. 10).

7. *Multifactorial explanations.* The relationship between religion and health is likely due to a combination of the factors listed and to hypotheses that have not yet been considered.

8. *Super-empirical explanations.* The preceding hypotheses are social, psychological, and biological. It may be that the best hypothesis is one for which concepts and measurement tools are not yet available. Consider, for example, the beliefs of ancient and contemporary religious traditions in a universal life force or "energy."

To date, this largely mysterious idea has been dismissed by Western researchers. In the future, empirical observations may be available to further understand this "energy" or life force.

9. *Supernatural influence.* Another possible explanation is supernatural, "in other words, a transcendent being who exists fully or partly outside of nature chooses when and why to endow and bless individuals with health or healing, presumably on the basis of their faithfulness" (Levin, 1993, p. 11). Such a hypothesis, by definition, cannot be studied.

At an ecological rather than an individual level, the degree of concentration or density of a religious group is another component of the religious influence on health that has been examined. Areas with a higher concentration of religious groups have been shown to have different morbidity and mortality rates than areas that are similar in all regards but lack religious density. For example, Fuchs (1974) compared the mortality rates of two similar western states: Utah, where there is a very high concentration of Mormons, a religion that, among other things, prohibits cigarette smoking, alcohol, and caffeine, and Nevada, a more secular state, which has relatively high rates of alcohol and cigarette smoking. There were also important differences in marital, family, and geographical stability in these two states. The death rates for cirrhosis and for cancer of the respiratory system were higher in Nevada. On the other hand, very conservative states tend to have higher rates of teen pregnancy (Strayhorn & Strayhorn, 2009), which may lead to a number of health problems both in the teen mother and in her offspring. The moderating variable in this case may be a decreased probability of using birth control. Nevertheless, it does indicate a situation in which religiosity may be linked to poorer health outcomes. Still, in general, religious people tend to be healthier than less religious people. Thus, having a population that practices a religion likely lowers health-care costs for businesses and governments (Newport, 2013).

Studies have been done on the relationship between religious and spiritual practices and health.

Overall, the evidence seems to suggest a moderate protective effect (Koenig et al., 2001). A wide variety of outcomes, including those related to both mental and physical health (as well as outcomes from specific diseases), have been included in these studies. We still do not understand the actual mechanisms for the effects. For instance, the relative importance of private religious and spiritual practices as compared to attendance at public religious events such as church services is not well understood. There appear to be gender differences in the impact on health of religious and spiritual practices (Maselko & Kubzansky, 2005). Perhaps surprisingly, Maselko and Kubzansky (2005) found that while weekly public religious activity was significantly associated with health and well-being, the relationship was stronger for men than for women. In other words, men seemed to get more health benefit from weekly church attendance than women and this was linked to denominational adherence. It appeared in this study that men's well-being increased from attendance at Roman Catholic services, but that of women decreased. The authors hypothesized that this might be related to the use of male language and imagery for God, as well as the patriarchal hierarchy and leadership within the church and in the Mass. Another explanation might be that men tend to be more socially isolated and thus the shared participation in Mass may be of greater benefit. Another study found that weekly attendance, but no more, was associated with decreased anxiety and depression. The explanations for this positive effect of moderate church attendance related to sense of meaning, interpersonal connections, and self-forgiveness, among other factors (Sternthal et al., 2010). Other scholars have looked at the consequences to health of switching denominations. Sheitle and Adamczyk (2010), for instance, compared switching from "high-cost" (theologically restrictive and culturally exclusive) religious groups such as Latter-Day Saints and Jehovah's Witness to less demanding mainstream denominations and found the benefits of staying in these high-cost groups were highly protective as compared to others. Being a member of a high-cost group has the potential to provide strong support and solutions for many if not most of the uncertainties of everyday life, but only as long as the person remains a member and perhaps only as long as he/she continues to believe or pretend to believe in those teachings.

Prayer and Health

Prayer for health is as ancient as civilization. Lately, under the modern positivistic scientific paradigm, a number of studies have been published establishing that prayer effects changes in human beings as well as in a number of other biological systems or organisms, including cells, fungi, yeast, bacteria, plants, single-celled organisms, and animals (Targ, 1997). It doesn't matter whether the prayer includes the laying on of hands or if the "prayer" and "person prayed for" are geographically separated, even by a wide distance and with or without intervening barriers. How does this work? Some people think the space–time continuum has not been adequately defined by science. Some people think scientists cannot investigate whether or not God heals through prayer because, by their definition, God is outside of and greater than any human ability to measure—God is infinite and perfect. Human powers of observation and measurement are flawed and finite. Thus, we cannot "study" God empirically. Still others contend that we do not adequately understand all of what our physical senses are capable of perceiving and that some people have learned how to extend the common ways of using their perceptual senses. But is there some empirical force, energy, or information whose effects, emanating from prayer, can be studied? Prayer is believed to be "communication" with the deity, the Creator, who "answers" the petitioner. Healing in this context is the response of God, including to the requests of people.

Prayer has been investigated as a natural phenomenon with some interesting results. Levin and Vanderpool (1989) have reviewed empirical studies and found a positive link between prayer and health. This link may be empirically explained as the result of (1) making behavioural adjustments, including dietary restrictions such as fasting as a way to "move into prayer"; (2) knowing that one is being prayed for may, in and of itself, lead to a feeling of being supported; (3) knowing that one is being prayed for and praying for oneself and others may be comforting and result in changes in the immune system; and finally (4) simply a belief in prayer may lead to well-being.

The classic and most cited study of prayer and healing was done by Randolph Byrd at the San Francisco General Medical Center in 1982–3 (Lerner, 1994, p. 128). A devoutly religious yet scientifically trained medical doctor, Byrd set out to investigate the effects of prayer on healing by looking at the health effects of being prayed for among 393 cardiac patients. He randomly assigned the patients to two groups and assigned people from nearby evangelical and Catholic prayer groups to pray for patients in the experimental group. Those randomly assigned to the control group were alike those in the experimental group in all respects at the beginning of the study. After the prayers, the experimental group was healthier in the following ways: (1) the lesser need to be ventilated or intubated; (2) the lesser need for antibiotics; (3) the relative infrequency of cardio-pulmonary arrest; (4) the relative infrequency of congestive heart failure; (5) the relative infrequency of pneumonia; and (6) the lesser need for diuretics. In this double-blind situation, prayer by distant and unknown others was effective in improving the outcomes of cardiac patients.

Another study, with parallels to Byrd's, is a double-blind clinical investigation of post-operative patients that also documented psychological and physical improvements. In this study, 53 males who underwent hernia surgery were divided into three groups. The first group received a pre-recorded tape with suggestions for a speedy recovery. The second group experienced distant healing during the surgery by a healer who was concentrating on the individual and sending him/her healing thoughts (prayers), and the third group was a non-intervention control. The group receiving distant healing/praying was more likely to experience recovery than either of the other two groups (Targ, 1997, p. 75). Other studies have noted the effectiveness of distant healing for various physiological measures, such as electro-dermal activity, heart rate, blood volume, and relaxation (Targ, 1997). Music, imagery, and touch (called MIT therapy) have been found to have a positive impact on the health of people in cardiac care (Krucoff et al., 2005). Brown (2012), a professor of religious studies, has studied the phenomenon of intercessory prayer (prayer for others) and found some evidence of lasting healing. The conclusion we must come to, then, is that empirical research on the effects of prayer can be done and that the findings so far are intriguing. More research needs to be undertaken to demonstrate empirically the potential effects of prayer on health.

The Illness Iceberg

The distribution of illness in a population has been described using the simile of an **illness iceberg** (Last, 1963). The image implies that most symptoms of disease go largely unnoticed by the people who have the symptoms, by health-care practitioners, and by epidemiologists interested in measuring the incidence and prevalence of disease. Illness goes undetected for a number of reasons. First, people often explain away or rationalize physical changes in their bodies in ways that seem to make sense and therefore do not require a medical explanation. Sudden or extensive weight loss and a long-standing cough that doesn't seem to get better both can be signs of very serious illness. They are, however, easily explainable in lay terms: "I've been too busy to eat" or "if it would only stop raining my cough would go away." In the second place, some signs of latent illness develop slowly, so that the patient is not alerted to them and, in fact, may normalize such changes over time. High blood pressure and cholesterol build-up in the arteries are two examples. Some diseases can only be detected by clinical tests such as X-rays, CaT scans, and blood and urine tests.

Practitioners, too, are limited in what illnesses they can detect. Some diseases that are not observable through any specific clinical measures can be diagnosed only by a myriad of complex tests, plus symptoms described by the patient and some element of luck or art. Also, practitioners are often limited in their ability to detect illness because their patients do not provide sufficient information. Epidemiologists face all of the obstacles described above. In addition, epidemiologists frequently rely on a wide range of data collection strategies all of which are subject to various limitations of validity, reliability, recall, response rate, truth-telling, and the like.

In the face of such ambiguity and variability in the recognition and acknowledgement of signs and symptoms of illness, what are the processes that lead some people to decide to do something about them and others to ignore them?

Why People Seek Help

What makes you decide to go to the doctor? Do you go when pain becomes severe? Is it when your symptoms interfere with your responsibilities at home, school, or work? Do you try to avoid going to the doctor? When you feel cold or flu symptoms do you generally just go to bed early or take a day or two off work? Do you go to the local drugstore to buy something from the shelf? Or do you go to a naturopath, chiropractor, nutritionist, allopathic physician, acupuncturist, or other therapist? The processes by which people come to notice signs they think may be symptomatic of illness, the kinds of attention they pay to these signs, and the action they decide to take are all a part of the study of illness behaviour. Whether someone seeks help and what kind of help is sought are the result of complex social, economic, and psychological determinants.

The first stage of illness is the acknowledgement or notice of symptoms or signs. Sometimes symptoms are noticeable as little more than a minor behavioural change, such as tiredness or lack of appetite. Some common symptoms, such as a cough, cause only a mild discomfort; others may cause a searing pain. Sometimes symptoms are noticeable as measurable physical anomalies such as a heightened temperature or an excessive blood-sugar reading. Other times, illness is not experienced until it is diagnosed after a medical examination.

People with similar symptoms may respond very differently to them. One may go straight to the doctor; another may "let nature take its course," even with severe symptoms. Although early responses may be quite variable, they will make sense within the context of the social, cultural, economic, and psychological conditions of each person.

An early study, "Pathways to the Doctor" (Zola, 1973), was based on interviews with more than 200 people at three clinics. For each person it was the first visit for that particular problem. According to Zola's analysis, the decision to seek treatment was based on a great deal more than the mere presence of symptoms. Rather, this decision was associated with one or more of the following:

1. occurrence of an interpersonal crisis;
2. perceived interference with social or personal relations;
3. sanctioning by others;
4. perceived interference with vocational or physical activity; and
5. a kind of "temporalizing" of symptoms (or thinking that they will go away in time or the reverse).

Mechanic (1978) proposed that seeking help depends on 10 determinants:

1. visibility and recognition of the symptoms;
2. the extent to which symptoms are perceived as dangerous;
3. the extent to which symptoms disrupt family, work, and other social activities;
4. the frequency and persistence of symptoms;
5. amount of tolerance for the symptoms;
6. available information, knowledge, and cultural assumptions;
7. basic needs that lead to denial;
8. other needs competing with the symptoms;
9. competing interpretations that can be given to the symptoms once they are recognized;
10. availability of treatment resources, physical proximity, and psychological and financial costs of taking action.

Mechanic and Zola take somewhat different points of view. In particular, Mechanic acknowledges the relevance of the symptoms themselves—their severity, perceived seriousness, visibility, frequency, and persistence—and the knowledge, information, and associated cultural assumptions people use in determining whether or not to take action. In Zola's 1973 model, "symptoms" per se are not discussed. They are a given. It is their place in the "ongoingness" of life of the individual that is examined.

Medical treatment has certain costs. In Canada most treatment, whether visiting the doctor's office or the emergency room or being treated in hospital, is essentially free (paid for through the taxation system). However, there are other costs, including time off work, transportation to and from medical help, purchase of pharmaceuticals, the anxiety of waiting for results, and paying for babysitting or child-sitting arrangements. All of these and others can be viewed as constraints within which the theories above must operate. Furthermore, since these studies were published some significant social changes have developed that affect the frequency of seeking medical help, including direct-to-consumer advertising of drugs as well as the many health websites on the Internet. People can use the Internet to find a diagnosis for the symptoms they may experience.

While a risky process, Internet advice can forestall doctor and other health-care visits or may increase the demand for doctoring. In addition, some people go to the doctor after they have read about or seen an advertisement for a new treatment or a new disease. Some diseases may even have an element of attractiveness to some people, as they seem to be so associated with camaraderie, fellow-feeling, and even popularity (high incidence). Thus, certain people may search for the possibility of a diagnosis and treatment. The Movember movement, for example, has highlighted prostate cancer as a possible diagnosis for men of a certain age for whom early and continued testing is recommended. Such positive campaigns can increase the probability that people will go to the doctor for examination. The results of the breast cancer movement can also be seen in the widespread attendance at mammography screening despite the equivocation regarding effectiveness. There are also new categories of people who visit the doctor, such as those who want to be "better than well" and better than "normal." Those who choose mood-altering drugs and cosmetic surgeries might select medical care because of their aspirations to feel and/or look better. Choosing to go to the doctor, then, is the result of a complex mixture of symptoms along with a variety of social experiences.

Summary

1. Stress is a process that occurs in response to demands that are either much greater than or much less than the usual levels of activity. Historically, the bodily reaction to stress has been termed "fight or flight" by Cannon. Later, Selye suggested that the General Adaptation Syndrome (GAS) is the body's reaction to all stressful events. It has three stages: an alarm reaction, resistance, and exhaustion. Exposure to stress in the third stage can lead to "diseases of adaptation."

2. Some researchers have developed scales to measure degrees of stress.

3. Several factors affect the amount of stress experienced. One important factor is social support, which has been seen to be a buffer against the degree of stress experienced.

4. Social capital and social cohesion are linked to health outcomes.

5. People are more likely to stay healthy when they have a feeling of comprehensibility, manageability, and meaningfulness in their lives and are able to develop a sense of coherence and a belief that things are under control.

6. There is a new focus on positive psychology as the study of what contributes to happiness.

7. Religion and prayer have been associated with healing both historically and, more recently, empirically.

8. The first stage of illness is the acknowledgement or notice of symptoms or signs. What people do about the illness, how illness is experienced and handled or treated, is called "illness behaviour." Illness behaviour varies according to the individual's social circumstances. Factors that lead an individual to seek treatment include the occurrence of an interpersonal crisis, the perceived interference with social or personal relations, sanctioning by others, the perceived interference with vocational or physical activity, "temporalizing" of symptoms that have continued "too long" or develop "suddenly" and "unexpectedly," and the availability of treatment resources, physical proximity, and psychological and financial costs of taking action.

Key Terms

illness iceberg
psychoneuroimmunology
psychosomatic
resilience
sense of coherence

social cohesion
Social Readjustment Rating Scale
social support
stress
tautological

Questions for Study and Discussion

1. Assess yourself with regard to all of the socio-psychological variables that seem to be related to health status. What changes can you make now to improve your health?
2. Design a study to measure the sense of coherence of students in your department. Consider how department relationships affect your well-being.
3. Critically evaluate the studies examining the relationship between prayer and health.
4. When do you go to the doctor? Do your reasons correspond to those of Mechanic and Zola?
5. Define, describe, and critically analyze ideas associated with the illness iceberg.
6. Examine the World Happiness Report for any year since 2012 and discuss what you have learned regarding the contributions to happiness.

Suggested Readings

Dossey, L. (2014). *One mind: How our individual mind is part of a greater consciousness and why it matters.* Hay House. Larry Dossey is a physician who has spent his life praying for his patients as he treats them conventionally

Fancourt, D., Ockelford, A., & Belai, A. (2014). The psychoneurological effects of music: A systematic review and new model. *Brain, Behavior, and Immunity, 36,* 15–26. A review paper investigating the role of music in health.

Gawande, A. (2017). *Being mortal: What matters in the end.* Henry Holt & Company. A very popular book on the socio-psychological experiences of illness, disease, and death that focuses on an answer to the question of the meaning of life in the end.

Helliwell, J., Layard, R., & Sachs, J. (2019). *World happiness report 2019.* Sustainable Development Solutions Network. An annual report (available online) that ranks countries around the world in respect to the happiness of citizens and offers explanations for the differences.

The Experience of Being Ill

Chapter Overview

- Illness is experienced in subjective and individual terms, although the personal experience is socially constructed and contextualized according to the cultural, social determinant, and socio-psychological discourses related to the issues we have discussed thus far.
- Disease and sickness need to be understood as socially constructed and distinct from one another but influenced by the circulating discourses and practices.
- Among the variety of popular personal and individual discourses of illness are the following: illness as choice, as carelessness or failure, as despair, as secondary gain, as a message of the body, as communication, as metaphor, as statistical infrequency, and as sexual politics, as aspirational, as potential, as candidate, and as survival.
- The insider's view of living with illness over time (chronic illness) describes it as involving a great deal of emotional, ontological, and philosophical work, along with the management of, among other things, treatments, symptoms, side effects of various treatments, and health-care providers.
- Illness, sickness, and disease are linked recursively to self and identity.

Introduction

What is it like to acknowledge for the first time symptoms of a potentially serious illness? For instance, how do men feel and how do they talk to themselves and to others upon first noticing a lump in a breast? How do women manage to cope with a diagnosis of myocardial infarction? How do people manage who feel awful but cannot get a diagnosis, such as some people with chronic fatigue syndrome, fibromyalgia, or environmental sensitivities? What is it like to be told that your child has epilepsy, Tay-Sachs disease, or Down's syndrome? What is it like for the doctors, the nurses, the siblings, and significant others? How do people talk to themselves when they learn that they have cancer, diabetes, or AIDS? How do people manage the uncertainty surrounding a diagnosis of HIV/AIDS and the possible or probable future prognosis of illness? How do people tell their significant others once they have received a diagnosis from the doctor? And how, then, do family members and significant others manage the news? These are the sorts of questions that might be asked about the experience of illness.

The purpose of this chapter is to describe and explain something of the socially constructed experience of being ill in Canadian society. Much published sociological research that we have examined so far in this text assumes that the object of sociology is the observation of the institutions and structures of society and of individual behavioural and attitudinal interpretations of these forces through their psychosocial dynamics. Both the social-structural and personal levels constrain and influence people's thoughts, feelings, beliefs, and actions. Chapters 2 through 6 in this book have been written largely in these traditions of positivist, conflict, feminist, intersectional, and anti-racist points of view, often using quantitative and "objective" data about social phenomena to provide description and causal explanations. These chapters do not examine the described experiences of those for whom these external "objective" forces come to be integrated into personal meanings and interpretations. This type of analysis has been largely absent in these previous chapters of the text.

Chapter 7 is written in the interpretive tradition: it draws attention to the meanings, interpretive discourses, and world views of human beings in relation to illness, sickness, disease, and death. The chapter examines the subjective reality, the consciousness of people making and finding meaning in interactive and social contexts. The analysis in this chapter is at the individual level. However, it must be emphasized that a person's views are constructed in the context of a particular society and a particular place at a unique point in time in that society. Attitudes and actions are the shifting results of accepting and resisting circulating social discourses related to power and knowledge in societies. Meanings and identities are constructed from social interactions in specific social, political, economic, and historical contexts. Meanings and identities reflect a person's position in the social structure and that person's relationships and experience. Cultural attitudes to illness vary. Definitions of health and illness alter over time and place.

Illness, Sickness, Disease, Survivor, and Aspirational Health

We begin by distinguishing among disease, illness, and sickness. **Disease** is that which is diagnosed by a physician; it is usually believed to be located in specific organs or systems in the body and potentially curable or treatable through particular biomedical treatments. **Illness**, by contrast, is the personal experience of the person who does not feel well or as well as possible. While illness is affected by the discourses of medicine it is also heavily influenced by the individual's social context and such characteristics as gender and racialization. What a person considers to be "normal well-being" reflects the social group within which norms are forged and maintained. **Sickness** refers to the social actions engaged in by a person as a result of illness or disease, such as taking medication, visiting the doctor, resting in bed, or staying away from work. Patients "feel illness" and "act sickness"; physicians "diagnose and treat disease." Aspirational health—the health that improves and enhances—results from a confluence of medicine, malleable bodies, new technologies, and, possibly, optimism about what medical interventions might deliver. In recent years, medical solutions have spread to everyday concerns. This includes, first, the use of medicine to change one's identity and improve or enhance the self, thus suggesting the notion of **aspirational health**. Second, other solutions result from technological change and powerful mass media representations and include (1) living with the statistically or genetically predicted expectation of disease, i.e., being a **patient-in-waiting**, (b) being a **survivor** of a disease, or (c) being in remission and seen by others as an **illness candidate.**

Sickness, disease, illness, and anticipatory or aspirational health, being a patient-in-waiting, a survivor, or an illness candidate may be independent of one another. This is confirmed by the fact that people can feel ill and act sick and yet not visit a physician. People can act sick without having a medical diagnosis, as when a student complains of

having flu in order to get an extension for an essay or an exemption from an examination. A physician may tell people that they are not ill and ought not to pretend to be sick. Have you ever thought of asking for a doctor's note to avoid doing something? Have you ever done something despite feeling very ill? People can fear Huntington's disease and avoid the genetic test even though they did not inherit the gene. In this case, sickness, illness, and disease may or may not occur together.

Figure 7.1 clarifies the relationships among illness, sickness, disease, and medicine for self-improvement. Illness, sickness, disease, and the desirable way to be a human being all are socially constructed experiences. People do not experience or talk about their illnesses or their ideal bodies and moods in a social or cultural vacuum. Everything that people feel, say, think, and do about their illnesses and body/mind aspirations is culturally and socially mediated. For example, a sore back conjures up one set of meanings, ideas, and actions when it happens to a person with bone cancer. A sore back conjures up a different set of meanings, ideas, and actions

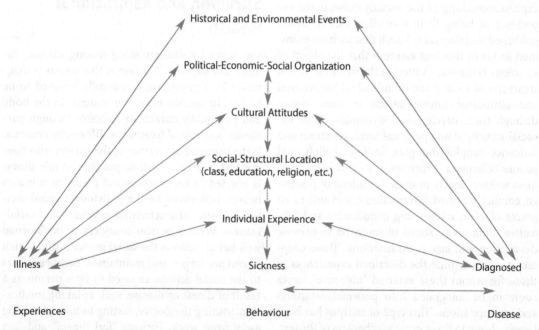

Figure 7.1   A Model of the Relationships among Illness, Sickness, and Disease

when it happens to a world-class skier just before the Olympics. In fact, noticing that a part of the body, such as the back, is sore is only possible within a particular social-cultural context and its resultant language categories. Small breasts have a certain value for a female runner or swimmer but might be perceived differently by a young woman who wants to be a Hollywood star. In respect to moods, sadness, for example, once elicited one sort of explanation as an inevitable part of difficult life situations. This was prior to the development of the popular anti-depressants known as SSRIs (selective serotonin reuptake inhibitors). This discourse has changed and been transformed into a widely accepted and medicalized meaning. It is now often pathologized as depression in the context of the availability of SSRIs (see, e.g., Metzl & Angel, 2004; Clarke & Gawley, 2009). And, too, what had begun years ago as "sadness" has turned to a discourse of anger and desperation as some people have discovered the vast array of physical and behavioural side effects, including addiction to SSRIs, that can lead to suicide.

Sickness behaviour is socially mediated. Whether a woman goes to the hospital at the first sign of labour or does not go until she is ready to deliver, or delivers at home with a midwife or doula, depends in part on cultural influences. Old Order Mennonite women, according to the nurses in the obstetrics department of a local hospital, often have their babies on the way to the delivery room because they tend to wait through several stages of labour before travelling slowly in buggies to the hospital. According to the same source, women from some other ethnic backgrounds usually enter the hospital at the first sign of contractions and, once there, are likely to engage in long, protracted, painful, and "noisy" labour.

Disease, too, is a socially and culturally mediated event. Doctors make their diagnoses of death from a complex mix of socio-cultural, historical, economic, medical, scientific, technological, and clinical data, and in the context of their own age, specialty, class, gender, and ethnocultural circumstances. That death, too, is socially mediated was described first sociologically by Sudnow (1967)

and later by Timmermans (1998) and then others. There are repeated examples in the news of people who are considered brain dead but can continue to live on life support. In these cases, the decision as to when and/or whether to withdraw life support can become a fraught and even legal battle (Gibson, 2019). Nordquist (2006) studied the effect of patient insurance on the interpretation of do-not-resuscitate (DNR) orders of doctors. He found (in the US) that doctors were more likely to write DNR orders for people who lacked private insurance. Thus, doctors were implicitly valuing life in economic terms. Extended life was available for those who could pay for it. Li and Arber (2006) have studied how palliative care nurses, in doing the emotionally invested work necessary to nurse the dying, constructed the moral identities of dying people as "credible" or "troubled." This, too, played into how dying patients were treated. Death is medicalized and even monitored by the medical care system in Canada today, as one recent study of the performance status and symptom displays of dying patients shows (Seow et al., 2011). McInerney (2006) has studied media discourses of death with particular focus on the "requested death movement" (i.e., "right to die movement") in the Australian press, and Shoshana and Teman (2006) have examined the construction of death through another medium—television—in the series *Six Feet Under*. These last two references are based on qualitative and interpretive media analyses and reflect evidence that media both mirror and influence everyday social practices even in the case of our understandings of death. Of course, as sociologists we need to critique the media portrayal of both the "normative" and extraordinary ways of dying.

Outrageous Acts and Everyday Rebellions is the title of a witty satire by Gloria Steinem (1983) illustrating how bodily changes including illness, sickness, and disease may also become social or, in this case, illustrations of gender behaviours. Steinem suggests, for example, that beliefs about menstruation are socially determined. If men menstruated rather than women, menstruation would have very different meanings and consequences. First of all, if men menstruated, it would be a laudable, dramatic event, symbolic of strength and manhood. Men would compete with one another about how large their "flow" was, how long it lasted, and whose blood was the brightest. Menstruation would be celebrated ritually as a recurring reminder of the power of masculinity. To prevent problems such as cramps and premenstrual syndrome (PMS), billions of dollars in research money would be spent. Doctors specializing in menstruation would be thought to hold the most prestigious specialty. It would be the most highly paid and desired of medical positions. Sanitary napkins and tampons would be free. Epidemiological research would demonstrate how men performed better and won more Olympic medals during their periods. Menstruation would be considered proof that only men could serve God and country in war, in politics, or in religion (Steinem, 1983: 338). How far-fetched do you think that spoof is?

Highlighted Issues

Box 7.1 • Social Value of the Patient: Death, Psychiatric Patients, and Children

David Sudnow (1967), in what has become a classic text, described in great detail, as the result of lengthy participant observation at two US hospitals, how the "presumed social value of a patient" affected the type of death and health care a patient received. For example, poorer people, less "functioning" people, and people who were deemed less "valuable" because of "race"/ethnicity or age were given less aggressive treatments in general hospitals. Timmermans (1998) has reinvestigated the question of whether or not and how a patient's social worth continues to be a factor in the type and quality of treatment received, especially in advance of death. In particular, Timmermans examined how the use of resuscitation technologies may have been influenced by the presumed value of the patient. How do health-care practitioners "make sense of engaging in a practice with the small chance of saving lives and the potential to severely disable patients" (Timmermans, 1998, p. 469)? Apparently, in the face of controversial options, health-care practitioners continue to distinguish between people on the basis of their social viability or their ability to contribute to society (according to the doctor's set of values). In sum, "in the liminal space between lives worth living and proper deaths, resuscitative efforts in the emergency department crystallize submerged subtle attitudes of the wider society" (Timmermans,

1998, p. 471). The greater the perceived worth of the patient the more aggressive the treatment offered. The social and economic value of a life also is of fundamental significance in the legal establishment of the amount owing in the case of a wrongful death.

Children, by this legal accounting, are worth substantially less than adults, particularly adult males at the peak of their earning capacity. The social and economic evaluations of psychiatric patients also affect the types and quality of treatment they receive (Lincoln, 2006). Some psychiatrists, concerned citizens, and children's rights advocates argue that children are essentially the victims of ongoing and dangerous experiments when they are diagnosed with mental illnesses. In the absence of valid and reliable diagnostic criteria they may be prescribed experimental medications, even in the absence of knowledge of their safety (Whitaker, 2010; Breggin, 2014). The question of whether this treatment is partly the result of the negative economic value of children begs to be asked in this case. Do we need more robust ethical guidelines when it comes to the well-being and even the basic human rights of people regardless of their presumed economic value to society? Health care is a human right according to the World Health Organization. However, in a situation lacking universal coverage that right is definitely not upheld.

Spotlight on Ethics

Box 7.2 • Prozac, a Cultural Precursor to Opioids: Feeling Well and Feeling Better Than Well

One of the most interesting public debates in the last few decades, within an increasingly medicalized society, has been the debate over "personality-changing" drugs such as Prozac, prescribed often for depression and anxiety (Kramer, 1993). The miraculous nature of the effects of such drugs on a wide variety of symptoms, coupled with their under-recognized side effects, has led to widespread use. Still, there is disagreement about the ethics of prescribing or refusing to prescribe a drug reputed to be a cosmetic pharmaceutical used to make people feel "better than well." The availability of Prozac raised the question of whether people ought to take drugs that change their very personalities. Prozac's wide obtainability also raised the question of whether doctors should have the right to prescribe or withhold this powerful "feel-good" drug. What makes this particularly timely is that today people have increasingly come to rely on the highly addictive opioid drugs as a way to feel better than normal. Initially opioids were prescribed to mask pain, but then people seemed to require such drugs just to cope with the normal exigencies of everyday life. We have to ask what cultural role the first generation of mass-marketed anti-depressants had in the later reliance of a broader and broader swath of people on opioids to manage uncomfortable feelings, pain, and discomfort.

To what extent should we be able to choose to enhance or suppress moods and cognitions by buying a medication or some other individual medical intervention? If we agree that people have the right to choose how they want to feel and see the world, we have to ask who should pay for such "cosmetic" pharmacology? Is this something that medicare should cover through all of our taxes—or not? Under what conditions, when, and for whom might this use of taxes be acceptable? In your experience have you observed that using anti-depressants is one way for women to "do" femininity, just as drinking excess alcohol is sometimes a way for men to "do" masculinity? How else is medicine sometimes enlisted to aid in "doing" gender? Opioid use is also gendered. Consider possible explanations for correlations among opioid use and gendering.

Highlighted Issues

Box 7.3 • Social Anxiety Disorder

Social anxiety disorder (SAD), along with a number of other types of anxiety disorders, is increasingly diagnosed in Canada and around the world (Dowbiggin, 2009; Horwitz & Wakefield, 2012). It is largely subjectively defined. This may be by the sufferer or parents, who feel that the anxiety is disproportionate and causes significant distress or impairment. There are a number of different and competing explanations for this. On the one side are commentators who point to the increasing stress of the modern world, economic and other sorts of competitiveness, and the spread of risk consciousness. Life is harder. Less social support is available. There is more to fear, according to this view. On the other side are those who argue that the increase in this and in many other "popular" mental illnesses such as depression is a result of the claims-making advertising, to doctors and patients, of the pharmaceutical industry. Now that drug treatments are available, detractors argue, markets must be found. In this context pharmaceuticals are promoted widely and advertised as if they are able to mitigate all sorts of anxiety and other suffering. Social anxiety in this view is just pathologized and medicalized shyness that has been captured by pharmaceutical marketing. Do you have an opinion on this issue?

Links between identities and political or social issues are well described by Klawiter (1999) in her research on breast cancer activists in the San Francisco Bay area. There are, she observed, three different ideas about breast cancer and its causes and remedies, represented in three different social movements. At times the movements operate in the interests of three fundamentally different and even contradictory goals, including (1) raising funds for traditional breast cancer research that focuses on conventional treatments such as chemotherapy and radiation; (2) advocacy and support for ethnic minority women and other marginalized women's groups and women's health in general; and (3) protesting the multitude of potentially health destructive cancer-creating industries and the countless potential environmental causes of breast cancer. The first was represented by the Race for the Cure, which focused on research and cure through biomedicine. They valorized heteronormative identities and promoted early detection through mammographic screening for all. Those who had cancer were called "survivors." They were enlisted to stand together and advocate for more and better conventional research and treatment. The second, the Women and Cancer Walk, emphasized support for the broader women's health movement along with other women's cancers. It explicitly included multicultural feminist issues, challenged the focus on survival alone, and critiqued the assumptions of equality and heteronormativity. This group expressed opposition to institutionalized conventional medicine and promoted social and economic equality, beginning with gender equality. The third group was called the Toxic Tour. Their focus was on environmental activism to change the environmental conditions and, thus, the preventable causes of breast cancer. Cancer was represented as "the product and source of profit of a predatory cancer industry" (Klawiter, 1999, p. 121).

King (2006) has taken ideas about the social meanings and constructions of breast cancer movements in a different direction. In *Pink Ribbons, Inc.: Breast Cancer and the Politics of Philanthropy*, King argues that breast cancer marketing has become the model for the extensive growth of marketing among corporations in the neo-liberal modern states. Just as fundraising for breast cancer research and treatments has increased exponentially in the last several decades, so has neo-liberalism. Breast cancer activism, she argues, serves to diminish the responsibilities of governments for health care and health-related research under neo liberalism. The fact that breast cancer is dense with meanings related to both sex and femininity is consequential and of great benefit for social or cause marketing. Breast cancer has become a popular charity because of social marketing in a sexist and heteronormative social world. King's analysis is chiefly relevant for the first group above, exemplified by the Race for the Cure, the largest and most widely known of the movements. This group has been aided by the support of many corporations that have "pinked" a multitude of their products, some of which are carcinogenic, to expand sales and contribute to breast cancer research. This pinking process has even included the "pinking" of a gun to support research for breast cancer. Race for the Cure was started in 1980 and has historically been enormously successful. It had raised $1.5 billion by 2010 for conventional medical care. Then, faced with internal administrative scandals, a number of chapters were closed. There seems, however, to be something of a resurgence of the national-level charity today (McCambridge, 2018; Charity Navigator, 2017).

Cultural Variations in the Experience of Being Ill

In all societies and cultures people experience illness, pain, disability, and disfigurement. Sorcery, the breaking of a taboo, the intrusion of a disease-causing spirit into the body, the intrusion of a disease-causing object into the body, and the loss of the soul all are seen as possible causes of disease in a cross-cultural context (Clements, 1932). All these explanations, except for the intrusion into the body of a disease-causing object, involve the supernatural or magic in an attempt to understand illness. Westerners tend to see illness as empirically caused and mechanically or chemically treatable. Although there often is a significant moral component to an explanation for certain diseases in the Western world, immorality is not usually viewed as the immediate cause. In most of the non-Western world, non-empirical explanations and cures for disease are readily available. Illness is seen as a combination of spiritual, mental, and physical phenomena.

The experience of pain appears to vary from one social and cultural group to another. In a classic study Zborowski (1952) compared patients hospitalized in a New York City hospital and found that patients differed dramatically in how they experienced pain. Those from Jewish and Italian backgrounds responded emotionally to suffering and tended to dwell on their painful experience with great demonstrations of anguish. Italians saw pain as something to be rid of and were happy once a way to relieve their pain was found. Jews were mainly concerned with the meaning of their pain and the consequences of their pain for their future health. "Old Americans" and the Irish, by contrast, reacted stoically. The different attitudes to pain were reflected in distinct behavioural and emotional responses of people from different ethnic groups. What is the ideal response to pain in your cultural or ethnic group?

What is viewed as disease or health varies from society to society. Disfigurement or illness may or may not be seen as normal among one culture or another. "Afflictions common enough in a group to be endemic, though they are clinical deformities, may often be accepted as part of man's natural condition" (Hughes, 1967, p. 88). Disagreement is widespread over which states of physical being are desirable and which are not. Among some people, an obese woman is an object of desire; others define obesity as repugnant or even as a symptom of emotional or physical illness. Among many Canadians today, obesity is considered a medical condition with associated treatments, symptoms, tests, and risk factors. For some, small breasts constitute a medical problem. There are many examples of how physical health and illness understandings depend on value and moral judgements (Clements, 1932; Hughes, 1967; Turner, 1987; Foucault, 1973). Moreover, notions

of mental health also vary widely from cultural group to cultural group and change over time, as a perusal of the academic journal *Culture, Medicine and Psychiatry* demonstrates. In one highly relevant and recent example, transgender identity was, until 2016, considered a mental health disorder by the World Health Organization but is not any longer (Vagianos, 2018). It is clear that, for many people, health and religion, morality and wellness, and the natural and the supernatural are closely related.

Popular Cultural Conceptions of Health, Illness, and Disease

The following sections describe a number of popular conceptions of health and illness.

Illness as Carelessness and Failure

Contemporary neo-liberal health promotion is built on the assumption that individuals are responsible for staying well and that individual carelessness and failure causes (most) illness. Therefore, individuals are held accountable for smoking cessation, losing weight, drinking alcohol only moderately, using condoms, and pursuing early cancer detection through mammograms, prostate-specific antigen (PSA) tests, PAP smears, submitting to the HPV vaccine, and the like. When individuals fail to stay well, the medical system intervenes. The medical care system is based on aggressive intervention once a disease has been detected. The assumption is that the earlier the detection the better. To be a good citizen and a moral person is to be a healthy person and to avail oneself of early detection testing of all sorts. To be ill is to be a victim and often a victim of one's own weaknesses (e.g., lung cancer in the case of an individual who smoked). People are advised to change their behaviour as individuals as if such change is sufficient or even possible for all. This idea ignores the social constraints that people live under because of, for example, the neighbourhoods in which they live, the presence or absence of parkland nearby, the level of air pollution due to the industries in the neighbourhood, the choices of food (and their costs) at the local supermarket or convenience store, and so on.

Illness as Choice

Some believe that illness is a choice. We choose when we want to be ill, what type of illness we'll have, how severe it will be, and how long the illness will last. Because the body and mind are connected, illness is a result of thinking and feeling as well as of biological bodily processes. We give ourselves illnesses to take a break from the busy obligations of everyday life. We choose to be ill to allow for time out from our routines: to rest, to take stock, to escape, and to withdraw. A host of research in fields such as psychoneuroimmunology and psychosomatic medicine attests to the prevalence of this belief, on both theoretical and empirical levels. A great deal of work has been done on the mind–body interaction in the case of cancer, in particular. Several physician writers have addressed mind–body relationships in various ways. For an overview of several of the most popular, consider the work of Deepak Chopra (1987, 1989; Chopra & Kafatos, 2017) and Larry Dossey (1982, 1991, 2013) or any of Dr Andrew Weil's books (2011; also see *Encyclopaedia Britannica*, 2015). In fact, holistic medicine that takes the body/mind and spirit seriously as necessary parts of treatment is now commonly known as integrative medicine. Integrative medicine is intentionally inclusive of both allopathic (conventional) medical systems of understanding and treatment and also complementary and alternative models.

Oncologist Carl O. Simonton and his colleagues were among the earliest contemporary "popularizers" of the role of the mind in both causing and healing the body of cancer. They argued that cancer arises from a sort of emotional despair. Simonton's book, *Getting Well Again*, is full of examples of people who come to recognize, with the help of the psychotherapeutic skills of Simonton and his staff, that their cancer had been, in a sense,

a personal choice. Once a patient understands the reason for the choice of cancer as a way of coping with a personal problem, he or she can confront the problem on a conscious level and, thus, seek a cure (Simonton et al., 1978).

Simonton's method includes a number of techniques. One of the best known is the systematic use of imaging—conjuring up mental pictures of cells. For example, people are directed to imagine their cancer cells as black ants and their healthy cells as knights in shining armour. The hypothesis is that the more powerful the imaging of the anti-cancer forces, the more likely the imaging will be effective in ridding the body of the disease. Effective imaging may, it was believed, result in one of the following outcomes: increased longevity; moderation of symptoms, including pain; increased sense of well-being, autonomy, and control; improved quality of life; and even, at times, remission of the disease.

Imaging may be the most dramatic of the techniques used to combat cancer "psychologically" and to choose to get well. Numerous other methods are being used around the world by psycho-oncologists, including, but not limited to, yoga, meditation, journaling, art, and group and individual psychotherapy. The effects of all of these techniques on quality of life, longevity, and the disease itself are under investigation. The point to be made here is that within this model of health/illness an important part of healing (along with medical interventions) and of improving the quality of life is taking responsibility for one's state of health and choosing to try to do something about it.

There is considerable ongoing research on the general topic of mind–body interactions in cancer outcomes and well-being with cancer. According to a systematic review of the evidence in some 329 trials of psychological interventions for cancer, there is reason to believe in the possible health benefits of individual and group therapy, informational and educational interventions, guided imagery, and cognitive-behavioural therapies for people with cancer (Schofield et al., 2006). A pilot study of the use of yoga also noted that "the initial findings suggest that yoga has significant potential and should be further explored as a beneficial physical activity option for cancer survivors" (Culos-Reed et al., 2006). The mind matters in cancer survival, according to Speigel (2012). In a review of the available literature he found that breast, lymphoma, gastrointestinal, melanoma, and lung cancers were all impacted positively by psychological interventions. A number of mind/body approaches to cancer treatment are being explored, including acupuncture, mindfulness, and Tai Chi, as a part of integrative medicine (Abrams & Weil, 2009). One way of conceptualizing the value of integrative medicine in cancer treatment is that the usual medical interventions for cancer (chemotherapy, surgery, and radiation) function to get rid of the weed (that is, cancer) while integrative medicine maintains and enhances the soil so that health will flourish (Abrams & Weil, 2009).

Illness as Despair

Closely related to the idea that illness reflects choice is the idea that illness reflects and results from a sort of despair. Lawrence LeShan (1978), a psychotherapist who counselled and then studied cancer patients, came to the conclusion that common types of emotional experience among the majority of cancer patients predated the development of the disease. Examples of these emotional experiences include long-standing, unresolved grief over the loss of someone close, such as the death of a mother or father in childhood, childhood loneliness or isolation, the loss of someone close in adulthood, and the loss of a job. For LeShan's patients, understanding their grief and expressing feelings of sadness and anger became pathways towards being healed.

Norman Cousins's work, which formed the basis for his book, *Anatomy of an Illness as Perceived by the Patient*, is the foundation of another similar and popular approach to illness, health, and healing. This book, a long-time best-seller translated into many different languages and "must" reading in a number of medical schools throughout the world, tells the story of the author's reaction to and

healing from a severe and potentially fatal case of ankylosing spondylitis, a degenerative disease of the connective tissues in the spine.

Cousins's story of his "miraculous" recovery focused on three aspects of his "systematic pursuit of salutary emotions" (Cousins, 1979, p. 35). The first was his partnership with his doctor. Cousins, for many years the editor of the popular American literary magazine *Saturday Review* and a renowned peace activist, asked his doctor to engage in a collaborative partnership. The physician had the traditional armaments to offer. Cousins had done some reading about how healing could be affected by the power of positive thinking and by massive doses of vitamin C. Because he found the hospital forbidding, noisy, and thoroughly unhealthy, Cousins asked his doctor to treat him in a nearby motel. The second important component of his recovery was that his doctor agreed to his request for enormous intravenous doses of vitamin C, in which Cousins, having done considerable research on his own, believed. The third aspect of his rehabilitation strategy was laughter. Cousins had books of jokes and cartoons, tapes, and old film comedies brought to his room for his enjoyment. Laughing deeply relieved his pain and generally made him feel better. As he says, "It worked. I made the joyous discovery that ten minutes of genuine belly laughter had an anaesthetic effect and would give me at least two hours of pain-free sleep. When the pain-killing effect of the laughter wore off, we would switch on the motion-picture projector again, and, not infrequently, it would lead to another pain-free sleep interval" (Cousins, 1979, p. 39). As he was interested in demonstrating the credibility of his experience, Cousins instituted some small experiments. He found that each episode of laughter decreased the level of inflammation in his connective tissues. Five years after recovering from this disease, and having achieved some renown in the area of holistic health (he was appointed senior lecturer at the School of Medicine, University of California at Los Angeles, and consulting editor of *Man and Medicine*), Cousins suffered a serious heart attack. Rehabilitation resulted in another book, *The Healing Heart* (1983), in which he further developed his arguments regarding the importance of positive emotions in maintaining and achieving health that he had first elaborated in *Anatomy of an Illness*. Cousins's work is based on the idea that the mind and body are a single entity; positive change in one, for example, in the body by the use of pharmaceuticals such as vitamin C, or in the mind by mood elevation through laughter, can lead to healing.

A related movement for well-being, laughter yoga, was begun in India in the mid-1990s by a physician, Madan Kataria. Today, laughter yoga numbers thousands of laughter clubs throughout the world devoted to enhancing health by "laughing for no reason." Research on happiness, laughter, and health continues. See, for example, the review paper by Bennett and Lengacher (2008) and Weil's work (2011). In one empirical study, Lockwood and Yoshimura (2014) found humour of help in social and psychological well-being during recovery from cardiovascular disease. Whether or not laughter heals, it undoubtedly contributes to well-being as the body heals. Strean (2009) says, after reviewing the relevant literature that a time may come when doctors recommend a period of perhaps 20 minutes of laughter per day in the same way that they recommend exercise and particular diets.

Illness as Secondary Gain

Sometimes illness has definite benefits. Do you remember the last time you were conveniently sick on the day of a big test for which you had not had time to prepare? Small children quickly learn to complain of sore tummies when they do not really feel like going to church, to school, or out to play. Illness may provide an opportunity or permit someone to behave in ways he or she would like to but otherwise would feel constrained from doing.

Or, illness may allow someone to meet needs that would otherwise go unmet. The benefits of illness are as varied as people's illnesses. To illustrate: Brett was a high school guidance counsellor

and history teacher who had also taken on the job of basketball coach and was supervising set building for the school play. Brett was married and had two preschool children in daycare while he and his wife Lucy worked. Lucy was required to do a great deal of travelling in her job as a buyer for a large department store. Brett was often responsible for driving the kids to and from daycare, as well as for feeding and bathing them. He hadn't expected so much responsibility; he had been raised to assume that his wife would handle the children, the house, the cooking, and most of their domestic life.

He felt trapped. On the one hand, he supported and applauded Lucy's success and realized that if she was really going to "make it" in her business of choice she would have to continue at her present pace for three or four years. On the other hand, he frequently felt overwhelmed by his responsibilities. The day his doctor diagnosed mononucleosis, Brett was secretly relieved. At least now he had a way out.

The question of **secondary gains** has been explained in a more systematic way in research on welfare mothers (Cole & Lejeune, 1972). In this case the focus was on whether and in what situations mothers on welfare would be likely to claim that they were ill. The researchers hypothesized that illness could be seen as a legitimation, or acceptable explanation, for failure. Being on welfare was thought by a substantial number of welfare recipients to be the result, and also a continual reminder, of a personal failure. This being the case, women on welfare would be likely to look for a rationalization and legitimation for their situation. Indeed, the researchers found that women on welfare who felt that they had little hope of changing their status were more likely to use illness as their explanation for being on welfare than women who hoped or expected to move off welfare. The point here is that sometimes claiming illness seems to be a better choice and to provide a greater level of reward than the other available options. In such a case illness can be thought of as providing secondary gains. Another postmodern version of this situation may be the claim of illness in order to get a day away from work or for some other personal advantage or just to use up the available sick leave. This strategy even has a popular name—"taking a mental health day."

Illness as Uncertainty

A major concomitant of disease in modern society is its chronic nature. People who live with chronic diseases live in a state of uncertainty and the possibility of or the belief that they are at risk. Because of the prevalence of disease remission or chronicity, some have said that we live in a remission society (Drew, 2003; Frank, 1997). This is a psychological place where people are perhaps better but never cured. You have probably heard the phrase "the five-year survival rate." Notions such as this reflect the fact that many people who have had a serious diagnosis or a problematic early detection pre-diagnosis indicator, say, an elevated level of PSA (prostate-specific antigen), understand what it means to live with uncertainty. McKenzie and Crouch (2004) investigated uncertainty in the lives of people living with cancer and found that the perception of being at risk can cause ongoing suffering and a feeling of emotional dissonance from "ordinary" others. The fear of a relapse, they argue, leads to a painful discordance or alienation from ordinary life as most people experience it. Living with uncertainty may be one of the most difficult aspects of the trajectory of this disease. L.E. Miller (2014) describes how seeking and managing information are ongoing, and comprise one of the basic aspects of coping with cancer that continue long after the end of active treatment.

More than 80 per cent of children diagnosed with cancer today survive the diseases and treatment. Drew (2003) investigated the narratives of long-term survivors of childhood cancer and noted how much work they had done to reconstruct or redefine themselves and imagine a personal future. To manage everyday uncertainty and lack of supportive networks, many people with a variety of diagnoses are turning to the Internet to offer and receive social support. There has been a great deal of research on illness experience using

these sorts of data (see, e.g., Seale, 2006; Pitts, 2004). The Internet (including blogs, listservs, chat rooms, and discussion groups) appears to be a very rich source of narratives about surviving and coping with all sorts of mental and physical illnesses and conditions. A quick look at the options that come up when I type into my browser suggests there are now online support groups for a wide variety of conditions. Included on the first page are groups for diabetes, Parkinson's, depression, anxiety, autism, Meniere's, Huntington's, heart disease, and others. Clearly, many people seek support in the wake of a diagnosis. In the case of chronic fatigue syndrome (CFS), a highly uncertain and even contested diagnosis (Bulow & Hyden, 2003), attempts to develop meaning, clarity, and certainty have even resulted in a school in Sweden for people with CFS to learn about what to expect from their illness.

Illness as a Message of the Body

At times, within the homeopathic perspective, illness is viewed as an expression of a unique person at a particular point in time and engaged in a special set of circumstances. Illness is also the expression of a whole person—body, mind, and soul. Illness and health are not polar opposites: both exist in a person continuously in a state of dynamic equilibrium. From this perspective symptoms are not signs of illness but indications that the person is responding to a challenge and is engaging in what is called a "healing crisis." The healing crisis (or the symptom) is a manifestation of what has been happening for a time but has been repressed and therefore unnoticed. Fever, rash, inflammation, coughing, crying, sleeplessness, and tension are revelations of a deep disturbance of the whole person. Such symptoms are valuable, however, because they allow the person to acknowledge the crisis and to seek help. The role of the healer is to support the person emotionally and spiritually and to enhance the natural recuperative powers of the physical body through the administration of minuscule amounts of natural medications that are known to create the symptoms the individual is presenting (see Chapter 13 for a more complete discussion of homeopathic and naturopathic medicine).

Illness as Communication

People communicate through words and by signs and by body language. People also send messages through the way their bodies are functioning. Illness sends a message that one part of the body is alienated from the "self." The body expresses the soul. Some even say that illness expresses the soul more impressively than health, in the same way that a good caricature expresses essential aspects of a personality more clearly than photographs taken in a studio situation (Siirla, 1981, p. 3). Ideas such as these may be considered relevant in integrative medicine, in complementary and alternative medicine, and in holistic medicine.

Through particular sets of symptoms or particular kinds of illnesses, people convey messages about themselves. A woman with breast cancer may be saying that her need and desire to nurture has been frustrated. Since the breast is important in mothering, feeding, and soothing, it becomes the most appropriate symbol for communication about frustrated nurturing. Thus, a person's needs may be expressed through illness. "If these [needs] cannot be expressed in a realistic, 'healthy' form, symbolic organ language takes over" (Siirla, 1981, p. 8).

In this view, different diseases express different frustrations. Rheumatism, a disability that affects the muscles and the joints, may express the frustration of a person who once liked to be very active, but who had to limit his or her activities and then developed joint pain, stiffness, and inflammation in the joints and muscles. Cold symptoms, such as runny nose and sneezing, may result from a frustrated desire to cry. All illnesses can be examined as attempts by the body to communicate when it is otherwise impossible. Here illness is viewed as an attempt to speak to the world about one's existential situation.

Illness as Metaphor

Related to the suggestion that illness is communication is the idea advanced by Susan Sontag that illness is metaphor. Illness communicates when it is taken to be conveying a particular message for a person at a special point in his or her life. Illness as metaphor reflects the idea that cultures bestow symbolic meanings on various illnesses. In Sontag's view metaphors are most likely to be related to illnesses that have no clear or obvious cause or treatment. The two examples that she examines in some depth in *Illness as Metaphor* (1978) are cancer in the twentieth century and tuberculosis in the nineteenth century. In 1988 she examined the metaphoric meanings of AIDS. Her basic argument is that the metaphors attached to diseases can be destructive and harmful. They frequently have punitive effects on the patient because they exaggerate, simplify, and stereotype the patient's experience. Metaphors may function as stigma or to reinforce stigma. They may serve to isolate the person with the disease from the community. Metaphors often imply adverse moral and psychological judgements about the ill person. They have perpetrated the view, for example, that cancer is a form of self-betrayal, a repression of the true desires of the person. A study of the portrayal of HIV/AIDS in popular magazines in 1991, 1996, and 2001 has shown how HIV/AIDS continued to be seen in the context of ongoing homophobia despite the ostensible focus in the Canadian and American media on transmission among heterosexual men, such as the former professional basketball star Magic Johnson. An ongoing emphasis polarized descriptions of the guilty victims as compared to the innocent victims of HIV/AIDS (Clarke, 2006). It is my impression, though, that with the spread of same-sex marriage and the declining levels of homophobia fuelled by the organizing and educating work within the LGBTQ and Pride movements, this bias is likely somewhat mitigated. Another study of the portrayal of HIV/AIDS in mainstream media is overdue.

A different study of magazines over the same time period (Clarke et al., 2007) found that most articles about heart disease were directed at men and depicted heart disease as if it were gendered. For men, heart disease was described as almost inevitable and as a badge of successful manhood. Its experience and treatment were described in terms both mechanical and aggressive, and its origin as the result of individual lifestyle choices that could be changed by the individual himself. In comparison, women's heart disease was portrayed as something of which to be ashamed, especially since diagnosis conflicts with the role of "caregiver." Women were described as ignorant, emotional victims with pathological bodies, especially after menopause. Depression, too, is associated with metaphors. In the eighteenth century, British writer Samuel Johnson called his depression "the black dog," as did British Prime Minister Winston Churchill in the twentieth century, and today the Black Dog Institute in Australia focuses on depression, and an award-winning crime novel about a detective suffering from depression is titled *Black Dog*. Sometimes, too, disease names are used as metaphors for something else. For example, we have all likely heard the phrase that terrorism is "the cancer of the nation." Schizophrenia, too, is sometimes used as a metaphor. For instance, "the weather is schizophrenic" was found in a study of metaphors in newspapers in the United Kingdom (Chopra & Doody, 2007).

Media Images of Cancer, Heart Disease, and AIDS

One study of the way cancer, heart disease, and AIDS have been portrayed in the mass print media illustrates how diseases come to have unique meanings, metaphors, and cultures associated with them. Disease is seen as much more than a mechanical failure—as a physiological pathology. This research is based on media that are now dated. Consider whether you think these images and metaphors have any currency today. Think, too, about movies and television shows you may have seen depicting people with different diseases. Can you offer any working hypotheses about media representations of cancer, heart disease, or HIV/AIDS currently? This study is presented for historical interest and to stimulate you to think about the ways in which the current portrayals of these diseases might be similar and/or different. Table 7.1 portrays the findings.

The moral worth of the person with cancer is attacked by the invasion of an evil predator so fearsome it is not even to be named, but fought as a powerful alien intruder that spreads secretly through the body. The person with cancer is not offered much hope of recovery. By and large, the media portrays cancer as associated with extremely nauseating chemotherapy, surgical mutilations, excruciating suffering, and finally death. To some extent the person with cancer is held to be blameworthy because the cancer could have been detected earlier through timely medical checkups that would have initiated early medical intervention such as mastectomy (breast removal) or would have prevented the disease through practising positive emotions (Ehrenreich, 2009). There is a great deal of uncertainty about the cause of cancer. There are numerous putative causes. They are usually described as the result of individual lifestyle decisions. Again, then, it is the individual who is ultimately culpable. It must be emphasized that the characteristics of the portrayal of cancer have changed to some extent and this change may be particularly evident in the portrayal of breast cancer. Cancer, though, is the classic disease for a remission society in that there is almost always a heightened chance of recurrence. Cure is described in terms of probability, usually as a cure rate within a particular number of years.

The media description is radically different when the disease is a heart attack. The heart attack is presented as an objective, morally neutral event that happens at a specific time and place and causes a great deal of pain. Heart disease is portrayed in optimistic terms. Not only are there very clear and precise steps to be taken to prevent it, but when it occurs it can be treated in a variety of mechanical ways, including using new technologies to replace parts of a malfunctioning cardiac system. Heart disease does not affect the whole person or the moral being of the person. It "attacks" one part only. Heart disease is an "outsider" that could be repelled through quick, decisive action and the use of medical marvels. The person with heart disease might have experienced acute fear and pain, but the period of recovery is likely to be dominated by

Table 7.1   Images of Cancer, Heart Disease, and AIDS

Cancer	Heart Disease	AIDS
Cancer is described as an evil, immoral predator.	Heart disease is described as a strong, active, painful attack.	Little is said about the nature of the disease; much is said about the moral worth of the victims of the disease.
Euphemisms such as "the Big C" are used rather than the word "cancer."	Heart disease, stroke, coronary/arterial occlusion, and all the various circulatory system diseases are usually called "the heart attack."	Acquired immune deficiency syndrome is called AIDS. The opportunistic diseases that attack the weakened immune system are often not mentioned.
Cancer is viewed as an enemy. Military imagery and tactics are associated with it.	The heart attack is described as a mechanical failure, treatable with available new technology and preventable with diet and other lifestyle changes.	AIDS is viewed as an overpowering enemy, as epidemic and as a scourge.
The whole self, particularly the emotional attitude of the person and the disease, is subject to discussion. Because the disease spreads and because the spread is often unnoticed through symptoms or medical checks, the body itself becomes a potential suspect.	It occurs in a particular organ that is indeed interchangeable with donor organs.	It is described as affecting the immune system and as resulting mostly from immoral behaviour and connotes "shameful sexual acts" and drug abuse (needle sharing).
Cancer is associated with hopelessness, fear, and death.	A degree of optimism prevails about the preventability and the treatability of the disease.	It is associated with fear, panic, and hysteria because it is contagious through body fluids, primarily blood and semen.
Prevention through early medical testing is advised.	The heart attack is described as very preventable. Suggestions for lifestyles that will prevent it are frequently publicized.	Prevention is advertised as possible through monogamous sexual behaviour or abstinence, and by avoidance of unsterilized needles and drug abuse.
There are innumerable potential causes listed. They range from sperm to foodstuffs to the sun.	There is a specific and limited list of putative causes offered again and again.	Initially the causes for AIDS were general: being homosexual, a drug user, or a Haitian.
There is little consideration of the socio-political or environmental causes, e.g., legislation that could limit smoking.	There is little mention of socio-political causes.	There is little mention of socio-political causes.
There is much uncertainty about cause.	There is certainty about cause.	There is uncertainty about cause.

optimism about a cure, replacement valves, pace-makers and other new technologies, and a resolve to (easily) change the lifestyle habits that led to the disease in the first place.

The person with AIDS is portrayed as a diseased person and as somewhat morally repugnant, a victim who is essentially powerless in the face of this scourge. He (usually a male in the developed world although equally male and female in the developing world) is described as hopelessly doomed and isolated from potentially significant sources of emotional support such as lovers and family members. The disease itself is described in biomedical terms. The media does not dwell on the painful or debilitating symptoms of the disease. They do not focus on the inevitable terminal stages of the disease, on death itself, or on the mortality rate. Rather, they focus on the fear of contagion and the uncertainty about the causes of contagion. The person afflicted with AIDS is stigmatized because of the connection with homosexuality or drug-taking. In addition, the perception of HIV/AIDS is somewhat racialized because of the media link made to Africa, where the incidence is so much higher and where the virus was known to have existed since the 1920s in non-human primate populations. The person with the disease is described as isolated and abandoned because people are afraid of the contagion that might result from being close. This fear of being close to the person with the disease affects not only the immediate friends and significant others of the person with AIDS, but also more distant others such as medical personnel. The media portrayal of HIV/AIDS today is considerably different because the causes and means of transmission are well known and pharmaceuticals have made HIV a fairly well-controlled chronic condition in Western society. As homophobia has decreased, so has the media stigma abated somewhat, especially in the North American context (see, for instance, follow-up articles by Clarke, 2006, and Clarke et al., 2006).

These images of cancer, heart disease, and AIDS were drawn from selected Canadian and American magazines—*Newsweek, Time, Mclean's, Good Housekeeping, Ladies' Home Journal, and Reader's Digest*—over a 20-year period. Think about whether this analysis fits your understanding of the mass print media stories that you have read on disease. These magazines were among the highest circulating magazines in North America. However, they are not the only magazines with a mass circulation available in North America. Furthermore, little research has been done on the impact of such media depictions on people in society.

Studies of the media portrayal of both prostate and testicular cancer have found them to be described as if they were "masculine" diseases, and descriptions of them are encapsulated in stereotypically masculine contexts such as sports, competition, money, and sexuality (Clarke, 1999; Clarke & Robinson, 1999). By contrast, breast cancer (although it also can occur in men) was described as a woman's disease and related to stereotypically female behaviours and attitudes, such as emotionality and a preoccupation with appearance (Clarke, 1999). Cancer in general is still widely associated with fear (Clarke & Everest, 2006).

Illness as Statistical Infrequency

From this point of view illness is a mathematically infrequent state of mental or physical malfunctioning. When a transient condition, no matter how uncomfortable, is prevalent among a group of people, it is usually not considered pathological. Illnesses such as the common cold and flu are so widespread as to be considered largely unimportant and have fewer research dollars allocated to investigating them. Still, the flu was associated with 35.5 million estimated cases, 16.5 million doctor visits, 490,561 hospitalizations, and 34,157 deaths during the flu season of 2018–19 in the United States alone (Centers for Disease Control and Prevention, 2020).

Illness as Sexual Politics

Many feminist thinkers have analyzed the ways in which disease can be seen as sexual politics. Reissman (1987) has written a theoretical/

empirical review of the medicalization of women's bodies and lives with a focus on medicalized child-birth, reproduction and contraception, premenstrual syndrome, "beauty," and mental health and illness. Currie and Raoul (1992) discuss "women's struggle for the body" in the face of culturally and historically entrenched bodily expectations and restrictions. From the feminist perspective the constraints and limitations of gender roles are associated with the conceptualization and the subsequent diagnosis of various diseases. For example, Ehrenreich and English (1978) document how the "mysterious epidemic" experienced in the nineteenth century by middle- and upper-class women was the outgrowth of the conditions that characterized their lives. The journals and diaries of women of the time give hundreds of examples of women whose lives wasted away into invalidism. The symptoms included headache, muscular aches, weakness, depression, menstrual difficulties, and indigestion. The diagnoses were many: "neurasthenia," "nervous prostration," "cardiac inadequacy," "dyspepsia," "rheumatism," and "hysteria." The diseases were not fatal. They frequently were treated with potions containing opium, which may have caused or exacerbated the symptoms. They usually lasted throughout a woman's life until her death. In the present day, several common diseases particularly reflect gender politics. For women, one of these is depression. Depression is associated with "just being a woman" and experiencing many of the stages that are a part of the lives of women. Take, for instance, those women's conditions relating to reproduction such as the menstrual cycle, pregnancy, and post-pregnancy. All of these have been accorded a new disease label in the DSM (*Diagnostic and Statistical Manual for Mental Disorders*). Post-pregnancy in particular has been **pathologized** (conceptualized as problematic and/or needing medical treatment) and is accorded new labels and new treatments. It seems that with the discovery of the SSRI anti-depressants the breadth of suffering related to just being a woman has grown exponentially along with extensive marketing. Another illness applied stereotypically to females is fibromyalgia, although it can

occur in men as well. Fibromyalgia is considered a woman's disease (Barker, 2005) and is thought to reflect something of the position of women in society. The lack of an effective pharmaceutical or other treatment may reflect gender politics as it determines the possible legitimacy of the contested illness (Barker, 2011).

A feminist analysis explains that these (popular) diseases in the past provided an appropriate role for women in the middle and upper classes. Many of these women were utterly dependent on their husbands, and their sole purpose in life was the provision of heirs. Household tasks were left to domestic servants. Hired help cared for children. The wife's job was to do precisely nothing—and thus to stand as a symbol to the world of her husband's financial success. Medical ideology buttressed this view of the appropriate role of middle-and upper-class women with the theory of the conservation of energy. This belief was that human beings had only a certain amount of energy available to spend over their lifetime. Since the primary functions of women of these classes were procreation and decoration, it behoved them to save all their vitality for childbearing and not to waste any in studying or in doing good works. Such activities would drain energy away from the uterus, where it was needed, into the brains and limbs, where it served no good purpose.

Contemporary feminists have suggested that the eating disorders bulimia and anorexia nervosa are logical expressions of women's role today (Currie, 1988). Eating disorders can best be understood, in this perspective, as the internalization of conflicts that result from the prevailing contradictory images of women. Anorexia is almost exclusively a disease of adolescent women, particularly those from middle- and upper-middle-class backgrounds, and occurs primarily in modern Western capitalist societies. Some have applied traditional Freudian psychoanalysis to these disorders and have attributed their causes to a fear of sexuality and an attempt to avoid the implications of their femininity. Others have explained the symptoms from a family systems perspective as a result of mothers who overprotect and over-identify with their daughters. Daughters differentiate from mothers and become separate individuals, in this perspective, by rebelling and refusing to eat. Several feminist authors have argued that eating disorders constitute a protest by women against the contradictory images of women as independent, competent wage earners and as sexual objects who earn only a portion of male salaries in work that is devalued precisely because it is work done by women (Currie, 1988).

During two discrete periods in the twentieth century—the 1920s and the 1980s and 1990s and into the twenty-first century—anorexia was a notable problem. During both of these periods, equality of opportunity for men and women was being stressed. These were times of expanded educational and employment options for women. They were also times of contradictions. In theory, choices for women were expanding; in practice, they were steered into certain occupations and earned only a fraction of men's incomes. Furthermore, women were and continue to be notoriously under-represented at all levels of the political process—municipally, provincially, and federally. Nor have their domestic responsibilities declined. Inadequately available and inaccessible child care coupled with excessive housekeeping and domestic responsibilities mean that women who work outside the home also have full-time jobs inside the home. Yet a woman's identity is still tied up with her appearance, and maintaining a suitable appearance takes a lot of work as well. In these circumstances eating disorders, as Orbach (1986) claimed, can be seen as a women's "hunger strike."

Illness as Aspiration

Aspirational postmodern uses of medicine enlist doctors and chemicals to make one "better" and "happier" through such interventions as cosmetic surgery to straighten the nose, enlarge or reduce the breasts, or reshape innumerable other aspects of the body (and psyche). Interventions such as surgery for physical changes may be augmented with pharmaceuticals for changes in moods or cognition. For instance, surgical sex changes may be accompanied by hormone treatments;

anti-depressants may be sought for happiness or for enhanced happiness (Elliott, 2003). In these cases, the idea is to use medicine not just to return the self to a "normal" or non-diseased state but to improve the body and the mind through the new technologies of medicine to reach a "new and better normal." Such medicine is transformative and not merely restorative. Even basic marks of identity can be changed. Faces can be "lifted" or even transplanted, as was done for a French woman, Isabelle Dinoire, who had been mauled in the face by her dog (Ansari, 2016). She said she had the surgery as she was desperately trying to save herself after she had tried to commit suicide. In this case the transplant was intended to repair injuries; but now that the technology has been tried and proven, can discretionary face transplants be far behind? Altering the face through a product such as Botox is already one of the most popular of cosmetic medical interventions. It is advertised on the highly respected Cleveland Clinic website as one of a number of "noon hour" procedures. The most popular cosmetic surgery in the United States is breast augmentation as women seek the perfect size, shape, and "perkiness." In 2017, 300,378 breast augmentations were done in that country (American Society of Plastic Surgeons, 2017).

Cosmetic surgery and other cosmetic medical enhancements are a significant component of medical care today. A whole new field of medicine called "anti-aging medicine" seeks to help people live longer and to look younger along the way. This is branded as a kind of clinical preventive medicine. One of the most popular cosmetic anti-aging interventions is "filler" of various kinds. The most widely known is Botox. It is used by people as young as their teens (American Society of Plastic Surgeons, 2017). The *Vancouver Sun* describes the case of a 25-year-old woman who, expressing the ease of use, calls herself "bo-jacked" (Reynolds, 2012). Although it is impossible to get exact numbers for all of the various types of cosmetic interventions, the point remains that a new kind of medicine and a new illness identity have arrived: aspirational health and aesthetics. See, for example, the website for the American Academy of

Anti-Aging Medicine for much more information about this phenomenon.

Illness as Potential or Patient-in-Waiting

The idea of illness as potential is perhaps best understood today in the context of the notion of the risk society where risk is seen as a ubiquitous, inevitable, and increasing consequence of modern life with its reliance on science and technology (Beck, 1992; Giddens, 1999). Consequently, we live in a state of uncertainty about all of the ways we, and our loved ones, can come to harm, be sickened, and experience accidents and violence. The underlying issue is that uncertainty and ongoing anxiety have become expected in the consciousness of the modern person (Horwitz, 2013). Major accidents, even nuclear accidents, according to Perrow (1999), are considered "normal." They are anticipated, at some time or another. Medical error is so common that numerous studies and policies and news reports are directed to understanding and preventing it (see Schwappach, 2010, for one example of this type of work written by one of the foremost researchers in the area of medical error). Medical error is thought to be the third highest cause of death (Makary & Daniel, 2016). Hospitalization is considered to have its own dangers and hospitals are thought to be unsafe places. They may generate their own set of diseases, as when a patient admitted for a fracture from a fall catches hepatitis B on the ward. "Iatrogenic illness" is illness that is inadvertent. It is caused by side effects or as an after-effect of medical treatment. Furthermore, interactions of patients with one another or with doctors and other health-care workers can sometimes cause psychosocial harm. Thus, engagement with the medical care system is known to present its own set of potentialities for illness.

In these contexts illness is an ongoing risk or possibility. Health promotion advertisements and media stories surround us. We are told to watch out for numerous potential dangers in our food, water, environment, pleasure pastimes, and so on. In a sense, everything about modern life brings with it a risk of illness or accident (see the journal *Health,*

Risk & Society, which covers this topic from various perspectives). Now, however, we are adding to the notion of the uncertainties of chronic illness a new idea, which is living with uncertainty without illness but under the ever-present possibility of succumbing to one disease or another. Consider, for example, the level of concern in the media, in the global economy, and among the public when a new coronavirus began to spread from China to other countries in early 2020, which led to stigmatizing anti-Chinese attitudes among some segments of national populations. The potential for illness also dogs us in another way in this Internet age. No sooner does a person think of a possible "symptom" than he or she can look it up on the Internet and find it is part of a syndrome or a disease that may need treatment. There was a time when interns were "expected" to develop the symptoms of one disease after another as they studied them in medical school and then saw them in patients. With millions of health/medical sites and as the widespread use of these sites has expanded, the potential for perceived and potential illnesses in the people who consult them has grown exponentially.

Medical and genetic advances have also altered the landscape of illness and disease. There is a new category of patient—the patient-in-waiting. It is now possible to know definitely that a person will be diagnosed with a disease. Huntington's disease, for example, is a very serious genetic disease with physical and mental health components. This genetic disorder doesn't usually begin until a person turns 40 and beyond. Offspring of someone with Huntington's have a 50 per cent chance of being diagnosed. However, one can have a genetic test that will tell whether or not the person will be diagnosed. Until the disease processes become overt, the person is a "patient-in-waiting" (Timmermans & Buchbinder, 2010).

Illness Candidates

From a slightly different perspective—that of outsiders to illness—it appears that people have ideas about what sorts of people are likely to succumb to what sorts of diseases. This tendency to assign the likelihood of a personality or type of person being diagnosed with a particular type of disease has been called lay epidemiology. Lay epidemiology may be an aspect of making sense of who gets ill and who doesn't. It is a way to cope psychologically with uncertainty. "Using explanatory models allows individuals to account for, and make sense of, poor health" (MacDonald et al., 2013, p. 575). You may have engaged in lay epidemiology if you spotted a person who smelled as if he/she had been smoking and immediately thought of lung cancer. Or perhaps you have thought of the highly tanned person as a candidate for skin cancer. The widely accepted and stereotypical coronary candidate is the middle-aged overweight man. One of the problems with lay epidemiology is that it may lead people who fit outside the cultural mould for candidacy to neglect signs and symptoms of disease because their personal characteristics don't seem to fit. One example is the case of Kerri Lee Brown, a 39-year-old woman who was a health and wellness journalist and editor of the fitness magazine *Oxygen*. Although her symptoms of pain in her arm (although as she says, it was her right arm) and utter exhaustion were very severe, she failed to go to the emergency room or her doctor for medical tests because she thought of herself as an unlikely candidate for a heart attack or any other serious diagnosis. Eventually, though, when Brown sought help, tests indicated that she had already had a heart attack. Consequently, she has changed her lifestyle and is aware that she has ongoing risk factors. She says, "Even today, I still can't believe what's happened, it's been such a huge wake-up call" (Brown, 2013, p. 150). In a different example but one that reflects the same processes at work, men with breast cancer are diagnosed at later stages than women because they tend to explain away the symptoms. This neglect can lead to a poorer prognosis (Block & Muradali, 2013).

Illness Survivors

The concept of "survivors" refers to the fact that many diseases are considered not ultimately curable but only in remission. In a remission society some people—for example, those who have once received a cancer diagnosis—can be treated and can live as though they are well, all the while knowing they are at a heightened risk for a return of the disease. The possibility that surviving childhood cancer may lead to a new kind of diagnosis is exemplified by the survivors' clinics at and near major cancer hospitals around North America and in the Western world. Considerable research is conducted on the probability of surviving various types of childhood cancer and for how long (see, e.g., Mariotto et al., 2009).

The next section of this chapter moves from a consideration of models of illness in contemporary society to some empirical analyses of the experience of illness from the perspective of the subject.

The Insider's View: How Illness Is Experienced and Managed

Many sociological analyses of illness have treated it as an objective phenomenon measured by questionnaires and by biophysical or clinical tests. From this perspective the varieties of personal experiences are irrelevant. What matters is the explanation of the incidence and prevalence of various types of disease. However, in keeping with the arguments and traditions noted in the work of people such as Weber, Husserl, Schutz, Blumer, Mead, Cooley, Simmel, Garfinkel, Goffman, and other interpretive and social constructionist thinkers, some researchers have turned their attention to the symbolic meanings and the social constructions of illness in the context of people's everyday experiences. These researchers focus on analysis of the experiences of illness at the individual level. It must be emphasized, however, that individual attitudes must always be set in a social context at a particular place and at a particular point in time.

Analyzing illness at the individual level has a long and noteworthy tradition in the sociology of medicine and the sociology of health and illness. One of the first published studies, mentioned earlier, was that of Mark Zborowski (1952, 1969), who compared the understandings and meanings of pain among Jewish, Italian, and "Old American" ethnic groups in New York City. Erving Goffman's *Asylums* (1961) described the experience of hospitalization from the perspectives of the mental patients or inmates and from that of the staff. Later, Goffman (1963) examined stigma associated with illnesses and other "unusual or abnormal" conditions.

Roth (1963) describes his own experience of hospitalization for tuberculosis. Myra Bluebond-Langer (1978) describes the world of children dying of leukemia and the experiences of their parents, their nurses, and their doctors. Her work is particularly instructive in illustrating the control and spread of information. Bluebond-Langer documents the children's extensive, detailed knowledge of their conditions, the next stages in their diseases, the probable side effects of various medications, and which medications they were likely to be given, even when parents and hospital staff would attempt to shield them from this information. David Karp, a sociologist who experienced serious depression and published several books based on interviews with others as well as on his own experiences, is another scholar to whom one can turn to learn about this "insiders' perspective" more fully (see, e.g., Karp, 1996). Sorrel King (2009) has written a book about how her daughter Josie died as the result of medical errors. She also documents her powerful reaction, and her founding of an advocacy organization, the Josie King Foundation, dedicated to eliminating medical error in the United States.

Sociologists have turned to narrative descriptions of illness experience, including emotional experiences. Marianne Paget, a sociologist whose work was the study of medical error, was coincidently the subject of medical errors. The series of errors made by different physicians was ultimately responsible for her death. Before she died, however, she wrote of her experience in *A Complex Sorrow*, which includes a play text. As she says:

> It was while attending the first trial [for medical negligence/malpractice] in late 1987 that I began to experience back pain. Eight months later, I

learned I had cancer. Almost simultaneously, I learned that the errors made in my diagnosis had jeopardized my life. I was told that my condition was incurable. (Paget, 1993, p. 5–6)

Such interpretive and **phenomenological** writing is becoming more frequent in a postmodern sociology of the body, emotion, and health and illness, but it represents a significant and reflexive move from studying others' meanings to studying one's own, as Arthur W. Frank does so compellingly in *At the Will of the Body: Reflections on Illness* (2002).

Strauss and Glaser (1975) studied the impact of a number of different chronic illnesses and noted that people with such illnesses and their family members had to face a variety of common concerns. Although the study is dated it remains relevant today. Strauss and Glaser distinguished all of the following issues that had to be managed: (1) preventing and managing medical crises; (2) managing medical regimens (taking medications, administering needles, physiotherapeutic exercises); (3) controlling symptoms and preventing symptom eruption; (4) organizing and scheduling time (including necessary rests and treatments) efficiently; (5) preventing or coping with social isolation; (6) dealing with uncertainty and adjusting to changes during the course of the disease; (7) normalizing social and interpersonal relationships; (8) managing stigma; and (9) managing knowledge and information. Each of these will be discussed in turn.

Crisis management requires constant vigilance on the part of the ill person and those who are taking care of him or her. A diabetic, for instance, must continually monitor blood-sugar levels and weigh and measure food intake and insulin levels. Such monitoring may not be completely accurate, nor are the results entirely predictable. A serious reaction to an imbalance may be infrequent, but it is a constant possibility.

Managing medical regimens is often a complex matter. The physician tells the patient to take a certain number of pills or to have injections at certain intervals. The patient often adapts and adjusts the quantity or frequency to a level at which he or she feels comfortable. Most medications have side effects. The patient must learn to balance the need for the medication with the need to be free of side effects.

The control of symptoms is a related issue. This involves managing the medical regimen daily, hourly, or even more frequently so that a crisis does not erupt. It also involves taking enough medication to prevent a crisis but not enough to cause intolerable side effects. Minor symptoms may lead to changing some habits; major symptoms may require major lifestyle changes.

Organizing and scheduling time can be important in many chronic diseases because available time is almost always limited. Time is needed to manage the required medications, to visit doctors and hospital, to change clothes or apparatus, to cope with restrictions, to be able to move about, and so on. Often the symptoms, too, such as migraine headaches and herniated disk backaches, require that the ill person drop the daily routine in order to go to bed to cope with the pain.

Preventing or coping with isolation and trying to maintain social relationships when the person can no longer do what "normal" people do is another never-ending struggle. Sometimes people restrict their friendships to others who have the same problem and, therefore, understand. The ubiquity of self-help groups for most chronic diseases attests to the importance of social relationships with similarly disabled people, and perhaps, also, to the isolation felt by these people.

Another underlying experience that seems to be common among people with a variety of chronic illnesses is *uncertainty*, which affects every stage of illness, beginning with the diagnosis and ending with cure, confirmation that the illness is chronic, or death. Most chronic illnesses have variable and unpredictable prognoses. Cancer is perhaps the archetypal disease of uncertainty. Its very cure is measured by the diminishing probability of recurrence one, two, three, or more years after the initial diagnosis and treatment. As noted above, uncertainty is an almost inevitable aspect of living in the risk society—but it is exaggerated after a serious diagnosis.

Uncertainty also prevails during the stages of treatment, of spread of the disease, and of resurgence or remission. Under such circumstances, it is difficult to *normalize social relationships*—to make plans for the future, to be considered and consider oneself a reliable friend, companion, spouse, parent, or worker when faced with a disease with an unknown prognosis.

People who have once experienced a heart attack may distrust their bodies for a long time. They may avoid work and exercise and radically alter their lifestyle. They may feel unable to count on being alive in six months or a year. Because a heart attack frequently occurs without warning, those who have had a heart attack may lose the ability to take their bodies for granted. Yet this ability is often the prerequisite for life satisfaction.

Managing stigma is another issue the chronically ill must face. The sociological use of the term "stigma" originated with the work of Goffman (1963), who examined varieties of social interactions that were impaired by people's identity problems. Goffman designated a stigma as an attribution that discredits the value of a person. Goffman distinguished between the effects of stigma that are known only to the person involved and those that are known to others, and analyzed various strategies designed to handle the stigma in each case. The discredited person, whose deviant stigma is known to others, is challenged to "manage impressions" when interacting with others in order to maintain acceptable relationships. The discreditable person whose stigma is not known has another problem to contend with: he or she must manage information to hide the stigma and prevent others from discovering it. Many chronic illnesses carry stigma that can radically affect both the sense of self-identity and interpersonal relationships because, as Cooley has said, the way that we see ourselves is related to (1) our imagined idea of how we appear to others, (2) our imagined understanding of how others view us, and (3) our resultant feelings of pride or mortification. Even cities can experience disease-based stigma, as with the SARS outbreak in Toronto in 2003. For a period of time people were warned by the World Health Organization to avoid the city. Toronto lost millions in tourist dollars. Chinese restaurants were stigmatized because the disease originated in China and subsequently lost customers and money. Some Torontonians and visitors stayed away, fearing transmission of the virus because of its (relatively) high incidence in China and the presence of visitors from China in Toronto's Chinese districts.

Schneider and Conrad (1983) emphasize the importance of the stigma of another disease—epilepsy. Epilepsy may imply disgrace and shame. Borrowing a term originally used by the homosexual subculture, people with epilepsy are living "in the closet." This means that, like gays and lesbians, those with epilepsy frequently have tried to manage their perceptions of being different by isolation and concealment. "Coming out of the closet" is a political move by gays and lesbians intended to end their shame and isolation, and to empower and to instil pride in people who formerly have felt stigmatized. People with epilepsy and their families have evolved a number of techniques designed to manage information about epilepsy and to come out of the closet. Rather than being entirely closet-bound, people with epilepsy go in and out through a "revolving door" (Schneider & Conrad, 1983, p. 115). Some people can be told, others not. Some can be told at one time but not at another. People with epilepsy have been denied drivers' licences, jobs, and even housing. Some people with the disease, therefore, have learned to hide their diagnosis when filling out application forms or applying for jobs, or when first meeting new people. Managing the anxiety that surrounds the concern about when and whom to tell is an ongoing problem.

People with epilepsy have also developed ways of telling—as therapy and as prevention. Sometimes telling others from whom the epilepsy has been kept secret has therapeutic consequences. It can be cathartic, for example, when a person has kept up a close friendship over a period of time, all the while keeping the truth of epilepsy secret. Telling can also serve preventive purposes. Sometimes this occurs when epileptics believe it likely that others will witness their seizures. They may hope that the knowledge that the seizure is due to a defined medical problem and that there are clear ways to deal with it will prevent other people from being frightened.

People with epilepsy have frequently said that these negative social attributions were often more difficult to manage than the disease itself. A superlative account of the processes through which mutual denial of a stigmatized disease is maintained on a verbal level is found in the work of Bluebond-Langer (1978) on children with terminal leukemia. She devotes considerable detail to documenting how doctors, nurses, and parents practised mutual "pretense" to provide the "morale" for the continuation of hope through often painful and debilitating treatments. Although they all knew the children were dying, they all agreed not to acknowledge this fact. Meanwhile, the children knew in astonishing detail how long they were likely to live.

There are times when the lack of evidence that a disease exists elicits negative attributions. People with psychosomatic illness may be viewed as malingerers. Because the symptoms of multiple sclerosis can grow and then regress, people with this disease may not seem ill, and friends and acquaintances may complain that they are poor sports or "just psychosomatically" ill. As one sufferer put it: "Knowing that I did have the disease was a great relief, but despite this I could not really believe it for some years to come. Other people could see nothing wrong with me and I feared that they regarded me as a malingerer" (Burnfield, 1977, p. 435).

Managing knowledge and information about the disease and its probable course and effects is crucial in the successful adaptation to chronic illness. In *Having Epilepsy*, Schneider and Conrad document the ways in which knowledge is a scarce and valuable resource in coping with epilepsy. Frequently, children with a diagnosis of epilepsy are kept in the dark about the name of the disease, about its duration, and about how to manage it. Often, parents are "shocked, embarrassed, fearful, and ashamed" that their children have epilepsy, or they are afraid that their child will be ostracized when the diagnosis is made known. Hiding it from the child, according to Schneider and Conrad's findings, is often a source of resentment in the child and leads to greater disability and dependence in the future. As one woman said, talking of her parents, "I mean, they, the fact that they had never told me and couldn't cope with me, I felt was a total rejection of a child by that parent" (Schneider & Conrad, 1983, pp. 86–8).

Two other paths in the work on the experience of chronic illness need to be highlighted. The first is the work of Corbin and Strauss (1987) on the BBC chain and the second is the work of Charmaz (1987) on the struggle for the self. Each brings to the literature a fresh focus on understanding the experiences of chronic illness. Corbin and Strauss consider that the essential social components of this experience involve what they call the **BBC chain**—*bibliography, body,* and *self-conception.* By this, they point out that all who suffer from chronic illness are confronted, through their bodies (and their illness-related constraints, pains, freedoms, change, and so on), with challenges to self-concepts and to personal biography (i.e., the detailed story that the individual tells oneself about his or her life). The point here is that as the body is changed, so, too, are integral parts of the person—the self and the self-story in historical and future context.

Charmaz focuses on one aspect of the chain: the self. She argues that when individuals live with the ambiguities of chronic illness they develop preferred identities that "symbolize assumptions, hopes, desires and plans for the future now unrealized" (1987, p. 284). Moreover, coping with or managing chronic illness requires a balancing of identities and abilities through what Charmaz thinks of as a hierarchy of preferences. In her studies of people with various types of chronic illness she observed a tendency for people to have a hierarchy of preferences (or levels) for identity. In particular, she suggested a hierarchy beginning with, as a first choice, a "supernormal" identity and ending with, as last choice, a "salvaged" identity.

The focus on the self has also been described by Arthur Frank (1993). His work is based on his analysis of published, book-length illness narratives. His research uncovered three typical change narratives: (1) the rediscovery of the self who has always been; (2) the radical new self who is in the process of becoming; and (3) the no-new-self assertion. Frank, a sociologist who survived two very serious illnesses in his late thirties, a heart attack and then cancer, has written an insightful book about his illness experiences (1991). He has done so from his point of view as a sociologist, and the book is a wealth of sociological theorizing based on bodily and health-related experience.

Summary

1. Disease is an abnormality, diagnosed by a doctor, in the structure and function of body organs and systems. Illness is the personal experience of one who has been diagnosed by a doctor or who does not feel well; it involves changes in states of being and in social function. Sickness is the social actions or roles taken up by individuals who experience illness or are diagnosed with a disease. All are socially mediated.

2. The cultural and popular meanings of illness in contemporary society are widely varied.

3. Cosmetic pharmacology is sometimes used for mental health issues.

4. Life experiences of individuals as they encounter illness and responses to their illness, such as stigma, are of interest to sociologists.

5. Uncertainty is another central experience among the ill.

6. Managing medical regimens is another issue for those who are chronically ill.

7. The media, including the Internet, are essential in understanding illness experiences today.

Key Terms

aspirational health
BBC chain
disease

illness
illness candidate
pathologized

patient-in-waiting
phenomenological
secondary gains

sickness
survivor

Questions for Study and Discussion

1. Describe a situation in which you experienced illness, sickness, and/or disease and consider the tensions among the three aspects of the experience.
2. Provide examples of five of the several popular conceptions of illness.
3. Examine a popular magazine for discussions of illness, disease, and sickness. What images of diseases are evident?
4. What is your ethical stance on cosmetic pharmacology for mood improvement?
5. Look for 10 websites on a disease or cause of death and disability of interest to you. What meanings are assumed and portrayed?

6. Do you think the images of heart disease, cancer, and AIDS described in the research discussed in the chapter are still relevant today? What might be the relevance of the portrayal of disease, illness, or sickness for the individual and family experience of the disease?
7. Do you suffer from or do you know anyone who has an addiction to opioids? Do the challenges articulated in this and previous chapters reflect your understanding of the experiences that you or this other person have?

Suggested Readings

Allen, S. (2018). *A kind of mirraculas paradise: A true story about schizophrenia.* Simon & Schuster. A story based on the words of a person with schizophrenia about his experiences. This is edited by the niece of the person with psychosis so as to maintain the stream-of-consciousness style.

Best, R.K. (2019). *Common enemies: Disease campaigns in America.* Oxford University Press. The socio-cultural and political-economic factors in various historical campaigns against disease that examines how disease meanings and threats change over time.

Ehrenreich, B. (2009). *Bright-sided: How positive thinking is undermining America.* Metropolitan Books. Critical analysis of the negative effects of the culture of optimism.

Geise, R. (2013, Mar.). The mainstreaming of mental health. *The Walrus*, 30–9. A brief critical commentary on the notion of mental health.

Horwitz, A.V., & Wakefield, J.C. (2012). *All we have to fear: Psychiatry's transformation of natural anxieties into mental disorders.* Oxford University Press. A book about the expansion of and meanings of "anxiety."

Kalanithi, P. (2016). *When breath becomes air.* Random House. This book describes the experience of a 36-year-old neurosurgeon diagnosed with a terminal illness, who contemplates the meaning of life as he faces his death.

Klawiter, M. (2004). Breast cancer in two regimes: The impact of social movements on illness experience. *Sociology of Health and Illness, 26* (6), 845–74. Illustrations of the experience of breast cancer in two different time periods.

Part III

Sociology of Medicine

The next eight chapters consider issues in the sociology of medicine. Rather than investigating and discussing the causes of death and disease, how they vary across different parts of the social structure, by social-psychological proclivity, or the experiences of sickness, illness, and disease, as has been done in the previous chapters, here we examine the ways that medical practitioners and scientists define illness and sickness as disease and how medical services are organized around those definitions. It needs to be understood that the definitions, the knowledges, and the discourses of the medical profession and related social forces are also imbricated in the everyday understandings of all of the various others outside of medical functionaries. Thus, what you and I think of as illness and wellness are in large part determined by the medical discourses developed by various medical and health experts. This is not just medicine from above or from below but medicine as it is internalized and made normative in our everyday world. This is the working of power/knowledge in our daily lives within the realms of medical diagnoses and care. In the next chapters we will also look at the medical care system in Canada, with a focus on doctors, nurses, complementary and alternative health-care provision, and the pharmaceutical industry. We finish this section with a critical examination of the impact of globalization on health and medical care around the world.

Chapter 8 highlights the social construction of medical knowledge. Starting from the premise that all we know, understand, and believe about the world is related to the social-structural and cultural environments in which we grow up and live and the relevant circulating discourses, the chapter analyzes how medical knowledge is related to the historical, social, cultural, and structural backgrounds of physicians and research scientists, as well as to the social organizations of which they, and all of us, are a part. This chapter also examines briefly how the social characteristics of patients affect the diagnostics and decisions of doctors. It demonstrates that medical treatment is not an objective higher order of reality that stands above the real-world machinations of human beings; rather, it is entirely integrated into that world and is socially constructed through circulating discourses.

Chapter 9 is a historical overview of the place of medicine as a world view and practice of relevance to human social behaviour. It also looks at some of the processes of medicalization through which the medical profession gained the power to define an increasing amount of human behaviour as within its realm of responsibility for diagnosis and treatment. The ways in which the doctor can be seen as a moral entrepreneur are discussed. The powerful forces of biomedicalization fuelled by technological change, pharmaceutical and other related major industries, and strong advocacy organizations of citizens are described. The Internet search capacity, social media, and e-medicine accelerate all these processes. Chapter 10 also takes a historical approach, examining the history, origins, and some of the current issues facing the Canadian medical care system. Some of the impacts of this system on the work of the doctor, on the disease profiles of the population, and on death rates are considered. Chapter 11 looks at allopathic medical practice as a profession. It discusses medical education in the past and today. Medical mistakes and how they are handled, malpractice, medical markets, and medical subcultures are discussed.

The next three chapters examine participants other than doctors who are involved in providing health care. Chapter 12 looks at the history and the work of nurses and midwives in their social contexts. It also examines some of the challenges currently facing nurses and midwives in their practice in Canada today. Chapter 13 briefly describes and analyzes the growing importance of various complementary and alternative practices related to health and health care. It describes in somewhat more detail the philosophies and work practices of chiropractors and naturopathic doctors. Where Chapter 13 explores some of the medical practices on the "periphery" of organized health care in Western society, Chapter 14 describes and critically analyzes activity at the "core" of Western allopathic practice—the medical-industrial complex, a significant reason why medical costs have continued to soar in Canada, the United States, and throughout the Western world. The chapter pays particular attention to the pharmaceutical industry, the major industry in this complex about which there is a growing body of research.

Finally, Chapter 15 looks at health care from an international perspective, with a focus on the work of the World Health Organization and extensive case studies of the health systems of the United Kingdom (a national universal system paid for out of the public purse), the United States (a primarily private, insurance-based system), and Brazil (a constitutionally established public system that could continue to extend its coverage and become akin to the British system or could veer towards the private-pay system of the US). In addition, the critical impacts of the economic and political forces of globalization are considered as they relate to the attempts to provide equitable health care in South Africa and to the global coronavirus pandemic of 2020.

Part III covers some of the subject matter traditionally studied in a course in the sociology of medicine. However, it discusses neither hospital structures and functioning nor the place of hospitals in society today. This is just one of the enormously important topics regarding health care that we have had to leave out. This is largely because much more sociological research on these topics needs to be undertaken in Canada and elsewhere.

The Social Construction of Scientific and Medical Knowledge and Medical Practice

8

Chapter Overview

- Both medical practice and scientific knowledge are products of the societies in which they occur. They also are affected by history, economics, politics, and numerous other social forces.
- The modern and Western medical model of disease is only one of many possible ways of understanding the attitudes and behaviours that are labelled as "disease."
- The medical model encompasses a number of value judgements. There is a gap between scientific values and the work of science and that of the doctor.
- Technology has powerful impacts and has the capacity to change other aspects of social

life experience and identities. Technological discoveries often result in social and practice changes, even before their medium- and longer-term consequences are fully understood.

- Medical science and practice are infused with cultural understandings, biases, and stigmas, such as those pertaining to gender role stereotypes.
- Medical knowledge is accepted and rejected by different parts of the population at different times.
- Doctor–patient communication reflects broader social structure and cultural issues.

Introduction: The Sociology of Medical Knowledge

Is scientific knowledge universally true? Is scientific knowledge objective? Medical knowledge is based on science, but is influenced also by human, cultural, and social factors. This complex of considerations makes choosing among possible diagnoses and treatments complicated for patients and for medical practitioners. For example, after a cancer diagnosis, patients, at times, along with their doctors, have to decide whether to use chemotherapy and/or radiation or to do visualization, botanicals, immunotherapy, or something else. The evidence as to which approach is the best, when, why, and how, may be confusing and contradictory. Within medicine, debates prevail about the "reality" of some diseases such as chronic fatigue syndrome, which some people believe is just "yuppie flu" experienced only by spoiled middle-class and upper-middle-class women. In the next chapters of the book, we discuss questions such as the following: Do allopathic doctors have a "better" theory of medicine than chiropractic or naturopathic doctors? Does the introduction of a new technology, for example, pharmaceuticals, the CAT scanner, or MRI equipment, occur as the logical final stage of a process of rational decision-making, including cost–benefit analysis and an evaluation of the efficacy and efficiency of the new technology? Or are such decisions influenced by, among other things, the profit motive? Do medical science and practice reflect problematic cultural attitudes, such as racism, sexism, and homophobia, or are they a neutral and dispassionate endeavour?

This chapter will investigate the sociology of medical science and medical practice. To say that there is a sociology of medical science is to say that it is reasonable to examine how medical and scientific knowledge are discourses that can be seen as determined, created, and constructed by social conditions. Medical ideas result from the productive link between power and knowledge. It is worthwhile exploring how medical science affects or constructs social conditions and how the social and the scientific/medical worlds are frequently mutually reinforcing. Moreover, in the tradition of conflict theory, we can ask whose interests are served by a particular form of medical knowledge, organization, and practice. The symbolic meanings and constructions of medical science and practice are also relevant topics for discussion.

The argument of this chapter is as follows. "Science" is not perfectly objective and universally true. Science is produced by humans. It has resulted in "institutions" and discourses that have become embedded in wider social structures and maintained and resisted through processes of negotiation by some actors who live in a particular time (history) and place (culture, society, social strata) and by the associated disciplinary bodies of knowledge and practices. Medical practice is based on aspects of this socially constructed science and is also influenced by other social forces, such as the particular social characteristics of the medical care labour force and the socio-economic backgrounds from which the members of the labour force have been drawn and within which they continue to live at any given historical time period.

Medical and Scientific Knowledge: Historical and Cross-Cultural Context

Positivism, the model of science on which medicine is based, is described by attributes such as objectivity, precision, certainty (within a specific degree of error), generalizability, quantification, replication, and causality. Its search is for a series of law-like propositions designed to explain the operation of the body, the operation of medicine, the causes of disease, and the optimum methods of cure and management. These formal characteristics portray science as if it is superior to other ways of perceiving the human body in the world. Science, in this view, is outside of culture and social structure; therefore, the subjects of its study, the methods of studying human subjects, the findings from study and their interpretations, and the publication and dissemination of scientific knowledge should be objective and thus be true everywhere and at every time in history. Medicine and medical practice are similarly valorized. However, there are many reasons to challenge these assumptions.

A number of social theorists and researchers have demonstrated that beliefs regarding scientific objectivity are problematic. Kuhn (1962) has described the historical development of science and how the methods, assumptions, and even the very subject matter of science are infused with cultural categories. In *Madness and Civilization* (1964), an abridges translation of his 1961 doctoral thesis (the entire work, translated into English as *History of Madness*, appeared in 2006), Foucault describes the different understandings of and ways of "treating" those called "mad" in various societies over a long period of history. Freund, McGuire, and Podhurst (2003) have specified the value assumptions of contemporary medicine as mind–body dualism, physical reductionism, specific etiology, machine metaphor, and regimen and control.

Mind–body dualism is said to have begun with Descartes, the philosopher who effectively argued for the concept that "mind" or "spirit" is separate from the body. Descartes's writing and thinking became possible in a historical context of increasing secularization, which allowed for his belief in the separation of the body from the soul/mind. Not until Christian doctrine determined that the "soul" could be sent heavenward after death, without the body, could the notion of a non-spiritual human body following death make the cadaver "acceptable" for scientific investigation. Foucault (1973) describes the changes in the eighteenth and nineteenth centuries that allowed the physician to view the patient's body directly through the "clinical gaze," and not merely indirectly through the patient's verbal, subjective descriptions. Technological inventions such as the stethoscope gave physicians direct access to bodily functioning. With a stethoscope the doctor could observe, categorize, and understand the patient's body (or a part of the body) without the conscious awareness or involvement of the patient. Dissection of cadavers opened up a new world of speculation surrounding the patient and of medical language for description and explanation.

Such inventions further entrenched the distinction between the soul/mind and the body as they made the body a precisely describable and observable empirical entity.

Physical reductionism emphasizes the physically observable at the expense of other aspects of the individual, such as the subjectively experienced mental, sensual, and emotional. It also leads to a disregard for the social, political, and economic causes of ill health. The modern notion of the body as a group of potentially pathogenic organs made visible through technologies such as MRIs, CAT scans, and X-rays illustrates this reductionism.

René Dubos (1959) was the first to write that the **doctrine of specific etiology** is another characteristic of modern medical science. The primary assumption of this view is that each disease is thought to be the result of a particular pathogen or malfunction. It developed from the discoveries of nineteenth-century researchers such as Pasteur and Koch, who noted the specific effects of particular micro-organisms on the body. It has led to an exaggerated emphasis on the discovery of a "magic bullet" to cure one specific disease after another. Dubos notes that this emphasis is overly restrictive because it ignores the fact that the very same micro-organisms may assault any number of people but only a certain proportion of these people respond by becoming ill. It is also problematic because it has tended to ignore how a treatment for one disease may lead to side effects that may cause other diseases. It can also be associated with ignoring subjectively described symptoms such as fatigue (e.g., chronic fatigue syndrome) and pain (fibromyalgia) that lack "objective" medical measurement by available tools designed to see organ pathologies and whose symptoms may change frequently.

The **machine metaphor** for the body emphasizes discrete parts, such as individual organs, and their interrelationships with other discrete parts. This idea has led to medical specialization (e.g., cardiology, otolaryngology, urology, gynecology) and to highly skilled types of interventions such as the removal and replacement of parts of the body, including the heart, kidney, liver, blood, bone marrow, limbs, patches of skin, and even the face.

Finally, **regimen and control** are outgrowths of the machine metaphor. They assume that the body is to be dealt with, fixed, and continually improved. Not only strictly medical procedures but even health promotion policies imply that the body is perfectible and under the control of the individual through such actions as exercise and diet, and by maintaining healthy habits, such as not smoking and consuming alcohol only moderately. An emphasis on control through such things as the correct number and spacing of medical checkups, as well as the use of early detection technologies, reinforces this notion of the medically perfectible body. The burgeoning field of cosmetic surgery, discussed in Chapter 7, is just one significant outcome of this perspective. Stein has noted how Western, particularly American, medicine has adapted to such American cultural values. As he says:

> disease conceptualization and treatment are embedded in the value system of self-reliance, rugged individualism, independence, pragmatism, empiricism, atomism, privatism, emotional minimalism and a mechanistic metaphor of the body. (Stein, 1990, p. 21)

In an expanded analysis of the foundations of the medical model, Manning and Fabrega (1973) articulate the elements of what they call the biologistic view of the body. The biologistic view of the body includes the following tenets: first, organs and organ systems, and their specific functions, are identifiable and observable as discrete entities; second, the normal functioning of the body goes on pretty much the same for everybody unless disturbed by injury or illness; third, people's sensory experiences are universal; fourth, disease and experience of disease do not vary from one culture to another; fifth, boundaries between self and body and between self and others are obvious; sixth, death is the body's ceasing to function; and seventh, bodies should be seen objectively to be treated medically.

Sociological research provides critiques of all of these assumptions about science and medicine. First, few people today consider the mind/ body to be separate. Awareness of the possibilities of research on the body/mind connection is, in part, the result of the Eastern medical tradition including that mind and body are one. This has led to greater interest in meditation in Western countries, as well as the discovery that the brain is "plastic" (Doidge, 2007) and that neural pathways can be reconstructed following such injuries as stroke.

Second, it has become clear that much of the research on the "normal" person has been on the male-bodied person. Thus, less is known about the functioning of the female body (except her reproductive function) with respect to a whole range of disease categories including heart disease. As a result, medical findings cannot necessarily be generalized from one gender to another. They have to take into consideration the whole sexed body. This challenges both the notions of the body as mere machine and the doctrine of specific etiology. The body is not a mere machine: it is understood to be much more complex than that now.

Third, cross-cultural, anthropological, and linguistic studies have shown how people's bodily experiences can be articulated only from their available language. Fourth, cross-cultural research has shown that what is considered "disease" in one culture may be accepted as "normal" in another. Fifth, contagious diseases such as AIDS demonstrate anew that the boundaries between people are vulnerable. Thus regimen and control exceeds, at times, the boundaries of the body. Sixth, even the definition of "death" is now acknowledged to be very problematic (and not organ-specific) because of the possibility that, for instance, respirators and defibrillators can keep people alive even when they are "brain-dead." Seventh, bodies cannot be seen objectively and as only a system based on organs. That is an impossible value to achieve. The values implicit in the medical model and in the biologistic view of the body reflect particular cultural histories, biases, and predispositions. Medical science and practice are not objective, are not consistent across the discipline, and are not necessarily superior to other treatments and social practices.

Medical Science and Medical Practice: A Gap in Discourses

A significant gap frequently occurs between published biomedical research and the scientific treatments documented by such research and the actual daily practice of medicine (see Montini & Slobin, 1991). To try to minimize the distance between researcher and practitioner, the National Institutes of Health in the United States, through the Office of Medical Applications of Research, began in 1977 to convene Consensus Development Conferences (CDCs). The Canadian government and medical associations have a similar ongoing process for developing agreement between science and practice called evidence-based medicine or evidence-based practice. The Cochrane Collaboration is perhaps the best-known organization to provide systematic reviews of evidence about various medical issues. Medical practice is said to be guided today by what is termed evidence-based medicine (EBM).

The goal of EBM is to provide practitioners with information gleaned from scientific studies published in reputable journals and evaluated for quality. The goal of the Consensus Development Conferences was to bring together researchers, to inform practitioners of the latest scientific findings, to inform scientists of the practical issues facing practitioners, and to work towards the development of timely, national standards of practice. Unfortunately, a number of obstacles to the immediate integration of research findings into medical practice exist. Montini and Slobin have shown how various differences in the work cultures of clinicians and researchers may play a role in limiting their amalgamation. These limitations relate to distinct value differences between researchers and practitioners, including: (1) certainty versus uncertainty; (2) evolutionary time versus clinical timeliness; (3) aggregate measures versus individual prescriptions; (4) scientific objectivity versus clinical experience; and (5) constant change versus standards of treatment. We now examine each of these limitations in more detail.

(1) *Certainty versus uncertainty.* Doctors' work involves patients who want and need immediate and certain responses. Scientific work does not depend on or even expect *certainty*; rather, *probability* is the focus of laboratory science. Time-related concerns are considerably different in those two contexts. The practitioner needs at least enough certainty to make decisions about caring for a particular patient at a specific point in time. By contrast, the scientist works within a world of probabilities—thus, uncertainty—in a time frame determined by funding, the nature of the investigation, the parameters of the experimental paradigm, the intrinsic limitations of equipment, the training and abilities of the researcher, imperatives embedded in the research institution, and so on.

(2) *Evolutionary time versus clinical timeliness.* Science does not progress by proof so much as by failing to disprove. Caution is always implied in drawing conclusions. Scientific truth develops in incremental stages as more and more hypotheses are disconfirmed. However, the clinician must make timely decisions in response to the expressed and observed needs of individual patients.

(3) *Aggregate measures versus individual prescriptions.* While the scientist, in working with probabilities, deals in aggregates, the practitioner must deal with the suffering individual. Again, because of the immediacy of the sufferer, clinicians are forced to rely on what they are learning from their experience and are finding to be "tried and true" in their practice. They may be uneasy about relegating a given individual to a clinical trial or a new treatment, the outcome of which is unknown and will likely remain unknown for a considerable period of time. They may, for example, use medications "off-label" because of word of mouth of their colleagues.

(4) *Scientific objectivity versus clinical experience.* The scientist tries to control all variables in the interests of objective and generalizable findings. The clinician, in contrast, is faced with a unique individual reporting subjectively experienced symptoms that the clinician cannot control and needs to deal with immediately for the patient.

(5) *Constant change versus standards of treatment.* The researcher is aware of continuous change in research findings as new hypotheses are

put forward and supported or rejected. The clinician must practise medicine under the direction and with the support of practice standards but must also make assumptions that current knowledge is "good enough" and its implementation will be beneficial to the patient. The doctor has to assume that current treatments will be helpful and have a longer "shelf life" than frequently changing scientific hypotheses on the frontiers of medical developments.

The idea of **evidence-based medicine** (EBM) has been growing in influence in medical practice. Evidence-based medicine involves using statistical and other evaluative techniques for the meta-analysis of scientific literature related to all manner of potential medical diagnoses in order to inform continually the everyday practice of medicine. The goal is that a patient's care be based on the most up-to-date, valid, and reliable medical/scientific information, rather than on the practices long in use. Further, EBM assumes that the best evidence is gathered and assessed through systematic and thorough means. Doctors need up-to-date knowledge because textbooks quickly become outdated; experts may be wrong and medical journals too prolific to allow any individual practitioner to stay current. In addition, doctors often are rushed in their everyday work. Now, however, as a result of the Cochrane Collaboration, physicians can access timely reviews of the best evidence published in refereed scientific journals for many of the medical issues they face. In addition to the limitations itemized above there are many limitations to EBM including the fact that published research may not be actually representative of the best and most recent research, partly because of the time it takes to undertake and then publish research. Some populations are under-studied (e.g., women, racialized groups, and people sick with more than one disease concurrently). When researchers are funded by private corporations such as drug companies, published findings may be restricted (by the terms of the grant) to those who support the use of the intervention financed by the company in question (see, e.g., Olivieri, 2003). Furthermore, not all evidence is accessible because negative findings often are not publishable.

Medical Technology: The Technological Imperative

New medical technologies continue to be developed, manufactured, distributed, and employed. Among the new technologies are cardiac life-support, renal dialysis, nutritional support and hydration, mechanical ventilation, organ and stem cell transplantation and various other surgical procedures, pacemakers, chemotherapy, MRIs, CaT scans, and new, more powerful antibiotics. The question that we ask here is: What is the relationship between medical science and this evaluation process that culminates in the use of new technologies? Available evidence suggests that practitioners tend to adopt new technologies before they are evaluated and that they continue to use them after evaluation indicates they are ineffective or unsafe (Rachlis & Kushner, 1989, p. 186). The power of new technologies has been called the **technological imperative**. The numerous people who are made sick or who die as the result of the technological imperative can be found in the statistics for medical error in Canada and the United States. In Canada, the Canadian Institute for Health Information along with Statistics Canada reported that between 30,000 and 60,000 Canadians die annually from medical error (Finlay, 2016). Not all of these are the result of new technologies or of improperly used technologies, but some are. Drugs introduced into the market or that stay on the market despite accumulating negative evaluations are cases in point. For example, the acne drug Diane-35 (a hormone-secretion modifier designed for birth control) is said to have killed 11 Canadian women and to have caused serious and minor side effects in hundreds of others (Zlomislic & Teotonio, 2013), and the proliferation of opioids has resulted in many deaths and broken lives.

The adoption of new medical technologies is vulnerable to social variables related to four social forces (Butler, 1993): (1) key societal values, (2) federal government policies, (3) reimbursement strategies, and (4) economic incentives.

(1) Among key societal values, a number of social commentators have described the love affair of North Americans with new technology of all sorts. Enthusiastic optimism rather than realistic caution typifies our attitude to new technology. While we have yet to understand all of the possible constraints to freedom, privacy, and democracy created by the Internet, plus other threats that may easily result from global electronic communication, it already exists and is in widespread use. Some people are protesting that we don't yet know enough about the long-term effects of "wireless" technologies to use them as widely as we do, even among children in their schools. For example, the effects of the use of cell phones have not been precisely determined, but an extensive WHO review of studies reports evidence of increase in glioma (a malignant tumour that begins in the brain or spine) and schwannoma (acoustic neuroma), a non-malignant brain tumour (Dellorto, 2011). Is this a situation calling for the precautionary principle? The development of other new and related technologies often precedes considerations of and safeguards for possible deleterious health and social impacts.

(2) In the health area, the federal government, through such bodies as the Canadian Institutes of Health Research, the Heart and Stroke Foundation, and the National Cancer Institute of Canada, quietly funds biomedical research. Taxation policies, free-trade agreements, support for education and science, and other federal incentives encourage the discovery of new technologies. Our national medical care system fosters growth and expansion of the use of medical technologies immediately upon their development. However, such undertakings have not always proven desirable or fruitful. While Butler's study is based in the US, there is no reason to assume that Canadian legislation provides greater safeguards, and, in fact, available evidence indicates that in some situations, e.g., the thalidomide disaster of the 1950s and 1960s, Canadian regulation may be much poorer. Further, post-market surveillance of the effects of the introduction of new technologies in Canada is far from perfect (Fuller & Saibil, 2005). Chapter 14 considers this issue in more detail.

(3) and (4) While there are no definitive studies of the costs of new technology, a variety of studies taken together suggest that 20–50 per cent of the annual increases in health-care costs during the past 25 years or so are the result of progressive innovations in medical technology, including pharmaceuticals. In fact, the increase in the use and cost of pharmaceuticals is the driver of the increasing costs of medical care in Canada. A few new technologies appear to save lives and costs. Most new technologies are expensive and some may be ineffective or lead to negative side effects; however, they add costs to the medical care system whether or not they work. A great deal of controversy is expressed about the ethics of including cost-effectiveness in health-care provision; thus, this conversation has been less likely to occur in Canada (see, e.g., Donaldson & Dunfee, 2002). As long as the medical-industrial complex is even partly guided by privatization and the profit motive, the development and dissemination of medical technological innovations will result, in part, from market principles rather than from planned, rational, health-benefiting, and evaluated strategies for change. Consider this example: babies weighing as little as one pound can now be kept alive at a cost of, at times, millions of dollars per baby through neonatal intensive care for several months, and then continuing care for those babies and children who may have ongoing medical and other health, educational, and social needs. By contrast, a low-technology approach to preventing low-birth-weight babies that would include feeding pregnant women nutritious diets and maintaining minimal equitable socio-economic standards—via, for instance, a guaranteed annual wage for all—is a much more cost-effective and efficient strategy for a healthy citizenry—but this prenatal support has yet to be implemented.

An example of the tendency to first adopt new technologies and evaluate them later is electronic fetal monitoring. Designed for use with high-risk births, the fetal monitor was to provide doctors with information regarding the health of the fetus during labour. If a fetus showed dangerous vital signs the physician could actively intervene in the labour process by, for example, performing a Caesarean section. Electronic fetal monitoring (EFM) was initially made available in the 1960s. By the 1970s EFM and ultrasound were widely available in most hospitals. By the 1980s, 30 per cent of all obstetricians had EFM in their offices to detect prenatal problems. Rapidly, EFM became a standard monitoring device, even for low-risk situations. Its widespread use was associated with an increase in the diagnosis of prenatal problems. The Caesarean section rate, at 4.5 per cent of all births in 1965, rose to 16.5 per cent by 1980 and 24.7 per cent by 1988. In 2001–2, C-sections accounted for 22.5 per cent of all in-hospital deliveries in Canada. Studies of this phenomenon have found that the rate varies substantially by region, ethnicity, socio-economic status, and availability of insurance for payment. According to the Canadian Institute for Health Information, in 2010–11 the C-section rate for first-time C-section was 18.1 per cent and for subsequent births by C-section the rate was 82.3 per cent. Despite the variation in rates across the country and in different hospitals, it is clear that many think the rate is too high and potentially dangerous (Murphy, 2015). Caesarian sections are also at least twice the cost of a regular vaginal birth. In 2016–17, C-sections in Canada comprised 28.2 per cent of all births (Young, 2018). It must be noted that not all C-sections result from perceived prenatal problems. Some are necessary because of a previous C-section; some are elected by women who want to schedule their births; and some are the result of complications during labour that prevent women from being able to deliver vaginally.

Despite the rapid growth in the use of electronic fetal monitoring, randomized, controlled trials undertaken since 1976 have failed to demonstrate benefits of EFM in comparison with simpler methods of monitoring, such as the stethoscope. Moreover, EFM leads to certain risks for fetus and mother. The safety of ultrasound still remains to be completely established. In addition, there is substantial agreement that the use of new technology is a major driver for the increase in the costs of health care. Other important examples of the introduction of a new technology prior to evidence of its safety

and value are: (1) the widespread uptake of Vioxx, a highly popular drug for arthritis pain used by millions of people that apparently caused up to 140,000 heart attacks before it was acknowledged and withdrawn from market in 2004 (although the pharmaceutical company knew much earlier it could cause seriously problematic cardiovascular events) (Bhattacharya, 2005); and (2) the ongoing prescription of hormone replacement therapy (HRT) to millions of women despite its association with breast cancer after three or more years of use (Australian Government, 2010). Furthermore, in an ironic turn of events, the use of some anti-depressants, not only among young people, has been linked to an increased rate of suicide (Nischal et al., 2012).

McKinlay and McKinlay (1981) developed a model—the seven stages in the career of a medical invention—that could be used to explain the social forces involved in the dissemination of new medical technologies before they are adequately tested.

Stage 1: A promising report.
Stage 2: Professional and organizational adoption.
Stage 3: Public acceptance and state (third-party) endorsement.
Stage 4: Standard procedure and observational reports.
Stage 5: Randomized controlled trial.
Stage 6: Professional denunciation.
Stage 7: Erosion and discreditation.

The most important point is that evaluation, which is purported and believed to be the bedrock of scientifically based treatment innovations, occurs at stages 4 and 5, long after the introduction and widespread use of a medical invention. The concept of "disease-mongering" introduced in the *British Medical Journal* (Moynihan et al., 2002) explains the tendency to active intervention as the result of the profit motive of pharmaceutical companies. **Disease-mongering** is the corporate construction of new diseases for the sole purpose of business profits, "extending the boundaries of treatable illness to expand markets for new products" (Moynihan et al., 2002, p. 886). Further, Moynihan et al. note that alliances between pharmaceutical companies, doctors, and patients are encouraged to frame new conditions as widespread, debilitating, and severe. In their argument they documented three case studies. The first involved the medicalization of baldness around the time that Merck developed a hair-growth drug. Merck sponsored news articles emphasizing the extensiveness of the problem of baldness and the severe level of suffering that people experienced as the result of baldness. The company suggested that panic and emotional difficulties were associated with baldness. In addition, the company sponsored the founding of a new International Hair Study Institute. Thus, baldness came to be considered a treatable "disease." The second case involved the pathologizing of mild digestive symptoms into the disease "irritable bowel syndrome" as a part of the marketing of a new drug by GlaxoSmith-Kline. The third instance, social phobia or social anxiety disorder, was introduced into the public and medical consciousness at the time of the development of an anti-depressant by Roche, and both the terms and such drugs can be overused in cases of what might be called excessive shyness. Most recently, the highly reputable Berkeley Wellness report underscored how ADHD drugs are sometimes over-prescribed. Certainly, the wide differences in different countries and in different geographic parts of the same countries suggest that more is at work in the prescription of ADHD drugs than objective science would merit (Tuller, 2014; Whitaker, 2010). In fact, ADHD has been shown by some researchers and clinicians to be an ear-based condition that can be treated without drugs but with high-frequency sound (e.g., Doidge, 2015, pp. 280–302; Bérard, 1993, pp. 18–37).

Perhaps two of the most interesting historical examples of disease-mongering in the interests of profit are from the nineteenth century: the diagnosis of **drapetomania**, which caused slaves to run away from their masters, and **dysaethesia aethiopis**, which referred to poor work habits among slaves. The first can be seen as an instance of a diagnosis used to serve financial interests because slaves could be costly to own and, thus, slave owners stood to lose money whenever a slave ran away. Similarly, slaves who had poor work habits were costly to their owners. Calling these actions "diseases" reinforced the moral superiority of the owners and justified the actions they "had" to take to return the slaves home or to demand better work (Freund et al., 2003: 197).

Are there any other diagnoses that you know of today that might be seen to further the interests of profit-making?

CRITICAL THINKING

Box 8.1 • Should Fertility Be Controlled by the Employer?

Should fertility treatments such as the freezing of eggs and sperm be encouraged so that people can put off pregnancy and parenthood until it is convenient in respect to career development? Should this medical care be one of the perks offered by an employing company? Should the possibility of medical intervention to promote a delayed pregnancy be used as a tool for employers to keep employees working until a project is finished? In 2014, Apple and Facebook made the news for an innovative human resources initiative. They offered to pay for fertility treatments for their employees. Apparently, it was thought to be a good tool for recruiting and for retaining employees. According to the companies, it would give employees a chance to get well established in their careers by allowing them to put off having children until they had achieved what they wanted in their working lives. This initiative has spread around the US. Now, one in 20 companies with health insurance includes fertility treatments as one of the benefits.

This is an example of the medicalization of a bodily function. Discuss the ethical issues of this spreading policy.

A study comparing the approval for commercial use of two drugs in Japan and the US demonstrates the potential role of social and political pressure to adopt or not adopt new drugs irrespective of drug safety and efficacy information (Hollander, 2006). The two comparison drugs were Viagra and an abortion pill in the US and Viagra and a birth control pill in Japan. In both Japan and the US, Viagra was shepherded through the drug approval processes within six months. In the US the abortion pill was approved 17 years after related research was first allowed and four years after application was made for distribution. In Japan, the birth control pill was approved for use 35 years after the first application for approval. Ostensibly, drug approval is linked to drug safety and efficacy and is the result of scientific investigation. However, Viagra has been associated with heart attacks, irregular heart rhythms, stroke, chest pain, and increased blood pressure. On the other hand, the side effects to the mother of the abortion medication and the birth control pill appeared to be minor and included cramping, nausea, vomiting, and bleeding. The most serious side effect required a blood transfusion. Clearly, then, other factors were at play in the adoption of these drugs in Japan and the US.

In another example, a tonsillectomy is a very common surgical procedure, yet there is considerable variation in its use from geographic area to geographic area and from hospital district to hospital district. The proper treatment for tonsillitis is debatable. One of the ways this debate is resolved appears to be along the lines of specialty preferences. For instance, pediatricians tend to favour recurrent use of antibiotics to control tonsil flare-ups, whereas otolaryngologists are more likely to prefer the surgical procedure and to remove the infected or inflamed organ. It appears that the ideology of the specialty is buttressed by scientific research based on clinical trials and published in specialty research journals tending to favour one procedure over another. Although it may seem that economics might drive the preferences for action chosen by each different type of specialist, even in jurisdictions where physicians are on salary these specialty group differences remain. These findings suggest that belief in one's own procedure may have more influence than direct material interests. The interests may be indirect and reflect the need to protect and promote the hard-earned skills necessary for the long-run success of the specialty (Chow, 1998). One implication of this conflict in treatment procedures is that the knowledge base of doctors is much greater in their own specialty and, at times, they may be myopic with respect to looking at all of the alternative treatments. A specialist should not be expected to be able to offer an evaluation of the exact health costs and benefits of different types of treatments (based on different specialties), even though this would likely be in the interest of the health of the patient and the costs to the health-care system.

Medical Science Reinforces Gender-Role Stereotypes

Scientific medical knowledge is portrayed as an objective, generalizable, and positive accomplishment. Yet, what is taken to be objective medical science has been shown to reflect fundamental cultural and social-structural beliefs (Clark et al., 1991). Normative categories of social relations, in fact, have infused medical conceptions. Findlay (1993) studied the 10 most highly circulating texts in obstetrics and gynecology in the 1950s in Canada, as well as a representative selection of academic articles from five major obstetrics/gynecology journals and from the *Canadian Medical Association Journal*. Her research showed that physicians' descriptions and understandings of the female body guarded and reflected family values. The scientific and medical publications emphasized the importance of separate spheres for men and women, of stable marriage and family life, and encouraged fertility among women (who were assumed to be white and middle-class). Findlay noted that the essence of the "normal" woman during this time period was portrayed as if she ought always to be potentially fertile. Women's bodies were described largely with respect to fluctuations in their hormones and menstrual cycles. They were described as living to reproduce. As Findlay reports, one influential obstetrician/gynecologist explained: "The desire for children by the normal woman is stronger than self-interest in beauty and figure, stronger than the claims of a career, [while] in the man it is less intense" (Jeffcoate, 1957, in Findlay, 1993). By contrast, the abnormal woman was defined as one who had sexual or reproductive problems.

The women's movement of the 1960s and beyond has focused on eliminating such prejudices. However, women still are seen as reproductive bodies and viewed as largely responsible for birth control and for accepting or refusing sexual intercourse. Women continue to be used for experimental treatments in regard to their reproductive systems. For example, the vaccination against the human papillomavirus (HPV) was initially approved for use in Canada among young women and girls. It was and continues to be advertised as a cervical cancer preventative despite the fact that the safety and efficacy of the vaccination over the long term are yet to be determined. Also, considering that HPV is a sexually transmitted disease, the initial rationale for excluding boys and young men in trials and utilization is not clear. The consequences of HPV to males may be as severe (predominately genital and anal warts and genital and throat cancers) as the consequences to females (cervical cancer; cervical cancer with metastases). However, the infection of males can lead to the infection of more females.

Emily Martin's *The Woman in the Body* (1987) also instructs us about gender biases in medical conceptions of women's bodies and their functions. She demonstrates how culture shapes what biological scientists see. One interesting illustration of her thesis is how assumptions about gender infuse descriptions of the reproductive cycle and its elements, such as the egg and sperm. For instance, the female menstrual cycle is described in negative terms. Menstruation is said to rid the body of waste, of debris, of dead tissue. It is described as a system gone awry. By contrast, while most sperm are also "useless" and "wasted," the life of the sperm

is described as a "feat." The magnitude of the production of sperm is considered remarkable and valuable. Whereas female ovulation is described as a process where eggs sit and wait and then get old and useless, male spermatogenesis is described as continuously producing fresh, active, strong, and efficient sperm. While the eggs are swept and drift down the fallopian tubes like flotsam, sperm actively and in a "manly" and machismo fashion burrow and penetrate.

Ideas such as these infuse the work of medicine and can be seen in differences in the care of men and women with the same conditions. Cho and her colleagues (2019) found that when elderly men and women broke a hip, women were more likely to be treated in a cursory manner without preoperative investigations. Women can also have poorer quality care from family doctors (Wexler et al., 2005) when it comes to diabetes. Women have a long history of poorer quality cardiac care and problem identification, and this continues to be so (Regitz-Zagrosek, 2010) even in regard to very high-tech interventions such as heart transplants (Humphries et al., 2001). In addition, current medical practice assumes unitary gender and gender identity as well as heterosexuality, meaning that medical practitioners may not be aware of or sensitive to the particular health concerns of LGBTQ or gender-diverse individuals. With the increased inclusion and acceptance of diversity in these areas in many aspects of life (such as the legalization and celebration of same-sex marriage) it is time that medical practitioners adopted more progressive attitudes and behaviours (Pinto et al., 2019).

There is evidence, as well, of stereotyping regarding hegemonic masculinities. For instance, these masculinities have long been seen as risk factors (e.g., risk-taking of males has been seen as the cause of their higher incidence of automobile accidents and homicides) and are now being medicalized (Rosenfeld & Faircloth, 2006). Erectile dysfunction is a case in point. Medical definitions of erectile functioning link the performance of masculinity to the ability to "accomplish" (Loe, 2006, p. 31) an erection. According to Moynihan (2006), another recently discovered disease is "motivational deficiency disorder," otherwise known as "laziness" or maybe "extreme laziness." In another example, attention deficit hyperactive disorder (ADHD) is a frequent diagnosis for children and young people that functions to control their behaviours, particularly in school. What has been less documented is the fact that the diagnosis of ADHD, and the subsequent prescription of Ritalin for its treatment, serves, in a way, as a medicalization of boyhood because the vast majority of prescriptions (approximately 75 to 80 per cent) are for young boys because of their "disruptive" or "boyish" behaviours in classrooms (Hart et al., 2006).

The recent development of pharmacogenetics—the study of how drug response depends on genetic makeup (Helman, 2007)—has led to the targeting of drugs to specifically racialized groups. For instance, in 2005 a heart drug was approved by the US Food and Drug Administration (FDA) for the treatment of heart failure among African Americans. The success of the Human Genome Project in mapping the genetic makeup of human beings is making it possible to design drugs with a more exact fit to genetic makeup. These developments raise important ethical debates. Some argue that such precisely targeted medical interventions, in a racist society, could be used to reinforce and even act on racism or against other marginalized groups. It is possible to imagine the "discovery" of a disease that leads to consequent stigmatization and isolation in only one "race" or marginalized group. Furthermore, the genetic makeup is subject to alteration, which is how species evolve; targeting the genes of individuals is a way of interrupting evolutionary processes that have been underway for millennia and are far more complex than is yet known.

Canada in a Global Context

Box 8.2 • Caesarian Sections in Brazil: Medicalization from Above or Below?

A Caesarian section is a birth method that involves surgery in order to birth the baby through the abdomen of the new mother. It can be lifesaving for mother and for baby, but it generally costs more than a vaginal birth and it takes more time in the use of the specific skill of specialized obstetrical doctors. Generally, midwives and non-specialists can manage vaginal births. There are also some advantages to C-sections for doctors. In particular because they can be scheduled and they involve less time uncertainty for doctors who otherwise have to wait until the labouring mother is ready to deliver. Labours are of variable length, so this waiting can be lengthy. Also, of course, mothers-to-be can avoid the uncertainty and disruption of waiting for a labour to begin by scheduling a C-section ahead of time. Pregnant women can also avoid the fear of the pain and discomfort of labour by planning a C-section because in this surgery they have strong anaesthetics. However, in some cases women suffer more complications from C-section (Grant, 2019). In Brazil, which has a very high rate of C-sections, the procedure is hotly debated. The question is, is this the result of women's choice or the will of doctors and the state?

The World Health Organization indicates that a C-section rate of between 10 per cent and 15 per cent in a country is ideal. This rate would be sufficient were medical interventions only done when necessary to preserve the health of the mother and baby. In Canada, the rate is about twice as high as this ideal rate at about 28.2 per cent (Grant, 2019). Across Brazil, the C-section rate is about 50 per cent, and in private hospitals the rate of Caesarians is between 80 per cent and 90 per cent. In some hospitals the rate is 100 per cent. These dramatically high rates are justified by culturally widespread ideologies of birth wherein, for instance, vaginal birth is often experienced as violent. Only about 5 per cent of women in Brazil who birth vaginally have an intact perineum after the birth (Filopovic, 2014). Surgical interventions such as episiotomies are prevalent, and some negative alteration of the sexual organs of the birthing woman is often deemed normal in vaginal births. Furthermore, women face verbal abuse from doctors during birth in Brazil (Filopovic, 2014).

There have long been reports of high C-section rates in Brazil. C-sections are much more common among wealthier women. In some areas they are seen as status symbols and celebrated by birthing parties complete with in-hospital mini-bars as friends and family watch the C-section from a viewing room. However, less wealthy women have also been said to use C-sections to choose the date and time of the birth so as not to inconvenience themselves, their employers, or customers. More recently, reports suggest that

the high rate of Caesarian sections in Brazil may be based on hospital policies and even budgets. Hospitals have a financial incentive to pursue surgical childbirth as often as possible because of the fees to the hospital. Jill Filipovic reports that some women have been forced to have C-sections by doctors who falsely claim they are necessary. There are cases of the police being called to a hospital when a woman has refused to agree to a C-section birth (Filopovic, 2014). Doctors have even been reported to accept bribes from women who want to be allowed to deliver naturally but fear being pressured into surgical interventions. The particular method of birth in Brazil is clearly fraught and exists in the midst of powerful competing interests.

Doing further research, discuss this situation.

The Sociology of Medical Practice

Just as medical/scientific knowledge is a social product with social consequences, so, too, is the everyday practice of medicine. Have you ever left your doctor's office only to realize that you had forgotten to tell or ask him/her about something? Have you ever left the office unclear about what the doctor has said about your problem/disease, your medication, or something else? Have you ever felt that you "couldn't get a word in edgewise" in a conversation with your physician? Have you ever seen a sign in the examining room to the effect, "Please restrict your visit to one symptom or medical problem"? Have you ever asked for a second opinion or been skeptical about a doctor's diagnosis?

Considerable evidence demonstrates that the day-to-day practice of medicine is profoundly affected by social characteristics of patients and doctors. First, with regard to patients, there is evidence that physicians tend to prefer younger patients and to hold negative images of elderly patients. Elderly patients tend to be seen as both sicker and less amenable to treatment than younger patients.

The older patient, "far in excess of actual numbers, represents the negative idea of the uncooperative, intractable, and generally troublesome patient" (Clark et al., 1991, p. 855). The elderly may be overtreated, in general (Hadler, 2011), particularly when they spend their last days, weeks, or months and then die in hospital. Or under health-care rationing, they may be under-treated (Smith, 2009).

Physicians' attitudes and actions in regard to racialized characteristics reflect those of the wider socio-cultural context of which physicians are a part. For instance, several US-based studies have demonstrated that black patients tend to be referred to specialists less often, are treated more often by doctors-in-training, are more likely to be placed on a ward, and are admitted less frequently to hospital except when they are involuntarily hospitalized for mental health problems (see Chapman et al., 2013). Black patients also tend to receive less aggressive workups and interventions. Differences have been documented in the way that physicians treat patients of different class backgrounds. For example, patients with poorer backgrounds are likely given poorer prognoses and less state-of-the-art treatment (see Chapters 4 and 5 for a more detailed discussion of racialization, class, and health).

The social characteristics of physicians themselves, including gender, age, professional training, education, and form of practice, have also been shown to influence their work (Chapman et al., 2013).

Cultural Variation in Medical Practice

In an intriguing study, Lynn Payer (1988), a journalist, travelled and visited doctors in several countries: the United States, England, West Germany, and France. To each doctor she presented the same symptoms. She also examined morbidity and mortality tables and read medical journals and magazines in each country. Using this casual and commonsensical method, Payer found strong cultural differences in diagnostic trends and patterns that seemed to reflect fundamental differences in history and culture. Diagnoses and treatments varied widely from country to country, even under allopathic medical care. "West Germans, for instance, consume roughly six times as much cardiac glycoside, or heart stimulant, per capita, as do the French and the English, yet only about half as much antibiotic" (Payer, 1988, p. 38). In general, Payer found that German doctors were far more likely to diagnose heart problems than doctors in other countries. English physicians, by contrast, are characterized as parsimonious. For this reason, Payer describes the British as the accountants of the medical world. They prescribe about half of the drugs that German and French doctors prescribe and perform about half of the surgeries of American doctors. "Overall in England one has to be sicker to be defined ill, let alone receive treatment" (Payer, 1988, p. 41). By contrast, the Americans are spendthrift and aggressive. They have a tendency to take action even in the face of uncertainty. They do not, however, focus on a particular organ. Among the French, most ills are ultimately attributable to the liver.

Payer argues that these patterns reflect the German emphasis on the heart—on romance, in literature and music, for instance; the French focus on the pleasures of eating and drinking; the English have a preoccupation with rationalizing the national medical care system; and the American emphasis is on getting things done and getting on with it. Payer's work suggests, in broad strokes, something of the relationship between culture and medical practice. More cross-cultural research needs to be done and more is being undertaken (see, e.g., Lakoff's 2004 work on the links between anti-depressant use and the economic crisis in Argentina).

Class and Resistance to Medical Knowledge

One way that lay people interpret, accept, or resist "medical knowledge" is described in relation to a cancer education project developed for a white, working-class, inner-city area in the United States that was known as a "cancer hot spot" because of the relatively high rates of cancer mortality (Balshem, 1991). The problem was believed by the local inhabitants to be largely the consequence of air pollution from nearby chemical plants and occupational exposure of those who worked in the plants. With this belief system in mind, the community rejected "health education" about nutrition and cancer. To illustrate the resistance, Balshem, who was working as a health educator at the time, describes the aftermath of her slide show and talk about the cancer prevention possibilities of a diet that is high in fibre and low in fat. Immediately after this talk Balshem asked if there were any questions. She was met with silence. Then she raffled off a hot-air popcorn maker. People responded warmly, with pleasure. After that, there was silence again. The meeting adjourned and the subtext of the silence emerged. One person talked about her old neighbour (93 years old) who ate whatever she liked and was still alive. Another teased Balshem: "You mean your husband will eat that stuff; mine sure won't." Still another confessed that the people in the room liked their kielbasa (spicy sausage) too much to eliminate it from their diets. Finally, Balshem was invited to their next church supper for some really good eating. Balshem describes the meeting finale as follows:

> Then, the social climax: I am offered a piece of cake. The offerer, and a goodly number of onlookers, can barely restrain their hilarity.

Time stops. Then I accept the cake. There is a burst of teasing and laughter, the conversation becomes easier, the moment passes. We eat, pack our equipment, and leave. (Balshem, 1991, p. 156)

While the general atmosphere of these meetings was amiable, the explicit health messages were ignored or indirectly criticized as impractical and as being of less importance than things such as pleasure, family feeling, and "human" nature in the pursuit of health. To the participants the environmental causes identified by the people who lived there were the obvious culprit and cause of cancer.

To understand the community and its responses, Balshem engaged in survey research, long open-ended interviews, and focus-group research strategies. One of the findings was that the community members had sharply contrasting attitudes towards heart disease and cancer.

The causes and treatments of heart disease were both fewer and considered more responsive to lifestyle alterations. Cancer, by contrast, was described as the result of a horrible fate. It was seen as caused by almost everything in their environment. Many of the respondents directly denied the dominant scientific discourses regarding cancer causation and prevention. In particular, there were direct denials of smoking and of fat as cancer-causing agents. By contrast, no one questioned the standard scientific discourses about the prevention and causation of heart disease. Balshem called this response "resistance" and explained that:

maintaining a rebellious consciousness is part of constructing a valued self, valued community, valued life, in a subordinate class environment. Self and community, valuing and supporting each other, process myriad insults, betrayals, and frustrations. Local belief and tradition, it is asserted, are superior, as is local insight into the workings of authority and hegemony. (Balshem, 1991, p. 166)

For an abundance of reasons, class and community solidarity proved to be more important than expert health knowledge, beliefs about disease causation, and prevention strategies.

Despite the power of "medicalization from above," there is always resistance, or as Cornwell (1984) says, "medicalization from below." Calnan and Williams (1992) demonstrate another type of resistance to medical thinking and hegemony. They studied lay evaluations of the trustworthiness of doctors with respect to nine specific medical care issues. In particular, they asked whether or not laypersons would unquestioningly accept medical opinion with regard to the following nine interventions: (1) prescription of antibiotics; (2) hernia operation; (3) operation for bowel cancer; (4) prescription for tranquilizers; (5) hip replacement operation; (6) hysterectomy; (7) heart transplant; (8) test-tube babies; and (9) vasectomy. Their findings indicated that in only one case, antibiotics, would the majority of respondents accept medical intervention without question: 54 per cent said they would accept antibiotics without question. Yet even here, 41 per cent said they would only accept the doctor's recommendation for antibiotics with an explanation. Moreover, the views of the public regarding all interventions varied according to gender, class, age, and health categories. Although this study is now old I wonder how many of you accept medical opinion without question, even with regard to antibiotics, in an age of antibiotic resistance.

Calnan and Williams note that in making their decisions respondents were guided by certain fundamental values of their own. A good intervention was characterized in the following ways: as life-saving rather than life-threatening; as enhancing rather than diminishing quality of life; as natural rather than unnatural; as moral rather than immoral; as necessary rather than unnecessary; as restoring independence rather than promoting addiction/dependence; and as giving good value for money rather than being a waste of money.

The lay population knows that medical knowledge does not form a consistent whole. Nor do the different conceptions of medical knowledge necessarily complement one another: "The medical world is a melting pot of contradictory theories and practices, controversies and inexplicable phenomena about which doctors and lay people are in constant debate" (Bransen, 1992, p. 99). For example, after decades of encouraging women to examine their breasts for suspicious lumps and to have regular mammograms, the medical profession has begun to withdraw those recommendations. Mammograms, for instance, are recommended at different frequencies and ages for women today. False positives and costly exploratory surgery have levied a significant toll on women and costs to the system. Controversy still swirls around whether the potential side effects from mammography testing are worth the few cases of breast cancer that are found early enough for treatment to make a difference, as this review of 25 years of mammography use indicates (Klarenbach et al., 2018). Similarly, the usefulness of PSA testing in men has been called in question in the event that the only "treatment" is watchful

waiting. HRT was first heralded as the new wonder drug for the prevention of breast cancer and then later found implicated in other diseases.

Patient groups are organizing to seek their rights in Canada and around the world. The World Health Organization states that everyone in the world should have the right to accessible, affordable health care. This is not yet the case, as you will see in Chapter 15. For example, the Affordable Care Act, which does not cover every American, was introduced in 2010 by President Barack Obama, then hotly debated and threatened with a rollback under President Trump.

Medical Knowledge Becomes Popular Knowledge

Magazines, newspapers, and audiovisual media have long been important as sources of health-related information and attitudes in modern

CRITICAL THINKING

Box 8.3 • Obesity: Social or Medical Phenomenon?

Obesity is a modern condition at the forefront of debates about medicalization, as is suggested by the figures in Table 8.1 on the increasing numbers of bariatric or weight-loss surgeries performed in the US in recent years. Is it a medical problem? Are people who are obese also sick? Are they more likely than others to have their lives shortened simply because of their bodily size? If so, most importantly, is the best remedy a medical solution?

Bariatric surgery and weight-loss products are increasingly popular and more widely used. At the same time, considerable research links obesity to social and economic behaviours such as the association between the prevalence of fast-food outlets and obesity rates and the linkage of increases in overweight and obesity to the use of various computer screens and devices associated with sedentary behaviour.

From another perspective, some people and various social movement organizations, such as the fat acceptance movement and Health at Every Size, argue that the stigma associated with fatness and the marginalization of obese people are the main problems associated with obesity, rather than the weight itself. Such groups oppose policies that discriminate against people of a certain size, such as requiring payment for two seats on airplanes.

At the same time, over the course of the last century and longer in Western societies, thinness has been idealized and venerated, especially for women, from the whalebone corsets of an earlier time to various beauty and health products and the images of celebrity models today. Furthermore, the financial interests of weight-loss products, diet foods, and other interventions feed into this glorification of the smaller body.

Discuss.

Table 8.1   Estimate of Bariatric Surgeries in the United States, 2011–2017

	2011	2012	2013	2014	2015	2016	2017
Total	158,000	173,000	179,000	193,000	196,000	216,000	228,000
Sleeve (%)	17.80	33.00	42.10	51.70	53.61	58.11	59.39
RYGB (%)	36.70	37.50	34.20	26.80	23.02	18.69	17.80
Band (%)	35.40	20.20	14.00	9.50	5.68	3.39	2.77
BPD-DS (%)	0.90	1.00	1.00	0.40	0.60	0.57	0.70
Revision (%)	6.00	6.00	6.00	11.50	13.55	13.95	14.14
Other (%)	3.20	2.30	2.70	0.10	3.19	2.63	2.46
Balloons (%)	—	—	—	—	0.36	2.66	2.75

Source: American Society for Metabolic and Bariatric Surgery (ASMBS).

mass societies. These channels are currently being surpassed, however, by information available through the electronic superhighway. This trend has been dubbed escaped medicine (Nettleton, 2004) and m-medicine, that is, mobile-medicine or mobile-health (Lupton, 2012). Daily updates of scientific/medical news are available through the Internet, where there are probably billions of pages of information available at the click of the mouse. Some websites are affiliated with major medical institutions or disease-related charities such as the Heart and Stroke Foundation and the Canadian Cancer Society. Many of these are professionally run and present dominant discourses that are widely considered to be scientific, valid, reliable, and current. Others are full of invalid and unreliable information. Privacy and confidentiality are not always protected. Some sites are outdated. Some represent various commercial interests. Some reflect the concerns of special disease or treatment preference interest groups. If you investigate any number of disease-specific websites for sponsorship you will notice that pharmaceutical companies are often behind-the-scenes financial supporters. The extent to which this "pharma" sponsorship biases the information available in favour of one drug or another needs further investigation. A related investigation examined direct-to-consumer (DTC) advertisements, which are legal in the US and said to be

highly regulated as to safety information. However, DTC advertisements present a rosy picture of the benefits while diminishing the possibilities of side effects and long-term effects. Undoubtedly, DTC ads also drive up pharmaceutical use and health-care costs. The information provided varies in accuracy and accessibility. Moreover, people interpret information according to their own culture and socio-economic, gender, age, educational, and psychological characteristics.

Studies of health information on the Internet paint a fairly pessimistic picture of its validity and reliability. One study sought to find out how people use the Internet by establishing a website to provide information about cardiology. The researchers found that users were seeking information "correctly," that is, 95 per cent of those who asked for information asked pertinent questions (Widman & Tong, 1997). Another study evaluated information regarding pharmaceuticals. Here the researchers found that about 50 per cent of the information provided was correct, another 50 per cent was incorrect, and 10.4 per cent of that incorrect information was potentially harmful (Desai et al., 1997). In an evaluation of the quality of information regarding how to detect and manage childhood fevers, researchers found that only about 10 per cent of the websites providing information on childhood fevers adhered closely to recommendations in peer-reviewed guidelines (Impicciatore et al., 1994). Clearly, these are issues of concern to those who use the Internet for health information. Another study, this one of breast cancer sites (Hoffman-Goetz & Clarke, 2000), found inadequacies with respect to the validity and reliability of information, the presence of references, dated information, dead-end sites, lack of acknowledged ownership, security and privacy protection, widely different reading levels from site to site, and the dominance of the English language.

Although the above research is quite dated, it still appears that the Internet offers a Wild West approach to health information. The quality of sites varies markedly, and as yet there are no enforced reliable standards (Fahy et al., 2014). People use the Internet widely for health information and can trust many well-known sites such as that of the World Health Organization and the Public Health Agency of Canada. However, validity and reliability are still elusive for many other sites. To date the Internet is open, free, and unregulated. Debates flourish about whether this is the best strategy in the long run. Some researchers and institutions are working to develop indices and software that would provide organization, guidelines, and maps for users. In the meantime, technology leads social change and people are running to catch up! Different people use different types of media, and people use different media for distinct types of information.

Moyer and her colleagues (1994) evaluated, over a two-year period, the accuracy of scientific information as it went from original research/ medical sources to the various mass media, including newspapers and women's, science, and health magazines. They began with 116 articles in the mass media. Of those, 60 included traceable citations. There were 42 content-based inaccuracies including misleading titles, shifts in emphasis, treating speculation as fact, erroneous information, omitting other important results, omitting qualifying information, over-generalizing findings, and inaccuracies in personal communications. Women's magazines had the highest percentage of inaccuracies in traceable citations, at 88 per cent.

"Quality" newspapers had the fewest inaccuracies, at 25 per cent.

Furthermore, readers typically misunderstand at least some of the information they receive through the mass media. Yeaton et al. (1990) surveyed a small sample of college students regarding their understanding of popular press articles on health issues such as surgical alternatives for breast cancer, drug treatment for congestive heart failure, use of starch blockers for weight reduction, dietary cholesterol, heart disease, and skin transplants for burns. The overall rate of misunderstanding was 39 per cent. The fact that this level of misunderstanding exists among college students raises serious questions about the accessibility and quality of the health information accessible to the average citizen. If media-based information is both inaccurate (to an extent) and misunderstood (to an extent), we have to wonder about the quality of the health information that exists among the general population.

It must be emphasized that the media do not just provide background noise. They can have very real effects on health and health behaviours. A recent study of suicide reiterated the findings that reporting on suicide increased the rate of suicide (Sinyor, 2018).

Doctor–Patient Communication

Doctor–patient communication reflects the broader social structure and culture. It also reflects the particular characteristics of both patients and doctors. Physicians and patients each embody their own particular social spaces as carriers of culture and structure. In a study based on ethnographic fieldwork that entailed joining the surgical ward rounds at two general hospitals, Fox (1993) examined the communication strategies used by doctors to maintain authority and power in their interaction with surgical patients. When patients tried to ask questions, such as why they felt the way they did, how soon they would feel better, and when they could go home, the surgeons tended to ignore them. Instead, the surgeons maintained verbal and other sorts of control by focusing on the success of the surgery with respect to the specific goals of surgery (e.g., absence of infection, minimal scarring) and its specific outcome. Fox demonstrates that ward rounds can be understood as a systematic strategy entered into by surgeons to capture and maintain their discursive monopoly. By keeping the discussion focused on surgeon-centred themes, the doctors allow patients few opportunities to introduce their own views, concerns, or worries.

One area of social life around which there is a great deal of ambiguity and ambivalence is sexuality. On the one hand, sexual relations are more openly discussed, portrayed, and symbolized in all of the mass media today than in the past. Acknowledgement of the pervasiveness of sexual activity outside of the bounds of monogamous marriage is widespread. Accompanying the "liberalization" of sexuality, and particularly of women's sexuality, is the belief that a satisfactory sex life is an important part of a satisfactory life as a whole. Yet, many are still ambivalent about sex and many still believe it to be a shameful duty to be kept secret. Today, people are more likely to consult doctors when dissatisfied with their sexual functioning (Weijts et al., 1993). Sometimes, women's dissatisfaction with their sex life seems to be hidden behind complaints about physical functioning, including such things as vaginal infections and pain during intercourse (Stanley & Ramage, 1984).

It is useful to understand how such ambiguity and ambivalence are manifest in personal relations and in talk between doctors and their female patients. One study of doctors' and patients' talk showed constructions of sexuality were managed in the doctor's office quite "sensitively" so as to reinforce gender stereotypes about the "shame" and "mystery" surrounding female sexuality (see Table 8.2). The strategies used to discuss such "delicate" matters are best characterized as delay, avoidance, and depersonalization. Reflected in the talk and in the silence is the construction of the "delicate and notorious" character of female sexuality in the context of the possible discourse with an often more powerful and male doctor (Weijts et al., 1993).

Sociological discussion of "talk" is not trivial. It is important both theoretically and practically.

"Delicacy"—or the shame and privacy norms passing as "delicacy"—with respect to sexuality, particularly female sexuality, is a major factor in unwanted pregnancies, sexually transmitted diseases, and the transmission of the HIV/AIDS virus in heterosexual populations. To the extent that women remain unable to talk clearly and confidently about their sexuality, about their genital and reproductive health, and about birth control and health and safety devices such as condoms, they may be more likely to be unable to refuse unwanted and/or unprotected sex. In a context in which there is a high prevalence of STDs and STIs (sexually transmitted diseases and sexually transmitted illnesses) and unprotected sex by teens and young people, often with several partners and without protection, it is important that sexually active people feel comfortable asking for regular STD and STI checkups.

One important aspect of doctor–patient interaction is the emotion regulation of patients and doctors. Some aspects of emotional display are expected or at least allowed among patients. Crying, withdrawal, and even modulated anger are appropriate emotions for patients to display when receiving bad news, for example. Doctors,

Table 8.2 Doctors' Strategies for Talking about Sex to Patients

Strategies	Device
Delaying	delaying discussions of sex refraining from answering "sensitive" questions acting agitated in the context of delicate terms
Avoiding	using vague, indirect, and distant terms avoiding certain delicate terms using pronouns
Depersonalizing	avoiding personal references using definite articles
Tuning/ Adapting	adopting and repeating patients' use of pronouns and their omission of delicate terms

Source: Adapted from Weijts et al. (1993, p. 4).

however, are expected not to show such emotions even when they are frustrated, disgusted, or angry. Talcott Parsons thought of this as a part of the affective neutrality that doctors were taught to show to patients. One recent study examined the effects of emotion regulation among doctors on their patients (Kafetsios et al., 2014). Patients' satisfaction was found to be dependent on the emotion regulation (or suppression of emotion) displayed by their doctors. Evidently, emotion work is an important part of the skill set required for good medical practice and patient satisfaction. Doctors join other service workers in selling their emotional labour as a part of how they work (Hochschild, 1983). This suppression of emotion can be detrimental to the life and job satisfaction of doctors.

Summary

1. Medical knowledge is socially constructed. It reflects cultural values and social-structural locations. It has varied historically and cross-culturally.

2. Some of the specific values of contemporary medicine include mind–body dualism, physical reductionism, specific etiology, machine metaphor and regimen, and control. Sociological research provides a critical overview of these medical assumptions.

3. A large and significant gap exists between the findings of biomedical research and the implementation of the consequences of these findings in medical practice. The values of medical scientists and medical practitioners are, in many ways, at odds with one another.

4. Available evidence demonstrates that new technologies are usually adopted (even widely) before their safety and effectiveness have been ascertained.

5. Medical science has been infused with cultural and gendered stereotypes such as those described by Emily Martin.

6. Research shows that medical practice, too, is infused with cultural stereotypes, including those that pertain to age, gender, class, and race.

7. One cross-cultural study of medical practice by Lynn Payer offers provocative evidence of cultural differences in diagnosis and treatment.

8. Significant class differences exist in public understanding and acceptance of medical knowledge.

9. Lay views of medical practice vary according to gender, class, age, and specific health categories.

11. Media information about medical knowledge is frequently inadequate or inaccurate.

12. Medical doctors employ various discursive strategies in an attempt to maintain control over their own definitions of reality in the face of patient questioning.

Key Terms

disease-mongering
doctrine of specific etiology
drapetomania
dysaethesia aethiopis
evidence-based medicine

machine metaphor
mind–body dualism
physical reductionism
regimen and control
technological imperative

Questions for Study and Discussion

1. Find examples of mind–body dualism, physical reductionism, the doctrine of specific etiology, the machine metaphor, and regimen and control in an online medical journal, such as the *British Medical Journal* or the *Canadian Medical Association Journal*.

2. Do a search of a major newspaper over a period of at least one year and compare and contrast the understandings put forward of the vaccine for HPV.

3. What are the advantages and disadvantages of the widespread availability of health-related information on the Internet for the doctor and for the patient?

4. What social, institutional, and organizational forces in the current way that medical care happens might tend to promote poor communication between patients and doctors in the hospital?

5. Do research on Caesarean sections in Canada. Were you born with surgical intervention? What are and were the sociological factors in this method of birth in Canada or in the country in which you were born?

Suggested Readings

Beck, U. (1992). *Risk society: Towards a new modernity*. Sage Publications. The classic statement of the risk society.

Burke, H. (2018). *The deepest well: Healing the long-term effects of childhood obesity*. Houghton Mifflin Harcourt. A look at how obesity is a challenge not only to physical health but also to mental health.

Foucault, M. (1979). *The history of sexuality. An introduction*, vol. 1. Allen Lane. The first volume of a three-volume study, which introduces the term "biopower" as a means of governing of populations.

Giddens, A. (1999). Risk and responsibility. *Modern Law Review*, 62, 1–10. A brief but excellent overview of some important issues in thinking about the "risk society."

Halfmann, D. (2019). Political institutions and the comparative medicalization of abortion. *Journal of Health and Social Behavior*, 60(2), 138–52. Analysis of the extent to which abortion is ensconced in political debate and is a pivotal issue in patterns of voting.

King, Samantha. (2006). *Pink Ribbons Inc.: Breast cancer and the politics of philanthropy*. University of Minnesota Press. A critical look at cause-marketing in the case of breast cancer.

Perez, C. (2019). *Invisible women: Data bias in a world designed for men*. Harry N. Abrams. What are the implications of a world of research based mostly on men? How does this bias affect such things as medical care and pharmaceutical prescribing?

Rose, N. (2003). Neurochemical selves. *Society*, 41(1), 46–9. A commentary on identity in a psycho-pharmaceuticalized society.

Timmermans, S., & Buchbinder, M. (2010). Patients-in-waiting: Living between sickness and health in a genomics era. *Journal of Health and Social Behavior*, 51(4), 408–23. An article that considers some of the effects of genetic testing on social relations and identities.

A Brief History of Medicine and the Development and Critique of Modern Medicalization

Chapter Overview

- Amid growing tensions Canada has become more medicalized in many ways over the last century and a half.
- Over the last 30-plus years the processes of medicalization have come to involve biomedicalization as well.
- Medicine, as treatment for illness, has a very long history in the world.
- Hippocrates, a Greek physician from before the common era, can be considered one of the founders of what has become the Western, or medicalized, view of illness, disease, and related

treatment. The Hippocratic oath of ethical practice is still used today.
- The process of medicalization has, in many ways, paralleled the process of secularization. Medicine and religiosity or spirituality, over time and across cultures, have often overlapped They both deal with matters of life and death.
- Important critiques have been made of medicalization as a cultural, socio-economic, philosophical, and technological system.
- The contemporary physician can be seen as a moral entrepreneur.

- Medical definitions of reality are powerful and have widespread consequences.

- Whether doctors are increasing or decreasing in power is a matter of debate.

Introduction

How do you react when your body or your mind seems different in a way you think of as problematic? What does it take for you to go to the doctor, nurse practitioner, clinic, or emergency ward? Is it easier to seek help when your problem seems to be rooted in your body than in your feelings, thinking processes, or mind? Today most of you would choose to go to an allopathic or conventional medical practitioner. A few of you may regularly choose chiropractors or osteopaths for your first attempt at help. Or maybe it depends entirely on what your symptoms are? The very idea that you understand the idea of symptoms and that you know your options is because you live in what is called a medicalized or biomedicalized society.

We have discussed the processes by which people notice signs and call them "illness" rather than "immorality" or just "inconvenience." What are the processes by which doctors recognize some of these signs, label them as symptoms, and provide a diagnosis? Medical diagnostic categories change over time and may differ in different locations. What are the relationships among medicine, law, and religion? In what sense is medicine an institution of social control? To what extent have medicine's powers of social control been increasing over the past century while the power of institutional religion has declined in Canada? These are the sorts of questions addressed in this chapter.

Medicine and illness are intertwined; they are not necessarily co-extensive. Today it is primarily the doctors within the medical care system who make the definitions and diagnoses of illnesses. Doctors operate, however, under the circulating discourses and powerful effects of pharmaceutical companies and other private industries in the field of health care. The signs or symptoms that people pay attention to, and those they ignore, are largely determined by medical and pharmaceutical definitions of illness and wellness or normality and abnormality. These processes are often **mediated** through the mass media and the Internet. The expectations people have of their bodies depend to some extent on categories of disease available as defined by the culture and power of the medical care system. Medicalization and biomedicalization provide dominant perspectives in the power/knowledge nexus overlaying other possible ways of understanding the world, our bodies, and our needs. Medicalization is a powerful cultural force and narrative infusing language, behaviour, and attitudes, in fact, affecting our total world view.

Some people experience their bodies and minds in ways they consider to indicate medical conditions or illnesses that doctors are not able or willing to diagnose. For example, sufferers frequently experience chronic fatigue syndrome long before they are able to find a clear diagnosis and medicalization (Clarke & James, 2003; Dumit, 2006). Lyme disease has a multitude of changing symptoms over time and, without the specific discovery of the bull's-eye rash in the immediate days after the bite by a Lyme-bearing tick, is a problematic diagnosis. Multiple sclerosis is notoriously difficult to diagnose because it lacks clear markers and symptoms, and at times mimics normal, though perhaps exaggerated, behaviour, such as periodic stumbling and slurring of words. Alzheimer's cannot be definitely diagnosed except through autopsy after death. Some conditions develop with so few symptoms in the early stages that the seriousness of the disease is not perceived; the rare autoimmune disease of Goodpasture Syndrome, which attacks the lungs and kidneys, and cervical cancer are two such conditions. At other times, medical diagnosis precedes a person's awareness of a physical problem. High blood pressure, for instance, is often detected only by medical tests, not by any physical sensations experienced by the person. The point is that sometimes what is defined as a deviant, unusual, or unacceptable feeling, behaviour, or attitude is also seen as a medical problem. Sometimes the problem may also fall within the realm of religion and/or of law. For instance, AIDS is viewed as a disease by the medical care system. It has also been seen as evidence of sin by some churches, in a homophobic focus on what they may consider to be the immoral sexual behaviour of the diagnosed person. Because HIV/AIDS is contagious, AIDS patients may also be subject to legal controls requiring that they disclose their diagnosis to others. At times criminalization and medicalization constitute overlapping discourses. For example, the prisons, including juvenile facilities, incarcerate a disproportionate percentage of people who suffer symptoms of mental illness. Ashley Smith, the young woman who choked (herself) to death while being watched by the prison guards at the Grand River Correctional Institution for Women in Kitchener, Ontario, is a case in point. She was treated by myriad mental health professionals and given different drugs to combat a variety of changing mental illness diagnoses and yet she was still incarcerated and punished in solitary confinement over several years before she died (*Canadian Press*, 2012).

The spread of medical definitions of reality or medicalization can be seen in many places today. Perhaps one of the best examples is the case of mental illness. "Diagnostic inflation" is a particular problem in the case of mental illness (Kudlow, 2013). *The Diagnostic and Statistical Manual of Mental Disorders* (DSM) is the "bible" or dictionary of mental illness. It lists all of the diagnoses considered acceptable to the medical profession and lays out their symptoms in lists. This type of empirical clarity was intended to provide consistency in diagnosis. It has been useful for monitoring and determining costs in the case of third-party payment for services by insurance companies and governments. The first edition of the DSM was published in 1952. It was 130 pages long and included

106 mental disorders. This first edition had little impact on the practice of psychiatry. Nevertheless, it was useful in the effort to quantify the incidence of various types of mental illness.

In the 1960s and 1970s the question of the definition of mental illness became increasingly fraught and divisive. On one side were the Freudian psychoanalysts who believed that mental illness was the result of deep internal conflicts stemming from the inadequate resolution of the various developmental stages of childhood. As such, it was counterproductive, in the view of the Freudians who then dominated psychiatry in North America, to label and to delimit symptoms without identifying the causes in early childhood and trying to remedy the effects. It was the cause that was important, they argued. Knowledge of the symptoms was not necessary. Symptoms were not to be explicitly treated. In psychoanalysis the purpose of psychotherapeutic treatment is to uncover the childhood causes of neuroses and through therapy develop self-knowledge and insight and find healing. "Talk therapy" is the preferred method of treatment. On the other side were those who thought mental illness was ultimately biological and that progress in understanding and treating it depended on biological observation and measurement of observable pathology, primarily in the brain. The past of the individual patient was considered to be unimportant. Detailed descriptions of specific symptoms and the ways they were patterned together and observable in brain lesions were thought to be the fundamental building blocks of specific cures for pathologies. Ultimately, specific symptoms and sets of symptoms were to be empirically studied in the brain and linked to specific, underlying biological aberrations.

In 1980 the third edition of the DSM (made by a group of expert psychiatrists working together to try to come to agreement and to represent the different types of suffering they saw in their practices) was published. It was to be a compromise between the two positions and the contrasting understandings of mental illness. To accommodate these differing viewpoints this DSM was much longer and more detailed. The DSM-III was 494 pages long and had 265 diagnostic categories. The DSM-IV (1994) was 886 pages long and included 297 disorders. The most recent DSM-V (2013) is "about the same length" but has added new diseases and removed others (Grohol, 2018). It resulted from a group process in which the committee charged with the revision posted the revision online three times. In response they received about 13,000 letters suggesting changes, amendments, and so on, plus thousands of other e-mails and messages. Critics say that now it contains a disease for everyone and a drug treatment for most of us.

A Brief History of Western Medical Practice

At the beginning of written history, the medical practitioners in the Tigris-Euphrates and Nile valleys were also priests. Illness was regarded as a spiritual problem, a punishment for sins or for violations of the norms of society by such acts as stealing, blaspheming, or drinking from an impure vessel (Bullough & Bullough, 1972, pp. 86–101). In Egypt under Imhotep, the Egyptian pharaoh who built the stepped pyramid, medicine began to receive some separate recognition. At this time, however, the medical functionaries' roles, by modern Western standards, were strictly curtailed. Medical practitioners could treat only external maladies. Internal illnesses were firmly believed to result from and to be treatable exclusively through supernatural intervention.

Modern Western medicine appears to have been derived primarily from Greece in the fourth and fifth centuries before Christ and from medieval Europe. In both time periods, the tie between the body and the spirit, the physician and the cleric, was strong. Early Greeks erected temples in honour of Hygeia, the Greek goddess of healing, and those who were ill sought treatment in these temples. Sometimes the sick simply slept in them in hope of a cure. Sometimes temple priests acted as physicians and used powers of persuasion and suggestion to heal. Early Greek physicians viewed their calling as holy or sacred.

One of the most important Greek physicians of the time, Hippocrates, perhaps best illustrates this view. He proposed the Hippocratic oath, still relevant to the practice of physicians today. The first sentence of the oath illustrates both the sense of calling of the physician and the dedication to the gods that medical practice involved:

I swear by Apollo Physician, by Asclepius, by Health, by Panacea and by all the gods and goddesses, making them my witnesses that I will carry out, according to my ability and judgements, this oath and this indenture.

The oath further states: "But I will keep pure and holy both my life and my art" (Clendening, 1960, pp. 1, 5). The Hippocratic oath, with the injunction, "First, do no harm," contains prohibitions against harming the patient, causing an abortion, or becoming sexually involved with a patient. It considers that words spoken by a patient to a doctor are to be kept confidential and treated as "holy secrets." Nevertheless, Hippocrates and the Greek physicians of his time and somewhat later also were distinguished by their efforts to secularize the concept of disease by making its treatment not the concern solely of priests and its focus not simply on the supernatural. They began to make medicine a practice based on repeated, systematic, empirical observation. Through this conscientious focus on method, "Hippocratic medicine achieved a level of excellence never again attained in the subsequent two thousand years, and surpassed only in the twentieth century" (Lewinsohn, 1998, p. 1262).

The idea of balance that dominated Hippocratic medicine in the fourth and fifth centuries before Christ persists today in a variety of forms. Returning to health after a stressful event is thought of as returning to balance—to homeostasis. To Hippocrates, health depended on a harmonious blend of humours (fluids)—blood, phlegm, black bile, and yellow bile—that originated in the heart, brain, liver, and spleen, respectively. Sickness resulted from an imbalance in any of these four humours. Symptoms reflected this lack of balance. Treatment relied largely on the healing power of nature and on the use of certain diets and medicines to return the organism to balance and its natural order.

There were two types of practitioners, each catering to a different social class. Private physicians cared for the aristocrats. Most large towns, partly for the prestige of having a doctor and partly to serve those who needed medical care, retained public doctors. Both the public and private physicians tended to cater to the wealthier classes. The poor and the slaves usually received an inferior quality of medical care from the physician's assistant (Rosen, 1963).

The Greek period, which encompasses the later Roman Republic and the Roman Empire, is considered to have culminated in the work of Galen (130–201 CE). His discoveries were influential for almost two thousand years after his time. Working with the principles of Aristotelian teleology, he thought that every organ had a purpose and served a special function. But Galen's greatest contributions were his anatomical and physiological works (his knowledge of anatomy was based on dissections of pigs and apes) and his systematic and logical speculation (Freidson, 1975, p. 14).

When the Roman Empire collapsed, medicine and other sciences fell into disrepute and religious scholarship developed greater prominence. Conflict emerged between two modes of thought: the spiritual and philosophical. In the spiritual, truth was deduced from accepted religious principles without any reference to the real world. In the empirical, truth could only be inferred from evidence based on observation in the real world. Medicine lost much of the scientific analysis and empirical practice developed by the Greeks and Romans. Religious dogmatism limited scientific advances by prohibiting dissection and by forbidding independent thought, experimentation, and observation. The only knowledge deemed acceptable was that found in ancient texts and approved by the Church. For medieval Christians, disease was (again) a supernatural experience with a physical manifestation. Secular medicine and public health measures were criticized as signs of lack of faith. The Church, its liturgies, and its functionaries were

believed to be the source of healing; sinning was believed to be the source of illness.

The Church influenced the practice of medicine. Medicine was taught in the universities by rote and faith, and by memorizing the canons of Hippocrates, Aristotle, and Galen. The clergy practised medicine, but they were not allowed to engage in surgery or to use drugs. These two forms of physical treatments were left to the "lower" orders. Barber-surgeons treated wounds, did other types of surgery, and cut hair. Even lower in status than barber-surgeons were the apothecaries, who dispensed medicines. Hospitals were taken over by religious orders, thus coming under the control of the Church.

Medicine did not progress much during the medieval period. However, epidemics of disease and death led to certain new methods of inquiry that were instrumental in the later development of scientific medicine. Faced with a horrendous death rate such as that during the bubonic plague—the Black Death is said to have taken one-third of the population of Europe in the fourteenth century—people began to raise practical, empirical questions about disease. In the first place, it was clear that the plague was contagious from person to person. Second, not all people succumbed to the plague. Questions about the background differences of those who did and who did not fall ill seemed relevant. The bases for quarantine, germ theory, and the case history were laid.

By the eighteenth century, scientific medicine was becoming distinguished from religious practice and folk medicine. Available medical knowledge was organized and codified. Many new medical discoveries were made. The universities, particularly in Western Europe and Scotland, became centres of exciting medical advances in research and treatment. Tools, such as forceps and the clinical thermometer, were invented. New medicines, such as digitalis, were made available. Edward Jenner demonstrated the value of the smallpox vaccine. At the same time, the popular climate was confused by competition among various types of healing. People visited shrines or used the services of a variety of alternative healers. Medical research was inadequately financed, lacked facilities, and had no specialties; the few practising doctors were overworked.

The modern separation of medicine and the Church is the result of a number of social processes. The secularization of the human body as an object of science was a part of this process. A doctrinal development that paralleled the philosophical discussions of Descartes—the changing Christian doctrine of the separation of the body and the spirit that came to be called the Cartesian duality—resulted in autopsies being allowed. If the body was no longer the house of the soul, then the integrity or wholeness of the body after death was no longer of great importance. Institutional secularization occurred, too, as the Church became separated from the state. Through these processes clearer distinctions were forged among "disease," "deviance," "crime," and "sin."

Growing belief in the potential power of science and the emphasis on individual rights and freedoms contributed to the development of modern secular medicine, too. In the nineteenth century, particularly the last half, an enormous number of new discoveries occurred, as did many dubious attempts at healing:

> The medical literature of those years makes horrifying reading today: paper after learned paper recounts the benefits of bleeding, cupping, violent purging, the raising of blisters by vesicant ointments, the immersion of the body in either ice water or intolerably hot water, endless lists of botanical extracts cooked up and mixed together under the influence of nothing more than pure whim, and all these things were drilled into the heads of medical students—most of whom learned their trade as apprentices in the offices of older, established doctors. (Thomas, 1985: 19)

In fact, most of these remedies did more harm than good, with perhaps the exception of morphine and digitalis. Biology moved from the level of the organ to that of the cell. Both physiology and bacteriology were established. Germ theory emerged.

Surgery grew in sophistication along with asepsis and anaesthesia. Table 9.1 outlines some of the most important discoveries in the history of allopathic medicine.

Medicalization: A Critique of Contemporary Medicine

Medical science became increasingly influential during the period that urbanization, industrialization, bureaucratization, rationalization, and secularization developed. Medical institutions began to increase their powers as agencies of social control. More and more types of human behaviour began to be explained in medical terms. As the medical system's powers of social control increased, so, too, did the religious institutions' powers of social control decrease. Behaviours once viewed as sinful or criminal became increasingly likely to be viewed as illnesses. Alcohol addiction is a case in point. There was a time when drinking too much, too frequently, was seen as a sign of moral weakness, i.e., a sin. Today, however, alcohol addiction is often seen as a medical problem. Treatment centres for what is now considered a disease are located in hospital settings, and treatment frequently includes medication. Treatment is under the control of the medical profession. Madness, too, has gone through many different definitions and treatments over time (Foucault, 2006) as distinctions between normality and abnormality have shifted. Unhappiness has, for some, become a disorder (Geise, 2013).

Medicalization would not have been possible were it not for the acceptance of the Cartesian duality: the separation of the "whole person" from the body. This separation allowed for the medical gaze (Foucault, 1973). It imbricated seeing the person as also a distinct body with discrete organs, with a skeleton, and so forth. Medical experts could see these organs from the outside. As the individual came to be seen as a collection of parts so, too, did doctors have things to say about the various parts and their functioning. This transition was a form of biological reductionism. It included the separation of the mind and body

Table 9.1   Making Medical History: A Timeline for the History of Western Medicine

400 BCE

- Hippocrates separates medicine from religion and philosophy, treats it as a natural science

100s

- Ancient medicine culminates with Galen; his influence will last until Renaissance

700s

- Arabs develop pharmacology as a science separate from medicine

1000s

- Persian physician Avicenna (Ibn Sina) writes the Canon, textbook used in medieval Europe

1500s

- First attempts to restrict right to practise to licensed and qualified doctors
- Advances in anatomy and surgery as influence of Galen wanes

1800s

- Medical specialties begin to develop

1840s

- Inhalation anaesthesia techniques developed
- Edwin Chadwick brings about public health reforms in England

300 BCE

- Anatomy and physiology develop in Alexandria

200s

- Growing Christian religion emphasizes healing by faith

800s

- Monk-physicians treat the sick in infirmaries attached to monasteries

1200s

- Thomas Aquinas describes medicine as an art, a science, and a virtue
- Human dissection practised at Bologna

1600s

- William Harvey discovers circulation of blood
- Descartes conceives of body as machine and sees medicine as part of developing modern science
- Hôtel-Dieu in Quebec City founded, first hospital in Canada
- Use of microscope leads to new discoveries

1810s

- René Laënnec invents stethoscope

1850s

- Nurses led by Florence Nightingale save thousands in Crimean War
- Dr Elizabeth Blackwell founds New York Infirmary for Women

100s

- Asclepiades brings Greek medicine to Rome; bases treatment on diet, exercise, baths, massage

400s

- Fabiola founds first hospital in Western world at Rome

900s

- Influential medical school founded at Salerno, Italy; students include women

1300s

- Urine sample first used in diagnosis
- Black Death kills one-third of Europe's population; medicine powerless to stop it

1700s

- First successful appendectomy performed
- Guild of surgeons formed in England separate from barbers, with whom they had been joined
- Advances in scientific knowledge begin to be reflected in medical practice
- Edward Jenner proves value of vaccination in preventing smallpox

1830s

- Theodor Schwann shows all living structures made of cells

1860

- International Red Cross founded
- Joseph Lister introduces antiseptic surgery
- Gregor Mendel discovers law of heredity
- Louis Pasteur shows that diseases are caused by micro-organisms

Table 9.1 *Continued*

1870s

- Robert Koch discovers tubercle bacillus

1800s

- Otto von Bismarck introduces first state health insurance plan in Germany (1883)
- Sigmund Freud begins to develop psychoanalytic method (use of hypnosis begins in 1885; psychoanalytic method per se is introduced in 1896)
- Founding of Johns Hopkins hospital in 1889 and its medical school in 1894 introduces systematic medical education in US

1890s

- Malaria bacillus isolated Wilhelm Roentgen discovers X-ray

1900s

- The hormone adrenalin is isolated
- Flexner Report leads to reform of medical education

1910s

- Influenza epidemic kills millions worldwide

1920s

- Banting and Best produce insulin for use by diabetics
- Iron lung invented
- Alexander Fleming discovers penicillin

1930s

- Norman Bethune of Canada introduces mobile blood transfusion unit in Spain, continues work in China

1940s

- Use of antibiotics becomes widespread
- World Health Organization founded

1950s

- J. André-Thomas devises machine needed to take over heart function for performing open-heart surgeries.
- Discovery that DNA molecule is a double helix provides key to genetic code
- Jonas Salk develops polio vaccine
- Ultrasound first used to monitor fetus during pregnancy

1960s

- First state health insurance plan in North America successfully introduced in Saskatchewan despite doctors' strike
- Michael DeBakey uses artificial heart to keep patients alive during surgery
- Christiaan Barnard performs first heart transplant

1970s

- Smallpox eliminated from earth
- First baby conceived outside the womb born in England

1980s

- Cyclosporin allows entire organ transplantation
- Nuclear magnetic resonance makes possible more accurate diagnosis
- A new disease, AIDS, will kill millions

continued

Table 9.1 *Continued*

1990s	2000s	2010s
• Mapping of the Human Genome	• International public health efforts successfully halt SARS and the avian flu • Spread of antibiotic resistance • Consumer advocacy to disease recognition increased • Direct-to-consumer advertising of pharmaceuticals in the US and New Zealand • Biomedicalization and pharmaceuticalization spread	• Development of CRISPR graphene device to manipulate genes • Rise of e-scaped medicine, telemedicine, social media medicine, and other initiatives related to the availability of the Internet • New medical interventions based on stem cells • Appears that there may be a "functional cure" for HIV • Novel coronavirus, COVID-19, identified in China in late 2019; becomes global pandemic by March 2020

Source: Adapted and expanded from *Compass* (May 1988), 10.

from the spirit. In the context of these epistemological changes a new set of truths or discourses about the normal and abnormal person and the body emerged. These discourses have affected not only the patient in the clinic or doctor's office but also the view that the whole population is composed of people with varying degrees of normality and abnormality. Abnormality could be measured and observed and then treated to eradicate the pathology.

Medical institutions, including hospitals, extended-care establishments, pharmaceutical companies, and manufacturers of medical technology, have grown in importance. A large part of the gross national product is spent on health care. These are instances of medicalization, from the work of Zola (1972), a process whereby more and more of life comes to be of concern to the medical profession. Zola portrays medicalization as an expanding **attachment process**, with the following four components:

1. the expansion of what in life is deemed relevant to the good practice of medicine;
2. the retention of absolute control by the medical profession over certain technical procedures;
3. the retention of near-absolute access to certain areas by the medical profession;
4. the expansion of what in medicine is deemed relevant to the good practice of life.

In this view, the first area of medicalization is the change from medicine as a narrow, biological model of disease to a broader concern with the social, spiritual, and moral aspects of the patient's life. As well as bodily symptoms, the entire lifestyle of the patient may now be considered of concern to the doctor. For example, some physicians now routinely include in their patients' case histories questions about eating habits, friendships, marital and family relationships, work satisfaction, and the like.

The second component is the retention of absolute control over a variety of technical procedures. A doctor is permitted to do things to the human body that no one else has the right to do. Doctors are responsible for surgery, prescription drugs, hospital admittance, and referral to a specialist or another doctor. Doctors are the gatekeepers to numerous associated services and provisions related to acting upon the human body.

The maintenance of nearly absolute control over a number of formerly "normal" bodily processes, and indeed over anything that can be shown to affect the working of the body or the mind, is the third component. This third feature is seen especially in four areas: aging, drug addiction, alcoholism, and pregnancy. At one time, aging and pregnancy were viewed as normal processes, and drug addiction and alcoholism were seen as manifestations of human weakness. Now, however, medical specialties have arisen to deal with each of these. Zola illustrates this point with a discussion of the change in the view and treatment of pregnancy. He points to the pivotal importance of the management of childbirth for the growth of medical power.

The last component is the expansion of what in medicine is seen as relevant to a good life. This aspect of medicalization refers to the spread of the inclusion of a wide variety of social problems and behavioural anomalies as medical problems. Depression, ADHD, obesity, criminality, and juvenile delinquency are among those "problems" that were once linked to the moral/religious realm and are increasingly seen as amenable to medical definition and treatment.

Ivan Illich's Critique of Medicalization

Ivan Illich offers another useful definition and critique of medicalization in *Limits to Medicine* (1976). His argument is that contemporary medical practice is *inherently iatrogenic*, that is, it creates disease and illness even as it provides medical assistance. Three sorts of **iatrogenesis** are separated out and explained.

[It is] clinical, when pain, sickness, and death result from the provision of medical care; it is social, when health policies reinforce an industrial organization which generates dependency and ill health; and it is structural, when medically sponsored behaviour and delusions restrict the vital autonomy of people by undermining their competence in growing up, caring for each other, and aging. (Illich, 1976, p. 165)

Clinical iatrogenesis, that is, injury and/or disability that results directly from the work of the doctor, nurse, or other medical care provider in the hospital or in the clinic, is the first problem addressed by Illich. The opioid crisis is a case in point as opioid addiction is often the direct result of a dependence on prescribed medications. Thalidomide, prescribed in the 1950s and 1960s in West Germany, Canada, and elsewhere to women with a history of miscarriage, resulted in untold tragedy when numerous children were born without limbs. DES (diethylstilbestrol), again prescribed (in the 1950s) to women with obstetric problems, was later found to result in thousands of cases of ovarian and cervical cancer in the daughters of those who used DES and in other cancers in their sons. Today, millions receive chemotherapy, radiation, and/or surgery as treatment for a variety of cancers. However, such treatments are often felt by the patients to be more painful and debilitating than the disease itself. Those for whom a cure is effective may feel that the cost is worth the pain. On the other hand, those who are not cured, and whose lives can be extended for only a limited period, may regret having submitted to such treatments. The spread of HIV/AIDS and hepatitis C through blood transfusions from Canada's blood supply, along with the development of antibiotic resistance, are two other widely known examples of clinical iatrogenesis.

The rise in hospital-acquired infections and numerous perceived medical errors is another impetus for critical thinking among the populace. The Canadian Institute for Health Information estimates, based on a survey of Canadians, that one in four Canadians has been affected by medical error. O'Hagan and his colleagues (2009) found that one in six Canadian patients said they had experienced a medical error of one sort or another. This amounted to approximately 4.2 million Canadians who were given the wrong drug or the wrong dose, the wrong report, the wrong surgery, and so on. These are just a few of the troubles that occur in a situation where the beneficence of medicine is assumed.

Social iatrogenesis is evident in the impact of medicine on lifespan. Medical and technological intervention begins at birth and ends with the care of the aging and dying. There are medical specialties to deal with pregnancy and childbirth (obstetrics), childhood (pediatrics), adult women (gynecology), adult men (urology), the elderly (geriatrics), and the dying (palliative care). The presence of medical specialists to deal with various normal stages of the human lifespan is symbolic of the trend towards the medicalization of life and the increasing addiction of modern people to medical institutions.

There is a growing dependence on medical interventions in Western societies. The huge growth in spending on medical treatment, on hospitalization, and on pharmaceuticals is just one example. The success of medicalization has played a part in the generation of the "risk" society (Beck, 1992). "In this view, risks are increasingly globalized and generalized in ways which are seen as out of the individual's control, bolstering the social and political significance of scientific institutions and expert knowledge represented by, for instance, medicine" (Howson, 1998, p. 196). Who in modern society is not aware of the myriad risks associated with just living? Air, water, and land pollution compete with fatty diets, botulism and dangerous bacteria in food, pesticide residues, excess alcohol consumption, and even sunshine as things we have to "watch out for." Many public health policies are based on "prevention," which is a form of early detection. Examples leap easily to mind, such as screening for breast, cervical, testicular, and prostate cancer. Such surveillance increases the development of "risk consciousness." The negative side effects of this monitoring are seldom factored into their adoption. Avoiding risks of disease and maintaining health have become moral imperatives (Lupton, 1993; Howson, 1998), a taken-for-granted part of everyday life and the maintenance of the identity of being a good citizen.

Considerable evidence suggests that pharmaceuticals are often prescribed to people for social problems. Women consistently receive more prescriptions for mood-altering pharmaceuticals such as tranquilizers and anti-depressants than men do. Women in the middle and older age groups are at

highest risk. Research has found that the majority of those who use tranquilizers do so for a variety of societal, familial, and occupational demands and expectations rather than for a physical need (Tone, 2009). Women's very bodily shape and appearance have become medically diagnosable by plastic surgeons who recently instituted a new disease category—small breast syndrome. Cosmetic surgeons now offer designer vaginas. Naomi Wolf in *The Beauty Myth* (1991) says that medical discourse tells women that "beauty" is equivalent to good health. As beauty and health come to overlap so, too, do beauty norms and medical solutions to perceived physical inadequacies. After many years of problems with breast implants France has recently banned those clearly linked to a certain rare cancer (*BBC News*, 2019).

By *structural iatrogenesis* Illich means the loss of individual autonomy and the creation of dependency. The responsibility for good health has been wrested from the individual and the community as a result of the imposition of the medical model. This medical model often offers a ready and speedy solution to problems. The solution is enabled by the prevalence of medical institutions and medical practitioners. Pain, suffering, disease, and death are important experiences for all human beings. They can encourage the development of service, compassion, and connectedness with others. But medical bureaucracy and technology minimize the possibilities for the fertile development of family and community-based models of care. The medical model and its institutions usurp individual initiative and responsibility and thus destroy humanitarianism and spiritual development. In sum, in Illich's view, we rely excessively on medical care, and this overdependence has many destructive consequences for people and their communities. To correct this problem he advocates the deprofessionalization and debureaucratization of medical practice, and the maximization of individual responsibility. Self-care, autonomy, and self-development should be the guiding principles for well-being in Illich's view.

Vicente Navarro, a leading Marxist critic of medicine, takes issue with Illich's explanation of medicalization. Navarro (1976) argues that medicine is a mere pawn in the hands of a much greater power—the power of the state directed through the dominant class. The health industry is neither administered nor controlled by medical professionals. Increasingly, members of the corporate class (the owners and managers of financial capital) dominate in health and other important spheres of the economy. They influence the health delivery sector of the economy through the pharmaceutical and medical device industries, medical insurance companies, and medical organizations providing related health-care service delivery. Doctors themselves are often invested in these quasi-medical corporations. The majority of those involved in health care as consumers and employees have no control over either the production or consumption of health services.

The state supports the dominance of conventional medicine. It also challenges medical dominance "through its attempts to rationalize health care" (Coburn et al., 1997). The numerous debates among doctors and nurses and the provinces and federal government attest to the conflicts that continue in these arenas. Medical organizations are constrained not only by state policies but also, through political processes, by the public at large. The numbers of hospitals, the payment schemes under which doctors, nurse practitioners, midwives and nurses work, the adoption of new medical technologies, medical insurance and investment in pharmaceuticals (among other relevant things) are all under the jurisdiction of the provinces.

The Medicalization of Human Behaviour

Conrad and Schneider (1980) have analyzed the impact of the medicalization process in a number of areas, including mental illness, alcoholism, opiate addiction, delinquency, **hyperkinesis**, homosexuality, and crime. In all of these situations they attempt to show how medicine has become increasingly an institution of social control. Their research on hyperkinesis (now called ADD or attention deficit disorder and ADHD or attention deficit

hyperactivity disorder) provides one specific illustration of the process of medicalization.

Hyperkinesis (ADHD) is a relatively new "disease" that has been "discovered" over the past three-quarters of a century or so. It is estimated that it now affects about 5 per cent of children and is the most prevalent of childhood psychiatric disorders (CADDAC, 2019). Although its symptoms vary a great deal from child to child, typical symptom patterns include some of the following: excess motor activity, short attention span, restlessness, mood swings, clumsiness, impulsiveness, inability to sit still or comply with rules, and sleeping problems. Most of these behaviours are typical of all children at least part of the time. In fact, all of these behaviours are probably typical of all people at least once in a while. Conrad and Schneider have explained the processes by which these "normal" behaviours became grouped and categorized as indicators of "disease." They argue that hyperkinesis was "discovered" for a number of social reasons.

The first step was the discovery in 1937 by Charles Bradley that amphetamine drugs had a powerful and calming effect on the behaviour of children who had come to him with learning or behaviour disorders. Only later, in 1957, were the "disorders" to become a specific diagnostic category—hyperkinetic impulse disorder. A national task force in the US, appointed to deal with the ambiguities surrounding the diagnosis of the disorder and its treatment, offered a modern name: "minimal brain dysfunction" (MBD). In 1971, Ritalin, a new drug with properties similar to those of amphetamines but with different negative side effects, was approved for use with children. Soon afterwards, Ritalin became the drug of choice for children with hyperkinesis or minimal brain dysfunction. MBD or hyperkinesis became the most commonly diagnosed psychiatric problem of childhood. Special clinics to treat hyperkinetic children were established, and substantial research funding became available for those studying the problem. Articles appeared regularly in mass-media periodicals in the 1970s, and many teachers developed a working clinical knowledge of the diagnosis. In short, once the drug to treat the disorder was synthesized, produced, and made available, MBD became a popular disease around which a great deal of lay knowledge and activity was organized. Since that time ADD and ADHD have grown in incidence around the world. These diagnoses have been associated with gender, social class, pesticide use, the prevalence of female primary school teachers, classroom structure, and curriculum, among other things (see Rose, 2006).

Three broad social factors aided the social construction of hyperkinesis as a medical problem. These same forces have continued and grown as MBD became ADHD and the diagnosis became more common: (1) the pharmaceutical revolution, (2) trends in medical practice, and (3) government action (Rose, 2006, p. 157). First, the pharmaceutical revolution has been marked by a great number of drug-related success stories, such as penicillin's success as a widely effective antibiotic and the behaviour-controlling effects of psychoactive drugs in a variety of mental illnesses. Such early "successes" encouraged hope for the potential value of medications in many areas of life. Further, MBD has become ADHD with the help of the powerful effects of advertising in the mass media, on the Internet, and directly to doctors. These efforts have assisted in what has been termed the **pharmaceuticalization** of society (Abraham, 2010). Second, as the mortality rate from infectious diseases in children has decreased, the possibility for concern with less-threatening disorders has emerged. Medical practitioners, especially pediatricians, began to seek other sorts of problems in children that they could work on and treat. In this process they began to pay more attention to the mental health of children and to child psychiatry. Third, government publications, task forces, conferences, and the actions of concerned parents, along with the activities of the pharmaceutical companies, reinforced the legitimizing of ADHD as a new diagnostic category to be managed by the medical profession. The points made in this analysis are several. First, the behaviour labelled "hyperkinetic" existed long before the diagnosis. Indeed, such behaviour was, and is, widespread throughout the population. Second, the

popularizing of the diagnosis corresponded to its recognition as a "pharmacologically treatable" disorder. Third, the expansionist project was aided by the entrepreneurial behaviours of government and the drug companies, along with the Association for Children with Learning Disabilities, based in the United States. To conclude, medicalization is seen, in this example, as a process by which common behaviours become codified and defined as entailing certain symptoms that are best managed through medical interventions (see Rose, 2006).

Forging the link between social problems and health issues is a process that includes five **sequential stages of medicalization** (Conrad & Schneider, 1980). The first stage involves the definition of the behaviour as deviant from the normative expectations and as problematic. The second stage involves prospecting for a medical angle on the newly discovered problem behaviour. The medical diagnosis begins to emerge. Often a confirmatory study or a new and effective treatment is developed to reinforce the new diagnosis. In the third stage the medical legitimacy is reinforced and the establishment of the physician as medical **moral entrepreneur** continues through the development of other medical interventions and treatments, further research, the mobilization of citizen groups for support and advocacy, and the like. Subsequently, as the legitimization continues and new specialties develop, the state and health insurance companies accept the reality of the diagnosis. The final stage is the institutionalization of the diagnosis as a "fact," followed by investments in new treatments. Further research on the developing diagnosis is funded and widespread acceptance occurs. There may be some flexibility in these stages and some moving back and forth over time.

In "The Shifting Engines of Medicalization," Conrad (2005, p. 3) defines medicalization again and focuses on the primacy of definitional aspects of the process. "The essence of medicalization became the definitional issue: defining a problem in medical terms, usually as an illness or disorder, or using a medical intervention to treat it." What have changed, though, according to Conrad, are the causes of the continuous growth in the tendency of medicine to define aspects of life as relevant to it. Instead of focusing on the drivers noted above (doctors, social movements, and other interest groups), Conrad argues that medicine is now more rooted in the pursuit of commercial and market interests. Medical doctors are still the gatekeepers in the system, but they are subservient to larger social and economic forces, which he pinpoints as biotechnological innovations, especially in the realms of pharmaceuticals and genetics along with increased consumer power and organization and managed care. The increasing privatization of the payment for medical care in Canada also contributes to the expansion of the jurisdiction of medicine.

Contemporary medicalization processes have become a great deal more complex in the past half-century or so and debates about the encroaching powers of medicine and medicalization continue and expand. Foucault was one of the most important theorists to add to the debates with his focus on medicalization as a central discourse in the demarcation between the normal and abnormal and the pathologizing of what was considered to be abnormal. Medical discourse was used as a bludgeon, a tool that, through its dominating and reflexive discourses and knowledge/power, infused the identity of the modern person. Through this introjection or internalization of discourses people learn to govern themselves and see themselves as well or as not in keeping with disciplinary knowledges (medical knowledges) and through **technologies of self**. In this context, through circulating discourses, people have come to think of themselves as bodies existing in health or illness and in need of intervention. For example, with respect to feelings of sadness, people might now think of themselves as depressed because of their neuro-chemistry or neuro-chemical selves (Rose, 2003). These technologies of self, internalized by us all, are used to govern the self in the interests of the prevailing medical power/knowledges.

Adele Clarke and her colleagues (2003) have built on some of Foucault's ideas and also on their observations of some of the changes in the political economy. They have changed the descriptive term from "medicalization" to "biomedicalization"

because of neo-liberalism and the ways in which neo-liberalism has increased the spread of medicalization.

Neo-liberalism is composed of five fundamental rationalities of "good governance": (1) minimal government intervention in the "free" working of the economy and markets under advanced capitalism; (2) a belief in the fundamental power for good of the market; (3) a focus on managing the risks associated with economic development; (4) the promotion of and reliance on the idea that individuals are essentially responsible for their own fate; and (5) the acceptance of inequality as an inevitable consequence of these views (Ayo, 2012).

In this context we are interested in governmentality (Foucault, 1991). Governmentality refers to how people become themselves and learn to govern themselves through engagement with discourses that surround them. This concept points to the processes whereby individuals govern themselves so as to become health-conscious subjects and adopt **healthism** as a crucial part of their identity as good citizens (Crawford, 2006). Biomedicalization takes into account the powerful discourses and economic and political forces of neo-liberalism, particularly through changes that are internal to the technologies (such as pharmaceutical innovation and expansion) associated with medicine. Whereas medicalization was viewed as one of the most powerful transformations of the last half of the twentieth century, biomedicalization, argue Clarke and her colleagues (2003, p. 162), has usurped medicalization. "Biomedicalization is our term for the increasingly complex, multisited, multidirectional processes of medicalization that today are being both extended and reconstituted through the emergent social forms and practices of a highly and increasingly technoscientific biomedicine." These technoscientific innovations depend on and encourage enormous corporate investments and neo-liberal governing principles. While most of this growth originated in the US, Canada has quickly absorbed many of the advances and adopted many of the medical innovations. Empirically, in Canada, we see the rise of various types of privatization, even in the context of the universal medical care system. The pharmaceutical and medical device companies are two centrally important institutional drivers of the increasing costs of medicare as well as out-of-pocket medical expenses in Canada. About one-third of medical care for Canadian citizens is based on out-of-pocket expenses. Further, and highlighting the increasing importance of a medical view of reality, medicare is seen as emblematic of Canadian identity and as a symbol of good nationhood. Its meaning has spread beyond that of technical, surgical, pharmaceutical, or other medical interventions so that it infuses the culture, values, and norms of the society. Its influence can be seen on all aspects of everyday life. The culture of biomedicine has become so pervasive that it can be considered a new and growing regime of truth (Foucault, 1980, p. 133, as cited by Clarke et al., 2003, p. 163). In many ways biomedicine is not fettered by governments but under neo-liberalism is autonomous, independently powerful, and cannot be controlled.

Clarke and her colleagues (2003) document five areas in which they observe the processes of biomedicalization spreading:

1. The economic growth of privatized biomedical and technoscientific research as a proportion of the GNP along with the commodification of health-related research findings.
2. A focus on governing and stratifying population and evaluating lifestyles and behaviours with respect to their relative risk for different diseases and conditions before actual disease diagnosis.
3. Increasingly sophisticated, **digitized medicine**, including record-keeping, interventions, evaluations, and developments in sciences, including, for instance, genetics, molecularization, cloning, genetic engineering, nanoscience, and cloning.
4. Transformation in knowledges and their development and dissemination through such publicly available means as the Internet, health columns in newspapers and magazines, online support groups, direct-to-consumer advertisements, and so on.

5. Alteration in bodies through such interventions as pacemakers, cosmetic and bariatric surgery, and other individualized and customized niche-marketed medical interventions.

Let us discuss each of these in turn with a focus on their relevance to Canadian society. The first point is that there has been an absolute growth in the percentage of the GDP devoted to medical care over the past several decades and the focus of the expenditures has changed. According to comparative World Bank data, Canada spent 11.3 per cent of its GDP and the United States 17.9 per cent of its GDP on health care in 2018 (Canadian Institute of Health Information [CIHI], 2019). These figures represent a change over time of almost 4 per cent annual growth rate since 2000 in Canada and constitute about $6,839 per person today. Second, over the past two decades pharmaceuticals have been one of the fastest-growing components of the health-care system, according to the Canadian Institute for Health Information, and today comprise 15.7 per cent of the budget as compared with for 28.3 per cent for hospitals and 15.1 per cent for physicians (CIHI, 2019). When compared to similar countries this growth rate is second only to that of the US. Between 1998 and 2007 the annual rate of increase for drug expenditures out of hospital was 10.1 per cent annually. This rate has slowed somewhat since the economic crash of 2008. There has been a decrease in the growth rate of expenditures for pharmaceuticals in Canada over the recent past from 4.5 to 3.3 per cent. Still, it is a pace of increase that sometimes surpasses that of doctors and hospitals. For example, in 2018 the increase in pharmaceutical spending was 3.2 per cent as compared to 3.0 per cent for hospitals and 2.2 per cent for physicians. About 31 per cent of medical care is now paid for privately in Canada. About 15.4 per cent is due to out-of-pocket expense, while 12.4 per cent is through private insurance and 3.3 per cent is categorized as "other" (CIHI, 2019).

The second point is the idea that the demarcation between normal and abnormal populations has continued and the definition of abnormal has expanded. This has been accompanied by enormous efforts in the area of what is called health promotion within public health. Biomedicine can be seen in the continuing encroachment of a "risk society" mentality (Beck, 1992; Giddens, 1999) among Canadians and in various public health initiatives. We have discussed the rapid implementation of the vaccine for HPV among young girls. This is a case in point of the spread of the risk society mentality. We also see striking levels of emphasis on mammography and PSA testing even in the continuing face of ambiguity about their value for health protection. Although there do not appear to be any physical iatrogenic effects of PSA testing, the fear and anxiety resulting when elevated levels of PSA are noted are consequential and can increase anxiety. Watching and waiting to see if high levels go up or down or remain the same can be a serious emotional issue for some men and their families. With respect to mammography, evidence indicates that, especially with older machines, there can be carcinogenic effects from the testing alone. Furthermore, the false positives can cause needless worry for the person who has to be tested and retested. A recently published 25-year review of screening mammography has found that it makes no difference in death rates from breast cancer but that it may cause harm from over-diagnosis (Miller et al., 2014). Populations are described and monitored as if they are merely so many bodies at risk for one medical problem or another. The rates of obesity among children and adults of differing ages and genders, for example, are calculated and published regularly. The links between the growth in body size and various health problems, most notably diabetes, are advertised on various popular and social media. Still there is some debate about what constitutes obesity and at what level of overweight there may or may not be negative health consequences. Moreover, the health consequences of obesity and overweight are still debated. The spread of disease categories and pre-disease categories of risk is also evident in the case of mental illnesses, as our earlier discussion of the DSM and its expansion suggests.

An analysis of ADHD (Hart et al., 2006) demonstrates market segmentation, particularly by gender, and has sought to show how it is actually more appropriate to think of ADHD as an instance of the medicalization of male behaviours. The authors note that ADHD is now the most prevalent type of childhood disability in North America (Hart et al., 2006, p. 132). With the diagnosis, the use of Ritalin has grown exponentially. Its use has increased 800 per cent since 1994, and 90 per cent of this utilization has been in the US, although Canada and Great Britain are among the countries whose populations are increasingly endorsing this new disorder. Apparently, too, between 75 and 80 per cent of those for whom this drug is prescribed are male. Hart and his colleagues propose that the use of Ritalin corresponds to a failure among parents (usually mothers) and teachers (usually female) to socialize boys into acceptable behaviours. Furthermore, the authors link higher prescription rates to states with higher proportions of white children, disproportionately high socio-economic privilege, and expectations of higher performance levels on standardized tests. In addition, the over-prescription of Ritalin has meant that it has become a common "street" drug—sometimes known as "kibble and bits," "vitamin R," or "kiddie cocaine"—and that many young people sell it or pass it on to others.

The third point in the argument about biomedicalization is perhaps best and most succinctly highlighted by reference to the enormous sway of genetics today through the Human Genome Project. Bilateral mastectomies have become a treatment of choice for women with a history of breast cancer in their families and the presence of the BRCA1 or BRCA2 gene. The myriad of genetic tests to which newborns are subjected is an aspect of the phenomenon "patients-in-waiting" (Timmermans & Buchbinder, 2010). We have discussed some of the issues involved in living with the knowledge knowing that one will inevitably be diagnosed with Huntington's disease. That there are debates over whether or not newly discovered genes can be patented suggests one of the ways that neo-liberalism is imbricated in this component of biomedicalization.

The fourth point refers to the enormous spread of the mass and social media along with the Internet in general as sites for the expansion of health information and disease-mongering. More and more people are using the Internet for information about health. In fact, in 2016, of the millions of Canadians 16 years and over who regularly used the Internet, about 30 per cent used it for health information (CIRA, 2016). The Internet is also regularly used for getting a second opinion (Underhill & McKeown, 2008). Offering a second opinion online has, in fact, become a business. Nowadays a number of sites offer second opinions. For example, there is one from Stanford that, in return for $700, will review all of your medical records and then send a report evaluating the first opinion to your local doctors (Stanford Health Care, 2019). Apparently, a sizable percentage of people prefer to go to the Internet not instead of but before or after consulting their regular general allopathic practitioner (Hesse et al., 2005). Even caregivers go to the Internet for health information (Sadasivam et al., 2013). The use of the Internet for second opinions perhaps signals the diminution of the power of the medical doctor and a growing critical consciousness about medicine and its limits. It may also reflect the spread of the risk society consciousness so that experts are no longer trusted unthinkingly. At the same time the use of the Internet does not necessarily suggest a rejection of the model of medicine but just a different vantage point for the patient. The medical patient has become more autonomous and as compared to the doctor has relatively more power than in the past. In a sense the patient now has the capacity to become a consumer who can compare diagnoses and treatments. Of course, this choice is actually still limited by finances and by the availability and accessibility of medical practitioners. Once treatment is requested and offered the consumer usually becomes a patient again and reverts to the more passive position. Many physicians say that their work benefits from the prior research of their patients, provided the online information was reliable, accurate, and relevant (Murray et al., 2003).

The final point refers to what in Chapter 7 we called "aspirational medicine," the spread of biomedical interventions to make one's life better or, as Elliott (2004) says, "better than well." One category of intervention is "brainpower from a bottle" (Kudlow, 2013). Apparently off-label use of stimulants to enhance concentration and to enable long nights of studying or working is significant.

CRITICAL THINKING

Box 9.1 • Health Care and the Digital Revolution: Digitized Health Care

How will access to and quality of health care change in the future as a result of the digitization of our lives? According to a recent poll most Canadians are not skeptical but believe that health care will improve as the result of the move to online records, appointments, test results, and the like (Vogel, 2019). Most Canadians are optimistic about the future of medical care under digitization. They believe that access would improve, records and outcomes would be better, and they could track their own health online. Some were concerned about the possible inroads resulting from limiting their health record privacy. More than 75 per cent thought that wearable devices would be linked to their health records, thus enabling a continuous and beneficent monitoring of their health. Forty per cent were willing to share their health data with Siri, Google, Alexa, and Fitbit and would be comfortable with these platforms monitoring and reporting their health-related measurements to their care providers (Vogel, 2019).

What about you? What do you think the issues are?

Approximately 25 per cent of the students at some Canadian universities use such stimulants as aids to schoolwork and exam preparation. About 10 per cent of medical students have reported that they have used stimulants off-label to improve their performance in school, and about 12 per cent of dental students admit to such use (Kudlow, 2013). The downside of such seemingly innocent and even, to some viewpoints, practical use of stimulants is that those who do use them are much more likely also to use alcohol, cigarettes, marijuana, cocaine, and ecstasy and to drive recklessly. Furthermore, studies suggest that while the use of stimulants may not improve performance it does often lead to over-confidence.

Three other newly discovered "diseases" linked to pharmaceutical innovation are premenstrual syndrome (PMS), menopause, and erectile dysfunction. Considerable medical attention—and then sociological, feminist, and other critical attention—has been paid to these. Metzl

and Angel (2004) document the increasing use of Prozac, a highly popular anti-depressant, for an expanding variety of women's issues, including PMS or what is now labelled "premenstrual dysphoric disorder." McCrea (1983) documents the history of the discovery of menopause as a disease and notes several parallels to Conrad and Schneider's analysis of hyperkinesis. McCrea dates the discovery of the disease to the 1960s when a gynecologist was given more than $1 million in grants by the pharmaceutical industry. Very soon, this gynecologist was writing and speaking about menopause. He described it as a deficiency disease leading to a loss of femininity and "living decay." The diagnosis was inevitably coupled with a pharmaceutical solution—ERT (estrogen replacement therapy). In a feminist analysis, Dickson (1990, p. 18) argued that the "mounting sales of oestrogen are a result of the expanding concept of menopause as pathology." Still, many argue that menopause is neither a "disease" nor

CRITICAL THINKING

Box 9.2 • Uncertain and Unequal Medicalization: The Case of Brian Sinclair

Consider Brian Sinclair, a First Nations man who sought emergency medical care but did not receive it. He died in 2008 sitting in a wheelchair in the emergency ward of a hospital in Winnipeg after he had spent 34 hours without the attention of the health-care staff. An autopsy discovered that he died from an easily treated bladder infection. Other patients in the ER waiting room and security staff had repeatedly reminded the health-care workers of the presence and increasing suffering of Mr Sinclair but they were ignored. In the end, the medical staff finally noticed Mr Sinclair after he had died in his wheelchair. He had been deceased between two and seven hours before being noticed by the medical staff. Had any of the 17 requests and reminders from the public or security staff been attended to, Mr Sinclair could have received a prescription medication resulting in

a complete cure of the bladder infection (Lett, 2010). Among the many reasons examined by the coroner's report for this calamity was the fact that the nurses routinely offered sustenance, food, drink, and a place to sit inside out of the cold to the homeless and needy Winnipeg citizens with no place to go in the daytime when the shelters were closed. The triage clerk had failed to note Brian Sinclair's presence and his need for emergency care. From the visual vantage point of the nurses whose site line was blocked by the recent new design of the emergency room he must have looked as if he was just keeping warm.

What social and health policies need to be in place to prevent such a tragedy from happening again? Read the coroner's report to get a full picture of the history and current events leading to Brian Sinclair's death.

CRITICAL THINKING

Box 9.3 • Medical Status as Identity: Disclosing HIV Status

Should people be required to disclose their HIV diagnosis? If so, under what circumstances should this be required? The Supreme Court of Canada ruled in 1998 that if significant risk of HIV transmission was involved then individuals ought to disclose their HIV status. In 2012 the Court decided that disclosure was required if there was a realistic risk of transmission—but with a caveat. If the HIV viral load was relatively low and if a couple engaging in heterosexual vaginal intercourse used a condom, then disclosure was not deemed to be essential.

These issues are highly contentious. A variety of viewpoints have been expressed, often acrimoniously.

What do you think some of the arguments might be? Two points follow. On the one hand, some people oppose the law because they think it would likely result in people being unwilling to be tested in the first place. On the other hand are those who argue that if the law is not in place then people would be able to get away with spreading the virus from sexual partner to sexual partner or via sharing apparatus for drugs as a form of intentional malfeasance. Clearly, this is an important but debateable issue. This is the same debate as the one about any sexually transmitted infection except that the consequences of the decision are more serious. What do you think?

an experience most women pass through with difficulty. Many women hardly observe any difference between menopause and the times before and afterwards. The discovery that the ingredients in the drug now called Viagra, initially developed to treat heart disease, had the side effect of causing an erection led to the marketing of the drug for the newly popularized disease of erectile dysfunction (Loe, 2006). This drug has been so successful that Viagra has become a metaphor for a bull market—a rapidly rising stock market is sometimes called a Viagra market!

Highlighted Issues

Box 9.4 • Disease Definition

There are a number of different, competing models of disease. Some classes of disease are virtually assertions about the cause, e.g., cut on finger; others are simply descriptions of visually obvious, technically measurable, or verbally presented symptoms, e.g., high blood pressure. Some are classified by site, e.g., diseases of the stomach; some are categories of symptoms, e.g., headache; others are the names of syndromes that include the nature, symptoms, cause, and prognosis, e.g., Tay-Sachs disease. This list of categorizations could be extended. But the point

is that disease diagnosis is not a consistent, straightforward, unequivocal procedure. Diseases vary fundamentally in their history of discovery, their certainty and clarity, ranging from the most clearly defined, e.g., major anatomical defects caused by trauma, to those of unknown etiology and variable progression and description, e.g., multiple sclerosis. Given variability in the meaning of disease, it is not surprising that the process of diagnosis is sometimes considered to be an art rather than a science (Blaxter, 1978).

Medicalization and Demedicalization

The link between health and illness and morality is a universal phenomenon (Freidson, 1970, 1975). Religion, medicine, and morality frequently are connected. This integration may become a problem, however, in a complex industrialized society such as ours, in which the medical and the religious institutions are separate. The official perspective is that doctors deal with physiologically evident illnesses, while the clergy and the courts deal with moral and legal concerns. The jurisdictions are believed to be distinct. Yet, the doctor is accorded a good deal more power, prestige, and influence in our society than the religious functionary or average lawyer. This power is granted in part because the doctor's work is seen as altruistic, related to the service of others, and impartial (and potentially needed by all, even the irreligious) (see Parsons, 1951, for further discussion). In fact, however, as we have demonstrated, the doctor makes moral

judgements in ever-widening spheres of life (Illich, 1976; Zola, 1972; Conrad, 1975).

Physicians tend to *act* in the face of uncertainty, to diagnose disease but not to diagnose **non-disease**, and to consider social characteristics of patients in their diagnoses and treatments of physical ailments. Thus, in a variety of ways, the doctor labels or "creates" a definition of illness for the person who consults her or him.

Some argue that demedicalization is more characteristic of contemporary society than is medicalization (Fox, 1977). Recently, evidence is mounting that the power of the medical model to determine how we think about health and illness has declined in one particular way. This is because alternative health-care providers are challenging the dominance of the conventional allopathic physician in the medical labour force. The prevalence of the medical model's way of thinking about health, illness, and treatment has been criticized frequently. Some point to the fact that increasing expenditures on the provision of medical care have not meant an

Remembering Our History

Box 9.5 • Anti-Black Racism in American Health Care

Many of us are familiar with the Tuskegee experiments in which African-American men with syphilis were allowed to go untreated, suffer, and die terrible deaths even though there was a widely accepted and effective treatment (antibiotics) available at the time. This gross neglect was justified as "necessary" for the scientific understanding of the course of untreated syphilis. Lesser known, perhaps, are the experiments designed to find treatments for fistula (a hole developing in childbirth between the rectum and vagina that allows leakage) on slave women by the revered father of American gynecology, James Marion Sims. Even today, African Americans are more likely to be recruited for dangerous clinical trials because this is a way of earning money available to the unemployed

and underemployed. The differences in death rates between black and non-black Americans for diseases such as breast and cervical cancers are just two of the many contemporary examples of inequity in the availability of early detection and effective medical treatments. Such racism is true in the case of mental illness diagnoses as well. According to Metzl (2010) there are repeated stories of black Americans being diagnosed under the DSM with schizophrenia because of their hostility and aggression in the face of discrimination, prejudice, and violence exhibited towards them. Thus, the Tuskegee experiments stand as an illustration of a widespread racism in diagnosis, access to medical care, prevention, and early detection of disease for black people that continues today.

increase in the level of good health in the population. The new disease profile, which demonstrates the prevalence of chronic illness, mitigates the pervasive power of the medical model.

Implicit in Freidson's argument about the dominance of the medical profession is the notion that it has control over (1) the content of care, (2) clients, (3) other health occupations, and (4) policy (Coburn et al., 1997). Many have argued that allopathic medicine is declining in power due to the proletarianization of the profession and the decreasing gap in education between physicians and patients (Coburn et al., 1997, p. 2). Others disagree. Coburn and his colleagues have recently examined this issue and concluded "the state in Ontario is increasingly controlling both the context, and, more indirectly, the content of medical care. Physicians' fees, incomes, numbers, and modes of representation have all been affected" (Coburn et al., 1997, p. 8). This shift has occurred largely through resource allocation. The boundaries of medical practice are increasingly critically examined and constrained by the state through (1) an increased reliance on health planners, health economists, evidence-based medical practice, and epidemiologists in the conceptualization of appropriate and inappropriate medical treatments via such things as cost–benefit and health outcome measures; and (2) an increasingly legitimated critique of the scientific basis of much of allopathic medical practice. The state has been able to "cut through" dealing with an increasingly hierarchical medical profession, i.e., a profession controlled via its colleges, professional associations, and other medical elites (such as specialists, and physicians at university hospitals). While medical professionals still comprise the most powerful occupational group in the overall medical system, as compared to their own previous position they have decreased in dominance.

Williams and Calnan point to larger cultural changes that are implicated in threats to medical dominance. In particular, they are persuaded that "the lay public are not simply passive and dependent upon modern medicine, nor are they necessarily duped by medical ideology and technology. Rather, in late modernity, a far more critical distance is beginning to open up between modern medicine and the lay populace" (Williams & Calnan, 1996, p. 1617). Contributing to this view that, in today's postmodern society, the medicalization thesis is overstated is the growth of social reflexivity—a process through which people now think about truth(s) as relative. The "chronic feature of late modernity" is "a never-ending cycle of reappraisals and revisions in the light of new information and knowledge" (Williams & Calnan, 1996, p. 1617). As more and more people pay attention to mass and social media and as these media reflect constantly critical and changing views of various aspects of social and cultural life—such as science, technology, and medicine—people tend to become more knowledgeable about issues that relate to health, illness, and medical care. The experience that everything constitutes a risk for some disease or misfortune—even the sunshine now causes skin cancer—leads the populace to be cynical, uncertain, and skeptical of esoteric knowledge, science, allopathic medicine, and claims to objectivity and truth. Thus, culture may be becoming demedicalized. The experience of risk is so widespread that it generalizes beyond medical risk to all sorts of other risks in the modern world, including environmental, industrial, and other such hazards (Beck, 1992), that may outstrip the fear of personal illness in some ways.

Summary

1. The definition and diagnosis of illness today are largely the result of the labelling activities of the medical profession. The medical profession labels "deviant" and "normal" feelings and bodily signs and symptoms, and these definitions become reality for social actors.

2. The chapter gives a brief overview of the relationship between medicine and religion through history.
3. Over the past two centuries, medicine has become a distinct discipline. Definitions of "sin," "crime," and "illness" have changed. Some criminal or sinful behaviours are now viewed as illnesses, e.g., drug and alcohol addiction, although the law may not reflect those medical viewpoints.
4. Medicalization and biomedicalization are increasingly powerful social influences.
5. The physician is not only a scientist but also a moral decision-maker or moral entrepreneur. Medicine can legitimate the illness it diagnoses on the condition that the patient adopt the "sick role" prescribed by the doctor. Medicine defines what is deviant from health and also how the patient is to react to that definition. Illness is "legitimated deviance" insofar as it has been identified by the physician and the appropriate steps are taken by the patient to get well.
6. Doctors must make other moral decisions such as the allocation of resources, choosing between the present and future interests of the patient, and balancing the needs of the patient versus those of his or her family.
7. Medicalization leads to medical action in situations of uncertainty.
8. Medicalization can be observed in the micro-situation of physicians' controlling verbal interaction between the patient and the physician.

Key Terms

attachment process
digitized medicine
healthism
hyperkinesis
iatrogenesis
mediated

moral entrepreneur
non-disease
pharmaceuticalization
sequential stages of medicalization
technologies of self

Questions for Study and Discussion

1. Take one behaviour that can been seen both as moral/immoral and as wellness/disease and elaborate on the consequences of each diagnosis or definition of reality.
2. Examine a search engine for websites on a controversial "disease" mentioned in the text (e.g., ADHD, menopause). Critique the information available from the conflict or feminist theoretical perspective.
3. After examining a major national newspaper for medical stories over the past year or so, what do you think are the major challenges to medical dominance today?
4. Doctors tend to act in the face of uncertainty. Discuss with respect to your personal experience.
5. To what extent is the health care you access digitized? What do you think are the consequences of digitized care? Are you concerned about health privacy?

Suggested Readings

Clarke, A.E., Mamo, L., Fishman, J.R., Shim, J.K., & Fosket, J.R. (2003). Biomedicalization: The technoscientific transformations of health, illness, and U.S. biomedicine. *American Sociological Review, 68*(2), 161–94. Discussion of the increasing dominance of technology in the practice of medicine and the delivery of health care.

Doidge, N. (2015). *The brain's way of healing: Remarkable discoveries and recoveries from the frontiers of neuroplasticity*. Viking. The most recent best-seller by the Canadian psychiatrist who has popularized the concept of "neuroplasticity," a significant recasting of neuroscience and psychiatry that shows how the brain can heal itself and be healed through non-surgical, non-pharmaceutical, and non-psychotherapeutic interventions.

Mercer, C. (2019). Health sector preaches patient privacy, but what about physician privacy? *Canadian Medical Association Journal, 191*(34), E949–E950. As technology makes it easier to share photos and texts around the world, is the right of physicians to privacy being neglected?

Nelson, A. (2016). *The social life of DNA: Race, reparations, and reconciliation after the genome*. Beacon Press. Traces and explores the history and genealogy of race relations in terms of genomic information.

Rose, N. (2006). Disorders without borders? The expanding scope of psychiatric practice. *Biosocieties, 1*, 465–84. A review article that examines different explanations for the increase in mental illnesses.

Timmermans, S., & Buchbinder, M. (2012). *Saving babies: The consequences of newborn screening*. University of Chicago Press. A book about the costs, benefits, and social impact of newborn screening.

Wachter, R. (2015). *The digital doctor: Hope, hype and harm at the dawn of medicine's computer age*. McGraw-Hill. Thanks to enormous investments, health care is going online. What will it take to make this revolutionary transition useful and beneficial?

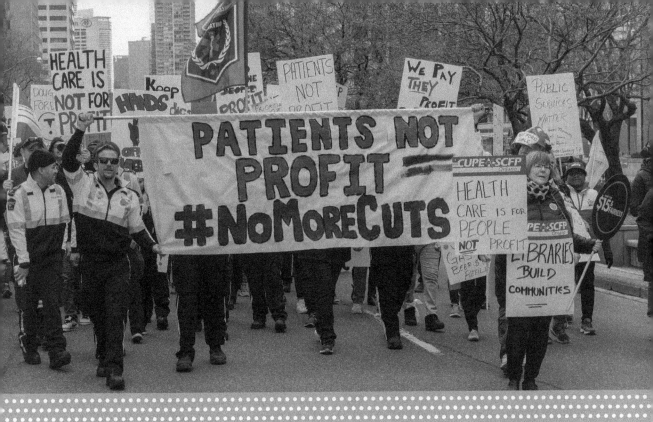

The Social Democratic and Current History of Medicare

Privatization and the State of Medicare in Canada

Chapter Overview

- The first Canadian medical "system" was composed of the various medical and religious practices of the many Indigenous peoples.
- The health of early settlers to Canada was severely threatened in a number of ways.
- Some of the first public health measures adopted in Canada resulted from the cholera epidemic brought to Canada first in 1832.
- Initially, medical practitioners from widely different backgrounds competed with one another for patients.
- Homeopathy was the first profession to be legalized and to establish its own

- licensing board. Soon after, other groups did the same.
- The development of medicare had both supporters and detractors.
- Tommy Douglas played an important role in the development of medicare in Canada.
- Medicare has had an impact on the class-based utilization rates of medical service.
- Medicare has had mixed consequences for medical practice and for doctor morale.
- Medicare is currently, and has been for the past decade or so, experiencing significant threats to public financing as its costs have continued to grow.

Introduction

Doctors in modern Western societies have been at the heart of the great forces of medicalization. Central to their role is that they have been highly respected and seen as extraordinary—the creators and keepers of esoteric knowledge. Understanding this is essential to considering the place of medicine in modern society. But have doctors always been dominant in the provision of medical care? What is the relationship between the state and physicians and how does it affect the practice of medicine in Canada today? How did medicare develop? How successful has medicare been in broadening and equalizing access to the medical care system for all Canadians? Has the change in accessibility to medicine led to changes in the overall health of the population or in the distribution of health in the population? What is privatization of health care and is it relevant to a thorough understanding of our health-care system today? What are the implications of trends towards restructuring and downsizing the health-care system? These are among the questions that will be addressed in this chapter.

Early Canadian Medical Organizations

The first Canadian medical "system" consisted of the various medical/religious institutions of the many groups of Indigenous peoples. Each of these groups had its own culturally unique definitions of what constituted health and what constituted illness, its own pharmacopoeia, and its own preferred types of natural and supernatural interventions. Since these peoples handed down their traditions orally, the only written accounts are from white settlers, priests, explorers, and traders. These writers tell us that medicine men or shamans were frequently called upon to diagnose and treat various types of injuries and disease. Shamans, as well as Indigenous people more generally, developed a number of very effective botanical remedies, such as oil of wintergreen, and physical remedies, such as sweat lodges and massages. In the following we will discuss several examples from Ontario.

In the seventeenth century, at the time of the arrival of the Europeans, the Native peoples of present-day Ontario were divided into two linguistic groups: the Algonquian and the Iroquoian. A study of Iroquoian bones dug from a burial mound near Kleinburg, Ontario, revealed that these people (around the year 1600) suffered from such well-known diseases as arthritis, osteomyelitis, and tumours (Holling, 1981). Evidence of a hole in a skull revealed the skill of a local surgeon. Some treatments devised by Indigenous peoples, when the cause was obvious, were empirical. Internal conditions of unknown cause were often attributed to supernatural origins, such as (1) the breaking of a taboo, e.g., mistreating an animal or showing disrespect to a river; (2) ghosts of humans, which craved company; (3) the evil ministrations of a menstruating woman; or (4) unfulfilled dreams or desires.

Many Indigenous people in what many now call Canada believed that everything in the world had a spirit or a soul, including animals, trees, rocks, the sky, lakes, and rivers. Thus, everything in the world was to be respected. In some Indigenous cultures all young people, especially males, were expected to search for a vision or a dream as a guide through life. To achieve this goal it was customary to spend at least a week alone without food. Hungry, lonely, and full of transient concerns, the young person would generally report that he or she had a vision, which was then interpreted by the medicine man or father. Medicine men were both the spiritual leaders and healers. They were able to cast out spells, predict the future, recover lost objects, diagnose and treat disease, and bring rain. Some were also magicians and jugglers.

A practical armamentarium of medicines evolved, which included treatments for widely differing medical problems, from fractures and wounds to freezing and frostbite, burns and scalding, rheumatism, arthritis, urinary problems, fevers, intestinal disorders, cancer, blood poisoning, and toothaches. Some of the herbs and plants used historically by the Native peoples continue to be used today.

Indigenous peoples in what is now Canada are known to have used over 500 different plants as medicines. Some were chewed and swallowed, some drunk in herbal teas, some boiled and the vapours inhaled, some infused and poured as medicine into the patient's ear. At times, plants were used only for ritual purposes. For example, thorny or spiny plants were sometimes used to ward off evil spirits or spirits of disease and death. At other times the value resided in the pharmacological effectiveness of a particular plant for a particular symptom or disease. A famous example of the use of a plant with specific and now scientifically substantiated medicinal benefit is the scraping of white bark of cedar, which is rich in vitamin C, for the treatment of scurvy. This intervention was taught to Jacques Cartier by the Mi'kmaq people. Pharmacologically useful treatments seem to have existed for a wide variety of symptoms such as wounds, skin eruptions, gastrointestinal disorders, coughs, colds, fevers, and rheumatism.

Remembering Our History

Box 10.1 • Canada's Cholera Epidemic

The worldwide epidemic of cholera reached Canada for the first time in 1832. Apparently, some Irish immigrants, who were escaping the potato famine and the beginnings of cholera in Ireland, were infected when they set forth for Québec City and Montreal. The boats they travelled on were built for 150 passengers but carried as many as 500. Such crowded conditions led to unsanitary circumstances and invited the spread of the virulent and contagious disease. Cholera attacked apparently healthy people, who could die within a matter of hours or days. It erupted in a number of symptoms, including severe spasms and cramps, a husky voice, a sunken face, blue skin colour, and kidney failure as various bodily processes collapsed. Doctors could do virtually nothing to help. Although there were various theories associating the disease with dirt and filth, its cause was not understood.

When the colonial government in Lower Canada realized the nature of the calamity, officials established a Board of Health with a mandate to inspect and detain ships arriving from infected ports. A Quarantine Act was passed in February 1832 and remained in effect for a year. Another Act provided a fund for medical assistance to the sick immigrants and to help them to travel to their destinations when they had sufficiently recovered.

In the spring of 1832 Grosse Isle in the St Lawrence, which was directly in the path of ships arriving from Europe, was established as a place of quarantine. All ships were stopped for inspection. Distinctions were made between ships arriving from infected and non-infected ports. Those from infected ports were required to serve a quarantine period, while the ships with ill passengers were thoroughly cleaned and those who were diseased were disembarked and treated; those who died were buried there. Some of the government actions were very unpopular because they restricted individuals' freedoms. This resulted in riots in various locations throughout the country. Crowds burned down some cholera hospitals.

Cholera invaded British North America at three other times—in 1834, 1852, and 1854. While statistics are not entirely reliable, it is estimated that as many as 20,000 people died in all the epidemics. While we have not seen cholera epidemics in Canada since the nineteenth century, they still occur on several continents where drinking water is contaminated and proper sanitation is lacking. Repeated outbreaks continue in various African countries. There are intermittent outbreaks elsewhere around the world today, including a recent epidemic in Haiti. Cholera is not necessarily fatal today and oral rehydration salts can be used to treat the majority of people when they are available.

Sources: Bilson (1980); Heagerty (1928, vol. 1); Marks and Beatty (1976).

The health of the early settlers in Canada was assaulted continually. Even before they arrived, immigrants, who were often malnourished to begin with, faced grave dangers from the overcrowded conditions on the boats in which they came to Canada. These densely packed quarters greatly increased susceptibility to the spread of contagious diseases. Pioneer life, too, was fraught with hazards. The winters were extremely cold, much colder than winters many of the immigrants had been accustomed to—and somewhat colder than we are accustomed to today, since the Little Ice Age extended from about 1450 to 1850, and today we are in the midst of climate change and global warming. The growing season was short and difficult. Accidents occurred frequently as people cleared the bush for timber and for farmland, roads, and buildings. Accidents happened on the rapidly flowing waterways. The building of roads, canals, and railways was extremely dangerous. Epidemics of smallpox, influenza, measles, scarlet fever, and cholera decimated the population from time to time. Childbirth in pioneer conditions was often dangerous for both mother and child (Heagerty, 1928). Local midwives, a few doctors trained in Britain and the United States, and travelling medical salespeople performed most medical treatment. Other treatments were based on folk remedies or on mail-order medicines.

The Origins of the Contemporary Medical Care System

The origins of the type of medical practice dominant today can be traced back to nineteenth-century Canada. At that time, various kinds of practitioners were offering their services and selling their wares in an open market. Lay healers, home remedies, folk cures, and other kinds of medicines were among the medical options available to the population. Whisky, brandy, and opium were used widely as medicines, as were numerous patent concoctions. Medicine shows were common from the 1830s and 1840s.

Most of the first allopathic medical practitioners in New France were either **barber-surgeons** from France, who had received primitive training as apprentices, or apothecaries who acted as general practitioners dispensing available medicines. Barbering and surgery both required dexterity with a knife: they were handled by the same person because of the ubiquitous practice of bleeding as a treatment for a wide variety of ailments. Surgery was practised only on the limbs and on the surface of the body. Internal surgery almost always resulted in death because bleeding and sepsis were not yet treatable or preventable. Two other common treatments were purging and inducing vomiting. Among the first doctors in Upper Canada were army surgeons. There were also some civilian physicians. Homeopathic doctors and eclectics (practitioners who used a variety of treatments) worked alongside allopathic or conventional practitioners. Lay-trained midwives delivered babies in the home, and other lay-trained persons performed surgery and set bones. No one type of healer was predominant.

Although the first medical school was established in Canada in 1824, theories about disease were varied and not scientifically based. The first involvement of the state in this hodgepodge of medical practices came in 1832 because advance warning had been received of the possible arrival in Canada of immigrants with cholera. The government immediately appointed a Sanitary Commission and a Board of Health, which issued directives for the protection of the people. Infected people were quarantined. Contaminated clothing was burned, boiled, or baked. Private burials were ordered. Massive outbreaks of cholera in 1832 and 1854 necessitated the establishment of a quarantine station at Grosse Isle on the St Lawrence for ship passengers who were infected and thus not allowed to enter Canada. Both Montreal and Quebec adapted buildings as hospitals to isolate disembarking passengers who had cholera. Public ordinances, which received the force of law in 1831, prevented the sale of meats from diseased animals and appointed civil authorities to inspect dwellings for their state of cleanliness. Early public health measures primarily emphasized quarantine and sanitation. Later the government became involved in other types of public health efforts. These included the Public Health Act of 1882 in Ontario, which was soon adopted in the rest of the country; the Food and Drug Act; the Narcotics Control Act; the Proprietary and Patent Measures Act; and the establishment of hospitals and asylums.

The Early Efforts of Allopathic Physicians to Organize

In spite of the primitive state of their medical knowledge, numerous attempts were made by **allopathic doctors**, dating from 1795, to have legislation passed that would: (1) prohibit any but allopathic practitioners from practising medicine; (2) provide the allopaths with licences under which they could practise; and (3) control admittance to allopathic practice. The allopathic practitioners often had high social standing in the new colony. In the English-speaking areas, they were usually British immigrants and often were ex-military officers (Torrance, 1987). Generally, they moved in the highest social circles, married into important families, stood for Parliament, edited influential newspapers, and provided care for the wealthier classes (Gidney & Millar, 1984). In small towns outside Toronto, allopathic practitioners were often among the most important businessmen, church leaders, and town politicians. In 1852 an informal group of these men established the *Upper Canada Journal of Medical, Surgical and Physical Science*.

The allopathic doctors expressed frustration with their working conditions. They claimed they were under-rewarded and under-esteemed because of the competition from "irregulars" and because of "quackery" and the disorganized state of the medical schools. Many of the "irregulars" were also educated, and because they did not engage in the heroic measures of the allopaths, such as the application of leeches, bloodletting, and applying purgatives, they were less likely to cause harm. But the allopathic doctors thought of them as uneducated, ignorant imposters who ruthlessly and recklessly administered untried, untested methods with dangerous results.

In fact, even at this time, the "irregular" doctors exhibited considerable strength and organizational skills. In 1859 **homeopathy** was the first profession to be legalized and to establish a board to examine and license practitioners. The eclectics were successful in consolidating their own board in 1861 (Gidney & Millar, 1984). Perhaps because of their relative success in organizing themselves, the homeopaths and eclectics and other heterodox practitioners were "contemptuously lumped together by the established profession as 'empirics'" (Hamowy, 1984: 63). The *Upper Canada Journal* denounced homeopathy as "so utterly opposed to science and common sense, as well as so completely at variance with the experience of the medical profession, that it ought to be in no way practiced or countenanced by any regularly educated practitioner" (quoted in Hamowy, 1984, p. 63). Opposition to the eclectics was equally passionate. They were called "spurious pretenders" and seen as embodying a continuous and strong threat to "true science."

Competition within the ranks of the allopaths, largely between "school men" (the university-trained and affiliated practitioners) and the Upper Canada practitioners (Gidney & Millar, 1984), prevented the unified stance necessary for the establishment of standards of education, practice, and licensing. In 1850 the "school men" held more power. By 1865 they had conceded some of their authority to the elected representatives of the ordinary practitioners. In the same year (1865) these ordinary practitioners succeeded in passing self-regulatory licensing legislation. This was revised in 1869 under the Ontario Medical Act to create the College of Physicians and Surgeons of Ontario. Much to the surprise of the "regular" or allopathic physicians, both homeopaths and eclectics were included under the same legislation. Homeopaths continued to be represented by the College until 1960. Eclectics were excluded in 1874. The regulation of homeopathy today will be discussed in Chapter 13.

Remembering Our History

Box 10.2 • The Flu Epidemic of 1918–19

In the fall of 1918 Canada's population was about 8 million. About 60,000 Canadians had died in World War I. During the fall of 1918 and continuing into 1919, between 30,000 and 50,000 people died in Canada as a result of the dreaded flu pandemic sweeping much of the world. Worldwide, according to estimates, 50 million to 100 million people died as a result of this influenza. Apparently the flu came to Canada on a troopship, the *Anaguayan*. One hundred seventy-five of the 763 soldiers on board took ill. The ship was quarantined at Grosse Isle. Yet, the disease was passed on to civilians. By the end of September it was clear that Canada had a serious problem. The epidemic spread quickly. New York and Massachusetts were hit. It spread up and down from the US into Canada and vice versa. It also spread westward along the railways and highways. It was attributed to Spain and called the Spanish flu, not because it started there but because, as Spain was neutral in the war, the Spanish press, unfettered by wartime censorship, was the first to report the virulent flu epidemic as it devastated the Spanish population.

It was unique because it tended to hit young adults and often killed them. Previously, the flu had tended to affect especially the very old and the very young. This flu epidemic attacked one in six Canadians. Schools, auditoriums, and various halls were opened as temporary hospitals. Children were left without parents. Quarantines were imposed. Public meetings were forbidden. But quarantines did not seem to work. Many people thought that quarantine was unjust. Others just did not believe that they worked because they saw people succumbing who had been very careful, while others, less careful, remained disease-free. Partly because of the impact of the flu, the need to establish a federal health authority was acknowledged. The bill to institute such a department received first reading in March 1919, and the new department became operational that fall.

Because quarantine did not seem to work, other measures were introduced. Laws were passed to ensure that people wore masks. But the laws differed. In some municipalities those who were caring for the ill were required to wear masks. In others, anyone who was in contact with the public was expected to wear a mask. Alberta required that anyone outside the home had to use a mask. Yet masks proved as ineffective as quarantine. Rather than boiling and sterilizing them frequently, and certainly between occasions of wearing them, people allowed the trapped germs to spread and multiply in the moist, warm environment inside the mask.

Most homes had their own trusted preventive measures and treatment. Mothballs and camphor in cotton bags worn about the neck were common. Travelling medical salespersons reaped profits from the salves and remedies they sold. Alcohol and narcotics were prescribed.

Losses to business were enormous. People were too sick to shop or were afraid to venture into the stores for fear of catching the disease. Many staff members, too, were off sick. Theatres and pool and dance halls suffered heavy losses. Some 10,000 railway workers were off at one time. Ice storms, blizzards, and below-zero weather had never exacted so heavy a toll as this epidemic. Telephone companies were heavily over-extended, both because people were relying on the phone rather than leaving the house and because so many employees were away sick. The insurance industry was one of those most heavily hit. Apparently some companies dealt with more flu claims than war claims. All in all, Spanish flu had an enormous effect on Canadian society. In addition, Inuit and settler communities along the coast of Labrador suffered among the highest mortality rates in the world, with two settlements—Okak and Hebron—experiencing a combined 71 per cent death rate.

Sources: Dickin McGinnis (1977); Heagerty (1928: vol. 1); Pettigrew (1983); Budgell (2018).

This 1869 legislation gave the practitioners, via their representatives on the College, control over the education of medical doctors. Proprietary (privately owned) medical schools were founded, but they were rapidly affiliated with universities in order to grant degrees. The power struggles between the university-based doctors and the other practitioners continued.

In Lower Canada the attempts to define and limit the work of physicians were complicated by the tensions between French and English doctors. The College of Physicians and Surgeons of Lower Canada, formed to regulate practitioners, was created in 1847. In 1849 legislation was passed to allow automatic incorporation of anyone who had been engaged in practice in 1847.

The competition and infighting that characterized much of the medical care system in the nineteenth century had receded by the beginning of World War I (Coburn et al., 1983). The year 1912 marked a turning point in the position of allopathic practitioners. The Canada Medical Act, which standardized licensing procedures across Canada, was passed. Finally, by this time a patient who sought the services of an allopathic practitioner apparently had a better than 50 per cent chance of being helped by the encounter. The passage of the Canada Medical Act followed another important event. The momentous Flexner Report, *Medical Education in the United States and Canada*, published in 1910, was sponsored by the Carnegie Foundation and the American Medical Association, financed by the Rockefeller philanthropies, and researched and written by Abraham Flexner, an American educator. The **Flexner Report** severely criticized the medical systems of Canada and the United States. It advised the elimination of the apprenticeship system, the standardization of entrance requirements to medical schools, and the establishment of a more rigorous scientific program of study. It recommended the closing of many medical schools, particularly the private schools, because they did not meet the criteria of scientific medicine.

Flexner's report radically changed medical education in the US and Canada. McGill University and the University of Toronto were the only schools in Canada given acceptable ratings. The medical schools in Halifax and London moved rapidly to become affiliated with Dalhousie University and the University of Western Ontario, respectively. Medical education began to be taught as a scientifically based, scholarly field under the aegis of universities.

The Flexner Report had a significant impact on the organization of Canadian medical education and the practice of, and training for, modern medicine. The report underscored and thus enhanced the legitimacy of positivistic science as the basis of clinical practice. It reinforced the importance of empirical science with its emphasis on observation, experimentation, quantification, publication, replication, and revision as essential to medical-scientific research. It emphasized the use of the hospital for the centralized instruction of doctors-to-be and the use of medical technology for observation, measurement, and standardization in diagnosis and treatment. By the 1920s the hospital-based, curatively oriented, technologically sophisticated medical care system that Canadians know today was firmly established.

One important side effect of the report was that the schools that were closed were primarily those that educated women and people of colour. Thus, the closing of the proprietary schools further entrenched the position of white, middle- and upper-class males in medicine.

A Brief History of Universal Medical Insurance in Canada

Mackenzie King first suggested a system of universal medical insurance in 1919 as part of the Liberal Party platform. It was recommended regularly by organized labour after the end of World War I (Walters, 1982). Later, universal medical insurance was proposed at the Dominion–Provincial Conference on Reconstruction in 1945. At this time, the provinces opposed the federal initiative, favouring free-market health insurance. In 1957 the federal government introduced the Hospital Insurance and Diagnostic Services Act, which provided for a number of medical services associated with hospitalization and medical testing. The federal government was to pay 50 per cent of the average provincial costs.

In 1961, the federal government appointed a Royal Commission on Health Services. The Commission, under Supreme Court Justice Emmett Hall, recommended that the federal government, in co-operation with the provinces, introduce a program of universal health care. The result was the Medical Care Act of 1968. Finally implemented in 1972, the new universal medical insurance scheme was to cover medical services, such as physicians' fees, not covered under the previous Hospital Insurance and Diagnostic Services Act. The scheme had four basic objectives or **principles of medicare**. (1) **Universality**. The plan was to be available to all residents of Canada on equal terms regardless of such differences as previous health records, age, lack of income, non-membership in a group, or other considerations. The federal government stipulated that at least 95 per cent of the population was to be covered within two years of the provincial adoption of the plan. (2) **Portability**. The benefits were to be portable from province to province. (3) **Comprehensive coverage**. The benefits were to include all necessary medical services, as well as certain surgical services performed by a dental surgeon in hospital. (4) **Administration**. The plan was to be run on a non-profit basis.

The Canada Health Act of 1984 added **accessibility** to make five principles. The costs for the new plan were to be shared 50/50 by the federal and provincial governments. They were also to be shared in a way that would serve to redistribute income between the poorer and the richer provinces.

Governments soon faced increasing financial pressure as health-care costs grew. Physicians who felt they were not paid enough "extra-billed" their patients. When a critical level of frustration and complaint was reached, the government appointed Emmett Hall again to chair a committee to re-evaluate medicare. In 1980, Hall reported to the federal government that unless extra-billing was banned, Canada's universal health-care system was doomed. In response, but amid much controversy, the Canada Health Act, which limited the provinces' right to permit extra-billing, was passed.

The Canadian Medical Association filed a lawsuit against the federal government, claiming: (1) that the Canada Health Act went beyond the constitutional authority of the federal government; and (2) that it contravened the Charter of Rights and Freedoms by prohibiting doctors from establishing private contracts with their patients. The Ontario Medical Association, the largest and most vocal provincial group, representing about 17,000 physicians, challenged the Act in court. The Ontario government passed the Health Care Accessibility Act (Bill 94) in June 1986 in response to the federal legislation, thus making extra-billing illegal. Members of the Ontario Medical Association staged a 25-day strike in protest, but eventually had to back down when the government refused to capitulate. Public opinion was decidedly against the strike action, and many doctors went back to work even before it was officially over. There have been many other doctors' strikes across the country, from British Columbia to Newfoundland and Labrador. Doctors have protested their incomes, working conditions, and the state of medical care for Canadians, among other things. There is continuing evidence of the dissatisfaction of some doctors with their working conditions across the country.

Medical care has continued to be a much-heralded Canadian value, on the one hand, and a site of continuing political controversy, on the other. It is often a major issue in Canadian elections. Debates about bringing back a parallel private system, about waiting lists for major tests and surgery, and about doctor shortages, compensation, and emergency room fiascos dominate the headlines of national newspapers at times. Several studies meant to optimize the system have been done, including *The Health of Canadians: The Federal Role* (Senate of Canada, 2002) and the Romanow Report (Commission on the Future of Health Care in Canada, 2002). The Canadian Medical Association and the Fraser Institute have argued for and continue to advance the possible benefits of a parallel private medical care system for Canadians who can afford to pay for extra or more rapidly delivered services and to keep down the tax costs of the system. These remain hotly debated topics across the country.

Remembering Our History

Box 10.3 • Timeline: The Development of State Medical Insurance

Germany and Western Europe introduce social welfare insurance, including health insurance, in the 1880s.

New Zealand introduces social welfare insurance, including health insurance, in the early part of the twentieth century.

Great Britain introduces national health insurance in 1948.

Canada

1919   Platform of the Liberal Party under Mackenzie King includes medicare.

1919   After World War I, organized labour begins what becomes an annual statement by the Canadian Congress of Labour concerning the importance of national health insurance, and in 1919–20 several US states pass medicare legislation that is later withdrawn.

1934   Canadian Medical Association appoints a Committee on Medical Economics, which produces a report outlining the CMA's position in support of national health insurance, with several provisos.

1934   Legislation passes for provincial medical insurance in Alberta. Government loses power before it can be implemented.

1935   British Columbia introduces provincial medical insurance legislation. Despite public support via a referendum, this legislation was never implemented because of a change in government.

1935   Employment and Social Insurance Act, including a proposal for research into the viability of a national medical insurance scheme, is introduced.

1942   Beveridge Report on Britain's need for a National Health Service published in Great Britain—the subject of much discussion in Canada.

1945   Dominion–Provincial Conference on Reconstruction includes proposals for federally supported medical insurance. Conference breaks down in the wake of federal–provincial dispute.

1947   Saskatchewan implements hospital insurance.

1951   A Canadian Sickness Survey completed. It demonstrates income differences in the populations affected by illness.

1958   Hospital Insurance and Diagnostic Services Act passes (federal).

1962   Saskatchewan CCF/NDP government introduces provincial medical insurance; Saskatchewan doctors' strike.

1962   Royal Commission, headed by Justice Emmett Hall, is appointed to investigate medical services.

1966   Federal legislation for state medical insurance passes.

1968   Federal legislation implemented.

1971   All provinces fully participate in medicare.

1972   Yukon and Northwest Territories included in federal legislation.

1977   Federal government changes the funding formula with the provinces—Established Programs Financing Act (EPF).

1984   Canada Health Act reinforces the policy that medical care is to be financed out of the public purse (penalties established for hospital user fees and physician extra-billing).

1987   Ontario doctors' strike.

1990   Bill C-69 freezes EPF for three years, after which future EPF growth is to be based on gross national product (GNP) minus 3 per cent.

1991   Bill C-70 passes to freeze EPF for two additional years before new formula (–3 per cent) comes into effect. Makes it possible for federal government to withhold transfer payments from provinces contravening the Canada Health Act.

1999   Throughout the nineties, medical care deteriorates across the country. Hospitals close; patients at times are turned away from emergency; emergency room waiting increases dramatically. Nurses, doctors, and other health-care workers strike in various actions. Evidence increases of a two-tiered medical system.

2000–3   Further debates occur between the federal government and the provinces on health-care funding. The provinces blame "the crisis in medicare" on the lack of sufficient federal funding and the federal

continued

government chastises the provinces for misspending. A number of investigations and reports are solicited, including the Alberta-sponsored report by former federal cabinet minister Don Mazankowski and the federal reports by Senator Michael Kirby and former Saskatchewan Premier Roy Romanow. Each report is received in a flurry of contradictory political discourse.

2005   In the *Chaoulli* decision of the Supreme Court in respect to a legal suit against the Quebec government for failing to allow private health care and thus subjecting a patient to a long wait for surgery, the Court finds that the refusal to allow private insurance for health care covered under medicare violates the rights and freedoms of the patient.

2006–20   The country continues to debate the advantages and disadvantages of a private parallel system for the provision of medical care in Canada even as the system is already partly privatized (about one-third of the system is currently for-profit) and dependent on consumers to pay some expenses out of pocket. For full coverage many Canadians already buy insurance to provide services additional to those provided through medicare, such as pharmaceuticals, a single room when hospitalized, and so on. Nor are dental or optometry services universally covered. In considering the advantages and disadvantages of a parallel private system the point is often argued that it would be more efficient and effective, and would provide greater access to care for the population. A national Pharmacare program is being discussed today (Pharmacare 2020).

Most hospitals across Canada are run as private non-profit corporations overseen by a community board, voluntary organization, church, or municipality. Although they are funded in large part by government, hospitals operate independently as long as they stay within budget. Some people argue that hospitals should be private for-profit corporations. This point of view, which has not yet been proven, asserts that private hospitals are more efficient.

Factors in the Development of Medicare in Canada

Today, Canada's health-care system, usually called medicare, is predominantly publicly financed and privately delivered by a combination of funds and policies established at the federal level and operational decisions executed at the level of the provinces and territories. It is considered a national system because its fundamental principles are federally based and federal funding reflects, in part, adherence to these principles. The federal government is also responsible for direct health service delivery to specific groups, including veterans, Indigenous peoples on reserves, military personnel, inmates of federal penitentiaries, and the RCMP. In addition, the federal government's health-related responsibilities involve such things as health protection, promotion, and disease prevention along with drug approval and regulation. It is important to note that the system is organized so that there are slightly more family and general practitioners, 119. 6 per 100,000 population, than specialists, who represent 114.8 per 100,000 (Canadian Institute for Health Information [CIHI], 2019). Family doctors are often the gatekeepers to the rest of the system, including specialty care, hospital admission, diagnostic testing, and prescription drugs. The ratio of physicians to population in Canada is relatively low in comparison with selected other OECD countries, most of which also have public systems of one sort or another. This ratio is growing, however (CIHI, 2019).

The development of medicare over the last half-century in Canada has been influenced positively or negatively by a number of significant social forces. The most important of these are: (1) the widespread movement in Western industrialized societies towards rationalized bureaucratic social organization and monopoly capitalism; (2) the spread in Western Europe and beyond of social welfare legislation in public education, old age pensions, family allowances, unemployment benefits, and medical care insurance; (3) the benefits to the medical profession in maintaining **fee-for-service**, cure-oriented, hospital, and technologically based medical practice; (4) the interests of the life and health insurance companies in perpetuating their share of a profitable market; (5) the interests of the drug, medical, and hospital supply companies in continuing to develop their increasingly profitable markets; (6) the interests of the urban labour unions and farm co-operatives in social welfare benefits for their members; and (7) the charismatic qualities and dedication of individuals such as Tommy Douglas, who had both a position of power at the "right" time in Saskatchewan and a commitment to universal medical care. Each of these will be discussed in turn.

First, the movement towards state medical insurance in Canada must be seen as part of a widespread trend in Western industrialized nations towards rationalization and bureaucratization in the context of monopoly capitalism and neo-liberalism. It was not until the twentieth century that the work of the physician came to be highly regarded as the most effective form of medical care. With the development of antibiotics to treat bacterial infections and neuroleptic drugs to control the psychosis associated with various forms of emotional despair and mental illness, the efficacy of the doctor became firmly established in the public mind. Along with the increase in legitimacy of allopathic medicine, medical practice began to alter as hospitals changed from being institutions for the dying and the indigent into being a place of work for the practice of medicine, especially surgery. Medical specialization increased and medical and paramedical occupations burgeoned. All of this growth and development served to enmesh the physician within enormous technically efficient bureaucratic structures.

Second, the introduction of medicare in Canada must be seen in the context of the spread of similar policies in the Western industrialized world. The first legislation was passed in Germany in the 1880s. By the time Britain first introduced universal medical insurance in 1912 (to be formally established as the universal National Health Service in 1948), much of Western Europe, as well as New Zealand, had already pursued this course. Talk of medicare and the passage of legislation in support of medicare occurred in the United States by 1919–20. The United States still does not have a universal system of health coverage and implementation of such a policy is still the subject of rancorous debate. The trajectory was different in Canada. From 1919 until the introduction of comprehensive state-sponsored medical care in Canada a half-century later, both federal and provincial governments made various attempts to draft legislation to implement medicare.

Third, the medical profession has had an impact on the timing and the nature of medicare. In 1934, the Committee on Medical Economics of the Canadian Medical Association completed a report that described the characteristics of the ideal medical insurance scheme. At this time the CMA expressed support for state medical insurance provided that: (1) it was administered by a non-political body of whom the majority would be medical practitioners; (2) it guaranteed free choice by physicians of their method of payment; (3) it provided for medical control over fees; and (4) it allowed for compulsory coverage up to certain levels of income (Torrance, 1987). It was in the financial interests of medical doctors to support this initiative because of the inability of many patients during the Great Depression to pay their medical bills. Thus, following World War II, after the return of economic growth when most patients were able to pay their bills either independently or through private medical insurance, the majority of the profession began to oppose medicare. The strongest statement of the opposition of the doctors to state medical insurance was the 23-day strike in 1962 by about 800 of Saskatchewan's 900 physicians.

Remembering Our History

Box 10.4 • Historical Impediments to the Development of State-Sponsored Medical Care in Canada

1. The traditional division, early in the century, between the urban industrial labour force and the farmers led to the consequent inability of these two working-class groups to form a unified labour lobby in favour of medicare.

2. The strengthening and unification of the Canadian Medical Association in 1920 with the appointment of Dr T.C. Routley as leader gave the CMA a unified voice and increased the power of the doctors' organization with respect to ensuring its vision of the limited conditions under which medicare might be acceptable.

3. The extensive representation of medical doctors in local, provincial, and federal politics and departments of health gave physicians the power to voice their individual views regarding medicare.

4. Through the British North America Act, 1867, the responsibility for health rested with the provinces.

5. Canadian Roman Catholics generally opposed state medical insurance.

6. The regional, ethnic, and occupational (labour/farmer) heterogeneity of Canadian society retarded the development of social democratic policies.

7. Private insurance companies steadily grew, especially during the fifties and sixties, and medical insurance became an increasingly common fringe benefit in collective bargaining agreements.

8. The Canadian Life Insurance Officers Association, the Canadian Chamber of Commerce, and the Canadian Manufacturers' Association repeatedly opposed state medical insurance.

Source: Walters (1982).

Fourth, the life and health insurance companies, through the Life Insurance Officers Association, opposed medicare. They argued that the role of the state was to provide the infrastructure for the development of such things as transportation and communication. State-sponsored medical insurance, they argued, should be limited to those who could not pay for their own policies and to assist in payment for catastrophic illnesses. The insurance companies were already making a profit and wanted to continue to do so.

Fifth, the drug, medical, and hospital supply companies and their representative body, the Canadian Manufacturers' Association, opposed government intervention in medical financing.

Sixth, the labour unions and farm co-operatives advocated national medical insurance. Except in the case of Saskatchewan, however, they did little actively to bring about state medicare.

Seventh, the importance of individuals such as Tommy Douglas cannot be overlooked. He was especially dedicated to the principle that medical care be accessible and available on a universal basis. He owed his well-being and perhaps his life to the fact that a physician operated on him without any fee and saved his leg from amputation when he was a boy. Partly as a result of this experience, his personal faith based in the Social Gospel movement (he was a pastor of the Baptist Church), and, of course, because of his socialist beliefs, Douglas made medicare a fundamental plank in his CCF platform (see Box 10.5).

Remembering Our History

Box 10.5 • Tommy Douglas

Tommy Douglas is one of the most important figures in the development of a universal state-supported medical care system in Canada. He was born in Scotland in 1904 and immigrated with his family to Winnipeg when he was a boy. An incident in his own life stands out because it was often cited as having provided the motivation for his determined fight for medicare. Before coming to Canada, Douglas injured his knee in a fall. As a result of the injury he developed osteomyelitis and was forced to undergo a series of painful operations. Despite these operations, osteomyelitis recurred while he was living in Winnipeg. The doctors in Canada felt that amputation was necessary. However, while Douglas was at the Children's Hospital in Winnipeg in 1913, a famous orthopedic surgeon, Dr R.J. Smith, became interested in his condition. Dr Smith took over the case and saved his leg. He did not charge the far-from-wealthy Douglas family. As Douglas says of this experience, "I always felt a great debt of gratitude to him, but it left me with this feeling that if I hadn't been so fortunate as to have this doctor offer his services gratis, I would probably have lost my leg."

In addition to this personal experience, Douglas was moved by the social conditions in Winnipeg in the early twentieth century. Unemployment was high. People lived with a great deal of uncertainty and were able to afford only the barest of necessities. These conditions made a lasting impact on Douglas. He was also sensitive to and strongly opposed to the discrimination and prejudice based on ethnic and racial differences that he saw around him in Winnipeg.

He acted out his commitment, first by becoming a Baptist minister in 1930 and then by becoming a parliamentarian. In 1932 he joined the Labour Party. In 1935 he was nominated as the Co-operative Commonwealth Federation (CCF) candidate for the Weyburn federal riding in Saskatchewan and was elected to the House of Commons. He was re-elected in 1940. From 1944 until 1961, Tommy Douglas was premier of Saskatchewan, the leader of the first socialist government in Canada. He worked towards economic security for the farmer, full employment for the urban worker, and the development of natural resources. Tommy Douglas promised that socialism would provide health and social services and lift taxation from the shoulders of the people and place it upon the "fleshy backs of the rich corporations."

By January 1945, free medical, hospital, and dental care was provided in Saskatchewan for pensioners and indigent people. Treatment for mental disorders and polio was made free to all. A school of medicine was opened at the University of Saskatchewan to increase the supply of doctors. Geriatric centres were built to provide care for the chronically ill elderly. Canada's first district-wide medical insurance program was established at Swift Current, where 40 doctors served a population of 50,000 people. This was financed by a family payment of $48 per year and a land tax. Thus, Swift Current became a testing ground for a provincial program.

By 1 January 1947, Douglas introduced the Hospital Insurance Plan. The premium at the time was $5 per person and $10 per family. At the end of 1947, the *American Journal of Public Health* stated that 93 per cent of the population of Saskatchewan was covered by the new scheme. The only exceptions were some remote northern communities.

In 1959 Douglas announced the introduction of medicare, which was to be based on five basic principles.

1. Medical bills would be prepaid and patients would never see a doctor's bill.
2. The plan would be available to everyone regardless of age or physical disability.
3. The plan would accompany improvements in all areas of health service.
4. The plan was to operate under public control.

continued

5. The legislation was to satisfy both patients and physicians before it went into effect.

A few days after Douglas stepped down in 1961 as premier of Saskatchewan to become leader of the newly formed federal New Democratic Party (NDP), the medical bill passed. In 1962 the Saskatchewan doctors' opposition to the government medical scheme intensified. A strike followed the announcement that the Act was in force. The strike lasted 23 days, during which time the government kept medical services in operation by flying doctors to Canada from Britain.

The Saskatchewan plan soon became the basis for a Canada-wide plan. In 1964 Prime Minister Lester Pearson announced that the federal government would give financial aid to any province that had a satisfactory medicare system. By 1969 most of the provinces were participating in the plan, with 50 per cent of the costs covered by the federal government.

After Tommy Douglas re-entered federal politics, he remained a member of the House of Commons from 1961 to 1979, first as the leader of the NDP, which had been formed in 1961 by a coalition between the Labour Party and the CCF.

Sources: McLeod and McLeod (1987); Shackleton (1975); Thomas (1982); Tyre (1962).

The Impact of Medicare on the Health of Canadians

The most important goal of medicare was the provision of universally accessible medical care to all Canadians regardless of class, region, educational level, religious background, or gender. To what extent has this goal been reached? Before the introduction of medicare a positive and clear relationship existed between income level and use of medical services. Before medicare it has been estimated that low-income groups visited the doctor over 10 per cent less often than did high-income groups. Now, however, the rates of health-care utilization across the social-class hierarchy are insignificant, if somewhat contradictory. For example, the likelihood of visiting a general practitioner is slightly higher among those who are poorer (ICES, 2011). Still, about 15.2 per cent of Canadians over 12 years of age reported that they did not have a regular doctor in 2010 (Statistics Canada, 2011). Men were significantly more likely than women to lack a regular doctor. Canada has a poor ranking when

it comes to rapid access to medical care (Power, 2017). However, the most common reason people gave for not having a regular doctor was that they had not looked for one. Those who had looked said that they did not have a doctor because the doctors in their area were not taking new patients, their doctor had moved or retired, or there were no doctors in their area. Still, when they needed health care, people said they found the help they needed through such resources as walk-in community clinics, emergency rooms, hospital out-patient clinics, and telehealth. Although statistics regarding class differences in access to doctors in Canada are not available, it is likely that differences do exist and that poor people have a more difficult time finding a doctor in a situation of shortage and a more difficult time going to a doctor because of the associated costs of taking time away from work, transportation, availability of babysitters, and the like. While differences in access do not appear to be obviously class-based, inequities continue (Kasman & Badley, 2004). Significant differences persist in the treatment received by visible minorities in Canada as compared to white people (Quan et al., 2006). Visible minorities are more likely to have contact with a general practitioner than white people, but they are less likely to be seen by a specialist, less likely to have had the early detection test for prostate cancer (the prostate-specific antigen or PSA test), and less likely to have received mammograms and Pap smears for breast and cervical cancer, respectively (Quan et al., 2006). Moreover, many medical services and products (such as pharmaceuticals) require out-of-pocket expenditures that are not affordable to every Canadian. In a system that relies so heavily on drugs and yet does not insure the out-of-hospital cost of drugs, it is impossible to claim universality.

Creeping Privatization

In a sense, much of Canada's health-care system is already private. Most hospitals and long-term care institutions are owned privately. Although approximately 70 per cent of health-care funds come from the public sector, 30 per cent are from the private sector (CIHI, 2014). This figure compares positively to the US, where about 52.2 per cent of the costs are private, but negatively to the UK, where 17.2 per cent of health funding is private (CIHI, 2014). Further, there are many new incentives across Canada for developing the private health-care sector, such as Timely Medical Alternatives, a brokerage for private health-care services. The website indicates that it can provide speedy medical care for such procedures as knee replacement, angioplasty, gall bladder removal, CT scan, MRI, ultrasound, weight-loss surgery, cardiac bypass, cardiac ablation, and hip replacement. Most of these private services are offered in the US, although there are pockets of privatized care in Canada. Advertised costs are said to range from the hundreds of dollars to thousands. This organization claims to have partnerships

with about 20 health-care institutions across the US and Canada and to be able to negotiate an 80 per cent reduction in cost. Periodically, a well-known Canadian politician will have been found, often amid huge controversy, to have travelled to the US to receive and privately pay for medical services. Danny Williams, when he was premier of Newfoundland and Labrador, is one example.

There is also evidence of personal and celebrity bias in access to care in Canada. A 1998 survey by the Institute of Clinical Evaluative Services in Ontario of some 1,150 health-care providers indicated that 53 per cent of the hospital executives and 80 per cent of the physicians admitted that they were involved in the care of a patient who received preferential access to treatment. Those most likely to have been favoured in these ways included relatives and friends, high-profile public figures, and patients and families who were well informed, aggressive, or likely to sue. Most of this preferential treatment was given for elective rather than necessary care (Alter et al., 1998).

Furthermore, many costs associated with use of the allopathic medical care system are not covered. To visit a doctor, one must be able to afford transportation, take time off work, understand how to make an appointment, and speak the language necessary for making an appointment. Following the doctor's orders, including taking medications or time away from work, frequently involves costs that may not be manageable to the non-working or working poor or to those receiving unemployment or social security benefits. Homeless people are another group who lack regular access to a doctor. As the costs of medications escalate it is noteworthy that access to prescription drugs will continue to decline. There are real consequences to this unequal access to care and treatment. For example, the death rates for people with diabetes were more than 50 per cent higher in 2012 among those with fewer financial resources (Booth et al., 2012).

Highlighted Issues

Box 10.6 • Health Care Online

Today most Canadians have access to the Internet, if not in their homes then through libraries and schools. Among the many uses of the Internet are social media (Facebook, Instagram, Snapchat, etc.), e-mail, instant messaging, entertainment, games, and shopping. However, in Canada, about 30 per cent of Internet usage is devoted to accessing information about health (Canadian Internet Registration Authority, 2016). Some Canadians have already started to use online platforms to access doctors and medical care. About 15 per cent of millennials have been diagnosed from a distance, and over 70 per cent of Canadians report that they are ready to rely on distance diagnosis (Barua & Globerman, 2018). About 66 per cent of Canadians are willing to go to an online doctor to prevent having to wait a long time for an appointment.

Access to online care is now available around the world. This may involve the sharing of lab tests and records, receiving a diagnosis, referrals, and prescriptions and related medical assistance. One Canadian company called Maple (https://www.getmaple.ca/for-you-family/how-it-works) claims that its online service makes it possible to speak with a doctor within two minutes. Since it offers service outside of medicare, Maple is private. Maple advertises a number of different ways to pay for its service, including a $30 per month individual membership or $50 per month family membership. These provide 30 or 50 virtual visits per year, respectively. One visit within this model is $49, unless it is on the weekend when it is $79, or overnight when it is $99. A subscription entitles the user to free pharmaceutical delivery, a print-out of the consultation, a unified place to store records, and essentially instant access. Started in 2016, Maple has about 200 physicians across the country working part-time (Owens, 2018). Some companies have purchased subscriptions as employee benefits.

Canada is actually behind in the uptake of tele-medicine. By 2016, Kaiser Permanente, the biggest health network in the US, conducted more visits online than in person, i.e., 52 per cent of 110 million visits. Studies have indicated that this distant care is as effective as in-person health care. It also achieved greater patient satisfaction, no more mistaken diagnoses than in-person consultations, and a decrease in malpractice claims (Owens, 2018). Questions still need to be asked about patients' long-term satisfaction with such health-care provision, as well as about health outcomes over time. Potential breaches of privacy should be of concern as disclosure of health status can possibly lead to such problems as the denial of medical or travel insurance or employment opportunities.

Debate the pitfalls and benefits of such an innovation.

The Impact of Medicare on Medical Practice

According to Naylor (1982), before the Great Depression, from approximately 1918 to 1929, doctors made more than four times the average Canadian salary. The Depression had a devastating effect on all incomes. In the period of recovery in the 1940s, doctors' salaries averaged about three times the national mean income. By 1989, with various private insurance schemes in place, doctors made about 3.7 times the average Canadian salary. Initially, medicare gave a dramatic boost to doctors' salaries. In the early 1970s doctors' salaries were approximately 5.2 to 5.5 times the national average. Wage and price controls, which were introduced in the mid-1970s, slowed the expansion of physicians' salaries during that period. Doctors' salaries have increased in the past decade by approximately 30 per cent in Canada. Family doctors and general practitioners make on average 2.8 times that of the average Canadian salary whereas the specialists make about 4.5 times that of the average Canadian (see Figure 10.1). Still, however, the salaries of Canadian doctors compare unfavourably to those of US doctors.

The average gross clinical income is approximately $277,000 for a family physician. Out of this doctors still have to pay their overhead, such as salaries for office/clinic staff, office rent, office and medical equipment, etc. Salaries also vary considerably by specialty, so that a family doctor makes much less than a neurosurgeon, for example. The average gross clinical income in 2017 for specialists was $357,000 and for surgical specialists $477,000 (CIHI, 2019). Moreover, the average gross clinical income varies considerably across the different provinces (CIHI, 2019: 26).

The number of doctors in Canada has grown much more quickly than the population and continues to grow. Between 1968 and 1978 the number of doctors grew by 50 per cent, the population by 13 per cent. The physician-to-population ratio has been narrowing for more than a century. In 1871, there were 1,248 citizens to every physician; by 1951 the ratio was 1:976; and by 1981 the ratio was 1:652. The number of specialists also continues to increase. Today the doctor–patient ratio is 228 per 100,000 and the rate of increase in the numbers of doctors from 2011 to 2015 outpaced the rate of population growth (CIHI, 2017). Figure 10.2 provides a picture of the physician-to-population ratio and how it changed in Canada from 1980 to 2015.

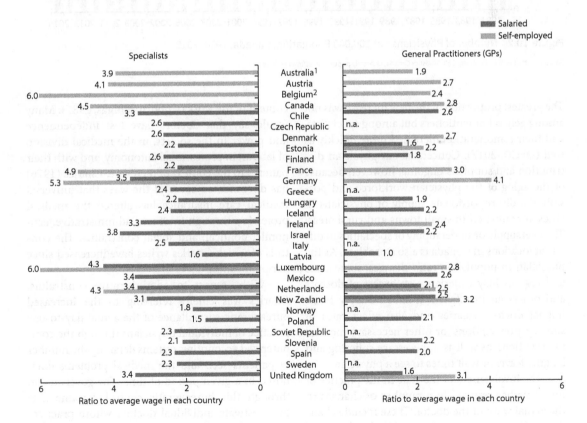

Figure 10.1 Remuneration of Doctors, Ratio to Average Wage, 2015 (or nearest year)

1. Physicians in training included (resulting in an underestimation).
2. Practice expenses included (resulting in an over-estimation).

Source: OECD (2017).

Figure 10.2   Number of Physicians per 100,000 Population, Canada, 1980–2015

Source: Scott's medical database, CIHI, Statistics Canada, Quarterly population estimates, 2016.

The greatest proportion of the new increase was not among general practitioners but among specialists, and their remuneration increased more quickly as well (OECD, 2017). Concern about physician distribution and supply is ongoing, however, because of the aging of the physician workforce and possibly the disproportionate supply of physicians in cities as compared to small towns and rural areas. The oversupply or undersupply of specialties in different locations in Canada is also a problem. As the physician-to-population ratio changes, some areas and regions may experience an excess of doctors and others an insufficient number. Supply levels impact doctors' salaries and also affect rates of surgery, prescriptions, or other necessary medical interventions, as well as unnecessary suffering and lengthy travel or wait times to see a physician.

The involvement of the state in the practice of medicine has resulted in a number of changes in the actual work of the doctor. These include changes in (1) working conditions, (2) the degree of control over patients and over other occupations in the medical field, (3) self-regulation in education, licensing, and discipline, and (4) the actual content of the work (Coburn & Biggs, 1987). Many would say that doctors have lost independence and power in the society, in the medical division of labour, in professional autonomy, and with their patients in the context of medicare. Charles (1976) has documented some of the ways that universal medical care insurance has altered the medical profession through increased administrative, economic, political, and social constraints. The controls of which Charles writes have increased since her publication.

With respect to administrative constraints, Charles was chiefly referring to the increased bureaucratic surveillance of the actual day-to-day practice of individual physicians through the computerized accounting systems detailing the number of patients seen and the medical problems diagnosed in a given period of time. The government, through this bureaucratic control, became able to investigate individual doctors whose practices varied substantially from the norms. The privacy of the independent entrepreneur was effectively eliminated through the powers of this bureaucratic and governmental surveillance.

Certain financial constraints resulted. While the salaries of physicians continued to increase under universal medical care, it was no longer possible for all individual doctors, as independent entrepreneurs, to reach the salary levels they might desire. The Quality Service Payment Formula dictated the maximum number of weekly "units" of service that could be provided by an individual physician without jeopardizing the quality of patient care.

The question of what proportion of the resources of a society should be dedicated to medical care, essentially a political concern, is the third area of constraint noted by Charles. One effect of universal medical care insurance is that physicians' fees are now negotiated between the provincial government and the provincial medical association. The government needs to keep down medical care costs and to ensure universal availability of service. It must also seek to minimize inequity among different medical care personnel such as nurses and others working within hospitals and clinics. The government needs to manage these competing demands within a global budget that includes hospitals and extended-care facilities, drugs, and expensive new technologies.

The final constraint noted by Charles is social. One such example is that in order to provide equitable medical care to people across Canada, even in remote and isolated areas, governments may implement quota systems that would allow doctors to practise in a given area only if their services were needed as determined by a standardized physician-to-population ratio. As a case in point, incentive systems to encourage doctors to work in less desirable places are offered at times.

Medical practice is a source of stress for medical students, interns, and residents as well. The University of Calgary's Department of Surgery studied stress among residents in surgery in 1992, 1994, and 1996 and found that most of the residents felt that their stress level was moderate to substantial. The most important causes of stress among these doctors were consistent pressure, overload, working conditions, and an ill-defined work role (Buckley & Harasym, 1999). In a stress survey from Kitchener–Waterloo in Ontario that involved 123 physicians, 42.5 per cent measured as highly stressed, 26.7 per cent were moderately stressed, and 30.8 per cent showed only low levels of stress. The physicians' scores on a series of stress measures tended to be high on emotional exhaustion and depersonalization and low on personal accomplishment (Lee et al., 2008).

The changing nature of medicine and the threat of an international pandemic, as occurred in 2020 with the novel coronavirus (COVID-19), also are causes for concern among doctors. As Chan and Huak (2004) have noted, the SARS crisis in 2003 had serious costs beyond those for patients and families. Many health-care workers in Toronto (an estimated 43 per cent of all diagnosed cases were among medical personnel) became ill, and two Toronto nurses and one doctor were among the 44 deaths recorded (*CBC News*, 2003). Twenty per cent of health-care workers suffered post-traumatic stress disorder (PTSD) in the wake of SARS. Oncologists or cancer specialists are another group of doctors who experience a lot of stress because they frequently work with seriously ill and dying patients, often over a period of time as their patients may increasingly sicken. Fully 53 per cent of oncologists reported being emotionally exhausted. Among the reasons cited are workloads, worry about patients, vicariously experiencing the trauma of patients and their families, and lack of self-care (Rutledge & Robinson, 2004).

The Impact of Medicare on Health-Care Costs

Clearly, health-care costs as a portion of GNP have increased during the period from about 1960 to the present. Figure 10.3 illustrates the increase in health spending in current dollars in Canada over the period 1975–2018. It shows that health care accounted for approximately 11 per cent of Canada's GDP in 2018. Figure 10.4 indicates the relative contributions of various components to overall health-care costs in 2018. This figure illustrates that the proportion of the health-care monies spent on pharmaceuticals has grown more quickly than that spent on either hospitals or doctors.

The National Forum on Health in 1997 recommended both national home-care and **pharmacare** programs in addition to the present medicare system. The World Health Organization has stated that all countries with universal medical care systems in place ought to establish parallel pharmacare programs. Canada is the only nation not to have done so yet, although the government to try to move in this direction (Morgan et al., 2015). The federal government, a number of provincial governments, and other organizations have studied and continue to study the "crisis" in medicare, as seen, for example, in waiting times for surgery and other procedures and in emergency room crowding, and have made various proposals. As long as medicare is subject to the fortunes of changing political parties and their accompanying ideologies it will be vulnerable. The provinces and territories manage their own health-care systems, educational programs, and health personnel and certification. Provinces vary in respect to the number of programs provided in addition to the basic medicare services. Some, for instance, provide additional benefits, including psychologists, dentists, optometrists, chiropractors, and podiatrists, as well as home care, drugs, and general preventive services. Many Canadians pay for private insurance plans for additional services. While pharmacare is on the national agenda, home care lags.

What is the impact of universal insurance on physician use in Canada as compared with the US, where there is no universal system and millions of Americans remain uninsured? Overall, Canadians of the lower classes and those with less education are more likely to visit a physician than are Americans (Pylypchuk & Sarpong, 2013). The wealthier are about equally likely to visit the doctor in both countries, and foreign-born people are more likely to visit the doctor in Canada. This difference is likely minimized if not eliminated among the elderly, who in the US have Medicare available to them. Medical care on average is more expensive in both Canada and the United States as compared to other OECD countries, and Canada has a lower physician-to-population ratio than many other OECD countries, at 2.5 per 1,000

population as compared to 4.3 in Germany and 4.1 in Spain, Sweden, and Italy, for example.

Despite significant numbers of hospital closures, hospitals continue to account for the highest component of the spending, which was 28.3 per cent in 2017. In recent years, spending on pharmaceuticals has climbed at a disproportionate and alarming rate, surpassing that spent on doctors within the Canadian system. In 2017, 15.7 per cent of the health-care dollar was spent on pharmaceuticals in comparison to 15.1 per cent on doctors (see Figure 10.4). In 1994 doctors accounted for 14.2 per cent and pharmaceuticals for 12.6 per cent. Clearly, the impact of increasing reliance on pharmaceuticals, along with the cost of drugs, is an important cost factor in the health-care system.

The 1990s saw dramatic changes in the medical care system across the country. Elected on a platform that involved eliminating the deficit, the federal Liberal government in 1996 withdrew funding to the provinces specifically earmarked for medicare with the introduction of the Canada Health and Social Transfer (CHST), which over the next several years meant less money to the provinces but with fewer strings attached. Consequently, between 1986–7 and 1994–5 the number of public hospitals declined by 15 per cent, and the number of beds in these hospitals was cut back by 11 per cent. The number of staffed beds per 1,000 people declined from 6.6 to 4.1 (Tully & Etienne, 1997). At the same time, the number of outpatient visits has increased while the number of in-patient visits has decreased. More surgeries that used to include a hospital stay have been relegated to day surgery that sends the patient home to be cared for by family or friends—or by no one. In the context of the control of hospital costs, due to federal transfer cutbacks along with provincial decisions, many hospitals across Canada posted negative annual growth in expenditures despite population growth. In 2012 there were approximately 2.7 hospital beds per 1,000 Canadians as compared to 13.4 per 1,000 people in Japan, 4.8 in Switzerland, 8.3 in Germany, and 2.9 per 1,000 in the US (OECD, 2014).

Cuts in the hospital sector may be reflected in some ill-health effects in the population. A retrospective before/after cohort study that included 7,009 infants born by uncomplicated

Figure 10.3 Health Spending as Share of GDP, 1975–2018

Source: National Health Expenditure Database, CIHI, https://www.cihi.ca/en/health-spending/2018/national-health-expenditure-trends/how-has-health-spending-growth-changed-over-the-last-40-years

vaginal delivery between 31 December 1993 and 29 September 1997 in a Toronto hospital compared the rate of hospital readmission among newborns born before and after the implementation of a supposedly cost-saving early-discharge policy. Before the early-discharge policy was implemented the mean length of stay was 2.25 days. Following the initiation of the policy the mean

stay decreased to 1.62 days. Deleterious effects of the new policy were observed in the higher rate of readmissions—11.7 per cent as compared to 6.7 per cent. The most frequent cause of readmission was jaundice (Locke & Ray, 1999). As healthy infants are one of the best predictions of a healthy population, this finding warrants serious attention.

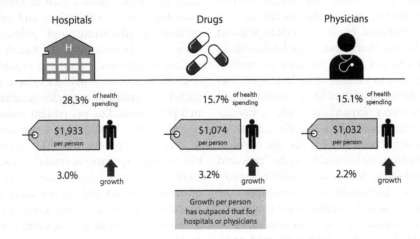

Figure 10.4 Health Expenditures in 2018: Hospitals, Drugs, and Physicians

Source: National Health Expenditure Database, CIHI, https://www.cihi.ca/en/health-spending/2018/national-health-expenditure-trends/where-is-most-of-the-money-being-spent-in-health-care-in-2018

The cost of medical care, along with the provision of other social services, has been front and centre in political debates during the years since the implementation of medicare. It is fair to say that the issue is critical—and has been dramatized by physician and nurse strikes, the closing of numerous hospitals through regionalization and debt, government caps on funding, globalization accompanied by the political focus on the level of deficit in the government financing, the expanded free trade agreements, and a variety of other initiatives designed to restructure the provision of medical care. Waiting times, chaos in emergency wards, and the links between medically provided prescriptions and the opioid crisis are among the predicaments facing the administration of medical care today. Still, medicare is an assumed and essential part of the Canadian identity.

As important as universal health care is to the Canadian identity it is also necessary to offer critiques. Using a model of analysis focusing on the inherent contradictions in a capitalist welfare state, Burke and Stevenson (1993) provide a critique of contemporary Canadian strategies for controlling costs and redesigning health services. They argue that the political economy of health care must be studied in relation to the wider national political economy. Furthermore, they suggest, current policies suffer from several biases, including (1) therapeutic nihilism (a critique of the medical model used to cut back on the various essential medical services without provision for an alternative); (2) healthism (a model that attaches health not only to medical services but also to various other issues, such as lifestyle), which can be used by the state to claim that almost every expenditure has a health-enhancing effect and thus specific "medical" care is less important; and (3) the discourse of health promotion, which can easily be "captured by neoconservative forces to further an ideology favouring decentralization, flexibility, the intrusive state, individual responsibility, and the sanctity of the family" (Burke & Stevenson, 1993, p. 70). All of these forces have been evident in the federal government's health emphases over the past three and a half decades, beginning with Marc Lalonde's 1974 report, *A New Perspective on the Health of Canadians*.

Over the years, various proposals have been made for cutting costs. A first set of proposals has included user fees, extra-billing, co-insurance, and deductibles. However, a number of researchers have found that such strategies do not work to control costs but rather to decrease equality of access to care, to deter use by the poor, and to redistribute the burden of paying for health care from taxpayers to sick people (Barer et al., 1979; Stoddart & Labelle, 1985).

A second set of proposals concerns controls over the supply of physicians and hospitals through limits on immigration of foreign physicians, on enrolments in medical schools, and on residency positions, monitoring of physician billing, hospital and bed rationalization and closings, decreasing budgets, and contracting out of services to the private sector. The problems associated with such provisions are that they are largely ad hoc and will, without explicit planning, inadvertently result in the dismantling of universal medical care.

A third set of proposals involves recognition of the increase in alternative models of health care (homeopathy, nurse practitioners, chiropractic); the introduction of alternative physician payment schemes such as medical savings accounts (MSAs), **capitation**, and salary; health promotion education; and publicly financed competition between types of health-care practitioners. Capitation is a system in which funding is given to service providers to take responsibility for the health of a specific number of people in a population, i.e., per patient annual payment to a physician. "The goal in a capitated system is to keep the population healthy so that they will not require expensive services" (Closson & Catt, 1996). There is a relationship between the type of funding system and service incentives as proposed by Closson and Catt. Even in the midst of a universal medical care system, dental, vision, and home care and prescription drugs are private expenditures.

Summary

1. The chapter provides an overview of the history of medicine in Canada. Indigenous peoples had medicine men and shamans who used a wide variety of effective herbal remedies. Early Canadian settlers relied on a variety of treatments provided by midwives, local doctors, travelling salesmen, and mail-order dispensers of remedies. During the nineteenth century the government started to institute public health measures to deal with cholera and to license homeopaths, allopaths, and other health-care providers.

2. The implementation of universal medical insurance in Canada, which was completed in 1972, was the conclusion of a long, uphill battle, yet that battle has continued to the present day.

3. There are several explanations for the development of medicare in Canada. Two of the most important are the movement in Western industrialized societies towards rationalized bureaucratic social organization and monopoly capitalism, and the spread in Western Europe and beyond of social welfare legislation.

4. The main goal of medicare in Canada was to provide equal health care to all Canadians, thus enhancing the general health of the population. To some extent, this goal has been reached; people in low-income groups visit physicians more often. Health, however, continues to vary by class.

5. Medicare has also had an impact on medical practice: doctors' salaries increased dramatically, but have since levelled off. The ratio of doctors to population in Canada continues to decrease. Working conditions, control over other occupations in the medical field and over clients, self-regulation in education, licensing, and discipline, and the actual content of the work have all undergone significant alterations. As well, the medical profession is now under increased administrative, economic, political, and social constraints.

6. Health-care costs as a portion of Canada's GNP have increased since the introduction of medicare. However, medicare seems to have controlled potentially spiralling costs of medical care. The greatest growth in medical expenditures until 1982 was in institutions; from 1982 to the present, the cost of drugs has represented the greatest growth in the health sector. In spite of some deinstitutionalization policies, the growth in the pharmaceutical sector is likely to continue as the population ages.

7. The cost of medical care is currently at the centre of a number of political debates regarding the provision of a universal social safety net.

8. The privatization of medical care continues to grow. Now about one-third of the cost of medical services to Canadians can be considered to be out-of-pocket.

9. The successes and failures of medicare continue to be debated.

Key Terms

accessibility
administration
allopathic doctors
barber-surgeons
capitation
comprehensive coverage
fee-for-service

Flexner Report
homeopathy
pharmacare
portability
principles of medicare
universality

Questions for Study and Discussion

1. Imagine living during the cholera and early flu epidemics in Canada. Describe how your life might have changed. Now think of and research the SARS outbreak or the recent coronavirus pandemic. Do you know anyone who was directly affected? How did the 2020 pandemic affect you at the time and how has it impacted your daily life since then?

2. Describe and critically analyze the early organizing efforts made by the allopathic doctors. Are there ways that the medical profession continues to maintain dominance in the division of labour among health-care providers?

3. Explain in detail why some forces supported the development of a nationally funded medical care scheme and others rejected it. Then discuss the arguments for and against the increasing privatization of the health-care system today.

4. How has medicare altered the health of Canadians?

5. How has medicare altered the work of doctors?

6. Consider the many implications of online of medicine.

7. Debate the public/private issues with respect to medical care in Canada today.

Suggested Readings

Armstrong, P., & Armstrong, H. (2016). *About Canada: Health care*. Fernwood. An explanation of some of the major values and practices of Canadian health-care policies.

Lavis, J. (2018). *Ontario's health system: Key insights for engaged citizens, professionals and policymakers*. McMaster Health Forum. A discussion designed to make the Ontario provincial health-care system comprehensible.

Miller, A.B., Wall, C., Sun, P., Baines, C.J., To, T., & Narod, S.A. (2014). Twenty-five-year follow-up for breast cancer incidence and mortality of the Canadian National Breast Cancer Screening Study: Randomized screening trial. *British Medical Journal, 348*. http://www.bmj.com/content/348/bmj.g366. The results of a 25-year follow-up of the impact of screening on breast cancer.

Starr, P. (2017). *The social transformation of American medicine*, 2nd edn. Basic Books. Pulitzer prize-winning book on the social history of allopathic and alternative medicine that charts the early battles for dominance among different types of care providers.

Tannenbaum, C., & Tsuyki, R.T. (2013). The expanding scope of pharmacists' practice implications for physicians. *Canadian Medical Association Journal, 185*(4), 1228–32. An article documenting some of the changes in the work of pharmacists now and in the future.

Ubelacker, S. (2013, 22 Jan.). MDs' gross income $307,000, report finds. *Globe and Mail*, http://www.theglobeandmail.com/life/health-and-fitness/health/mdsgross-income-307000-report-finds/article7640498/. Discussion of Canadian doctors' incomes.

Usher, W., & Skinner, J. (2012). EMPIRE and health website recommendations: Technologies of control. *Social Theory & Health, 10*(1), 20–41. A thought-provoking piece on the power of the Internet in health.

The Medical Profession, Autonomy, and Medical Error

11

Chapter Overview

- Medical practice is considered to be a professional occupation.
- Three somewhat different theories of professionalization are occupation, process, and ideology.
- The medical profession has consolidated its position through the subordination, limitation, and exclusion of other types of health-care providers.
- Norman Bethune and Banting and Best are notable Canadians in the history of medicine.
- Medical education has changed substantially over the past few centuries.

- Medical students tend to be from relatively high socio-economic backgrounds.
- The proportion of female and visible minority medical students is increasing.
- Medical responsibility and clinical experience are among the values that doctors learn during their education.
- There are several useful critiques of contemporary medical education.
- Some of the critical issues in medical organization and practice today are autonomy, control, authority, technical and moral mistakes, and variations in practice norms and variations.

Introduction

Why is the occupation of the physician thought of as a profession composed of especially dedicated people? What is it about medical practice and medical knowledge that enabled medicalization to become such a profound social force, infiltrating so much of everyday discourse? What is a profession? How does the medical profession fit into the whole medical care system? Are doctors losing or gaining power, prestige, and income? Membership in a professional occupation has long been associated with a sense of high moral calling and dedication to service. Such values are not necessary, however. Medical education is not focused on such topics. Doctors do not learn all that must be learned about diagnosis and treatment in medical school. They ought to continue to study and learn for the rest of their working lives. As we all do, doctors face conflicts at work. How do doctors handle mistakes or conflicts? To whom are doctors accountable? What is the place of physicians in the discourses of medicalization and biomedicalization? These are among the issues that interest medical sociologists. The purpose of this chapter is to analyze the work of the physician as a professional and to describe the process of medical education in the context of North American society, both today and in the past. The chapter will examine the division of labour and medical practice, the issues of social control and autonomy within the profession, ideas about physicians' networks and their cultural environment, their handling of mistakes, and medical education.

The "Profession" of Medicine

The idea that the practice of medicine is based on a scientifically educated profession is relatively new. Yet, in the last century or so, the medical doctor has become the archetypal professional to the lay public and to those other occupational groups aspiring to reach professional status. That the status of the doctor reflects and reinforces the dominating processes of medicalization and biomedicalization, two of the most influential discourses of the day, makes understanding the medical profession crucial to appreciating these socio-cultural phenomena.

Sociology has had three distinct ways to think about professions and professionalization: the trait approach, the process/power approach, and the ideological approach. Each of these will be considered in turn.

Profession as Occupation: The Trait Approach

The first view of the profession is as an accumulation of traits, that is, the **profession as occupation**. The basis of this view is that the medical profession as an occupation is quantitatively different from other occupations. It became a profession through a numerical accumulation of traits. William Goode (1956, 1960) thought that professions were special occupations that embodied two basic characteristics: (1) prolonged training in a body of specialized, abstract knowledge; and (2) a service orientation. Goode (1960) broke these two characteristics down further and described the traits of a profession as follows.

1. It determines its own standards for education and training.
2. There are stringent educational requirements.
3. Practice often involves legal recognition through some form of licensing.
4. Licensing and admission standards are determined and managed by members of the profession.
5. Most legislation with respect to the practice of the profession is shaped by the profession.
6. The profession is characterized by relatively high power, prestige, and income.
7. The professional practitioner is relatively free of lay control and evaluation.
8. The norms of practice enforced by the profession are more stringent than legal controls.
9. Members are more strongly identified and affiliated with their profession than members of other occupational groups.
10. Members usually stay in the profession for life.

The characteristics of the medical profession in Canada today are similar to those suggested by Goode. Physicians themselves largely determine what constitutes appropriate subject matter for the study and practical experience of physicians-in-training. Medical schools have some of the most stringent admittance criteria of any educational programs. In addition to grades, many medical schools consider the personal qualities of the applicants, such as their ethical views, behaviour, self-presentation in an interview, volunteer work, ability to work with others, leadership abilities, and, increasingly, and whole-person communication skills, as well as the Medical College Admissions Test (MCAT) scores. The profession, too, determines licensing and admittance standards. Medicine is characterized by the relatively high power, prestige, and income of its professional practitioners. Physicians are largely controlled via various profession-managed committees and

organizations, such as the College of Physicians and Surgeons. Such committees are composed primarily of practising doctors. Their own norms, incorporated in the *Code of Ethics* (Box 11.1), are more exacting than the law, in some ways, although they are not necessarily strictly enforced. A doctor's identity as a person is tied to his or her occupation. This affects all other aspects of his/her life, including family life. Usually, a career in medicine is a lifetime career. That doctors have their own code of ethics is just one more reflection of their claim to professionalism. The following box offers some highlights of the *Code of Ethics* developed by the Canadian Medical Association (CMA).

Goode's view of professions has a number of limitations. First, it is based on a self-serving

Highlighted Issues

Box 11.1 • Canadian Medical Association's *Code of Ethics*

The CMA's *Code of Ethics* includes 54 statements of principle under eight different categories. The following is a small representation under just two of the categories, the "General Responsibilities" and "Responsibilities to Society."

General Responsibilities

1. Consider first the well-being of the patient.
2. Treat all patients with respect; do not exploit them for personal advantage.
3. Provide for appropriate care for your patient, including physical comfort and spiritual and psychosocial support, even when cure is no longer possible.
4. Practise the art and science of medicine competently and without impairment.
5. Engage in lifelong learning to maintain and improve your professional knowledge, skills, and attitudes.
6. Recognize your limitations and the competence of others and, when indicated, recommend that additional opinions and services be sought.

Responsibilities to Society

1. Recognize that community, society, and the environment are important factors in the health of individual patients.
2. Recognize the profession's responsibility to society in matters relating to public health, health education, environmental protection, legislation affecting the health or well-being of the community, and the need for testimony at judicial proceedings.
3. Recognize the responsibility of physicians to promote equitable access to health care resources.
4. Use health care resources prudently.
5. Recognize a responsibility to give the generally held opinions of the profession when interpreting scientific knowledge to the public; when presenting an opinion that is contrary to the generally held opinion of the profession, so indicate.

Source: Canadian Medical Association, *Code of Ethics*, 2018.

ideology put forward by the professional group itself. The ideology of a particular occupation cannot help but be self-serving. Second, it ignores the fundamental importance of the power, not just as a characteristic or specific individual trait but as a force behind the very ability to define the features of the professional group. This power enables the group to maintain the prevailing ideology in society at large, not simply by the addition of more and more factors or traits of what it is but through its claim to a superior status on the bases of these traits. Third, this analysis does not take into account the fight for changes in the profession over time. Fourth, it ignores the relationship between the profession and the rest of society—the state, the economic and political structure, and the social organization of the society. In brief, the trait approach ignores the historical development of the profession and its political, economic, and moral place in society.

Profession as Process

The second designation of profession is that it is a social construction resulting from a process through which various occupational groups progress or aspire to progress over time under various conditions (see Table 11.1). The accomplishment of the title and status of being a profession is the goal. Wilensky's (1964) work is representative of this **profession as process** approach.

The steps to becoming a professional in this perspective are as follows: first, the members of the occupation engage in full-time work; second, they establish a relationship with a training/education program; third, they establish an association; fourth, they gain legal status; and fifth, they construct a code of ethics. This approach brings a historical perspective to the concept of the profession. It also has the advantage of showing that occupations can be seen as falling along a continuum with respect to the degree of professionalization they manage to incorporate at any one time or another. Underlying this model, as well as the trait approach, is the view that the profession is a more desirable and higher calling than other occupations. The people who hold the status of professional are expected to be of a finer character than others. Their occupational prestige scores tend to be high.

Johnson's (1972, 1977, 1982) model of the professions bridges the process and the ideology approaches in a power-analysis approach. Johnson describes professions with respect to process, too, but he focuses on how occupational groups come to think of themselves, present themselves, and

Table 11.1 Profession as Process

	Non-Profession	Profession
Education	Very little, very simple concrete educational training not associated with a university.	Complex, abstract, esoteric, lengthy education associated with university.
Licensing	No licence is required. Anyone can call themselves a _____.	Profession itself determines eligibility and continuously evaluates ongoing suitability to maintain professional status.
Code of ethics	Each person for himself or herself and to his or her own benefit.	Altruism, higher calling, collectivist orientation and identity.
Association	Each person for himself or herself and to his or her own benefit.	Organized group encompassing people actively pursuing the profession and maintaining its status and remuneration.
Peer control	State-based laws to control individual behaviour and discipline.	Professional association determines standards of education, professional activity, and disciplines members in violation.

fight to be identified as professions as they increase in power. He sees power as the ability of the professional practitioners to define their work and its compensation as well as other aspects of "reality" in an increasingly broad way, and even to define "the good life" for their clients.

From this viewpoint, the fundamental characteristic of a profession is the ability of the group to impose its perspective and the necessity for its services upon its clients. Professional power arises out of the social distance between the two parties. Three crucial variables determine the degree of power held by a professional group: (1) the more esoteric the knowledge base of professional practice and the less accessible this knowledge is to the lay public, the greater the power of the profession; (2) the greater the social distance between the client and the professional (e.g., when the professional is, for instance, of a higher income level and social class than the client), the greater the power of the profession; and (3) the greater the homogeneity of the professional group in contrast with the heterogeneity of the client group, the greater the ability of the group to organize and assert their power.

Subordination, Limitation, and Exclusion in the Medical Labour Force

In the process of becoming a profession and maintaining this status, doctors have also sought to restrict the scope of the work of other types of practitioners. According to Willis (1983), the allopathic medical profession achieved the level of dominance it has come to enjoy in the division of labour within medicine by three distinct processes. The first is **subordination**. This refers to the process whereby potentially or actually competing professions come to work under the direct control of the doctors. Nursing is an example of this process, because the practice of nursing has been severely restricted and constrained so that the primary legal position of most nursing practice today is subordinate to the medical profession (see Chapter 13).

The second process is called **limitation**, and is illustrated by such occupations as dentistry, optometry, and pharmacy. Such occupations are not directly under the control of the allopathic practitioners, but they are indirectly controlled through legal restrictions that serve the power of the medical profession. The process by which pharmacy came to be subordinate to medicine is a case in point. In the nineteenth century, pharmacists operated as primary caregivers. They prescribed medicines to patients who came to them for help, particularly to the poor and those without doctors. The roles of the pharmacists and the doctors overlapped at that time because most doctors made and dispensed their own drugs. When the pharmacists in Canada became self-regulating in 1870–1, they agreed on an informal compromise with the doctors. Pharmacists gave up prescribing, and doctors generally gave up dispensing drugs.

The third process, **exclusion**, is the process whereby certain occupations that are not licensed and therefore are denied official legitimacy and tax-based financial support come to be considered "alternative" practices. The Australian example given by Willis (1983) is that of chiropractic. Chiropractors in Canada have an ambiguous position today (see Chapter 13). Perhaps a better Canadian example would be naturopaths. Because naturopathic medicine is based on a different model of science than allopathic medicine and is not yet the subject of a sufficient amount of traditional scientific research confirming its effectiveness, it is not considered a mainstream medical practice and its practitioners are not funded under medicare.

Significant changes have occurred in the legal status of complementary and alternative healthcare practice across the country in the last few decades. In Ontario, for example, the Regulated Health Practitioners Act came into effect in 1991 and was amended in 2010 (Ontario Government, 2018). This landmark legislation restricts allopathic monopoly. However, consumers have to pay privately for such alternative services.

Profession as Ideology

An ideology is a group of descriptive and prescriptive beliefs used to explain and legitimize certain practices and viewpoints. Doctors profess these beliefs, as Freidson (1975) implies in the title of his book *The Profession of Medicine*. Parsons (1951) adopted the prevailing ideology of professionals when he argued that a profession has the following characteristics: (1) universalism, (2) functional specificity, (3) affective neutrality, and (4) a collectivity orientation. In this view of the **profession as ideology** a physician is expected to apply universalistic, scientifically based standards to all patients. Physicians are not to differentiate between patients or their treatments on the basis of social differences such as gender, education, income level, or race, for instance, or on the basis of other personal preferences, attractions, or repulsions. The work of the physician is also functionally specific to the malfunctioning of the human body and mind. Functional specificity requires that the physician not offer advice to a patient on non-medical matters such as real estate or choice of a career, but restrict advice to health and disease. The doctor is expected to refrain from emotional involvement, in other words, to be affectively neutral. Finally, the physician is expected to exhibit a collectivity orientation, that is, to provide service to others out of a sense of calling and an altruistic desire to serve. Self-interest, whether expressed in terms of financial rewards or other aspects of working conditions, is not appropriate within the ideology of medical practice.

This view is ideological—and it has served the medical profession well. Through the spread of such a view the public came to believe that doctors

Remembering Our History

Box 11.2 • Norman Bethune

Norman Bethune, born in 1890 in Gravenhurst, Ontario, became a prominent Canadian thoracic surgeon who served in three wars and distinguished himself as a surgeon and a political activist on three continents.

Bethune came from a family with high standards and widely recognized achievement. His great-great-grandfather, Reverend John Bethune (1751–1815), built Canada's first Presbyterian church in Montreal. One of his sons, John Bethune (1791–1872), became Rector of Montreal and Principal of McGill University. Two other sons, Alexander and Angus, also achieved prominence in their chosen professions: Alexander became the second Anglican Bishop of Toronto; Angus became a successful fur trader and businessman who was involved in the two great Canadian fur-trading companies, the North West Company and the Hudson's Bay Company, and later was a director of the Bank of Upper Canada. Angus's son (Norman Bethune's grandfather) was educated in Toronto and learned surgery in Edinburgh before returning to Toronto to become one of the co-founders of Trinity Medical School in 1850. Norman himself was one of three children of Elizabeth Ann Goodwin and Malcolm Bethune.

Bethune worked in a number of jobs, as a lumberjack and as a teacher, teaching immigrants how to read. From 1909 to 1911 he was registered in pre-medical studies at the University of Toronto. Just before his third year of medicine, Bethune joined the Royal Canadian Army Medical Corps. After he was wounded at Ypres he returned to Canada to complete his medical degree. In 1923 he married Frances Campbell Penney with whom he had a stormy and ambivalent relationship. They were divorced and later married again. In 1927–8, Bethune contracted tuberculosis and was treated at Trudeau Sanatorium in New York. As a result of his experience of illness, Bethune developed an interest in thoracic surgery and entered practice with Dr Edward Archibald, a renowned thoracic surgeon at the Royal Victoria Hospital in Montreal. Here Bethune engaged in research on tuberculosis. During this time, he invented a variety of surgical instruments that became widely used in North America.

Bethune is, however, best known for his political activities. In 1936, Bethune tried to establish a state-supported medicare system for Canadians. He organized a group of doctors, nurses, and social workers, called the Montreal Group for the Security of People's Health. Outraged at the refusal of the Canadian Medical Association to support plans for socialized medicine, he sailed for Spain at the outbreak of civil war in October 1936 to aid in the struggle against the Nationalist forces of General Franco. In Spain he devised a method to transport blood to the wounded on the battlefields.

As a professed communist, it was almost impossible for Bethune to remain in Canada. When war broke out in China, Bethune decided to help in the fight for communism. Medical treatment was needed. With funds donated by the China Aid Council and also from the League for Peace and Democracy, Bethune purchased much-needed medical supplies. He arrived in Yannarv in 1938 and quickly moved to the front lines in the mountains of East Shanxi. Travelling with the Eighth Route Army, he devoted his remaining years to fighting fascism and saving the lives of the soldiers who stood for the cause he, too, believed in. His fame reached China's political leaders. Summoned to meet Chairman Mao Zedong, Bethune convinced the leader of the need for surgical knowledge in the front lines of the Chin-Cha'a Border Region.

Bethune founded a medical school and model hospital that would later be renamed the Norman Bethune International Peace Hospital. He has a place in history's pages as a great surgeon and humanitarian. Bethune died in China of septicemia on 12 November 1939.

Sources: Gordon & Allan (1952); Shephard (1982); Stewart (1977).

Library and Archives Canada

Bamboo scroll painting of Norman Bethune; unknown artist. Bethune is still known as a hero in China; in 2003, when the SARS outbreak in China was recognized by the government, those who went to treat the ill became known as "Bethunes."

are "morally superior" individuals who deserve to be trusted, to dominate the practice of medicine, to hold a monopoly in the construction, maintenance, and spread of what is taken to be official "medical knowledge," to control standards for their training, and to discipline their errant members themselves. The power and beneficence attributed to the medical profession have been instrumental in the growth of medicalization.

Deprofessionalization

Widespread debate is ongoing today about the extent to which deprofessionalization or a proletarianization of medical work is occurring (Broom, 2005). Erosion of professionalism is seen in the increasing control experienced by doctors from insurance companies and government bureaucracies. It occurs in the demystification of medical knowledge through widespread access to the Internet and to health information there and in other places (Broom, 2005). A number of health and social movements, such as the women's health movement, the HIV/AIDS movement, and the breast and prostate cancer movements, also are indications of an increase in consumer power and, indeed, an increase in citizen knowledge about health matters and a decrease in medical power. More recently, the widespread citizens' response to the "liberation" treatment for multiple sclerosis (MS) demonstrates the growing power of engaged citizens (Ubelacker, 2017). MS patients and their supporters rallied and organized to get medicare to pay for and Canadian doctors to undertake "liberation therapy." Before systematic research was done, this was touted as a treatment with huge potential. Organizing occurred via online support groups, listservs, and other social media. About 3,000 people with MS left Canada and paid the cost of the surgery. Recently, however, Canadian research found that the surgery was ineffective (Ubelacker, 2017). Nevertheless, the organizing by patients enabled research and some limited treatments that would otherwise not have been done.

The view that medicine is a profession above reproach is also challenged today in the wake of increasing costs without parallel improvements in life expectancy or health quality, mounting evidence of doctors' mistakes, growing rates of errors associated with hospitals and pharmaceuticals, and media reports of individual doctors being criminally charged for sexual assault of patients. Moreover, in the wake of the "financial and debt crises," the future growth of the increasingly specialized occupations in medicine was, for a time, curtailed. During the last few decades, hospitals have been closed across the country. Home health care was to have been expanded. The federal government appears to have been increasingly supportive of what has come to be called "health promotion and disease prevention." Alternative health-care providers such as midwives have become legalized, with their own colleges, in various parts of the country (Canadian Midwifery Regulators Council, 2018). After effectively practising outside the law for most of the last century, midwives today have been granted a degree of professional autonomy. Challenges to the exclusive rights of allopathic doctors to dispense medical care are evident elsewhere. The growing autonomy of nurse practitioners challenges the exclusive knowledge of medical practice, as well. Questioning the expertise of groups and occupations such as allopathic doctors is also one telling aspect of what has come to be called the "risk society" (Beck, 1992, 1994).

Another threat to medical dominance is the easy availability of medical information via the Internet. Physicians today have to deal with patients coming to their offices primed with information gleaned from the Internet. They may have already decided on their diagnosis and be visiting to demand a particular type of drug or treatment they have learned about through the Internet or other media. Interestingly, the evidence suggests that patients are not only more likely than not to get a prescription when they ask for one but also to get a prescription for the particular brand name for which they have asked (see Ford & Saibil, 2010). Nettleton (2004) calls this increasing reliance on the Internet "e-scaped medicine."

An important blow to the Canadian popular belief in the altruism of the medical profession arose at the time of the 1962 doctors' strike in

Saskatchewan. A more recent and equally dramatic demonstration was the strike over extra-billing by many Ontario doctors in 1986. Still, however, in regard to public perception of ethics, nurses, medical doctors, and pharmacists continue to be at the very top of the occupational ranking by a Gallup poll (see Brenan, 2017 and Table 11.2). This percentage was higher than that for police officers and even clergy. Moreover, there are many examples of doctors, nurses, and medical organizations fighting for the health and well-being of the most vulnerable around the world. The NGO Doctors Without Borders is a case in point.

The altruism of many in the medical profession is evident in a number of other new initiatives. Doctors have become increasingly militant in their fight for what they consider to be improvements in health-care accessibility and funding. Strikes, lawsuits against the government, and legal efforts against limitations in access to medical care are among the job actions taken by doctors in British Columbia, Quebec, Alberta, and Manitoba in the latter part of the twentieth century and into the twenty-first century (Sibbald, 1998). Another indication of the willingness or necessity of doctors to fight for what they believe can be found

Table 11.2   Americans' Ratings of Honesty and Ethical Standards in Professions

	Very high/High %	Average %	Very low/Low %
Nurses	82	16	2
Military officers	71	24	3
Grade school teachers	66	27	5
Medical doctors	65	31	4
Pharmacists	62	32	6
Police officers	56	32	12
Day care providers	46	43	7
Judges	43	41	15
Clergy	42	41	13
Auto mechanics	32	53	14
Nursing home operators	26	48	22
Bankers	25	54	21
Newspaper reporters	25	39	35
Local officeholders	24	53	20
TV reporters	23	39	37
State officeholders	19	47	33
Lawyers	18	53	28
Business executives	16	54	28
Advertising practitioners	12	49	34
Members of Congress	11	29	60
Car salespeople	10	48	39
Lobbyists	8	31	58

Source: Gallup (2017, Dec. 4–11). https://news.gallup.com/poll/224639/nurses-keep-healthy-lead-honest-ethical-profession.aspx in the Supreme Court decision in *Chaoulli*. On 9 June 2005 the Supreme Court of Canada ruled on a case in which a physician and patient sued the Quebec government after a year-long wait for hip replacement surgery. The high court struck down a Quebec law prohibiting the purchase of private insurance to cover procedures already offered within the public system. In response to the Supreme Court decision, the Quebec government asked for time to implement changes and proposed the introduction of guaranteed wait times for some procedures, such as radiation treatments, cardiac and cataract surgery, and knee and hip replacements (Schumacher, 2005). Private health-care services within Canada are widely available and readily identifiable through a quick online search of the topic for those who can afford to pay for them. More recently, doctors have organized against the federal government's refusal of medical care to refugee applicants and have been part of a movement that had the Supreme Court strike down the cuts to health care for refugees proposed by the federal government (*CBC News*, 2014).

A Brief History of Medical Education in North America

After 1800, a growing number of proprietary medical schools (profit-making institutions that were generally owned by doctors who also served as teachers) began to open in North America. The quality of the education they offered was poor. They were usually ill equipped for teaching, but then medical theory was still very simple (Wertz & Wertz, 1986, p. 137). Bleeding, the application of leeches, and the ingestion of purgatives to cause vomiting were still the treatments of choice. At this time people were as likely to be harmed as helped by the prevalent and accepted methods of cure.

The most advanced medical training of the time was in Europe, especially France and Germany, where medical research was well supported. Louis Pasteur's germ theory, proposed in the mid-nineteenth century, had a remarkable effect on medicine and, with the new "medical gaze" (Foucault, 1973), provided the basis for the discovery, classification, and treatment of numerous diseases. By the end of the century German physicians had made significant discoveries in the world of medical science. Rudolf Virchow described a general model of disease development based on cellular pathology (1858), and Robert Koch discovered the bacilli for anthrax (1876), tuberculosis (1882), and cholera (1883). Because of these exciting developments in European medical science, American doctors began to cross the ocean for their education and training. Approximately 15,000 American doctors studied in German-speaking universities from about 1870 to 1914.

European training soon became a symbol of status among Americans. Those with such training were able to establish more prestigious and specialized practices than American-trained doctors. By the beginning of the twentieth century, medical research was well funded by the Carnegie and Rockefeller families. The United States began to move ahead as a leader in the development of scientific and medical resources.

Medical education was radically revised and upgraded at the beginning of the twentieth century. As discussed in Chapter 10, the Flexner Report, published in 1910, reviewed medical education in the US and Canada. Sponsored by the Carnegie Foundation, Abraham Flexner visited every medical school in the two countries. Only three American medical schools, Harvard, Johns Hopkins, and Western Reserve, were given approval. The others were severely criticized and were characterized as "plague spots, utterly wretched." Flexner's observations about Canadian medical schools were very similar to those regarding the American schools. As he said:

> In the matter of medical schools, Canada reproduces the United States on a greatly reduced scale. Western University (London) is as bad as anything to be found on this side of the line; Laval and Halifax Medical Colleges are feeble; Winnipeg and Kingston represent a distinct effort toward higher ideals; McGill and Toronto are excellent. (Flexner, 1910, p. 325)

According to the report, 90 per cent of the practising doctors lacked a college education, and the vast majority had attended inadequate medical schools (Wertz & Wertz, 1986, p. 138). Flexner recommended that medical schools consist of full-time, highly educated faculty and be affiliated with a university. He suggested that laboratory and hospital facilities be associated with universities. He recommended the establishment of admission standards. Medical education, he argued, should be at the graduate school level. However, the effects of the Flexner Report were not as devastating to Canadian schools as to the American schools because Canadian medical schools had already been limited and controlled in their growth. In addition, there were far fewer proprietary (profit-making) schools in Canada. Proprietary schools were gradually closed, and medical education was upgraded slowly. Large American foundations donated monies to Canadian medicine and a scientifically based practice was established.

Remembering Our History

Box 11.3 • Sir Frederick G. Banting and Charles H. Best

Banting and Best are known for their discovery of how to extract the hormone insulin from the pancreas. This made possible the treatment of diabetes mellitus, a disease in which an abnormal buildup of glucose occurs in the body. In 1923 Banting was a co-recipient of the Nobel Prize for physiology and medicine for his research and the development of insulin.

Banting's interest in medicine was aroused as the result of a childhood incident. One day, while on his way home from school, he stopped to look at two men who had just begun the first row of shingles on the roof of a new house. As he watched, the scaffolding on which they stood suddenly broke. The two men fell to the ground and were badly injured. Banting ran for the doctor, who arrived in a matter of minutes. As Banting watched the doctor's skilful intervention, he decided that he wanted to be a doctor.

He studied at the University of Toronto and became committed to his idea that insulin, a hormone secreted by certain cells within the pancreas, would cure diabetes. However, Banting's qualifications as an investigator of carbohydrate metabolism were limited. He needed an assistant.

Realizing Banting's dilemma, Professor J.J. Macleod at the University of Toronto mentioned to his senior class in physiology that a young surgeon was carrying out research on the pancreatic islets and the isolation of the antidiabetic hormone. Two students, C.H. Best and E.C. Noble, had previously been engaged in experimental studies of diabetes and had an understanding of carbohydrate metabolism as well as the specific skills required to perform the necessary tests. Both were chosen assistants for a period of four weeks each. They tossed a coin to decide who would work the first four weeks and Best won. Mr Noble never did return to assist Banting. Best became his permanent assistant. Banting and Best made a good team. Their skills complemented each other. The younger man's knowledge of the latest biochemical procedures complemented the surgical skills of the older man.

On 16 May 1921 Banting and Best were given 10 dogs and the use of a laboratory for eight weeks. Their first task was to ligate the pancreatic ducts of a number of dogs. The next step involved trying to produce experimental diabetes. Many animal rights activists argued against the use of dogs in Banting and Best's experiments. However, Banting adopted a very caring attitude towards these "assistants." He made sure the dogs were always spared unnecessary pain.

By 21 July 1921, a depancreatized dog and a duct-tied dog with a pancreas were available. Banting opened the abdominal cavity of the latter dog, removed the shrivelled pancreas, and chopped it into small pieces. This mass was ground up and saline was

continued

added. Banting and Best administered 5 cc intravenously to the depancreatized dog. Samples of blood were taken at half-hour intervals and analyzed for sugar content. The blood sugar fell and the clinical condition of the dog improved.

On 11 January 1922, after months of research to perfect the extract, Banting and Best were ready to experiment with a patient. The first patient was a 14-year-old boy suffering from juvenile diabetes. When he was admitted to the Toronto General Hospital he was poorly nourished, pale, weighed a meagre 65 pounds, and his hair was falling out. A test for sugar was strongly positive. He received daily injections of the extract. An immediate improvement occurred. The boy excreted less sugar, and he became brighter, more active, and felt stronger. This 14-year-old boy was the first of many children who were helped by the discoveries of Banting and Best.

In 1923, Banting and Professor Macleod jointly received the Nobel Prize in physiology and medicine for their investigations into and research on insulin, the active principle of the islets of Langerhans of the pancreas and regulator of the sugar level in the blood. Macleod received this joint recognition for sharing his laboratory facilities and for finding Best to collaborate with Banting. Macleod insisted on the verification of the initial work and the repetition of certain controlled experiments. However, Macleod did not create the serum. Banting was somewhat annoyed that Best did not receive any recognition or award for his work, so he divided equally his share of the award money ($40,000) with Best. Furthermore, Banting always assigned equal credit for the discovery of insulin to his friend and assistant, Best.

Sources: Bliss (1982, 1984); Castiglioni (1941); Stevenson (1946); *Awareness* (1980, p. 71); *Colliers Encyclopedia*, vol. 3 (1973, p. 602); *Encyclopaedia Britannica*, vol. 3 (1976, p. 134).

By the mid-1920s the medical profession in America had clearly established itself as a leading profession. Its standards for training had been improved and were considered excellent. Medical research had reached great heights. The power of the doctor as a healer and as a scientist was widely assumed.

Medical Education in Canada Today

The first Canadian medical school, established in 1824 with 25 students, was at the Montreal Medical Institution, which became the faculty of medicine of McGill University in 1829 (Hamowy, 1984). By the turn of the century six other university medical schools had opened their doors—Toronto, Laval (Montreal and Quebec City campuses), Queen's, Dalhousie, Western, and Manitoba. From the early 1980s to the late 1990s, the number of students admitted to the first year of medical school declined.

In 1983, 1,887 students were admitted. By 1997 only 1,577 students were admitted to medical schools in Canada—a 30 per cent decline in the number of first-year positions per 100,000 Canadians—in spite of population growth and aging (Buske, 1999, p. 772). Since then, the number of physicians per 1,000 people has continued to grow as a result of the high rates of immigration of physicians, as well as increased medical school enrolments.

The process of becoming a doctor requires three different steps: an undergraduate education in science and/or arts, graduate study leading to the MD, and a minimum one-year internship in which the graduate MD works in a hospital or clinic under the supervision of practising doctors. During the internship year students write qualifying exams through the Medical Council of Canada, after which a licence to practise medicine is issued by any one of the provincial medical licensing bodies. Many doctors continue after the internship to specialize in family practice or any of a number of different specialties recognized by the Royal College of Physicians and Surgeons of Canada. Today, 17 Canadian universities grant an MD degree and there are new programs around the country, including in northern Ontario and northern British Columbia.

Medical students have been and continue to tend to be drawn from middle- and upper-middle-class family backgrounds, although some medical schools are making a concerted effort to admit people whose first language is not English and who come from poorer backgrounds. Grades are of fundamental importance. The proportion of women graduating from medical school has altered significantly: 6 per cent of all graduates in 1959 and 44 per cent in 1989 were women (Williams et al., 1993). By 1990, women comprised almost 50 per cent of all medical students, and since 1995 there have been more women than men enrolled. Of the medical students enrolled in 2016–17, 56 per cent were female (Table 11.3). This trend is likely to continue, as the rates of female university enrolment in all fields, with the exceptions of math and engineering, are higher than the rates of male enrolment, according to Statistics Canada (Ferguson, 2016).

Medical education is both expensive and lengthy. This means that it is generally more difficult for young people from less affluent families to attend. Tuition has continued to increase with the growing privatization of universities and professional schools in particular. Currently, medical school tuition varies considerably from school to school and province to province, in 2017 ranging from a high of over $27,000 per year at McMaster down to below $5,000 for in-province students at Quebec medical schools (Association of Faculties of Medicine of Canada [AFMC], 2017). Despite the high cost, applicants to medical school today far exceed the available spaces. Although doctors are well remunerated financially as compared to the average employed Canadian, the attraction of gaining a medical education and becoming a licensed practitioner certainly involves more than simply making a comfortable income. In business- or finance-related occupations, for example, with less education (possibly an MBA) a bright and hard-working person can hope to make a lot more money.

The Process of Becoming a Doctor

The most influential and complete sociological studies of medical education were done in the 1950s and 1960s. The two most notable were the studies done at the University of Chicago by Howard S. Becker and colleagues—*Boys in White: Student Culture in Medical School* (1961)—and at Columbia University by Robert K. Merton et al.—*The Student Physician: Introductory Studies in the Sociology of Medical Education* (1957). Each in its own way contributed to our knowledge of the socialization of the physician. Each explained some of the processes whereby young men (the vast majority of students were male in those days) pass through one of the most rigorous, busy, lengthy, and pressured educational programs and come to adopt the values, norms, skills, and knowledge expected of a medical doctor.

Becker and his colleagues observed and spent time doing participant observation with medical students during their years of medical education at the University of Kansas Medical School. These researchers noted that the major consequences of medical school were that physicians-in-training became aware of the importance of two dominant values: clinical experience and medical responsibility. These two dominant values then guided and directed the strategies used to manage the potentially infinite workload involved in learning all that had to be known before graduation. **Clinical experience** essentially refers to the belief that much of medical practice is actually based on the "art" of determining, from complex and subtle interpersonal cues and in interaction with the patient, the nature of the disease and the appropriate treatment. Along with clinical experience, doctors-in-training were instilled with the notion of **medical responsibility**. By this, Becker and his colleagues stressed the "enormous" moral responsibility of the life-and-death decisions that frequently confront doctors in practice.

These two values were the most important aspects of learning. They enabled the medical students to choose, from the masses of detail presented in books and in lectures, what actually had

Table 11.3 Enrolment in Canadian Faculties of Medicine by Gender, 1968–9 to 2016–17, Selected Years

Year	Men	Women	Total	% Women
1968–9	4,012	669	4,681	14.3
1969–70	4,259	795	5,054	15.7
1970–1	4,457	967	5,424	17.8
1971–2	4,690	1,162	5,852	19.9
1972–3	4,936	1,389	6,325	22.0
1973–4	5,127	1,632	6,759	24.1
1974–5	5,181	1,831	7,012	26.1
1975–6	5,167	2,042	7,209	28.3
1976–7	5,065	2,197	7,262	30.3
1977–8	5,002	2,306	7,306	31.6
1978–9	4,877	2,432	7,309	33.3
2006–7	3,828	5,323	9,151	58.2
2007–8	4,052	5,588	9,640	58.0
2008–9	4,254	5,894	10,148	58.1
2009–10	4,427	6,091	10,518	57.9
2010–11	4,592	6,261	10,853	57.7
2011–12	4,802	6,340	11,142	56.9
2012–13	4,990	6,385	11,375	56.1
2013–14	5,096	6,469	11,565	55.9
2014–15	5,144	6,466	11,610	55.7
2015–16	5,242	6,443	11,685	55.1
2016–17	5,149	6,549	11,698	56.0

Source: AFMC (2016).

to be learned. The notion of clinical experience guided the selection of facts that had to be memorized to pass the examination. It tended to lead the students to disregard basic science and focus on classes where they were provided with practical information of the sort that was not typically found in medical textbooks. Furthermore, the focus on medical responsibility tended to produce an emphasis by the student on interesting cases that involved life-and-death medical judgements rather than on the more common and mundane diseases. It also tended to guide the choice of specialties. The most desired specialties frequently were those with the potential of saving patients (or killing them), such as surgery and internal medicine.

Merton and his colleagues described medical education and socialization as a continuous process by which medical students learn to think of themselves as doctors and in so doing absorb sufficient knowledge to feel comfortable in their new role. Accordingly, two basic traits are developed: the ability to remain emotionally detached from the patient in the face of life-and-death emergencies, great sorrow or joy, or sexuality; and the ability to deal with the inevitable and constant uncertainty. Fox (1957) observed three sources of uncertainty in doctors in training. The first occurs because it is impossible to learn everything there is to learn about medicine and its practice. The second stems from the awareness that, even if the student were able to learn all the available medical knowledge, gaps would remain because medical knowledge is itself incomplete. The third source of uncertainty arises from the first two: the uncertainty in distinguishing between lack of knowledge on the part of the student and inadequacy in the store of medical knowledge.

Over time, disease and death, to the physicians-in-training studied by these researchers, ceased to be frightening, and emotional issues came to be seen as medical problems. The researchers elucidated the processes by which the students learned, in the face of enormous amounts of information, what they would be quizzed about and thus what they had to know to pass their courses and to graduate. In *Boys in White*, Becker et al. also describe the conversion of the idealism of the new student to the cynicism held by students in later years. When graduation approached, the original commitment to helping patients and practising good medicine tended to return.

These two studies are more than a half-century old. Some things have changed but there are similarities. Doctors still have to work and learn within a situation where uncertainty is inevitable and, in fact, is a basic aspect of the process of diagnosis—called differential diagnosis. This means that every diagnosis essentially involves ruling out other possible explanations for the presented symptoms. Further medical knowledge is changing all the time as new studies and new technologies are developed. Keeping up with everything is impossible and doctors have to live with that sense of inadequacy constantly. Clinical experience is still important in determining each diagnosis, but this increasingly has to be done in the context of what is called evidence-based practice or evidence-based medicine (EBM). This puts a powerful burden on doctors to base their decisions on more than clinical experience. Moreover, in the context of increased specialization, doctors have to decide whether or not to refer patients to specialists or order more tests to help in diagnosis. This personal responsibility, while still a feature of medical work, takes place in an increasingly complex field of possibly fraught definitions of the limits of personal responsibility and knowledge.

In addition, medical education has been shown to be sexist both in textbooks and in clinical examples used in classroom lectures (Giacomini et al., 1986; Zelek et al., 1997). In the past, an unwritten quota system governed the admittance of women into medical school (Woodward, 1999). In fact, the practice of medicine has been shown to be built around a masculine prototype (Zelek et al., 1997). A great deal of published research, the basis of medical practice, has used the male body as the norm (McKinlay, 1996). Doctors have to be aware of this and question their own gender and other biases. Sexism currently is being addressed in a variety of programs in medical schools across the country and, as noted previously, the majority of new students now, and in the past 20 some years, are female. Increased gender equality in education, training, and research is undoubtedly underway.

Doctors did and do reflect the heterosexism of the rest of society and lesbians, gays, and bisexual and transgendered people may not always receive the most appropriate health care as a result (Tortelli, 2016). Lesbian and gay doctors, too, are subject to discrimination (Druzin et al., 1998). The number of "out" gay and lesbian doctors is increasing and they are organizing. This movement undoubtedly will have benefits for lesbian, gay, bisexual, and transgender patients (LGBTQ+) patients, as well as for other sexual minorities. Same-sex marriage and the immense success of the Gay Pride movements in Canada and around the world are among the important contributors to a more open-minded attitude on the part of the majority of Canadians to LGBTQ+ issues. The Canada-wide association of lesbian, gay, bisexual, transgendered, and queer (LGBTQ+) medical students will most likely add to the progressive thrust of the treatment of LGBTQ+ patients and doctors alike. Teaching medical (and other) students about broader diversity issues than gender and sexual orientation continues to be a challenge although it is one upon which some posi- tive movement is visible. Racism is evident both in doctors and in patients. According to a report in the *Canadian Medical Association Journal*, visible minorities are still minorities in medicine. Only 16 per cent of hospital senior management and 14 per cent of board members are not white (Vogel, 2018). Twenty-five per cent of family medicine residents reported intimidation on the basis of gender, race, or culture (Vogel, 2018).

Getting Doctored

Shapiro (1978), in one of a number of autobio- graphical accounts of medical school, has critically evaluated his own experiences of becoming a phys- ician in a book entitled *Getting Doctored*. Although this book is older now, the principles are worth discussing and continue to be relevant. In this an- alysis the two most important features of medical education are the concepts of alienation and the au- thoritarian personality. Alienation is evident in the relationships of medical students to one another, in the relationships of doctors, interns, and residents towards one another, and in the approach of the medical student to studies, medical school, and pharmaceutical companies and other related insti- tutions. The authoritarian personality, which breeds alienation, is experienced at most stages of medical education and, later, in medical practice. Four types of alienation are discussed: alienation of labour or productive activity, alienation from the product of labour, alienation of people's relationships with others around them, and alienation from life.

Alienation of labour is seen throughout the medical care system, from the workers at the top to those at the bottom. Shapiro provides numerous ex- amples of alienated labour in medical school. These include: fierce competition between medical stu- dents, an enormous workload, and little direction re- garding what, out of the mountains of information, is most relevant. "Students, especially in the early stages, spend extraordinarily long hours at study without any assurance that they have mastered what is necessary" (Shapiro, 1978, p. 29). Shapiro uses the phrase "doc around the clock" to encapsulate the doctor's experience of being tied to medical work.

Alienation from the product of labour exists when the worker does not feel that the product of his or her labour is a true reflection of his or her self and values. The way doctors learn to talk about patients and their illnesses provides some illustrations of their lack of identification with patients. Patients were called "crocks" when their complaints were believed to be psychosomatic. They were described as having "two neurons" when they were believed to be lacking in intellec- tual functioning or were uncooperative (Shapiro, 1978, p. 168). The racism and sexism some doctors feel from their patients is another source of alien- ated work (Vogel, 2018).

Alienation of relationships, too, is repeatedly evident in Shapiro's description of medical school. One set of interpersonal strategies will be used to illustrate this. Competition is a central feature of the interpersonal interaction of physicians-in-training. Fear of failure is widespread. Students compete for rank in class. Students vie for the best internship, residencies, and for the position of chief resident. Apparently "a record number of medical school graduates missed out on residency programs" in 2017 (Woods, 2017), but the problem of some missing out is a serious and continuing one. There are not enough spots for those who graduate from medical school and some have to wait several years before they get the opportunity for practical experi- ence and can practise medicine.

In another study of medical students, Conrad (1998) analyzed four autobiographical studies of medical school and practice. His findings paral- lel those discussed previously and indicate a lot of continuity in the issues involved in education. Some of these issues then become practice behav- iours and may be linked to the high rates of burn out, depression, and anxiety found among doctors.

- The culture of medical education discourages caring.
- Doctors' clinical perspective focuses almost entirely on the disease rather than the illness or the suffering person.
- Doctors are not taught how to talk to patients. Although this is changing, there is still a way to go.

- "Medical school does an excellent job at imparting medical knowledge and technique, but it is inadequate in conveying humane and caring values." (Conrad, 1998, p. 343)
- "Technological medicine, with its disease orientation, myriad lab tests, complex interventions, and 'fix-it' mentality, pays scant attention to teaching about doctor–patient relations." (p. 343)
- Medical students' life of long hours, sleep deprivation, excessive responsibility, and (arrogant) superiors inhibits the growth of compassion and empathy.

Medical students today experience high rates of stress and depression (Glauser, 2017). For instance, about 37 per cent of Canadian medical school students meet the cut-off point for being

burned out. When other types of "mental health" problems such as substance abuse are included, the rates of "mental distress" in the profession are higher. Understandably, perhaps, in the face of the constant temptation, doctors apparently are more likely to use illicit drugs. The suicide rates for doctors are higher than those for Canadians as a whole, according to studies undertaken and reviewed by the Canadian Medical Association. About one in 10 practising doctors reported that they had thought of suicide at least once in the previous year (Vogel, 2018). Medical students tend to have high personal standards for work and achievement. These traits are sometimes associated with maladaptive perfectionism and an extraordinary concern with performance. Linked to this, medical students tend not to seek help, reporting that they lack time or are afraid of a lack of confidentiality. Even while

Spotlight on Ethics

Box 11.4 • Sexual Sterilization: Purifying the Gene Pool? And Controlling Populations

In 1928 the legislature of Alberta enacted the Sexual Sterilization Act to be overseen by the Alberta Eugenics Board. BC joined in this effort (Kersten, 2013). The Act was passed during the period in which eugenics was becoming a powerful idea. At the time it was believed by many to be a way to "purify races" and ensure a healthy and intelligent gene pool. Mental illness and retardation, epilepsy, and even criminal behaviour and prostitution were among the conditions thought to be genetically transmitted. Initially in Alberta, the primary group targeted to be sterilized were "mentally disabled or defective" people. Before a person institutionalized for being mentally defective was discharged the Alberta Eugenics Board insisted on sterilization to ensure that there would be "no danger of procreation" once the inmate had left. The rationale was to mitigate the risk of the "multiplication of the evil by the transmission of the disability" (Elgie, 2014). Later, people with Huntington's, syphilis,

and epilepsy were included. Indigenous women were over-represented in the practice of these policies. This legislation was finally repealed in 1972 in Alberta and 1973 in British Columbia (Kersten, 2013).

Perhaps the most widely known case of a person who was sterilized is that of Leilani Muir. She sued the Alberta government in 1995 for sterilizing her without her consent during an appendectomy. Muir had been institutionalized in a training school at 10 years of age because she was an abused and unwanted child. She was successful in her suit, and the Alberta government was forced to compensate her financially. Subsequently, more than 700 other victims of forced sterilization sued the Alberta government, which settled these suits out of court. A National Film Board video about this is case, by Glynis Whiting, can be found online. While people with intellectual disabilities may not face sterilization today, they still face oppression and are often discouraged from reproducing.

being expected to provide a form of care for others, they are not encouraged to care for themselves in their education or in the fee-for-service structure of their work. Instead, they cannot rely on a constant secure income but are incentivised to work more and more to increase their income.

Another one of the ongoing difficulties of medical practice is that doctors have to deal constantly with suffering, pain, and emotional fragility in their patients. Some patients are difficult at times but doctors have few options but to offer care and treatment. Among patients with life-altering or life-threatening medical issues doctors may have to

live with the feeling of failure and that they are not able to help. Generally, patients do not visit their physicians to report on how happy they are and how well they are feeling. These existential issues related to the job of being a doctor can perhaps be mediated, but they will not go away. In addition, there are the physical stressors such as long hours, overnight calls, and bodily stresses resulting from poorly designed work locations, sitting and standing for long hours, and sometimes bending repetitiously. As a service profession emotional labour is a basic part of their work. They have to manage their emotions in front of their patients. There

Canada in a Global Context

Box 11.5 • Forced Sterilization of Indigenous Women in Canada Gains the Attention of the UN Committee against Torture

In February 2018, a Saskatchewan-based law firm applied to certify a class action lawsuit against the government of Canada on behalf of a group of about 100 Indigenous women to protest what lawyer Alicia Lombard described as a practice of coerced sterilization in Saskatchewan hospitals (Zingel, 2019). In the meantime, Indigenous women have been reporting similar experiences of sterilization without full, informed consent in several provinces and territories, including Saskatchewan, Alberta, the Northwest Territories, Yukon, Manitoba, and Ontario. Some women report that the procedure was not fully explained by hospital staff, making it impossible for women to give informed consent, and other women did not understand that they had the right to refuse it. Other women were harassed to sign consent forms while in active labour or were told by hospital staff that they could not leave the hospital or see their newborn babies until they consented to be sterilized (*CBC Radio*, 2018).

Forced sterilization targeting Indigenous women has been occurring in Canada since the 1930s. Sterilization laws enacted by Alberta and British Columbia between 1928 and 1933 allowed women to

be sterilized without their consent if they were deemed "mentally defective"—a highly dubious term—and Indigenous women were disproportionately designated as "mentally defective," with 77 per cent of the Indigenous women who were sterilized thus designated. These forced sterilizations were particularly significant in the small towns of the Far North. For example, in the Nunavut town of Igloolik, 26 per cent of the women between the ages of 30 and 50 were apparently sterilized. Half of the women in Naujaat, another Nunavut community, were sterilized. New laws made the forced sterilizations illegal in the early 1970s, but as this class action lawsuit alleges, the practice continued.

The Canadian Medical Association has spoken out forcefully against this practice as a serious violation of medical ethics (Kirkup, 2018). The UN Committee Against Torture has called for the criminalization of forced sterilization. The Chief of the Assembly of First Nations (AFN), Perry Bellegarde, has supported the UN committee's view (Smoke, 2018), as has NDP MP Don Davies, who has written to the RCMP asking for an investigation into what the UN calls criminal assault and torture (Barrera, 2019).

are workload issues, physician shortages and, at times, excesses, family pressures and responsibilities, and monetary requirements, and also, among other stressors, possible harassment and intimidation, the difficulties of transitioning into clinical work, and the enormous responsibility of finally being the diagnostician and treatment provider. Upon graduation, doctors need to learn not only to manage their own finances but also how to run an office, with all the accounting, management, hiring, and firing this involves.

Organization of the Medical Profession: Autonomy and Social Control

Physicians are self-regulating. Through their organizations they decide what constitutes good medical practice, determine the requirements for training a physician, set standards of practice, and discipline colleagues who depart from these standards. The way that practice is organized, its locus of activity, and the payment modality are all affected by the regulatory power of doctors. The profession has established two major control bodies, the College of Physicians and Surgeons and the Canadian Medical Association, which are recognized by the federal and provincial governments. These organizations attempt to define expectations of medical behaviour, to improve standards of performance, and to protect the status and economic security of their members. The Canadian Medical Association is an amalgamation of the provincial medical associations. The CMA represents physicians as a national lobby group. The provincial bodies negotiate with the respective medical care plans for fee scales and other matters of relevance to the practice of medicine. The situation is somewhat different in Quebec.

The Medical Act requires that the Medical Council of Canada be responsible for the licensing of qualified medical practitioners, for supervising what these practitioners do, and for preventing unqualified practitioners from practising (Medical Council of Canada, 2019). The provincial colleges

have the power to eliminate from the register all those who are convicted of certain offences, although monitoring this can be difficult (Ansari, 2014). And while practitioners may appeal the judgements of the Medical Council in court, the view of the Council is almost invariably upheld. The courts thereby have long tended to support the idea that the profession is the proper judge of the actions of its colleagues.

Autonomy and power are crucial characteristics of the profession of medicine. However, self-regulation depends on the type of practice in which the doctors are engaged (Freidson, 1975, p. 71). Freidson distinguishes among doctors practising alone, colleague networks, large group practices, and university clinics. Those who practise alone enjoy the greatest freedom from outside control. Pure forms of solo practice generally are quite rare. Solo practice, nevertheless, has been lauded as the model of the ideal-typical modality for an entrepreneurial professional who is free from control. In this model the doctor treats the patient privately and confidentially, without the interference of colleagues, insurance companies, governments, or any other outsiders. This patient–doctor relationship is described as a "sacred trust." Assurance of continuous competence by the physician in private practice is based primarily on the assumption of adequate recruitment policies, educational programs, and licensing procedures. In fact, the ongoing day-to-day control of practice ultimately rests with the individual practitioner. In Canada doctors are subject to some regular control and oversight by the government as they are paid through public funds.

One of the primary sanctions against behaviour deemed inappropriate by professional colleagues is ostracism—by not referring patients or by denying certain privileges, such as hospital privileges. This is useful only to the extent that the particular medical practitioner depends on colleagues and hospitals for her or his practice. Specialists usually are colleague-dependent to a greater extent than are general practitioners because access to these specialists by patients can occur only through the medical referral system.

The number of doctors in solo practice is decreasing. Most receive at least some of their income from fee-for-service payments. Seventy-three per cent of the payments to physicians in Canada are fee-for-service and 27 per cent are derived from alternative payment types (Picard, 2016). Some doctors are paid by more than one method. Fee-for-service has been the preferred method of payment in the past because it has seemed to reflect on physician autonomy. Group practices may be preferred by women and by younger doctors, and thus the trend towards group work might continue. Furthermore, work satisfaction may be higher for some in group situations.

Today, the power and autonomy of the physician within the hospital are severely restricted. Doctors used to be the only gatekeepers to the hospital system: they determined which patients, medical colleagues, and various paraprofessionals would be admitted. Now, hospital administrators, many of whom are graduates of university-based hospital administration programs, are the pivotal figures organizing the hospitals (Wahn, 1987). Doctors now function in the hospital as the middle managers whose work is likely to be constrained, organized, and directed by the hospital administrators and observed and critiqued by the nursing staff and others below them in the hospital hierarchy. Hospital administrators are guided by different primary goals than are doctors. They are chiefly concerned about managing the organization in a rational and efficient manner and eliminating "unnecessary" services and costs so as to balance the hospital budget. This, of course, involves satisfying the goals of promoting and maintaining good, safe, and efficient medical care. But these medical goals must be met in the context of rationalizing services and balancing the interests of many specialty groups who work within the hospital.

Coburn et al. (1997) have argued that the medical profession has, in part, declined in autonomy and control because of the involvement of the government in payment. Payment for medical services is a significant part of the budget of each province. It ranges from 43 per cent of the total program spending in Ontario to 34 per cent in Quebec (Barua et al., 2017). In this context, the government necessarily has some of the moral authority that once belonged to the individual doctor and is able to intervene at times to limit expenditures and to monitor individual practice. In particular, "in recent years, the state has introduced changes in the structure and functions of the self-regulatory college, has intervened with a number of cost-controlling mechanisms—denying funding for new technologies, tightening controls on insured service, and promoting explicit guidelines for medical decision-making" (p. 17). The autonomy of the medical profession is fragile and complex, and threats to that autonomy are real. Biomedicalization theory (Clarke et al., 2003) also reflects a diminution in the independence and autonomy of doctors not only vis-à-vis the state but also in the face of huge for-profit organizations such as pharmaceutical and medical device companies and various types of insurance providers.

The Management of Mistakes

Mistakes happen to all of us. They happen both on and off the job. They are an inevitable part of life. Which student has ever received 100 per cent on all tests, essays, and exams? Which teacher has never made an error in adding or recording marks? Doctors are no exception: they also make mistakes. But when doctors make mistakes the results can be devastating—they can result in death or serious disability for the patient. One question Marcia Millman asks in *The Unkindest Cut* (1977) is how doctors handle their mistakes. Millman carried out her research for two years at three university-affiliated hospitals, where she was a participant-observer working with doctors at all status levels. Because these hospitals were teaching hospitals attached to universities, their standards can probably be considered above average.

Millman's work highlights three basic points. First, the definition of what constitutes a mistake is variable. In fact, the old joke that the operation was a success but the patient died has a basis in fact. Results that patients interpret as mistakes are not necessarily considered **medical errors**. And doctors in different specialties may have different

Highlighted Issues

Box 11.6 • Medical Practice and Errors

An interview study of 40 doctors' interpretations of what constitutes mistakes in their work demonstrated the "anguish of clinical action and the moral ambiguity of being a clinician" (Paget, 1988). Mistakes, the interviewed doctors noted, are absolutely inevitable in the work of the doctor. Mistakes are intrinsic to medical decision-making: they are essential to the experience of doctoring. Clinical practice involves risks because it requires the application of finite knowledge to specific situations. Mistakes often occur not because doctors are at fault or incompetent; rather, medicine by its nature is an essentially "error-ridden activity." Because of the method of interpretive understanding based on interview data, Paget was able to describe medical practice with empathy for doctors. As she says, "mistakes are complex sorrows of action gone wrong" (p. 131).

The doctor knows that she/he is making decisions based on some but not all of the information available. Moreover, even if the doctor has all the available information, it may not be enough to diagnose or treat a disease. Medical practice inherently encapsulates a degree of uncertainty. Yet, it usually results in, even requires, action. Paget's work enables us to see the definition of mistakes from the perspective of the practising clinician. Based on open-ended interviews and using a phenomenological approach, she shows the everyday struggles of doctors who make decisions in an error-ridden climate.

Treatments can be dangerous; the potential for deleterious results from mistakes has grown enormously. Irreparable mistakes are inevitable: they occur in spite of good intentions, good education, and care.

---

understandings of what constitutes a mistake. Actions that would be considered reprehensible in an attending physician are considered permissible in an intern who is, after all, "just learning." The point here is that there is no universal standard of perfect or imperfect medical practice. Norms are worked out in practice.

Second, while the designation among doctors of what constitutes a mistake is problematic, some results of medical practice are considered undesirable enough to warrant investigation. One example would be an unexpected death during surgery. When such an outcome occurs, Millman notes, doctors tend to use two mechanisms for dealing with it: (1) neutralization, and (2) collective rationalization. As Millman says:

> By neutralization of medical mistakes I mean the various processes by which medical mistakes are systematically ignored, justified or made to appear unimportant or inconsequential by the doctors who have made them or

those who have noticed that they have been made. (Millman, 1977, p. 91)

Thus, an action that results in harm to a patient can be ignored, or it can be justified because of the intricate nature of the surgery involved or because it was the patient's fault for not informing the physician of a drug reaction. In justifying themselves, doctors may emphasize unusual or misleading clues; or they may focus on the patient's unco-operative attitude or "neurotic" behaviour. Even though "doctors may have differences and rivalries among themselves with regard to defining, blaming, and acting on mistakes, all doctors will join hands and close ranks against patients and the public." According to Millman, the assumption made is, "there but for the grace of God go I" (p. 93). In the face of mistakes, doctors will tend to band together to support one another and to explain the behaviour leading up to the "mistake" as blameless or at least as being as logical as possible given the circumstances.

The third point of Millman's work is that hospitals have instituted formal mechanisms for dealing with mistakes, for using errors as a source of education, and for investigating culpability. The Medical Mortality Review Committee, one such mechanism, she described as meeting monthly to discuss deaths within the hospital and to review each death in which there may have been some possibility of error or general mismanagement. The fundamental yet unspoken rule governing such a review was that it was to be "a cordial affair." Even though the atmosphere might sometimes be slightly strained, and the individual physician whose decisions are being reviewed might be embarrassed, rules of etiquette and sociability were stringently enforced. All members of staff who had a part in the mistake used the committee meeting as an opportunity to explain to the others how the conclusion made sense to them. Emphasizing the educational aspect of the event rather than its legitimate investigatory nature minimized the discomfort level.

About 20 years ago in Canada a significant minority of patients (7.5 per cent) experienced negative effects as a result of medical error, or about 185,000 events a year, and it was estimated that between 44,000 and 98,000 people died annually in the US as the result of error (Canadian Foundation for Healthcare Improvement [CFHI], 2004). No data suggest that these numbers have

improved. Sometimes the error is dramatic, such as when bandages are left inside a patient after surgery or when patients are given the wrong medication. Sometimes they may be more equivocal errors. One study, for example, found that 25 per cent of people surveyed said that they had experienced an "adverse event" in either the hospital or the community (CFHI, 2004). In the past, errors were seen to be the result of individual "bad apples" who were then blamed as individuals. Now, however, error is believed to be often the result of system failures and to result, in large part, from understaffing, multi-tasking, the myriad of new equipment needing monitoring, and a rushed environment. There are a number of new trends for managing and minimizing errors, including critical incident reporting (Iedema et al., 2006), electronic health records, and bar codes on medications (CFHI, 2004). In 2007, the Canadian Institute for Health Information, drawing on a variety of data sources, reviewed patient safety in Canada. The analysis estimated the frequency of a range of adverse events. Of the events examined, nosocomial infections (i.e., infections acquired in the course of health care) were most common, occurring in around 10 per cent of patients. At the other end of the scale, the least common incident in the analysis was a fatal event due to blood transfusions, which occurred in 0.001 per cent of patients (see Table 11.4).

Table 11.4   Types and Rates of Adverse Events

Event	Number Affected per Event
Adults contracting a nosocomial infection while in an acute-care hospital	1 in 10
Children contracting a nosocomial infection while in an acute-care hospital	1 in 12
Obstetrical traumas during childbirth (vaginal delivery)	1 in 21
Birth trauma: injury to neonate	1 in 141
Post-admission pulmonary embolism or deep vein thrombosis	1 in 279
In-hospital hip fracture for adults aged 65+	1 in 1,263
Foreign object left in after procedure	1 in 2,998
Adverse blood transfusion events	1 in 4,091
Fatal events definitely, probably, and possibly related to transfusion of blood components	1 in 87,863

Source: Adapted from CIHI (2007).

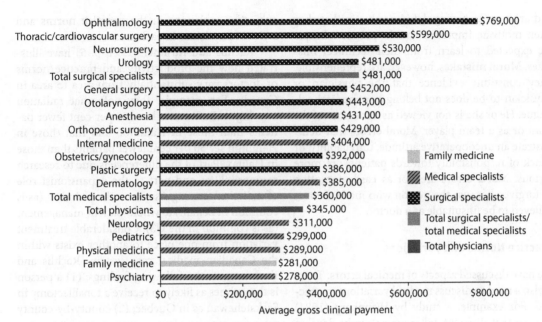

Figure 11.1 Average Gross Clinical Payment by Physician Specialty, 2017–18

Source: CIHI (2019).

Medical errors are often the result less of individual mistakes than of system failures. Among the documented systemic errors, according to Charney (2012), are the following:

- the profit motive or the need to make a profit to stay in business and/or to thrive;
- inadequate levels of staffing (e.g., patients hospitalized with a 1:4 nurse-to-patient ratio are 31 per cent less likely to die than those with a ratio of 1:8);
- shiftwork, which can lead to potentially dangerous consequences for patients;
- hospital working conditions (e.g., work hours, ergonomics, work flow, and autonomy, for instance);
- intimidation and harassment from colleague to colleague;
- accountability and laws that may prevent some reports of errors (from fear of censure or prosecution);

- failure to report or the under-reporting of errors, which means that the systems are not as likely to be changed;
- new and complex technologies.

Technical and Moral Mistakes

Bosk's (1979) work on mistakes among doctors adds another theoretical dimension to our understanding of medical error. Bosk studied the ways surgeons and surgeons-in-training at a major university medical centre regulated themselves. He noted that the medical centre's hierarchy is structured and managed so that those at the bottom levels are more likely to have to bear the responsibility for mistakes than those at the top.

There were, he noted, two different kinds of mistakes—technical and moral. **Technical mistakes** are to be expected in the practice of medicine and, usually, colleagues are forgiven them. They are viewed as an inevitable part of medical work and are seen as having definite value in that they often motivate improvements in practice. People are expected to learn from their technical mistakes. **Moral mistakes**, however, are reprehensible. They constitute evidence that the physician or physician-to-be does not belong as a medical colleague. He or she is not viewed as a member of the team or as a team player. Moral errors that demonstrate an uncooperative attitude, unreliability, or a lack of responsibility towards patients are more serious. Moral errors are not as easily forgotten or forgiven because the person who made them is believed to be unsuitable as a doctor.

Practice Norms and Variations

We have discussed aspects of medical errors. There is also a need to discuss medical variations in practice. For example, a study by Wennberg (1984) showed that different colleague networks develop different sets of beliefs, norms, and practices regarding diagnosing specific diseases and the appropriate treatment for them. Wennberg compared rates of hospitalization and surgery in the states of Iowa, Vermont, and Massachusetts and found tremendous variations from state to state and within states. He then divided the different areas into what he called "hospital markets" or hospital service areas (populations using one hospital or a group of hospitals). He found that different hospital service areas had highly variable rates of all measures of hospital and surgery utilization. For instance, he noted that the rate of hysterectomy (among all women under 70) varied from 20 per cent in one market to 70 per cent in another. The rate of prostatectomy varied from 15 per cent in one market to 60 per cent in another. Tonsillectomy rates varied from 8 per cent to 70 per cent in two different markets. In trying to explain these wide differences, he examined the roles played by (1) illness rates, (2) insurance coverage, (3) access to medical services, (4) age distribution, (5) per capita hospital bed ratios, and (6) physician–population ratios. None of these factors made a significant impact on the utilization of hospitals or surgery. Wennberg concluded that the differences must be due to

subjective variations in the **practice norms** and styles of physicians in each area.

Rachlis and Kushner (1994, p. 5) have illustrated how the productivity and practice norms of doctors vary substantially from area to area in Canada. For example, they note that radiation oncologists in Toronto have 50 per cent fewer patients than those in Hamilton and that those in Hamilton see 50 per cent fewer patients than those in Halifax. Part of the difference is due to research responsibilities and part to the expansionist role of radiation oncologists—from the technical (as is common in Britain) to whole-patient management (as is common in the US). Considerable treatment variation from one place to another exists within the Canadian medical care system. Rachlis and Kushner note the following findings: (1) a person is three times as likely to receive a tonsillectomy in Saskatchewan as in Quebec; (2) county-by-county rates for coronary bypass surgery vary 2.5 times throughout Ontario; (3) the length of stay for hospitalized heart attack patients ranges from 6.6 to 12.9 days (within just one province). Also, substantial differences in diagnosis and treatment sometimes exist from province to province in Canada (Revah & Bell, 2007). At times, this is likely the result of different levels of coverage for different procedures. Ongoing issues are also related to the differences in personal values and religion, which lead some doctors to refuse to provide certain treatments (birth control and abortion are the two most widely known of these).

According to John P. Bunker (1985), such variation occurs because medicine is an art and not a science, and therefore a great deal of uncertainty is involved in the practice of medicine. Most surgery is not for life-threatening problems but for conditions of discomfort, disability, or disfigurement. Moreover, in most cases the benefits just about equal the risks. Surgery may be equally likely to improve the health, comfort, and lifespan of the patient as it is to cause an increase in morbidity. There are no clear differences in mortality rates in different hospital markets. Hospitalization or surgery rates are not correlated with declines in either the mortality or morbidity rates.

CRITICAL THINKING

Box 11.7 • Another Look at Medical Practice and Errors

The medical system, like all systems, is mistake-ridden. However, under-reporting of mistakes is common. This is partly because the culture of medicine in many ways emphasizes individual responsibility, professional autonomy, and self-regulation. Such an individualized system does not easily foster shared responsibility and the opportunity of learning from mistakes. Rather, it encourages denial, fear, and blame. In addition, the population served by doctors is increasingly litigious and numerous lawyers are ready to take medical error cases. In this context admitting a mistake can be enormously costly to various parties to the mistake. Sometimes errors result from faulty equipment. In an environment increasingly dependent on new and complex technologies, errors may seem inevitable. They are certainly explainable. They are not, however, acceptable. In the absence of systematic reporting of errors, improving the quality of health care is hampered.

The most extreme case of medical malfeasance to come to light in the recent past is that of a British doctor, Harold Shipman, who was found to have murdered at least 215 of his patients and to have done so without any suspicion being directed towards him for a very long time. He was caught only when he crudely altered the will of his last victim in a way that apparently made detection inevitable. It has been suggested that the doctor was addicted to pethidine (an opioid painkiller). He may have also been addicted to murder. How did these murders go undetected for so long? The medical error lies in the fact that these murders could have gone on so long without detection. The lack of

adequate surveillance of medical practice reflects error in the functioning of the medical system. How did he manage to get corroborating signatures from other doctors on certificates of cremation? Donna Cohen (2002) suggests that he was able to avoid detection, in part, because of prevalent ageism. She argues that because the elderly are more likely to die of all sorts of conditions, family members and friends are much less likely to ask questions when a death is unexpected or unexplained. All of the people killed by Shipman were at least middle-aged, 82 per cent were women, but many had been healthy. Elizabeth Wettlaufer was a Canadian nurse who was a serial killer of eight nursing home residents. This again underscores the particular vulnerability of the elderly to unnoticed murder (McQuigge, 2017). In this case the murders were only detected when Wettlaufer, who confessed again and again, was finally believed. She was then reported to her professional governing body, which took immediate action leading to her losing her license to practice and being charged with murder. None of the family members or friends of those murdered asked questions about the sudden and unexpected deaths of their loved ones. Until the end none of the people to whom she had confessed, including a lawyer and a pastor, took action to report her.

How much of a role does ageism play in the fact that the serial murders occurred and were ignored for such a long time? How much of a role does the lack of adequate monitoring of medical practice play? What other factors might help to explain such repeated murders and a corresponding lack of recognition of them?

Wennberg, Bunker, and Barnes (1980) studied seven different types of surgery, including hysterectomy, tonsillectomy, gall bladder surgery, prostatectomy, and hemorrhoidectomy in Canada, the United Kingdom, and different locations in the United States. Generally, the rates were highest in Canada and lowest in the United Kingdom. The authors suggest that while such differences have enormous implications for costs, and for morbidity and mortality rates, they are not the result of malpractice but occur because diagnostic and treatment procedures are not perfect.

Norms of practice develop out of colleague and network interaction.

Malpractice

One type of social control of medical practice designed to minimize errors and punish individuals for malfeasance is the malpractice suit. Malpractice insurance policies are now a necessity, and fees for malpractice insurance have grown substantially. Despite common misperceptions, the numbers of lawsuits against Canadian doctors have been declining in the recent past. The number of lawsuits peaked in 1995, at 1,415. In 2004 there were 1,083 (CFHI, 2006). The number of lawsuits continues to decrease. It was 16.1 per 1,000 members in 2004 and 9.5 per 1,000 members in 2013, according to the annual report of the Canadian Medical Protective Association (2013). This is a 40 per cent drop. This may be the result of a diminution in errors or of fear of reprisal in the case of initiating a suit or something else. Most complaints originate in hospitals or other health-care institutions. The provincial/territorial licensing bodies are required by law to examine all complaints against their members that are brought to them. Still, the numbers are high: in 2004, according to the Canadian Institute of Health Information, anywhere from 9,000 to 24,000 Canadians were said to die annually as a result of medical error (*CBC News*, 2004).

As a consequence of these trends, doctors are now spending hundreds of millions annually on insurance for claims of injury alone. This rate, however, is still not close to the malpractice insurance rates in the US. The Canadian Medical Protective Association was established in 1913 by an Act of Parliament. It provides legal defence, liability protection, and risk-management education for physicians in Canada, according to the home page of its website. It also seeks to maintain standards, inspect practices, and provide financial and legal support in the case of a charge of medical error. The Canadian Medical Protective Association had approximately 97,688 members across Canada in 2017. According to the annual report, membership fees vary considerably from specialty to specialty. The highest fees, reflecting the highest rates of legal complaint, were for physicians working in obstetrics and some surgical specialties. In Ontario, in 2017 the annual fee for an obstetrician was $99,072. The lowest rates in Ontario—$780 annually—were for doctors doing humanitarian work or teaching/research work abroad. Annual fees vary by region, and there are different schedules of fees for Quebec, Ontario, and then the rest of Canada. The Canadian Medical Protective Association (2017) has developed a number of courses, tips, and strategies to help doctors to increase safety and to minimize lawsuits.

Summary

1. The medical profession can be thought of as an occupation, a process, a power group, or an ideology. There are certain strengths and limitations to each of these descriptions and it is possible for them to overlap.
2. As an occupation, medicine has two basic characteristics: prolonged training in a body of specialized, abstract knowledge and a service orientation. However, the view of profession as occupation accepts the profession at its own valuation and ignores the power of the group, changes over time, and the relationship between the occupation and the rest of society.
3. As a process, doctors are seen as fighting for dominance and professional status over time. Members engage in full-time work, establish a training/education program, belong to an association, gain legal status, and construct a code of ethics. The members of the occupational group must have esoteric knowledge

and social distance from the rest of the population and must be more or less homogeneous.

4. As an ideology, the medical profession holds descriptive and prescriptive beliefs that explain and legitimate certain practices and viewpoints. The ideology includes universalism, functional specificity, affective neutrality, and a collectivist orientation. This ideology has been effective in promoting the dominance and monopoly held by doctors over time.

5. There are three steps to becoming a doctor: an undergraduate education, graduate study leading to the designation MD, and, at minimum, a one-year internship. Medical students generally come from middle- and upper-middle-class family backgrounds. Physicians-in-training become aware of two dominant values: "clinical experience" and "medical responsibility." Medical students learn emotional detachment and the ability to deal with inevitable and constant uncertainty; they also encounter alienation and may develop authoritarian personalities.

6. Power and autonomy of the medical profession have been somewhat curtailed by the emergence of hospital administrators and the involvement of governments, as well as by the provincial Colleges of Physicians and Surgeons and the Canadian Medical Association.

7. Doctors make mistakes. The definition of what constitutes a mistake is variable; doctors use two mechanisms for dealing with undesirable mistakes: neutralization and collective rationalization. There are two kinds of mistakes: technical, which are to be expected and usually are forgiven, and moral, which may indicate that the person who made them is unsuited to be a doctor.

8. Different colleague networks within the medical field develop different sets of beliefs, norms, and practices regarding specific diseases and their appropriate treatment.

9. Medical malpractice and complaints against doctors are diminishing in frequency in Canada.

Key Terms

clinical experience
exclusion
limitation
medical errors
medical responsibility
moral mistakes

practice norms
profession as ideology
profession as occupation
profession as process
subordination
technical mistakes

Questions for Study and Discussion

1. Assess the different views of the meaning of profession and the processes of professionalization with respect to allopathic doctors.

2. What are the characteristics of a good doctor? Critically examine the list of responsibilities mentioned in the Canadian Medical Association *Code of Ethics*. Use your own experience to do so.

3. Explain the reasons for the socio-demographic backgrounds of medical students today. Do you expect that this will change? Why or why not?

4. What are some of the consequences to the increasing number of women as medical students and doctors?

5. Explain the distinction between technical and moral mistakes. Is this difference relevant for any other occupation? Discuss.

Suggested Readings

Lapointe-Shaw, L., & Bell, C.M. (2019). Measuring the cost of adverse events in hospital. *Canadian Medical Association Journal, 191*(32), E877–E878. doi: 10.1503/cmaj.190912. An article about new research and policies measuring error or adverse events in hospitals across Canada.

Stanbrook. M. (2019, 23 Apr.). Gun control a health issue for which physicians rightfully advocate. *Canadian Medical Association Journal, 191*(16). A debate about the role of the Canadian Medical Association and individual doctors in advocating for gun control.

Starr, P. (2013). *Remedy and reaction: The peculiar American struggle over health care reform*. Yale University Press. Discussion of the debates about national health care in the United States.

Nurses and Midwives

The Stresses and Strains of the Privatizing Medical Care System

12

Chapter Overview

- Nursing in some form has always existed.
- The history of nursing as an occupation is associated with the history of religion and the status and role of women as carers.
- Some of the critical issues facing nurses today include sexism, managerial ideology, hospital organization, and financial cutbacks in the context of neo-liberalism.
- Florence Nightingale is a central figure in the history and present practice of nursing.

- Midwifery has very recently become regulated in a number of provinces in Canada.
- Some birthing mothers are assisted by doulas as well.
- Impediments remain to the widespread acceptance and utilization of midwifery for birthing women and their families.
- The safety and effectiveness of midwifery are supported by good evidence.

Introduction

Nurses are fundamental to the modern medical care system. Hospitals, community clinics, long-term care institutions, home-care organizations, and most doctors' offices could not function without the essential work of nurses. Nurses and nurse practitioners are often responsible for the health of remote communities on a day-to-day basis. Midwives, who have long helped women give birth and continue to do so in most of the world, have been given legal status across many Canadian provinces for maternity care and birth.

What are the sociological forces that continue to affect the recruitment, retention, employment venues, and quality of working life of nurses? Who, socio-demographically speaking, are nurses and midwives—in Canada today and historically? What is the relationship of the work of the allopathic doctor to these other health-care providers? Can the work of the nurse be seen as "separate but equal" to the work of the doctor? Are the rates of mother and infant mortality higher, lower, or the same among midwifery-assisted births as those of obstetricians and gynecologists? Are the birth experiences of the mothers and of the babies born with the assistance of midwives better than those born in hospital under the care of doctors? These are among the questions addressed in this chapter.

Nursing: The Historical Context

Some form of nursing has always been available for sick people, even if it was only unskilled assistance such as help with feeding and being made comfortable. Such nursing usually was women's work, an extension of domestic responsibilities. Often, today, nursing is a complex paraprofessional occupation run by rigidly hierarchical bureaucracies segregated "according to sex and race, power and pay, specialty and education" (Armstrong et al., 1993, p. 11) and equipped with complex technology (the vast majority of all Canadian nurses work in hospitals). The duties of the hospital nurse are extremely varied and specialized, and are clearly articulated within a complex division of labour. Some nursing roles, such as those in the coronary care unit (CCU) or the intensive care unit (ICU), involve highly skilled medical management and quick decision-making in operating sophisticated machinery and other technologies, including multiple drug regimens. Thus, one nurse in an ICU or CCU may spend her/his working hours monitoring and recording the readouts on a series of machines that are keeping a patient alive. Another, working in a psychiatric clinic, may spend her/his days in group and individual therapy, where the tasks involve listening and communicating on an emotional level with patients. But wherever nursing is taking place, it is usually under the jurisdiction of a physician. Interesting exceptions occur, however, such as occupational nursing in which nurses work in industry as on-site caretakers for minor injuries and sickness, including emotional stress caused by such things as work burnout, and develop and administer workplace wellness programs. Nurses are also employed as stand-ins for doctors in remote communities at times. In such cases, they may handle the majority of the day-to-day health complaints of their community members.

The rise of Christianity led to distinctive roles for nurses. Healing and caring for the sick came to be thought of as acts of Christian charity, and nursing became a full-time occupation for the sisters of the Church. They worked with the sick, founded hospitals, and provided bedside care. Commitment to the sick was an acceptable role for devout Christian women because it was an occupation controlled by the Church. Nursing sisters worked for the Church as well as for medical practitioners. This arrangement gave them the autonomy to refuse the orders of doctors, and even to refuse to work for certain types of patients when such work violated their Christian convictions and the values and doctrines of the Church.

Military nursing, too, has a long history. As early as the thirteenth century the Knights of St John of Jerusalem admitted women into their order so they could nurse the wounded. In the seventeenth century, the Knights of Malta maintained a type of nursing service in their hospital at Valetta. Two knights were assigned to each of the towns surrounding the harbour. Each pair of knights had four nurses "to assist them in their rounds," their duties being to carry supplies to the sick and the poor, to see that the physicians appointed to visit them attended to their duties, and to ensure that patients received the proper care and medicine (Nicholson, 1967, p. 16).

After the Protestant Reformation of the sixteenth century, nursing disappeared as a respectable service for devout Christian women in countries where the Catholic Church and its organizations were diminished. Those who could afford to pay for services were doctored and nursed at home. Hospitals were built, but they were primarily for the poor and indigent, and were filthy, malodorous, and overcrowded. They usually lacked clean water and adequate drainage. The bed linens were seldom changed. Patients shared the same dirty sheets. It was not realized that fresh air was healthy and so windows frequently were boarded up. Germs spread and multiplied in such a filthy and airless atmosphere.

Women working in these hospitals were those who had no choice—the poor, infirm, old, and sometimes patients who had recovered but had nowhere else to go. At this time, a stereotype emerged of the nurse as a drunken, poverty-stricken old woman who lived and ate with the sick. Hospitals were considered places to move to die, or when there was no other choice. Frequently, they were infested with rats, had contaminated water supplies, and were inhabited by patients with contagious diseases such as cholera, typhoid, and smallpox: it is no wonder that the mortality rate, even among the nurses, was often as high as 20 or 30 per cent.

Marie Rollet Hébert is thought to have been the first person to provide nursing care in what is now Canada. She and her husband, a surgeon-apothecary, worked together to help the sick from the time of their arrival in Quebec in 1617. Later, nursing sisters, members of various religious orders, emigrated to what are now Quebec City and Montreal, established hospitals, and treated those wounded in skirmishes and battle. Those nurses were more like doctors and even pharmacists than modern nurses; they made and administered medicines and performed surgery. They headed the hospitals and the missions they founded.

By the eighteenth and nineteenth centuries, epidemics of smallpox, influenza, measles, scarlet fever, typhoid, typhus, and tuberculosis threatened the health of the people. In response, nursing sisters from various orders established hospitals as places where the sick could be segregated and cared for. Still, the hospitals were used especially by the homeless and poor. Over time the hospital system expanded. Today, the hospital has become a place for all classes of people when they are acutely ill and need the specialized, and often high-technology, services offered by doctors, nurses, and others. People are expected to go to the hospital to be treated and to return home. They are not expected to die.

Nursing Today: Issues of Sexism, Managerial Ideology, Hospital Organization, and Cutbacks

Nurses comprise about half of all medical care providers. Altogether there were 425,757 nurses licensed to practice in Canada in 2017; 398,845 of these nurses indicated that they were employed in their profession. This figure includes registered nurses (281,673), nurse practitioners (4,967), licensed practical nurses (106,854), and registered psychiatric nurses (5,651). More than 80 per cent of nurses work in health-care institutions—hospitals, community health agencies, and long-term care institutions (Canadian Nurses Association, 2017). Nursing is one of the most "female" of occupations today—92 per cent of all the workers in the field of nursing are female. A small minority of registered nurses in Canada are male, but their numbers are growing. In 1985, about 2 per cent of RNs were male; by 1995 about 4 per cent were male and today about 8 per cent are male. Males tend to be over-represented in certain fields such as psychiatry, critical care, emergency care, and administration. There tend to be few males in such specialties as maternal/newborn care, pediatrics, and community care. Male nurses, on average, are older than female nurses. This trend may reflect the fact that nursing tends to be a second career for male nurses.

Critical analysis of the work of the contemporary nurse tends to follow one of four lines: (1) the patriarchal/sexist nature of the content of the work and of the position of the nurse in the medical labour force; (2) the impact of the managerial revolution in nursing practice; (3) the impact of the bureaucracy of the hospital on the working life of the nurse and on patient outcomes; and (4) the impact of neo-liberalism through cutbacks on the numbers of nurses and the quality and safety of nursing work. These will be discussed in turn.

Sexism

Sexism is ubiquitous in the medical labour force. Historically, doctors have usually been men and nurses have usually been women (Zelek & Phillips, 2003). Today, this is changing. In 2019, the majority of those entering medical school in Canada were women, as has been the case for the past 25 years (see Table 11.3). As these women move into positions of power in medical schools and in various organizations for doctors such as the Canadian Medical Association we can expect some consequences in the interests of equity and a diminution in the culture of sexism. However, Canadian nurses are still predominately women.

The role of the nurse, in fact, the origin of the word, refers to female functions. "Nursing" comes from the Latin *nutrire* and means to nourish and suckle. Both historically and today, "nursing" refers both to a mother's action in suckling or breast-feeding her baby and to the act of caring for the sick. Because the earliest nurses were nuns working for the glory of God, nurses have long been called "sisters." The very concepts of caring, nurturing, feeding, and tending to the sick are inextricably tied up with ideas about women

(Reverby, 1987; Growe, 1991). The few men who train or are educated to be nurses usually end up moving up the administrative ladder or work where their size and strength are definite assets, such as in psychiatry where sometimes restraint of the patient is required.

Florence Nightingale, born in 1820, was the founder of the modern practice of nursing. Her views of nursing and nursing training reinforced a subservient, feminine image of the nurse. She believed that while nurses could be trained in some of the detailed duties of bedside care, the most fundamental aspects of the nursing occupation could not be learned. Just as it was impossible to train a person to be a mother, it was impossible to train a woman to nurse. The essential components of a nursing woman's character—her selfless devotion to others and her obedience to those in authority—could not be studied or taught. Thus, entrance requirements to nursing schools traditionally included an interview in which these nebulous characteristics were evaluated.

Fine-tuning was still necessary, but it could only be managed if the woman was first of all "successful as a woman." One of the first hospitals to train nurses according to the Nightingale model, the New England Hospital for Women and Children in Boston, included among the requirements for admission "that an applicant be between 21 and 31 years old, be well and strong, and have a good reputation as to character and disposition, with a good knowledge of general housework desirable" (Punnett, 1976, p. 5). The need for womanly "care" is still a preoccupation today, as discussed in the *British Journal of Nursing* (Wood, 2014). There is, however, some recognition that this emotion labour can be costly to the well-being of the nurse (Peate, 2014).

This sexism in ideology is reflected in differences in pay, authority, responsibility, prestige, and working conditions between men and women in the health-care labour force. Physicians have the advantage over nurses in all of these respects. The nurse has responsibility for carrying out the doctor's orders, but no authority to change them when they are incorrect.

Royal Inland Hospital of Nursing, Kamloops, graduating class of 1948. Can you see some of the gendered (and racialized) assumptions about what makes a "good" nurse reflected in this photo? Look at their disposition, dress, age, and race.

Canadian Museum of History: Canadian Nursing History Collection

Managerial Ideology in Hospitals

The second critical issue today is the managerial ideology in hospital management systems. This ideology is the outcome of a historical trend that reflects the development of the money economy, bureaucracy, capitalism, and rationalization. In particular, this method of financing in the public sector reflects the pressure to keep costs low under neo-liberal governance. **Managerial ideology** assumes that managers are to run organizations as efficiently as possible so as to provide adequate service at minimal cost. In Canada, hospitals are funded chiefly through the public sector; federal and provincial funding provides operating grants; local municipalities also provide funds, as do local fundraising initiatives. They are run under the jurisdiction of provincial government authorities. Hospital managers are accountable to boards and the boards to the provinces. They are faced with limited financial resources and the necessity of setting priorities within the context of extensive other interests. Payments for nursing services must compete with needs for cleaning, equipment upkeep, purchase of new and increasingly expensive technology and pharmaceuticals, as well as payments to the many other hospital personnel, including

occupational and physical therapists, social workers, staff physicians, and others. In this context, nurses often work on overcrowded and understaffed wards in the midst of patients who are increasingly sick (Urban, 2012).

Several rationalized management systems have been developed for use in hospitals. These management systems are modelled on the manufacturing sector. They embrace a type of piecework, but in this case, rather than a widget, the piece to be worked on is an organ or a specific set of symptoms related to a particular diagnosis. One management system is case mix groupings (CMGs), introduced in 2007 in Canada according to the Canadian Institute for Health Information. It is a technique for detailing the specific tasks and the time each task takes with reference to the average patient with a particular diagnosis. Productivity and cost-effectiveness are the goals. Nurses must try to work within the specified time limits and still provide adequate nursing care to the patients. CMGs are a set of mutually exclusive categories that can be used for describing patients' clinical attributes. Patients within a particular CMG are believed to require roughly equivalent regimens of care and hence are believed to consume similar amounts of hospital resources (May & Wasserman, 1984, p. 548).

The problem with case mix grouping or any other rationalized and predetermined workload determination and measurement is that it assumes that all patients with a particular medical condition will require similar medical treatment and psychosocial care (e.g., childbirth by Caesarean section, or chemotherapy with stage-one lung cancer). A cost is then assigned to the nursing care required by the typical patient with that specific diagnosis. Each of the patients in the hospital is accorded a particular time/cost value. Nurses, nursing assistants, orderlies, and other medical care personnel can then be assigned to various wards for specific lengths of time to provide predefined services.

This rationalization, or what Rankin and Campbell call "accounting logic" (2006, p. 14), seems very reasonable, but it has numerous deleterious effects on the working lives of nurses (Campbell, 1988;

Rankin & Campbell, 2006). Such a system demeans the authority and autonomy of the nurse and diminishes her/his powers of decision-making. Individual patient needs are not assessed holistically as a result of experience gained during the practice of the art and science of nursing, but by a predetermined, quantified, and remote system. Nurses know that individual patients always vary from the norm in some way or another. Yet, time for each patient has been allocated by an external—and claimed to be objective—classification system. The nurse, thus, is constrained, by virtue of the time allotted, to behave towards all patients within certain predefined strictures, regardless of their individual differences. Not only is such a requirement destructive to the morale and autonomy of the nurse, but also it may be dangerous or harmful to the patient. Staffing assignments based on the information provided in such systems do not allow for the fact that, just as patients differ from the norm, so, too, do nurses. For instance, a small nurse may need help in turning a large patient. Turning may be required hourly. Yet, if the assignment has not considered such characteristics of staff/patient interaction as relative size, it cannot predict costs accurately. In this case the smaller nurse will have to get the assistance of a larger nurse, a nursing assistant, or an orderly. Finding the person to provide such assistance will take additional time; the person who provided the assistance will have to deduct the time taken from his/her total time available for care. A generous allotment of flexible time could enable the nursing staff to manage such situations. However, such flexibility does not exist in the climate of cost containment that typifies the contemporary hospital system. For nurses, the outcomes of such management systems include decreased job satisfaction, burnout, and stress (Conley & Maukasch, 1988; Austin, 2007; Rankin & Campbell, 2006). For patients, the outcomes can include poor quality of care, slower recuperation, possibly medical error, and, ultimately, greater long-term susceptibility to recurrent ill health.

Clearly, such newer managerial techniques, combined with restructuring and downsizing in hospitals and in the medical care system more generally, are reducing the autonomy of nurses and making it increasingly difficult to meet the standards of their profession and to care for patients

holistically. At the same time, in a new era of awareness of the extensiveness of errors in hospitals brought to light by the Institute of Medicine report in 2000, *To Err Is Human*, government policies are making it easier for patients to complain about the services provided by individual nurses. Despite the emphasis on errors as problems in systems, as outlined in this report, blame may still be obfuscated by individualized "accountability" or "responsibilization" and passed down the hospital hierarchy to those nearest the bottom. The new managerialism has also sometimes exacerbated differences and has polarized groups such as RNs and RPNs, degree-holding nurses against diploma nurses, and management against staff nurses.

Finally, as a result of the dominance of sexism coupled with managerial perspectives, under neo-liberalism most hospital nurses work shifts, an arrangement shown to have deleterious effects on health. Their working conditions are problematic in a number of other ways as well: (1) their working hours usually are rigid, except in that they may necessitate unexpected overtime; (2) night and evening shift work is regularly required; (3) they are often restricted in their work to a hospital; (4) they are at risk because of the frequent and often serious occupational health and safety conditions in hospitals (Canadian Nurses Association, 2017); (5) their workloads are excessively busy and yet demanding of precision and attention to detail, as well as great carefulness and care; (6) they are, because of underfunding, often forced to do housekeeping and other non-nursing work. Thus, sexism restricts women to an occupational ghetto, and that ghetto provides them with few rewards; much demanding, detailed labour; and little or no authority as compared to the doctors in the system (Cassidy & McIntosh, 2014).

Bureaucratic Hospital Organization

The third area for the critical analysis of the nursing profession today is related to the effect of the hospital's bureaucratic structure on nursing. Job opportunity consists of the available career expectations, ambitions, and goals and the probability of reaching these (Kanter, 1977). The structure of opportunity within an organization is determined by rates of promotion, locations for promotion, jobs that lead to promotion, and the like. People who have little opportunity tend to: (1) have lower self-esteem and sense of self-determination, or lack confidence in their ability to change the system; (2) seek satisfaction outside of work; (3) compare themselves with others on the same organizational level rather than with people on a higher level; (4) limit their aspirations; (5) be critical of managers and those in powerful positions; (6) be less likely to expect change; and (7) be more likely to complain (Kanter, 1977).

Opportunities for nurses are lacking in modern hospital organizations. The structure of promotion in the hospital limits vertical mobility for nurses. The major option open to a nurse with aspirations is to leave nursing and become an administrator. The first step would be to become a head nurse on a ward, with day-to-day responsibility for running the ward and for managing a team of nurses of various types and levels of responsibility. Further movement up the system takes the nurse further and further from the actual practice of nursing.

Power can be defined as the capacity to mobilize resources (Kanter, 1977). Power includes the discretionary ability to make decisions that affect the organization, the visibility of the job, the relevance of the job to current organizational problems, and opportunities for promotion. Nurses, by these criteria, have very little organizational power.

Highlighted Issues

Box 12.1 • The Doctor–Nurse Game

Leonard I. Stein's paper "The Doctor–Nurse Game" (1987) describes one strategy used by doctors and nurses to manage the contradictory position of the doctor, who may have more power and authority, and the nurse, who frequently has more information and knowledge, both about particular patients and their health while in the hospital, and about hospital routines and common medical practices. This contradiction is especially acute when the doctor in question is a resident, intern, or new graduate. Stein's point is that nurses frequently make suggestions to doctors about how to treat certain situations and cases but that such suggestions must be handled with great subtlety and caution and even disguised. The object of the game is for the nurse to make recommendations to the doctor, all the while pretending to be passive. On the other hand, the doctor must ask for advice without appearing to do so. A typical scene might proceed as follows:

Nurse A: Mr. Brown has been complaining of pains in his legs for more than six hours today. He appears to be quite uncomfortable.

Doctor G: Is this a new symptom for Mr. Brown or is it recurring?

Nurse A: Mr. Brown complained of a similar pain last week when he was admitted. He was given xxxx and it seemed to diminish.

Doctor B: OK. Let's try xxxx. What dosage did he require to get relief?

Nurse A: 3 m/hour.

Doctor G: OK. xxxx, 3 m/hour, nurse, please.

Nurse A: Thank you, doctor.

Stein suggested that the game plan is taught to the nursing students at the same time as they learn the other aspects of nursing care. Doctors usually start to learn once they actually begin to practise in a system with nurses. Holyoake (2011) claims that despite the fact that the game was first observed 40 years ago, it continues to exist today. It is just one way of managing in an unequal bureaucratic system where the specific detailed knowledge may reside in a lower part of the hierarchy while those in the higher part are charged with the responsibility of acting on that knowledge.

The arrest of Susan Nelles on 25 March 1981 for the murder of four infants at the Hospital for Sick Children in Toronto exemplifies the powerlessness of nurses who have responsibility without authority. Even though physicians and others were routinely on the ward and were also frequently involved with patients, it was a nurse who was first suspected and charged in the case of the infant deaths. Furthermore, many nurses (and others) were incensed by the fact that the televised hearing showed that the **Grange Inquiry** treated doctors differently from nurses—dramatically so. Doctors, on the assumption that they were innocent, were questioned with deference and respect. Nurses were questioned under the assumption of guilt and suspicion. "It was as if the police assumed, if it wasn't this nurse who committed the crime, which nurse was it?" (Wilson, 1987, p. 27). Through this and other incidents, nurses discovered that they were the first to be blamed, but had little respect or authority within the hospital system. Box 12.2 provides more detail.

Cutbacks

Today, cutbacks to the health-care system, province by province and by the federal government, represent a grave threat to the public nature of the health-care sector and have had significant effects on hospitals. The overall number of beds in hospitals has declined but hospitals are actually treating more patients, hospital patients are sicker, and medications and treatments are more frequent and more complex (McGillis Hall & Kiesners, 2005). A report from the Ontario Council of Hospital Unions (2014), *Pushed Out of Hospital, Abandoned at Home: After Twenty Years of Budget Cuts Ontario's Health System Is Failing Patients*, reiterates this perspective. The consequence of these budget cuts means that patients may be more likely to be readmitted. The report also found: (1) there is a decline in referral for various home-care services; (2) there is an increase in hospital-acquired infections; (3) people suffer in emergency wards while waiting to be admitted; and (4) especially elderly and chronically ill patients may wait seemingly interminably for admittance to long-term care.

Remembering Our History

Box 12.2 • The Registered Nurses Association of Ontario Responds to the Events at the Hospital for Sick Children and the Grange Inquiry

"The Grange Inquiry was the highest-priced, tax-supported, sexual harassment exercise I've ever encountered," said Alice Baumgart, the Dean of Nursing at Queen's University. The Registered Nurses Association of Ontario agreed, and in a little booklet called *The RNAO Responds* the Association explains why. The following discussion summarizes its arguments.

The arrest of Susan Nelles exemplified sexist bias for a number of reasons.

1. The police and others jumped to the conclusion that the unprecedented number of deaths—36 between 1 July 1980 and 25 March 1981 on wards 4A and 4B at Toronto's Hospital for Sick Children—were the result of murder. They

neglected to investigate the possibility that the theory of digoxin overdose was questionable because digoxin is notoriously difficult to measure. It is normal to find some digoxin after death, and there is some evidence that digoxin levels may increase after death. No control groups were used for the baseline data.

2. Once the police and hospital officials decided that the deaths were due to murder, they neglected to examine systematically all the possible sources of digoxin "overdoses." They failed to consider that the drugs might have been tampered with in the hospital pharmacy, or in the manufacturing or distributing branches of the pharmaceutical companies; or that the drugs

could have been administered secretly by any of a number of other hospital personnel who had regular access to wards, such as physicians, residents, interns, dieticians, lab technologists, or even a member of the general public who might unobtrusively have entered the hospital on a regular basis. Instead, the focus of suspicion was immediately placed on some of those with less power in the system—the nurses. Because, according to the first analysis, Susan Nelles appeared to have been the only nurse on duty during a number of suspicious deaths, she was questioned. When she asked to see a lawyer before answering questions, the police assumed that she was guilty and arrested her. The case against her was strengthened because she apparently had not cried when the babies died. Both aspects of her behaviour—asking to see a lawyer, which was, of course, responsible adult behaviour, and her failure to cry—violated gender stereotypes; thus her behaviour was taken as evidence that Nelles must be guilty.

Other sources of bias in the investigation were evident.

3. The focus was on individuals within the bureaucratic system (the hospital) rather than on the malfunctioning of the system itself.
4. The media were accused of biased and sensationalized reporting of unfounded allegations and suspicions. As criminal lawyer Clayton Ruby stated, the media, when reporting on the inquiry, ignored their usual rules of fairness and thus held some responsibility for the damage done to reputations.
5. Justice Grange tended to assume that a nurse was responsible for the murders and to ignore other evidence. He also disregarded the evidence that tended to raise questions about whether or not the "excess" digoxin could have resulted from measurement error or some alternative explanation.
6. The television coverage overemphasized the putative guilt of the nurses. The cameras tended

to zoom in on the nurses' faces or hands as they were giving evidence, but rarely seemed to focus on those of the police or the lawyers. Such camera work emphasized the discomfort of the nurses and encouraged a picture of them as probably guilty.

Among the issues raised for nurses by the events at Sick Children's and the Grange Inquiry are the following.

1. Nurses have little status or authority within the hospital, yet they are held responsible or accountable for their work.
2. In contrast to the continuing low status of nurses, their clinical roles have grown for three reasons: (a) the increased number of critical-care patients in hospitals; (b) the increased number of specialists involved with each individual patient; and (c) the increased use of technology, all of which the nurse must co-ordinate.
3. The Associate Administrator: Nursing—the highest level in the nursing echelon—was three administrative levels below that of the senior management of the hospital. Nurses thus had no access to the most senior levels of hospital management.
4. Nurses are expected to be generalists and to move easily from one part of the hospital to another and from one type of care to another. They are expected to perform duties at night that they are not permitted to perform in the day, because during the day only the doctor is thought to have the ability to perform them.
5. The bureaucratic structure, the assumption that nurses are generalists, and the low level in the hierarchy held by top nursing administrators limit the opportunities for nurses' advancement. In addition, nurses suffer from burnout, job stress, low job satisfaction, and the like.
6. The events surrounding the inquiry also reinforced the notion that the "feminine" skills of nurturing and caring are much less

continued

important than the "masculine" skills of curing and analysis.

7. It became clear that the image of nursing was infused with negative stereotypes and myths, similar to the negative stereotypes of women in society.

By articulating the issues, promoting their views, lobbying various levels of government, and dealing with the hospital bureaucracy, nurses and nursing unions responded by making some changes in the quality of the work environment of nurses. Destructive as the events at Sick Children's were, the outcome for the nursing profession in the long run may be hopeful. The Ontario government apparently compensated Nelles for her anguish after her ordeal, which included the arrest and public accusations. No one was ever charged for these deaths. In fact, the deaths may not have been homicides at all (Pruden, 2016). Probably the most significant result of the case was the way that the nursing profession rallied around one of their own and in many ways became increasingly empowered. The nursing profession has maintained a very public and political face in subsequent issues faced by the health-care system in Canada, and has often been responsible for broadening the debate beyond a limited medicalized view of health to include a public health and prevention focus. One of their current concerns is advocating for the introduction of new technologies such as a national system of digital records and communications for health care (St Denis, 2017).

More recently, when 12 children died after cardiac surgery in Manitoba in 1994, the warnings and ongoing reports given by the nurses of problems with the new cardiac surgeon were repeatedly ignored (Ceci, 2004) until an inquest report was finally published (Sinclair, 2000). The inquest took almost three years, involved testimony from over 80 witnesses, and resulted in more than 60,000 pages of transcripts. In his report, Judge Murray Sinclair made what he considered to be the subordinate position of the nurses in a bureaucratic environment an important part of the explanation for how the deaths were allowed to continue in spite of numerous attempts by the nurses to bring the serious and life-threatening problems to light.

While the Grange Commission occurred several decades ago the characteristics of nursing work articulated above have not changed substantially. Nurses are still in a very difficult situation in which they have responsibility for their patients but do not have authority. Each one of the points enumerated above continues.

Source: Registered Nurses Association of Ontario (1987).

Nurses report that they are increasingly overworked, and frequently they have to work overtime, without pay, just to get their necessary work done and the patients and charts ready for the next shift. Jobs are being eliminated or made insecure; nurses are being laid off and those who remain must work harder, under worsening conditions, with decreasing opportunity to provide the care they are trained to provide. A research report, *Nurse Fatigue and Patient Safety Report* (Canadian Nurses Association, 2010a), has documented some of the costs of the excesses in nursing work, including long hours and other stresses and strains. In this case the report also discusses the consequences for patient safety. In this regard it is important to note that nursing shortages are associated with an increased rate of infections contracted in hospital (Taunton et al., 1994).

Of the nurses working in Canada, significant numbers still work on a part-time or casual basis. Thirty per cent were employed part-time and 10.4 per cent were employed on a casual basis in 2017 (Canadian Nurses Association, 2017). Approximately 59.5 per cent worked full-time. The lack of a sufficient number of stable and committed jobs makes the work even harder for all concerned. Moreover, benefits often only accrue to those who work on a non-casual basis. Some nurses have had to work at two places of employment to make ends meet (Canadian Nurses Association, 2010a). Some, lacking sick days, undoubtedly have to go to work sick.

The picture of the nursing workforce in Canada as compared to other OECD countries is complex. Canadian nurses earn more than the average salary in US dollars of OECD nurses (see Figure 12.1). However, the ratio of the average earning of nurses in Canada to the average wages

of the whole workforce is slightly lower than that of nurses elsewhere (see Figure 12.2). Nevertheless, the salary for nurses is above the average salary of workers in Canada. The proportion of nurses per 1,000 population is just slightly above the OECD average and the ratio of nurses to doctors is above the OECD average. These figures do not point to a clear conclusion about the relative quality of the work environment for nurses in Canada. Instead, they paint a nuanced and complex picture.

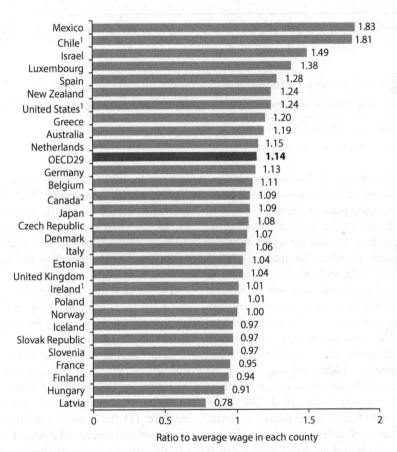

1. Data refer to registered ("professional") nurses in Chile, the United States and Ireland (resulting in an over-estimation).
2. Data refer to registered ("professional") nurses and unregistered nursing graduates.

Figure 12.1 Remuneration of Hospital Nurses, Ratio to Average Wage, 2015 (or nearest year)

Source: OECD Health Statistics 2017, doi: http://dx.doi.org/10.1787/888933604818

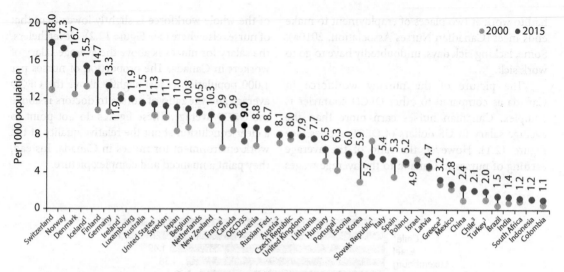

Figure 12.2   Practising Nurses per 1,000 Population, 2000 and 2015 (or nearest year)

1. Data include not only nurses providing direct care to patients, but also those working in the health sector as managers, educators, researchers, etc.
2. Austria and Greece report only nurses employed in hospital.
3. Data in Chile refer to all nurses who are licensed to practise.

Source: OECD Health Statistics 2017, doi: http://dx.doi.org/10.1787/888933604742

Some of the changes in health-care services, such as financial withdrawal of some federal funding to provinces, aging populations, sicker patients, increasingly advanced technology, and downsizing or restructuring, have affected the world of nurses in the last several decades. The nursing profession is extremely vulnerable to such changes in the national and provincial socio-economic and political environments because nurses usually are paid via the government or government-financed institutions. The increase in the numbers of better-educated nurses who are paid more (those with baccalaureate or higher nursing education) has resulted in health benefits to patients such as lower surgical mortality (Aiken et al., 2003) and more positive patient outcomes in respect to "functional status, pain and patient perception of nursing care" (McGillis Hall et al., 2003). Both patients and physicians in Ontario feel the staffing is inadequate and adversely affects the health of patients. Several coroners' juries, as a result of unnecessary deaths, have recommended "safe" ratios of trained nurses at various places in the hospital. The Canadian Nurses Association (2011) published a report on the supply and demand for nurses in

Canada to 2011 indicating a shortage of at least 60,000 registered nurses by 2022. This projection took into account the age distribution of registered nurses, the current number of nurses, ages of students in nursing schools, and population growth predictions. With respect to the age distribution the research found that the average age of nurses and of nursing students is increasing. In addition, just a few years ago there were an estimated 5,050 nursing job openings in the country that were not filled (Tencer, 2016).

An optimal number of nurses is crucial to the well-being of all of us, especially hospitalized patients. According to Potter et al. (2003), as hours of nursing for the patient in hospital increase: (1) the level of patient pain decreases; (2) the patient's perceived health status increases; and (3) the patient's post-discharge satisfaction increases. Furthermore, according to Rogers et al. (2004), the likelihood of making errors increases as (1) the number of hours of work increases (the odds of making an error were three times higher when RNs worked shifts 12.5 hours or longer); (2) when RNs work overtime; and (3) when RNs work more than 40 hours per week.

Table 12.1 Workplace Violence: Nurses and Personal Support Workers

More than 770 frontline nurses and personal support workers in Ontario were asked about workplace violence. In one year:

68% experienced at least one incident of violence	20% experienced nine or more incidents of violence
42% experienced at least once incident of sexual harassment or assault	83% experienced at least one incident of non-physical violence
75% witnessed at least one incident of violence against a co-worker	26% lost time at work due to violence on the job

Source: Data from Ontario Council of Hospital Unions.

Nurses often experience job strain as a result of many factors, especially overwork, understaffing, and excessive overtime (McGillis Hall & Kiesners, 2005). McGillis Hall and Kiesners have documented how the current workforce patterns are associated with many work–life issues for nurses. In this study, nurses expressed guilt and remorse over their inability to do the job the way they know it needs to be done, because they have too many patients who are too sick, and they simply don't have enough time to provide an adequate level of care (McGillis Hall & Kiesners, 2005, p. 2482). They said they felt frustrated, guilty, and stressed by the lack of adequate time and staffing to do a good job at work. Nurses also reported that this work frustration spills over into their family and home life, personal health, and patient outcomes. Their study is a richly documented qualitative study of the difficulties of nursing today. It includes numerous examples of these challenges in the words of the nurses themselves. Nursing unions have done their own research, and a study published in 2012 found that nurses had almost twice the rate of absence due to illness or disability of all other occupations (Canadian Institute for Health Information [CIHI], 2012). Moreover, to compensate for the mismatch in planned and actual staffing needs, 29 per cent of the work done by nurses was in overtime, and only half of this was in paid overtime while the rest was in unpaid overtime that nurses felt they had to do for the well-being of their patients.

Although violence occurs in all walks of life, nurses and personal care workers are in a particularly vulnerable position as compared to workers in other occupations in the general workforce and other occupations within the health-care labour force (Mojtehedzadeh, 2017). Canadian nurses report a high incidence of emotional abuse (Aiken et al., 2003). Moreover, even compared to prison guards, police officers, bank personnel, and transport workers, health professionals are at the highest risk of assault at work (Kingma, 2001). A survey of 19,000 nurses working in Canada found that 29.6 per cent had been physically abused by a patient over the previous 12 months (Priest, 2008). A recent survey found that nurses and personal support workers experienced significant amounts of physical violence, sexual assault, and non-physical violence at work. Twenty-six per cent of those surveyed said that they lost time at work as a result of violence (see Table 12.1).

Nursing as a Profession

Nurses have been striving in many ways to reach professional status. They have done this through: (1) increasing educational requirements; (2) forming their own "college" to handle questions of practice and the discipline of members; (3) carving out a body of knowledge that is separate from that used by other medical care workers; and (4) emphasizing the special qualities and skills that nurses have and that physicians do not have.

Fifty years ago, Freidson (1970, p. 49) argued that nursing was a paramedical occupation, as were the occupations of laboratory technicians and physical therapists, because of four characteristics they all shared: (1) the technical knowledge used by the paramedical occupations is usually developed and legitimated by physicians; (2) the tasks of paramedics usually are designed to help physicians fulfill their "more important" duties; (3) paramedics usually work at the request of the physician; and (4) they are accorded less prestige than the medical profession. Despite the efforts of nursing organizations to gain greater autonomy and full professional status for their members, these characteristics have not changed. The medical profession is unique in that no other profession has such a bevy of supportive occupational groups enabling it to do its work. While lawyers use members of other occupational groups regularly, these groups (e.g., accountants, real estate agents, court clerks, bailiffs, and so on) are autonomous and are not considered paralegals.

The modern occupation of nursing has developed out of the context of a historical subservience of women to men and of nurses' subservience to the doctors. Nursing tasks, roles, rights, and duties have arisen to serve the needs of physicians in patient cure and care. From the day that Florence Nightingale and her nurses in the Crimea first waited to nurse until the doctors gave the orders, nurses have waited on doctors. Contemporary nurses, in an effort to enhance their position in the medical labour force and/or to achieve the status of a profession, have taken a number of job-related actions. Krause (1978, p. 52) lists these:

1. the shift to university training;
2. the taking over of physicians' dirty work;
3. the use of managerial ideology;
4. taking control of technology; and
5. unionizing.

The Shift to University Training

Nurses used to be "trained" while they worked in hospitals for a period of several years. Their days were long in the hospital. They took classes outside of their work as well. Subsequently, for several decades, the most popular program for training registered nurses in Canada was the community college, with some hospital placement. Now, there

are programs at community colleges and universities, and joint programs between colleges and universities. The Bachelor of Science in Nursing degree program is designed to increase the credibility of the nurse by providing a theoretical background and greater training in critical thinking as it applies to nursing practice. As of 2010, 57.6 per cent of employed nurses had a diploma, 38.8 per cent had a baccalaureate, 3.3 per cent had a master's, and 0.1 per cent had a doctorate (Canadian Nurses Association, 2010a). Despite these intentions and hopes, the Canadian government has increasingly invested in licensed practical nurses who have less training and are paid much less. They are given responsibilities that were once restricted to registered nurses but lack the expertise in some cases to provide safe bedside care and health monitoring.

The Canadian Association of University Schools of Nursing is attempting to put a unique focus on nursing education and training. Many different specialty certificates are open to graduate nurses. Nurses with particular types of advanced training can be licensed as nurse practitioners (NPs). The nurse practitioner role has been expanded and includes many responsibilities that were once the sole purview of doctors (Figure 12.3). Nurses with a bachelor's degree in nursing and additional training to a level at least parallel with a master's degree have been working as independent practitioners in many Western countries for many decades. For a period, NPs were being trained in Canada as "physician extenders." These courses were terminated for a time in the last part of the twentieth century but have been redeveloped. Originally, nurse practitioners were to work especially in primary care with children. Today, NPs are regulated and covered by legislation in 12 provinces and territories in Canada. In all of these jurisdictions they are able to act autonomously. They are able to diagnose, order diagnostic and screening tests, and prescribe medication (CIHI, 2006). In 2010, 2,554 nurse practitioners were working in Canada (Canadian Nurses Association, 2010b).

Nurses and nurse practitioners are being encouraged through education to engage in critical thinking, independent decision-making, research,

NURSE PRACTITIONERS – Untapped Resource

NURSE PRACTITIONERS (NPs) IMPROVE TIMELY ACCESS TO HIGH-QUALITY, COST-EFFECTIVE CARE in a broad range of health-care models. Through their practice and collaboration with other health-care providers, NPs reduce pressure on the health-care system[1].

Education
Minimum 6 years of academic training plus clinical experience

Baccalaureate degree in nursing + RN licence/registration + Graduate NP education + NP licence/registration

93%
of Canadians

are confident that NPs can meet their day-to-day health needs[2]

Number of Canadians receiving primary care from an NP:

3 million

Estimated 800 patients per NP[3]

AUTONOMOUS ROLES FOR NPs:

PERFORM PHYSICAL EXAMS — ORDER TESTS — DIAGNOSE & TREAT ILLNESSES — WRITE PRESCRIPTIONS — ADMIT / DISCHARGE — PROVIDE REFERRALS

IMPACT

IMPROVED ACCESS TO CARE[4]

Decreased appointment wait times by offering same-day appointments for urgent patients or **within 3 days**[5]

20% **reduction** in emergency department admissions from long term care[6]

24% **increase** in family satisfaction with quality of care[7]

55% **reduction** in the use of multiple medications[8]

WHERE DO THEY WORK?

24% Other
4% Nursing home
36% Hospital
36% Community health

- YT (0.16%) — 10
- NT/NU (0.75%) — 46
- BC (8.35%) — 514
- AB (9.27%) — 571
- SK (3.83%) — 236
- MB (3.5%) — 217
- ON (56%) — 3,451
- QC (8.85%) — 545
- NL (2.97%) — 183
- PE (0.7%) — 43
- NB (2.26%) — 139
- NS (3.31%) — 204

Timeline

1960s Begin practising to increase the quality of health care in northern and underserved locations

2006 1,162 NPs; Canadian Nurse Practitioner Initiative formed

2012 Federal government passes *New Classes of Practitioners Regulations*, granting additional prescribing authority for controlled drugs

1997 Becomes a regulated profession to address the increasing demand for primary health care

2009 New regulations broaden scope of practice

2019 6,159 NPs

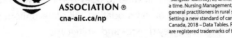

CANADIAN NURSES ASSOCIATION ®
cna-aiic.ca/np

[1]Canadian Nurses Association. (2017). The nurse practitioner [Position statement]. Ottawa: Author. [2]Nanos, N. (2016). Canadians' opinions on home healthcare and nurses. (Nanos Polling Series 2016-854). Ottawa, Canada. [3]Martin-Misener, R., Donald, F., Kilpatrick, K., Bryant-Lukosius, D., Rayner, J., Landry, V., Viscardi, V., & McKinlay, R. J. (2015). Benchmarking for nurse practitioner patient panel size and comparative analysis of nurse practitioner pay scales: Update of a scoping review. Retrieved from https://fhs.mcmaster.ca/ccapnr/documents/np_panel_size_study_updated_scoping_review_report.pdf [4]Sangster-Gormley, E., Griffith, J., Schreiber, R., Feddema, A., Boryki, E., & Thompson, J. (2015). Nurse practitioners changing health behaviours: One patient at a time. Nursing Management, 22(6), 26-31. [5]Roots, A., & MacDonald, M. (2014). Outcomes associated with nurse practitioners in collaborative practice with general practitioners in rural settings in Canada: A mixed methods study. Human Resources for Health, 12, 2-11. [6]Klaasen, K., Lamont, L., & Krishnan, P. (2009). Setting a new standard of care in nursing homes. Canadian Nurse, 105 (9), 24-30. [7]Ibid. [8]Ibid. [9]Canadian Institute for Health Information. (2019). Nursing in Canada, 2018 – Data Tables. Retrieved from https://www.cihi.ca/en/regulated-nurses-2018 ● CANADIAN NURSES ASSOCIATION and the CNA flame design are registered trademarks of the Canadian Nurses Association. © Copyright 2019 Canadian Nurses Association. July 2019

Figure 12.3 Nurse Practitioners—An Untapped Resource, 2017

Remembering Our History

Box 12.3 • The Story of Florence Nightingale

The story of the transition of hospital nursing from a duty performed out of charity and for the love of God, or by poor women who had no option, to an occupation requiring training must begin with Florence Nightingale. She revolutionized nursing work and laid the foundations for the modern, full-time occupation of nursing. As she described her calling, "On February the 7th, 1837, God spoke to me and called me to his service." Another time she wrote, "I craved for some regular occupation, for something worth doing instead of frittering away my time with useless trifles" (Bull, 1985, p. 15). She said that she chose nursing to serve the sick despite years of opposition by her wealthy mother and sister and the pleas for marriage made by several ardent suitors.

Nightingale was born into a wealthy English family in 1820. The upper-class Victorian woman was expected to marry, to provide heirs for her husband, to run his household, and to be a decorative companion at social events. In this scenario, her days would have been taken up with organizing the servants and governesses in the household, perhaps engaging in some embroidery or fancywork, and meeting with other women concerning some charitable cause. Nursing at that time was for the most part done by the indigent. It most certainly was not a "suitable" occupation for someone of Nightingale's social standing.

Nevertheless, she was committed to making something special of her life in the service of God. Her first experience of the kind of service to which God might be calling her came one summer when the family was holidaying at their summer place, Lea Hurst, in Derbyshire. Nightingale met and helped a number of poor cottagers, taking them food, medicine, and clothing. Later, she nursed her sick grandmother and an orphaned baby. When she learned of a school for the training of nurses located in Germany, the Kaiserwerth Hospital, she visited it.

Her father, having seen Nightingale refuse suitors, read and study mathematics late into the night, and maintain her fervent commitment to God's call, finally weakened and allowed her to study nursing. When she returned to England after her studies, two rich, aristocratic friends, Sidney and Elizabeth Herbert, supported Nightingale and spread the word that she was England's leading expert in matters of health. When a director was required for a nursing home, the Institution for the Care of Sick Gentlewomen in Distressed Circumstances, the Herberts recommended Nightingale. She accepted the position in 1853 and turned the nursing home into a very good and well-run hospital.

Slightly more than one year later, after she had gained invaluable experience through running the hospital, Sidney Herbert, who was then Secretary of War, asked Nightingale to go to Turkey to nurse British soldiers injured in the Crimean War (1853–6). The war, to that point, had been disastrous for the British. They had been unprepared. There were widespread shortages of equipment, food, bedding, and medical supplies. The soldiers were expected to live on mouldy biscuits and salt pork. They slept in the mud in clothes and blankets that were stiff with blood and crawling with lice. In the infirmary, there was no water for washing, and all the drains were blocked. Almost every man had diarrhea, but there were neither diets nor special medicines to relieve it (Bull, 1985, p. 35). There were no hot drinks because the necessities for lighting a fire were not available.

Nightingale was asked to recruit, organize, and take a group of 40 nurses into this chaotic and squalid situation. She advertised in London and beyond, but was able to find only 38 women, some of whom were religious sisters, with the qualities she required. Nightingale and her staff set out for the Crimea. She laid down strict orders to be followed: all were to be considered equal; all were to obey her. They were to share food and accommodation. All wore uniforms comprised of grey dresses and white caps.

Nightingale and her nurses arrived at the Barroch Hospital in Scutari, in late 1854, ready to work and armed with financial resources. They were met with hostility by the doctors, who refused to let them see patients and offered all 38 women only six dirty, small rooms (one of which had a corpse in it). They were given no furniture, lighting, or food. Nightingale had experienced opposition in her life: she was prepared to wait. She told her nurses to make bandages and offered the doctors milk puddings for the patients. These tasks seemed "suitable" for women, and so the doctors accepted the milk puddings. Less than one week later there was another battle and a huge number of casualties. The doctors, overwhelmed by the enormity of the disaster and the tasks that lay ahead of them, and reassured that the nurses were willing to obey (they had waited) and that they could provide "feminine services" (make milk puddings), asked the nurses to help out.

Nightingale ordered food, cutlery, china, soap, bedpans, and operating tables. Her nurses sewed clean cotton bags for straw mattresses. Men were hired to clean the lavatories and basins. The floors were scrubbed for the first time in anyone's memory. Soldiers' wives were recruited to wash clothes and bedding. Still the mortality rate did not decline significantly. Nightingale, who knew far more than the doctors about the importance of fresh air, cleanliness, and clean water, had the plumbing inspected. The pipes were blocked and the water supply contaminated. Once this was cleaned out, the mortality rate dropped dramatically.

Nightingale was viewed as a heroine both within the hospital and without. Within the hospital she was known as "the lady with the lamp." She offered all kinds of services, even banking and letter-writing, to her patients. At the end of the war, the grateful soldiers dedicated one day's pay to her for the establishment of the Nightingale School of Nursing and the Nightingale Fund. Outside the hospital, once she returned home to Britain in 1857, she was heralded as the most important woman of her time, except for Queen Victoria. At this time, there were no female judges, MPs, or civil servants. No woman had ever taken charge of an institution.

Florence Nightingale was a heroine to Britain and to the Western world.

Her greatest achievements were in public health reform. Her writing and lobbying in this area continued long after she returned from the Crimea, even though she spent the rest of her long life essentially bedridden. It has been suggested, in fact, that Nightingale's work was the beginning of modern epidemiology. Her work is also thought to have provided the model for the early training of nurses. Eventually, after several unsuccessful attempts, the first nursing school, on the Nightingale model, was established at the General and Marine Hospital in St. Catharines, Ontario, in 1874. A few years later, the Toronto General (1881) and Montreal General (1880) hospitals were established. Nursing students who were "in training" often comprised almost the whole staff of these hospitals (Jensen, 1988).

The long-term effects of Nightingale's work on the practice of nursing are often considered to have been equivocal, however (Reverby, 1987). On the one hand, she herself exhibited enormous strength and commitment, and was able to garner extensive personal power as a leader in epidemiological research models, in health-care policy, in the management of hospitals, in military nursing, and as the most important role model for the secular occupation of nursing in her society. On the other hand, she ensured that the women who worked as nurses for her were taught to be handmaidens to doctors and to be "mother-surrogates" to patients. Even though Nightingale studied hard to become educated and rejected her own assigned gender role, she expected her nurses to be subservient, obedient, and docile in their relationships with medical doctors.

Nursing, under Nightingale, was to be a woman's job. Only women had the necessary character and qualities. While carving out a respectable occupation for women, she also reinforced a ghettoized and subordinated female labour force that is still in place today. This model of nursing supported the traditional stereotype of the physician as father figure and the nurse as mother.

Florence Nightingale died in 1910 at the age of 90.

and leadership. However, the hospital structures in which they work usually limit their ability to do so. Thus, while there is a definite move towards requiring a university degree in order to practise, there is still no significant change in the hospital authority structure. Even nurses with PhD degrees are not able to claim professional autonomy as practitioners vis-à-vis the physician. Nevertheless, an increase in the numbers and the authority of nurse practitioners will relieve some of the pressure on medical care costs and on the "shortage" of doctors because the tasks for which NPs are being trained include those that were formerly done only by medical doctors. NPs can work independently outside of hospitals in free-standing clinics as well as in community health centres (Canadian Nurses Association, 2010b).

Several creative initiatives have been designed to address other critical health shortages. For instance, the Saskatchewan Indian Federation College in Regina (now First Nations University of Canada) started a collaborative program with the University of Saskatchewan to assist Indigenous students to prepare for nursing. Across Canada other nursing specialties are being developed as well, including parish nursing, school nursing, nursing informatics, forensic nursing, mental health nursing in the schools, and legal nurse consultation.

Taking Over the Work of the Physician

Nurses have taken over some of the **"dirty work" of physicians**, including such routine tasks as monitoring blood pressure, setting up intravenous infusions, and giving medications. At the same time, they have passed some of their own "dirty work" down the line to occupations such as registered practical nurses and personal care workers, e.g., making beds, bathing, feeding, and other actions for the personal care of patients. Both of these changes have been partly attempts to shore up the relative importance of nurses in the medical labour force: they have accepted some of the higher-status tasks of physicians and rejected some of their own less desirable tasks. Still, the presence

of registered nurses on the ward makes important differences in the health of patients even after they leave the hospital. A positive relationship has been found between nurses engaging in ward rounds and a higher level of independence, less pain, better social functioning, and greater satisfaction with care for discharged patients (Amann et al., 2018).

Managerial Ideology and Nursing

Managerial ideology applied to nursing has led to a multitude of divisions within the occupational group. These include divisions among nurses by specialty (e.g., intensive-care nurses, pediatric nurses), divisions by type of training (hospital, community college or university-based training), and divisions by level of responsibility (head nurse, staff nurse). Furthermore, registered nurses have divided the occupations below them in the medical labour force into various classes of subordinates, and have sought to maintain control as the governing body over various types of registered nursing assistants. The impact of managerial ideology is noticeable both in the increase in the introduction of such efficiency measures as case mix grouping and other means of speeding up the delivery of nursing care and in the "ideological subordination" of nurses to the interests of the organization or hospital rather than to the patient or the nursing community (Rankin & Campbell, 2006).

Seeing the Future

Some nurses in Canada are seeking advancement for their occupation in part through an anti-technology ideology. Rather than emphasizing their skill and expertise in handling new technologies, these nurses are rejecting the value of the medical model and arguing that medical care should be based much more broadly on holistic care, health promotion, and disease prevention. They emphasize the importance of their caring approach versus a curing approach. This argument is particularly persuasive given the current demography of illness, i.e., the increasing rates of

Spotlight on Ethics

Box 12.4 • Diversity in Nursing in Canada

A recent study found that Canadian nurses continue to be largely Caucasian and identify as heterosexual (Jeffries et al., 2019). One effect of this homogeneity is that nursing students tend to reflect the demographics of the nursing population at large—the majority of applicants to and students in nursing programs are also white and heterosexual. This trend affects the quality of care that nurses are able to provide for the increasingly diverse populations in Canadian health-care venues. A recent commentary in *Canadian Nursing Journal* advocates for addressing this problem by focusing first on enlarging the numbers of visible minority applicants to nursing schools and increasing the numbers who are accepted into training. This aim would be supported by the targeted removal of financial barriers and the development of mentoring programs to support a diverse range of students, programs, and incentives to attract nurses from around the world, thus challenging oppressive policies and increasing the levels of cultural competency among practising nurses. Systematic promotion of visible minority nurses is another essential aspect of the policy some are advocating. These are some possible ways to enhance diversity in the nursing workforce. What do you think?

chronic illness and the aging population. Others are taking up new technologies with enthusiasm and advocating for digital health care, digital records, and the uptake of online medical and nursing care services (Canadian Health Infoway, 2017).

Relatedly, while unionization has had a positive effect on at least one particular aspect of the status of nursing—income—at the same time unionization has also served to proletarianize nurses and to establish their position as members of the skilled working class who work for wages. More research needs to be undertaken on the short- and long-term consequences of the unionization process.

Midwifery

Have you thought about your own experience of birth? Have your parents told you about it? Was your father in the delivery room with your mother? Did your mother have any surgical intervention when she gave birth to you? Do you know anyone who has given birth at home or in an institution other than a hospital? Are you aware of the sorts of services that midwives offer to the mother and father before, during, and after the birth?

The final section of this chapter describes the history of midwives, their work, and their contemporary situation. The term "midwife" comes from Old English and means "with the women." The French term is *sage-femme*, or "wise-woman." Essentially, the work of the midwife is to assist women as they prepare for and give birth and as they learn to care for their new offspring. Midwives have usually practised their work in the home, where the woman is surrounded by her family and friends. Birth in this environment is seen as a healthy natural event, not an illness or disability.

Thus, midwives have tended not to use artificial or mechanical means to assist with birth. Their assumption is that birth is fundamentally a natural event. Among the other assumptions are that a midwife would predict a breech birth (upside down, feet- or buttocks-first presentation) through a manual examination. Massage of the fetus in the uterus would be used to turn the baby for a normal delivery. Manual manipulation rather than forceps would be used to move the baby down the birth canal. Pain would be handled by rubbing the back, shoulders, and neck of the woman in labour, and with encouraging words and assisting women in controlling the pace and depth of their breathing.

The woman in labour would be relaxed and comforted by the familiar atmosphere and the presence of a person or persons with experience.

A brief overview of the history of **midwifery** is necessary for understanding its position in Canadian society today. The practice of midwifery can be traced to ancient history. The Bible includes a number of references. Exodus 1:15–22 is one example: two midwives, Shiprah and Puah, refused to obey the orders of the king of Egypt that all male infants be put to death. The written work of classical Greek and Roman physicians such as Hippocrates and Galen documents the prevalence of midwives. Male physicians were summoned only when special difficulties developed (Litoff, 1978). Until the Middle Ages, women who themselves had given birth were acceptable attendants at other births.

Up to the fourteenth century, midwifery flourished in Europe. Then came the witch hunts in which women healers of all sorts, and particularly midwives, were put to death. Midwives were especially vulnerable because of their close association with the placenta, which was believed to be an essential ingredient in witchcraft. By the end of the fifteenth century, witch-hunting had declined. In Britain, and soon elsewhere in Europe, midwives gained formal legitimacy under the Medical Act of 1512. This Act was to be administered and enforced by local churches. Licensing depended on the good character of the aspiring midwife and required that she be hard-working, faithful, and prepared to provide service to both rich and poor whenever it was needed. She was also forbidden to use witchcraft, charms, or prayers that were not dictated by the Church. Men were not allowed to be present at birth (Litoff, 1978). Then, in 1642, the College of Physicians gained authority to license midwives. For the next 300 years the legitimacy, recognition, and power of the male midwives, now obstetricians, gradually grew in England and Europe while those of female midwives declined.

In the last quarter of the nineteenth century, British midwives made numerous attempts to gain legitimacy and recognition as an autonomous professional group. In 1893, a committee of the British House of Commons reported on the significant rate of maternal and infant mortality. These deaths were attributed to poorly trained, unregulated midwives, and the committee report recommended that midwives be registered (Eberts, 1987). Most doctors rejected this suggestion because they argued that midwives did not have the necessary training. The Royal British Nursing Association supported the proposal to create a new occupational category: obstetric midwives or nurses.

Public opinion in favour of midwifery seemed to be growing. By the early part of the twentieth century, midwives in Britain were legitimized through regulation. With the establishment of the National Health Service in 1948, midwives were employed as a form of public health nurse. In 1968, legislation in Britain expanded the role of the midwife.

The earliest mention of midwifery among Euro-Canadian women appears in a deed in the Montreal archives, which reveals that the women of Ville-Marie, in a meeting held on 12 February 1713, elected a community midwife named Catherine Guertin. Also, in the English settlement of Lunenburg, Nova Scotia, Colonel Sutherland, the commander, wrote to the British government in 1755 asking that two pounds per year be paid to the two practising midwives. Apparently in no other regions in Canada were midwives on government salary (Abbott, 1931).

Until the mid-nineteenth century, most births in Canada took place at home in the presence of midwives (Oppenheimer, 1983), although from this time on home births were attended by physicians. From 1809 until 1895 the legal position of midwives was uncertain and changeable. Whenever midwives did not pose a threat to the work of allopaths they were allowed to practise; but where they did compete with allopaths, primarily in the cities and among the middle and upper classes, there were attempts to restrict them (Wertz & Wertz, 1977; Barrington, 1985; Ehrenreich & English, 1979; Biggs, 1983).

Statistics indicate that in 1899 midwives attended about 3 per cent of all Ontario births and doctors attended 16 per cent (Biggs, 1983). This means, of course, that about 81 per cent of births were formally "unattended." However, as the legal status of the midwife was unclear, the percentage given for midwife-attended births is probably an underestimate. Over the duration of most of the nineteenth century, apparently, midwives garnered a significant amount of community and media support. The *Globe* newspaper in Toronto opposed a medical monopoly of childbirth until 1895, when a bill to reinstate licensing of midwives was vehemently defeated in the legislature. At this juncture the *Globe* reversed its position (Biggs, 1983).

In the last part of the nineteenth century and into the twentieth century, the importance of the doctor's exclusive right to attend births grew. However, midwifery was legitimated and legalized in Canada at the end of the past century. It is now regulated and legal across the country. In Canada, presently, legislation ensures that midwives are qualified to practise. The term

"midwife" is protected and the practice of midwifery by those who are unlicensed is illegal, just as it is illegal for someone who is unlicensed to practise medicine. It is estimated that more than 1,690 midwives are in practice across the country and hundreds are being trained annually (see Figures 12.4 and 12.5).

Issues in the History of the Practice of Midwifery

There has been considerable resistance to midwifery in Canada until recently. In addition to sexism and patriarchy, other social forces responsible for the contemporary pattern of the tendency to high-tech, hospital-based, interventionist-oriented, physician-attended births include: (1) bureaucratization and hospitalization, (2) the profit motive, (3) the public health movement, (4) the emphasis on safety and pain relief in childbirth, and (5) the campaign for ascendancy waged by physicians.

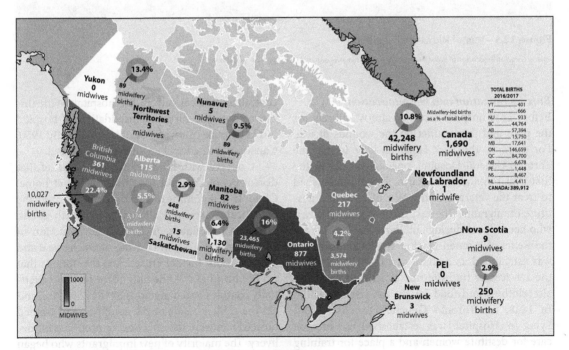

Figure 12.4 Registered Midwives and Midwifery-Led Births

Source: Canadian Association of Midwives. (2018). *Annual Report*. https://canadianmidwives.org/wp-content/uploads/2018/08/CAM-Annual-Report-map-2017-E-1-1024x592.jpg

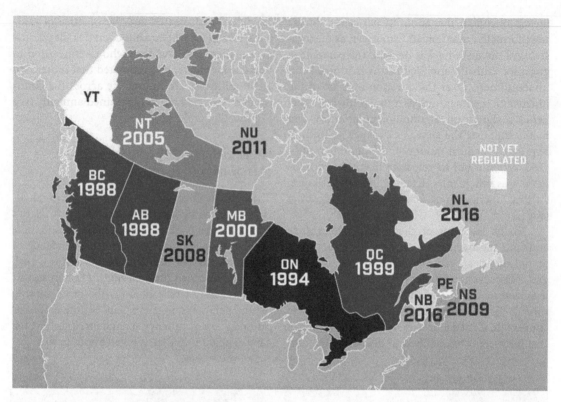

Figure 12.5 Year of Midwifery Regulation

Source: Canadian Association of Midwives, https://canadianmidwives.org/2016/10/19/year-of-regulation

Bureaucratization and Hospitalization

Before 1880 hospital care was almost entirely for the poor and those suffering the wounds of war. For example, the York Hospital, later to become Toronto General Hospital, opened in 1829 as the first real hospital in Ontario. It was established to treat the veterans of the War of 1812 and destitute immigrants. The first institution for women who needed care during childbirth, the Society for the Relief of Women During Their Confinement, was established as a charity in 1820. It provided the services of midwife-nurses and doctors, and also clothing and food for the mother and child. In 1848, the Toronto General Dispensary and Lying-In Hospital was established to provide care for destitute women and a place for training medical midwives. Around the beginning of the twentieth century a concerted effort was made to

centralize medical care in the hospital. With this move came the further consolidation of hospital births by male midwives or obstetricians. By 1950, Canadian midwifery had all but disappeared.

Concern with modesty spread the belief that decent people did not have their babies at home. Childbirth literature of the time emphasized the complicated, scientifically managed birth event. The new techniques, including the induction of labour, anaesthesia, and the use of mechanical and surgical tools, further entrenched the notions that (1) the hospital was the only place for this potentially complex and dangerous birth procedure, and (2) the skilled hands of the equipped and trained obstetrician were the only ones appropriate for delivery. The majority of new immigrants who began to populate the cities and used midwives supported these views. Middle-class and upper-class women tried to distance themselves from the poor and immigrant women who could not afford doctors and hospitals and from their typical childbirth practices. This, too, reinforced the growing belief in the appropriateness of the hospital as the place of choice for childbirth for the middle classes.

World War I had an impact on the growth of scientifically managed hospital births. Childbirth came to be described as a dangerous process, and women, with war casualties fresh in their minds, were increasingly concerned to deliver their babies in a safe environment. Many were impressed with the physicians' argument that infant and maternal mortality rates could only be substantially decreased when childbirth was recognized as a complicated medical condition (Litoff, 1978). The growth of hospitals provided additional beds. Automobiles and roads reduced the time it took to get to the hospital after labour contractions had started. The advantages of hospital births as a realistic possibility began to emerge and garner support.

Profits for Doctors

Physicians had a lot to lose if midwives were given free rein to practise. According to Biggs, midwives (in about 1873) charged approximately two dollars per birth, whereas male doctors charged five dollars. Biggs states that physicians felt that they should be "protected most stringently against the meddlesome interference on the part of old women," and that the amount of money lost through the competition with midwives would constitute a "decent living for [his] small family" (Biggs, 1983, p. 28).

The Public Health Movement

During the last half of the nineteenth century and into the twentieth century, Canada, along with the rest of the Western industrialized world, witnessed a dramatic decrease in mortality rates. The decline in maternal mortality rates corresponded to the general decrease in mortality and coincided with the increasing prestige of the physician and the growing belief that medicine could cure all ills. This, too, provided ideological support and furthered the move to obstetrician-centred, hospital-based births.

The Emphasis on Safety and Pain Relief in Childbirth

Another element in the move to birth taking place in hospitals was women's search for relief from the pains of childbirth. Among the causes of such pain for nineteenth-century women were the cultural constraints on middle-class women, which demanded a certain delicate beauty. This could best be achieved by wearing boned corsets that constricted their waists, rib cages, and pelvises. Sensitivity to pain was considered feminine, and thus women's pain threshold tended to be low. Women were encouraged to see themselves as fragile, sickly, and weak. Thus, middle-class women at the beginning of the twentieth century began to envision comfort during birth as the obliteration of consciousness through "twilight sleep." Since twilight sleep (a combination of morphine and scopolamine) could be monitored more effectively in the hospital, middle-class women sought to give birth in hospital.

Precautionary measures, including the enema and shave in preparation for birth, were developed to preserve hygienic conditions and prevent puerperal fever. Forceps were designed in the nineteenth century. Their use became standard because they could speed the birth process if it were slow. A Caesarean section, a potentially life-saving procedure to be used when labour was ineffective or the pelvis was too small, became a frequent and even dangerously overused procedure. By the 1930s there were real safety advantages, including blood transfusions and antibiotics, in treating problematic births at the hospital. Yet, as Barrington (1985) ruefully points out, the necessity for blood transfusions and antibiotics often resulted from hospital-caused infections and doctor-caused hemorrhages.

The Campaign for Ascendancy Waged by the Physician

Doctors described midwives as "dirty, ignorant and dangerous" (Biggs, 1983, p. 31). Devitt (1977) quotes a midwife's statement, from 1906, that the obstetricians thought of her as the "typical old, gin-fingering, guzzling midwife with her pockets full of forcing drops, her mouth full of snuff, her fingers full of dirt, and her brains full of arrogance and superstition." Biggs (1983) quotes a doctor's view of midwives from the *British American Journal of Medical and Physical Science*:

> And when we consider the enormous error which they [midwives] are continually perpetuating and the valuable lives which are frequently sacrificed to their ignorance, the more speedily some legislative interference is taken with respect to them, the better the community at large.

Physicians gained ideological superiority over midwives by portraying their own work as based on science and buttressed by apparently safe and efficient tools such as forceps. Given that physicians were educated men from good families and were coming to have high status, social power, and also often much political influence, it is no wonder that they were successful in advancing the view that their births were the best births.

The Present Status of Midwives

Worldwide, midwives deliver approximately 80 per cent of babies today. The North American situation is different, largely because of the presence and ideological success, as well as the institutional dominance, of allopathic doctors, particularly the specialists in birth, obstetricians. In the past almost half-century the women's and feminist movements have been powerfully critical of the medical profession for denying the autonomy of women in childbirth. Women also have spearheaded a movement for women's rights over childbirth. Romelis (1985) discussed five specific components of this movement, including groups advocating (1) natural childbirth, (2) the Leboyer method, involving gentle birthing and immersion in water, (3) alternative in-hospital births, (4) home births, and (5) non-hospital birth centres. The role of midwifery fits within this view that abhors an unthinking reliance on modern hospital practices, such as "invasive diagnostic procedures, induction and acceleration of labour, reliance on drugs for pain,

routine electronic fetal monitoring, dramatically increasing Caesarean-section rates, and separation of mother and baby after the birth" (Romelis, 1985, p. 185).

The increasing legitimacy of midwifery reflects both the strategies taken by the state to control health-care costs (e.g., in Ontario midwives are now on salary through the provincial government) and the increasing political influence of women's groups and organized midwives on state policy (Bourgeault et al., 1998). The shift in attitude also reflects the type of service offered by the midwife, who provides more holistic care and a minimum of 44 hours of prenatal and postnatal care, education, and support and emphasizes the importance of the values of the mother-to-be in the choice of birth, allowing births at home, in birth centres, or in hospitals, as well as medical exigencies.

Midwifery has been found to be safe in homes, hospitals, and birthing centres in a wide variety of studies. Moreover, mothers attended by midwives are less likely to use drugs for pain or to have surgical interventions such as episiotomies or Caesarean sections. Midwives are less likely to use forceps, vacuum extraction, or other interventions, and mothers who choose midwives tend to be very satisfied with their care. In jurisdictions without enabling legislation, midwives risk prosecution if anything goes wrong.

Today, the practice of obstetrics and gynecology has lost some of its attraction for doctors because of its relatively high malpractice insurance costs and the 24/7 work load. Many family doctors, too, for a variety of reasons including insurance costs and time away from general practice, seem to be happy to turn childbirth over to midwives. Still, only a small percentage (about 10.8 per cent) of Canadian births are attended by midwives (see Figure 12.4). Nevertheless, the training institutions will soon have produced many more graduated midwives, and a growing number of provincial and territorial governments cover the costs of midwives. We can expect this proportion to increase.

In addition to midwives, some women who are giving birth are now choosing doulas. They are non-medical birth coaches who pay attention to the desires and wishes of the birthing woman. They are not trained to help in the actual physical birth process. Instead, they are trained or simply volunteer to be the emotional voice for women during the process of giving birth. This is particularly important because the role of the midwife has grown in responsibility to encompass the actual safety and efficacy of the birthing process, even in a hospital setting with all of the "high-tech" tools available. Birthing involves physical, intellectual, and spiritual aspects of human experience—the body, the mind, and the spirit. The mind and the spirit are the focus of the support offered by doulas.

Summary

1. Some sort of nursing function has always been associated with illness and treatment. Florence Nightingale was the founder of the contemporary system of nursing care. She led a handpicked team of 38 nurses to serve in the Crimean War. Nightingale pioneered sanitary practices and caused the mortality rate to drop. She also provided many other services for the patients.

2. Although Nightingale established nursing as an important profession in society, she did so by reinforcing a ghettoized and subordinated female labour force. The view of nursing as a woman's job is still in place today.

3. Critical analysis of the work of the contemporary nurse tends to follow one of three lines: the patriarchal/sexist nature of the content of the work and the low position of nursing in the hierarchy of the medical labour force; the managerial revolution in nursing practice; or the impact of the hospital bureaucracy on the working life of the nurse.

4. Nursing associations have been striving to achieve professional status by increasing educational requirements, forming licensing bodies, attempting to carve a body of knowledge separate from that of physicians, and emphasizing nurses' special qualities and skills. However, some argue that nursing is a paramedical occupation, not a profession, because the technical knowledge that nurses use is created, developed, and legitimated by physicians, the tasks nurses perform are deemed less "important" than those of doctors, and nursing has less prestige than the medical profession.

5. Midwifery is based on the belief that birth is a natural process, and therefore the use of artificial or mechanical means to interfere with birth is avoided. Midwives have almost always been women. Attempts by midwives to gain legitimacy have been met by rejection because doctors argue they do not have the necessary training, and because their presence threatens the work of allopaths.

6. The social conditions that allowed allopathic practitioners to achieve a monopoly of the childbirth process also contributed to the contemporary pattern of high-tech, hospital-based, interventionist-oriented, physician-attended births. These social conditions include patriarchy and sexism, bureaucratization and hospitalization, the profit motive, the association of the medical model with the success of the public health movement, the growth in measures for safety and pain relief, and the campaign for ascendancy waged by the physician.

7. While the legal status of midwives is still ambiguous in some provinces, it is changing. With legal recognition of midwifery in all Canadian jurisdictions except Prince Edward Island and Yukon, salary and workload levels have been established and institutionalized as part of the health-care delivery system.

Key Terms

"dirty work" of physicians

Grange Inquiry

managerial ideology

midwifery

Questions for Study and Discussion

1. Do a media content analysis of the portrayal of nurses in different time periods. Assess if and how the media representation may reflect gender stereotypes.
2. What organizational challenges in hospitals do nurses face today?
3. What can be done about the degree of violence experienced by all levels of nursing practice?
4. Are nurses today faced with having responsibility but lacking authority?
5. How do you evaluate the move to increase the status of nursing? In other words, are nurses "professionals" or "paraprofessionals"?
6. Critically evaluate case mix grouping. What are the major drivers of this policy?
7. What is the legal position of midwifery in your province? How does the pay level of midwives compare to nurses and doctors? Discuss.
8. Do you favour the use of a midwife for yourself, your partner, or your surrogate in pregnancy and childbirth? Explain your decision.

Suggested Readings

Karbeah, J., Hardeman, R., Almanza, J., & Kozhimannil, K.B. (2019). Identifying the key elements of racially concordant care in a freestanding birth center. *Journal of Midwifery & Women's Health*. doi:10.1111/jmwh.13018. Study of the importance of racial concordance in health care and midwifery.

Peate, I. (2014). Compassion fatigue: The toll of emotional labour. *British Journal of Nursing, 23*(5), 251. A study of the emotion work in nursing.

Scarf, V., et al. (2018). Maternal and perinatal outcomes by planned place of birth among woman with low risk pregnancies in high income countries: A systematic review. *Midwifery, 62*, 240–55. A review of studies of birth outcomes finding support for the value of home birth with midwifery support.

Sutherland, N.C., et al. (2018, 19 July). Discourses reproducing gender inequities in hospice palliative home care. *Canadian Journal of Nursing Research*, 189–201. A discussion of gender inequity in the experiences of palliative home care and how to respond as nurses.

Urban, A.-M. 2012. Nurses and their work in hospitals: Ruled by embedded ideologies and moving discourses. PhD diss., University of Regina. http://ourspace.uregina.ca/bitstream/handle/10294/3553/Urban_Ann-Marie_188003945_PhD_EDUC_Spring2012.pdf?sequence=1. A dissertation about the hospital work of nurses today.

Wood, C. 2014. Choosing the "right" people for nursing: Can we recruit to care? *British Journal of Nursing, 23*(10), 5. An article about whether "caring" can be used as a criterion for recruiting nurses.

Complementary and Alternative Medicine

13

Chapter Overview

- The acceptability of complementary and alternative medicine (CAM) is growing among Canadians.
- The views and practices of allopathic doctors with regard to CAM appear to be changing.
- Chiropractic, a major alternative to allopathic medicine, is based on a very different understanding of the nature and cause of disease.

- Chiropractors have a unique place in medicare in Canada.
- Naturopathy has a different understanding of disease and its causes.
- Naturopathic practice is increasingly accepted as legitimate in Canada.

Introduction

Some of you have been to a naturopathic doctor. Others of you routinely use chiropractic services. Some of you meditate or perform regular relaxation training. Some of you may belong to support groups. Some of you exercise regularly. Some of you are vegetarians or follow a macrobiotic diet. Some of you attend church and/or pray regularly and believe that spirituality can be healing. Such actions as these may be examples of complementary and alternative healing practices. Notice the breadth of these options. Note, too, that some involve professional services while others are done without cost and even invisibly. These various health-related actions are the types of issues we will address in this chapter.

Alternative, Complementary, and Allopathic Medicine

As is often the case with a new concept, its definition can be amorphous, expansive, and variable. There are debates about whether the descriptive term ought to be "unconventional," "alternative," "unorthodox," or "complementary" medicine or health care. Each term has its proponents. It is becoming conventional (as unconventional medicine becomes conventional) to use the term **complementary and alternative medicine (CAM)** to describe the methods of treatment used both separately (alternatively) and often preventively, on the one hand, or in association with or complementary to allopathic medicine, on the other. Basically, CAMs are all those health-care practices that differ from allopathic medicine. They have tended not to be taught at allopathic medical schools and most are generally unavailable in North American hospitals (although there are some important exceptions such as therapeutic touch). However, a growing number of variations to that generalization exist. For instance, about 50 medical schools in Canada and the US include CAM in various ways in their conventional medical education (Howell, 2012).

Conventional or **allopathic medicine** is the subject matter of most of the second half of this text. It refers to the type of healing based on a theory of opposites, or on the assumption that opposites cure. Health is the biologically natural state, not just the preferred state of the body. Disease is an unwanted aberration caused by germs, bacteria, or such things as trauma from outside that attacks the equilibrium of the body. The germ theory of disease provides some of the basic assumptions upon which allopathic medicine has developed. It is the root from which the monumental scientific and biomedical research industry has grown. Insofar as disease is fundamentally an unnatural, abnormal invasion into an otherwise healthy body, treatment involves an attack on the enemy—the disease. Such treatments as surgery, medication, and radiotherapy are the outcomes of this type of thinking.

A variety of criticisms of this medical model have been offered. Advocates of **holistic health care** and CAM criticize the medical model for a reductionist focus on, and limited mechanical and biomedical treatment of, the physical body and, in fact, narrower and narrower components of the human body—e.g., genes. Instead, they advocate treating the whole person—body, mind, and spirit—through a combination of methods best suited to each particular and unique individual. Among the myriad methods included are massage, acupuncture, visualization (imaging a healthy body), herbs, vitamins, hydrotherapy, meditation, prayer, psychic and faith healing, chiropractic, and naturopathy. Sometimes people choose CAM as an alternative when they are sick and do not go to a conventional medical doctor. Approximately 20 per cent of Americans do not receive conventional medical care in an average year (Nahin et al., 2009). They do this for a number of different reasons, including rejecting its theoretical foundation or because it is inaccessible or too expensive.

Theories of the relationship between allopathic medicine and CAM are undergoing radical change. The latest available national survey of 31,044 adults over 18 in the US found that 62 per cent used some type of CAM in the previous 12 months (this includes prayer for health). It also found that CAMs were most often used to treat back pain or back problems, colds, neck pain or neck problems, joint pain or stiffness, and anxiety or depression (Barnes et al., 2004). Of those surveyed, 19.3 per cent did not use any conventional care, and of these about one-quarter used alternative medicine (Nahin et al., 2009).

Eisenberg and colleagues (1997) estimated (conservatively) that the out-of-pocket expenses for American people for CAMs were $12.2 billion and the total expenditures (again conservatively) were about $27 billion. Today, the total spent on CAMs, according to the National Center for Complementary and Alternative Health Care in the US, is $33.9 billon. This comprises about 10.2 per cent of the total out-of-pocket expenses on health care (http://nccam.nih.gov/news/camstats/costs/costdatafs.htm). These figures also may suggest that the majority of the money spent on CAMs is funded through health insurance plans. This also underscores the finding that CAM is most likely to be used by the middle and upper classes who either can afford "extra" health care or have insurance to cover such care. This was comparable to the estimated out-of-pocket expenditures for physician services. Clearly, alternative medicine and therapy among basically "well" American people is already substantial and is growing. While this American survey is probably one of the most widely cited of such studies, research in numerous other Western countries currently dominated by allopathic care indicates that unconventional medicine and alternative health practice are mounting elsewhere, as well.

The number of alternative practitioners appears to be growing at a faster rate than that of allopathic physicians, and it is predicted that it will continue to do so. In one instance, Cooper and Stoflet (1996) predicted that the per capita number of alternative medicine clinicians would grow by 88 per cent between 1994 and 2010, while the supply of physicians would grow by only 16 per cent. Whether these predictions have proven accurate or not is very difficult to know, as there are no complete listings of all of the various CAM practitioners in Canada or the US. Some of the CAM practitioners work "underground" and want to remain invisible to regulatory bodies. Because there is not usually such an investment of years in education,

as with allopathic care, and because it is sometimes difficult to make a living, some practitioners may stay in their occupations for only a limited amount of time or work only part-time. Some types of practitioners, such as psychic healers, are fairly widely viewed as "sketchy" and may not be counted in any census of CAM. In any case, the legitimacy of many CAM practitioners is less secure than that of conventional doctors. This is certainly the case historically. At one time, referral by a physician to an alternative health provider was considered such a serious violation of medical practice that it resulted in loss of membership in medical societies and even the loss of medical licence. Indeed, one physician, in 1878, was reputedly murdered because he consulted with a homeopath (who was also his wife) (Rothouse, 1997).

Many other signs indicate that unconventional medicine is moving into the mainstream. In 1992 the US Congress established an Office of Alternative Medicine at the National Institutes of Health (see www.nccam.nih.gov/health). The National Library of Medicine in the US has increased access to research and other articles about complementary and alternative medicine. A number of medical schools and hospitals in the US and Canada have developed programs or departments for the study of alternative medicine. Beth Israel Hospital at Harvard University has raised millions of dollars for a Center for Alternative Medicine and numerous medical schools, including such large and important institutions as Georgetown, Columbia, Harvard, Maryland, and Wayne State in the United States and a number of post-secondary schools in Canada, offer courses in alternative medicine. A growing number of scientific and academic journals devoted to alternative medicine and intended for physicians and other health providers are in circulation. In addition, many insurance companies now provide coverage for alternative health care. At least one, American Western Life, actually offers a "wellness" plan that uses naturopathic rather than conventional physicians as gatekeepers and offers naturopathic remedies as the first stage of treatment. Some insurers reimburse for particular types of CAM only, such as **acupuncture**, which is among the most widely accepted of alternatives, especially for pain and substance abuse. Certification as an acupuncturist is often needed for reimbursement. Across Canada, naturopaths, acupuncturists, and Chinese medicine practitioners, among others, are working towards inclusion in health practitioner regulatory legislation. The Vancouver Hospital has established an alternative medicine clinic to perform research on various CAMs. This hospital has also opened a Healing Touch Centre for energy-balancing therapies such as therapeutic touch. **Therapeutic touch** has become a recognized treatment and one found among the skills of many nurses across Canada and the US. Finally, several schools that train CAM practitioners,

such as the College of Naturopathic Medicine in Toronto, have expanded or are planning to expand (Imman, 1996, p. A3). More and more people are seeking help from CAM specialists for a variety of ailments, especially pain, arthritis, anxiety, insomnia, and headaches.

Today, CAM is often called integrative medicine to indicate that it is being adopted by and integrated into conventional systems. We can gain more information on the utilization numbers of CAM by including an examination of the health problems most often treated by CAM (Table 13.1). Table 13.2 explains some of the details of attitudes to CAM and how these may have changed since 1997 and Table 13.3 lists the top 10 most common health problems that led people to use CAM.

Table 13.1 Top Three Health Conditions Treated by Therapy for the Most Commonly Used Therapies (Lifetime), 1997, 2006, and 2016

	1997		2006		2016	
	Condition	% of Respondents	Condition	% of Respondents	Condition	% of Respondents
Massage	Back or neck problems	42	Back or neck problems	39	Back or neck problems	28
	Relaxation	12	Relaxation	8	Back problems/ back pain	14
	Stress	8	Stress	6	Stress	10
Chiropractic Care	Back or neck problems	75	Back or neck problems	61	Back or neck problems	39
	Frequent headaches	6	Back problems/back pain	7	Back problems/ back pain	28
	General overall health and back problems/back pain	4	Joint problems	7	Joint problems	6
Yoga	General overall health	19	Back or neck problems	14	General overall health	17
	Back or neck problems	18	General overall health	13	Stress	7
	Relaxation	15	Relaxation	8	Relaxation	7

Table 13.1 *Continued*							
Relaxation Techniques	Stress	22	Stress	13	Stress	29
	General overall health	14	Back or neck problems	10	Anxiety attacks	17
	Relaxation	14	Anxiety attacks	9	General overall health	11
Acupuncture	Back or neck problems	30	Back or neck problems	30	Back or neck problems	16
	Frequent headaches	13	Joint problems	11	Back problems/ back pain	15
	Arthritis or rheumatism	8	Any sprains or strains	10	Frequent headaches, muscle pulls/ problems	10

Source: Fraser Institute, Complementary and Alternative Medicine: Use and Public Attitudes 1997, 2006, and 2016, p. 34.

Table 13.2 **Attitudes towards Complementary and Alternative Medicines and Therapies in Canada, 1997, 2006, and 2016 (%)**

	1997	2006	2016
Conventional medicine does not have all the answers to our health problems.	77	76	72
Alternative medicine has been used for centuries in other countries; there must be something good about it.	74	68	66
Just because alternative medicine hasn't been scientifically tested and approved by Canadian and provincial medical bodies doesn't mean it isn't effective.	69	67	63
When it comes to my health, I don't like to try anything new that hasn't been proven.	53	52	49
I like alternative medicine because it takes my whole lifestyle into consideration rather than just my physical well-being.	46	45	46
If my doctor doesn't recommend I use alternative medicine, I'm not going to try it.	35	36	38
I just don't know enough about alternative medicine to want to try it.	44	42	36
I don't think alternative medicine works.	18	20	22

Base: All respondents.

Note: Percentages are those who agree with each statement, or all who rated their level of agreement as 5, 6, or 7 on a 7-point scale where 1 means "completely disagree" and 7 means "completely agree."

Source: Fraser Institute, Complementary and Alternative Medicine: Use and Public Attitudes 1997, 2006, and 2016, p. 54.

Table 13.3   Use of Alternative Therapy for 10 Most Frequently Reported Principal Medical Conditions, 2016

Condition	% Reporting Condition	% Using Alternative Therapy in Past 12 Months	% Who Saw a Provider in Past 12 months	Three Most Commonly Used Alternative Therapies
Back or neck problems	34	70	38	Massage therapies, chiropractic care, relaxation techniques
Allergies	27	64	33	Massage therapies, relaxation techniques, osteopathy
Arthritis or rheumatism	23	61	28	Prayer, massage therapies, relaxation techniques
Difficulty with routine walking	20	61	27	Relaxation techniques, chiropractic care, massage therapies
Gynecological or menstrual problems	16	77	50	Relaxation techniques, massage therapies, chiropractic care
Frequent headaches	15	70	41	Relaxation techniques, massage therapies, chiropractic care
Anxiety attacks	14	76	50	Relaxation techniques, massage therapies, chiropractic care
Digestive system problems (ulcers, inflammatory bowel disease, hepatitis, or constipation)	13	70	36	Relaxation techniques, massage therapies, yoga
Lung problems (asthmas, bronchitis, emphysema)	12	57	25	Chiropractic care, relaxation techniques, yoga
Impotence	10	47	13	Massage techniques, prayer, relaxation techniques

Source: Fraser Institute, Complementary and Alternative Medicine: Use and Public Attitudes 1997, 2006, and 2016, p. 39.

Canada in a Global Context

Box 13.1 • Acupuncture

Acupuncture can include use of herbs, tuina (Chinese massage), exercise, and diet, and generally refers to the insertion of fine needles to various parts of body to stimulate the flow of energy (qi). Points are located along 14 main meridian lines or channels through which the body's energy flows. It stimulates the body's natural healing abilities, relieves pain, and restores internal regulation systems. There are two basic approaches. (1) Traditional Chinese medicine includes a holistic system of health care that aims to bring the body, mind, and spirit into balance, and includes such methods as moxibustion, i.e., application of heat, generated by burning dry moxa leaves on or near an acupuncture point; Chinese herbology; tuina, i.e., massage of acupuncture points; nutritional counselling; and therapeutic exercises such as qi gong and Tai Chi. (2) Medical acupuncture or "anatomical acupuncture" stimulates the body's production of endorphins. Electro-acupuncture uses needles with mild electrical impulses; laser may be used in place of needles.

Acupuncture has been widely adopted by a wide variety of health-care providers, including conventional doctors, because of the growing number of studies documenting its effectiveness for various conditions. It is used in childhood cancer to control pain and nausea, and is the most frequently used CAM in the UK, where fully 7 per cent of the adult population has received acupuncture. Providers of acupuncture include allopathic doctors who have taken short courses, Chinese medicine specialists, some of whom have specialized over five years in acupuncture, and physiotherapists.

What is the evidence for its benefits? A review article (Vickers et al., 2002) found studies to support acupuncture for post-operative nausea and vomiting, chemotherapy-related nausea and vomiting, and post-operative dental pain. A meta-analysis of 21 studies done on 1,421 people found that acupuncture improved cognition after a stroke (Liu et al., 2014). Among other things, the studies do not take into account the level of expertise or the amount of experience of the practitioner. The modern and Western use of acupuncture does not reflect the thousands of years of history or the theories of yin and yang and so on under which the Chinese have developed and still use the treatment, and thus to study its effectiveness is complicated. More research is needed.

Two widely known American allopathic and conventionally trained doctors have been enormously influential in the processes involved in legitimating CAM in the US and Canada. They exemplify the power of the celebrity, or what has been called "celebritization," in influencing health and medical treatments (Beck et al., 2014; Frith et al., 2013; Lernere, 2006; Noar et al., 2014). One is Dr Mehmet Oz, a graduate of Harvard and the University of Pennsylvania School of Medicine as well as of the Wharton Business School, who worked as a surgeon at Columbia Medical Center until 2001. Since 2009 Dr Oz has had a daily (Monday to Friday) television show on which he discusses and features both conventional medicine and CAM. *Time* magazine listed him as forty-fourth out of the 100 of the most influential Americans in 2008 and *Esquire* magazine listed him in the top 75 most influential people in the twenty-first century. He appears to be extremely open-minded about the various possibilities of healing outside of allopathic care (see Box 13.2). The other doctor who has achieved a level of fame (he graduated from Harvard Medical School and has been on the *Dr. Oz* show, for example) is Andrew Weil. He has published many best-selling books on CAM, or what he calls integrative medicine. He even started a school called Arizona Center for Integrative Medicine (see www.integrativemedicine.arizona.edu) where MDs and medical students, among others, do extra training in integrative medicine.

The recognition of these two conventional doctors in areas of CAM reflects the growing acceptance of various ways to understand healing. It also reflects a growing "healthism" (Crawford, 2006) or focus on health as a symbol of good citizenship and good morality. In this sense, public health campaigns and the emphasis on health in everyday life call on people to pay assiduous attention to their bodies and minds and to ensure that, as good citizens, they make good health a focus of living (Rose, 1999). It is in this context of the uptake of healthism that the expansion of CAMs can best be seen and understood. Indeed, the very idea of a television show dealing with how to be healthy

and healthier in an ever-broader way reflects a postmodern sensibility and the biomedicalization of everyday life. The so-called "wellness" focus of CAMs includes body/mind/soul and spirit as relevant for treatment and upkeep, and this emphasis reflects the powerful discourses of healthism and biomedicalization.

At the same time that the broad social trends imbricate discourses of healthism into everyday life as essential to being human, skeptics repudiate the effectiveness of various CAMs because of their lack of research evidence. Thus, another movement involves bringing CAM under the purview of medical science so that it succumbs to the very same research designs and rules of evidence that have captured the practices of major medical research funding bodies in the Western world and in the powerful World Health Organization. In this context, new publications include systematic

Spotlight on Ethics

Box 13.2 • Complementary and Alternative Medical Advice on Dr. Oz

CAM medical advice abounds. You can find it in advertisements on social media, in magazines, and even on billboards, to name just a few places. You can find it at your local yoga studio or gym. One apparently influential source of information is television. Have you ever watched *Dr. Oz*? He is an immensely popular television celebrity whose program on heath and unconventional medicine, *The Dr. Oz Show*, debuted in 2009. His award-winning show has made it into an afternoon television spot and is among the most highly rated daytime shows (Specter, 2013). He was first championed by the virtually universally known celebrity, Oprah. Dr Oz is on the faculty of Columbia University and a surgeon, but he is unconventional in his views and open-minded about competing ideas of health and healing. The idea of evidence-based medicine—the bulwark of conventional medicine—seems to be irrelevant to Dr Oz. On his show, he introduces and seems to support many

different but unproven remedies for assistance with health problems.

Research published in the British Medical Journal found that, on average, Dr Oz recommends 10 different products or services on each show. Researchers found that approximately 46 per cent of the suggestions were at least partly supported by evidence, but 15 per cent were contradicted by evidence, and there was no evidence found for 39 per cent of the remedies or interventions that Dr Oz proposed. Using a slightly higher standard of evaluation, these researchers found that 33 per cent of the endorsements were supportable. By comparison the degree of correspondence between practice and evidence ranges from 10 per cent to 75 per cent among conventional medical practitioners.

What are the ethical issues in promoting unfounded cures and prevention products on television? Should anything be done about this practice?

reviews of the small studies that have been done of various CAMs. One interesting review article in a mainstream medical journal examined the available research literature included in the databases PubMed, Medline, Google Scholar, and Quertile on the topic of CAM use with mood disorders (Qureshi & Al-Bedah, 2013). The authors of this study justified taking the time to do the review with the comment that between 30 per cent and 40 per cent of patients with major depressive disorders did not respond to conventional anti-depressants but that 30–40 per cent of people with major depressive disorders would respond to CAM. In particular, they found evidence that light therapy, St John's wort, *Rhodiolarosea*, omega-3 fatty acids, yoga, acupuncture, mindfulness therapies, exercise sleep deprivation, and S-adenosylmethionine are effective in mood disorders. The results for some other interventions were either negative or ambiguous. This review paper is one example of the attempts being made to bring CAM "into the fold" of medical science and evidence-based medicine.

The use of unconventional medicine is clearly increasing. Why are such approaches growing in popularity? To be sure the creeping spread of the concern with healthism is a part of it (Crawford, 2006). However, there is also a move to be more critical of allopathic doctors and allopathic medicine as a part of the expansion of the risk society (Beck, 1992). Because risks are everywhere, expertise in the avoidance or management of risks is not assumed in the same way that it was at one time. People think of themselves as having the ability and indeed as having to take the responsibility for determining what sorts of experts to trust and for what sorts of conditions. In this way, people may be more and more willing to question their allopathic doctors regarding the medical treatments they provide. They need to ask: Are all of the various sorts of treatments effective? Are none of them effective? Is context important to whether they are effective or not? For what sorts of problems are they effective or not? Are there similarities and differences among them?

CAM includes a great deal more than that which is offered by various trained practitioners who provide health services such as massage, acupuncture, homeopathy, and the like. It also includes the services offered by various conventional practitioners. In some areas of medicine there is a history of the inclusion of CAM with regular allopathic treatment. In the case of childhood cancer CAM use has been reported to be as high as 84 per cent. This includes services offered by professionals such as chiropractors, osteopaths, and acupuncturists as well as over-the-counter vitamins, botanicals, and spiritual healing and yoga, among others (Valji et al., 2013). Although most patients were taking these treatments along with their regular chemotherapy drugs, most do not tell their regular physicians. The relationships between conventional doctors and CAM practitioners and practices are variable and sometimes fraught, and while some allopathic doctors are supportive of alternatives, others are not (Verhoef & Sutherland, 1995; Kelner et al., 2004). Formal leaders in public health, allopathic medicine, nursing, physiotherapy, and clinical nutrition argue that CAMs lack standards of evidence, standards of education and practice, and self-regulation (Kelner, 2004, pp. 920–1). In sum, it is difficult to draw conclusions about the relationships of CAM and conventional medicine because of contradictory results from numerous studies, the use of different concepts and measurements in studies, and various other methodological and theoretical reasons (Hirschkorn & Bourgeault, 2005).

One of the most difficult issues for medical doctors is that they have been trained to trust only research published in good medical journals and using the "best" research designs. This often means the gold standard of designs—the double-blind experimental design in which there is a control group and an experimental group whose reactions to treatment are investigated. What makes this a double-blind study is that no one knows who is in the experimental group and who is in the control group. Most CAM has not been investigated with this model. Much of CAM has not been evaluated for health effects at all. In fact, many CAM providers and theorists argue that such research is impossible because every treatment is individualized and thus calculated for the unique needs of the particular person. On the other hand, allopathic medicine is concerned with smaller and smaller parts of the human body, such as the gene, and the effects of treatments at this level. When treatment systems are not commensurate with the accepted experimental design, then financing, policy, and planning become very difficult. Nonetheless, scholars are thinking about this and attempting to devise ways of proving or estimating the varied legitimacy of CAM for health outcomes. As Boon and her colleagues (2007) say, CAM researchers are

Highlighted Issues

Box 13.3 • Some Alternative Health-Care Methods

Acupressure: Use of finger pressure on acupuncture points on the body to stimulate the flow of energy and promote the body's ability to heal itself. No needles are used. The most widely known form is shiatsu.

Feldenkrais (Russian Method): System of retraining the body to improve its movement and reduce pain from disease or injury; relies on the interaction between the sensory pathways of the central nervous system carrying information to the brain and the motor network carrying messages from the brain to the muscles. It may be particularly useful for accident victims; those with back problems, cerebral palsy, and multiple sclerosis; and musicians, athletes, and others whose careers may benefit from improved body movement.

Herbalism: Plants for healing and preventive medicine. Suggested benefits: skin problems (psoriasis, acne, eczema), digestive disorders, heart and circulation problems, gynecological disorders, allergic responses.

Homeopathy: The use of highly diluted traces of botanical, mineral, and other natural substances to stimulate the body's self-healing abilities; "like is cured by like." A substance that would create symptoms of disease in a healthy person is said to trigger the immune system of the ill person; the homeopathic practitioner's skill lies in matching a person's symptoms and body type correctly with the hundreds of remedies available. It is believed to assist the body's process of healing, particularly in the case of chronic conditions, such as asthma, cold, and flu, and to alleviate certain emotional disorders and injuries, arthritis, hay fever, PMS, gout, constipation, headache, migraines, children's colic, earache. Homeopathy does not treat structural problems but works with the body's soft tissue, muscle, and ligaments to improve joint movement, back pain, spinal and joint problems, asthma, carpal tunnel syndrome, cramps, migraines, sciatica, respiratory disorders, chronic fatigue syndrome, allergies, digestive disorders, high blood pressure, and cardiac diseases.

Reflexology: Natural healing therapy based on the principle that there are "reflex" points on the feet and hands that correspond to every part of the body. Stimulation of those areas of the extremities causes changes in distant body tissues. It also is used to reduce stress and tension, and is considered an effective relaxation technique.

Rolfing: Manipulates the muscles and connective tissue to shift the body into alignment; pressure applied with the fingers and knuckles, etc. It is thought to be especially beneficial for athletes, dancers, students of yoga, musicians, and people suffering from chronic pain.

Shiatsu: Practitioner applies pressure to points on the body using fingers, palms, knees, or cushioned elbows to relax the body to promote its natural ability to heal.

Source: For further discussion of these and other CAMs, see Harden & Harden (1997).

especially interested in this because of the issues of legitimacy and evidence base raised by insurers, purchasers, providers, regulators, and patients. CAM school students report that they do address research methods and evidence-based care along with working with conventional medical practitioners (April & Gaboury, 2013).

The many types of CAM can be organized and categorized in various ways. The US Office of Alternative Medicine organizes them into seven categories: diet and nutrition, mind/body techniques, bio-electromagnetics, traditional and folk remedies, pharmacologic and biologic remedies, manual healing, and herbal medicine. Muriel J. Montbriand

Remembering Our History

Box 13.4 • Christian Science: A Religion and an Alternative Form of Health Care

Religion and medicine are irrevocably intertwined among several major contemporary religious groups. One such group is Christian Science, founded by Mary Baker Eddy in 1866. Born in New Hampshire in 1821 to a Puritan family, Mary Baker Eddy spent the first 45 years of her life poor and in bad health but committed to the self-study of various medical systems, including allopathy, homeopathy, and hydropathy. She met and was influenced by a hypnotist healer named Phineas P. Quimby.

In 1866 Mary Baker Eddy fell on a patch of ice and was said to have been told by doctors that her life was at an end. Within a week she was well and walking. She claimed that she healed herself with the aid of God and the power of the mind over the body. Overwhelmed by this experience, she told others. She trained students, the first Christian Science practitioners, in a series of 12 lessons for which she charged $100. She wrote *Science and Health with a Key to Scriptures*, she said, under direct inspiration from God. By 1879 Mary Baker Eddy was able to found a church, the First Church of Christ, Scientist, in Boston. In 1881 she established an educational institution, Mrs Eddy's Massachusetts Metaphysical College. The church grew quickly and by 1902 there were 24,000 church members and 105 new churches. By 1911, the year Mary Baker Eddy died, there were 1,322 churches in Canada, Great Britain, Europe, Australia, Asia, and Africa.

Today the church is worldwide, and each church around the world follows the same lessons and readings simultaneously while seeking holistic health. While there are no ministers, there are practitioners who must graduate with a Christian Science degree. The basis of

the philosophy of Christian Science is that sin and sickness are not real but represent the lack of knowledge of God. According to Mary Baker Eddy:

Sickness is part of error which truth casts out. Error will not expel error. Christian Science is the law of truth, which heals the sick on the basis of one mind on God. It can heal in no other way, since the human mortal mind so-called is not a healer, but causes the belief in disease. Then comes the question, how do drugs, hygiene and animal magnetism heal? It may be affirmed that they do not heal but only relieve suffering temporarily, exchanging one disease for another. We classify disease as error, which nothing but truth can heal, and this mind must be divine not human. (Eddy, 1934)

Treatment for sin and sickness involves prayer. Thinking about God and concentrating on God both lead to and constitute healing. Sickness is the result of incorrect, sinful, or ungodly thoughts. Healing, therefore, involves changed thought:

To remove those objects of sense called sickness and disease, we must appeal to the mind to improve the subjects and objects of thought and give the body those better delineations. (Eddy, 1934)

Christian Science constitutes an archetypal modern example of the tie between religion and medicine. Today it has an estimated 2,300 churches or congregations in 60 countries around the world (http://www.-religioustolerance.org/cr_sci.htm).

(1994), a nurse researcher and professor at the University of Saskatchewan, has organized CAM into three categories: spiritual, including prayer and psychic surgery (such as is practised in the Philippines); psychological, including visualization, distraction, and cognitive strategies, e.g., adopting a positive attitude or a one-day-at-a-time philosophy; and physical. Clearly, some of these involve a practitioner but most do not. The following sections describe the philosophies and the occupational status of each of two complementary/alternative practitioners: chiropractors, because they are the largest competing alternative health-care occupation in Canada and in the world; and naturopaths, because of their growing importance in Canadian society.

Chiropractic

Chiropractic has been misunderstood frequently. It is passionately supported by some and passionately repudiated by others. The central tenet of spinal manipulation is an ancient technique legitimated even by Hippocrates: "look well to the spine, for many diseases have their origins in dislocations of the vertebral column" (cited in Caplan, 1984). In the beginning, American allopathic doctors vehemently opposed chiropractic. The American Medical Association (AMA) as late as the mid-1980s claimed that not only was there no scientific evidence for chiropractic but also warned the public against the untold dangers of submitting to such treatment (Caplan, 1984). One chiropractor commented that when he first started to practise about 50 years ago, he was refused admittance to service clubs, and people would make a point of stopping him on the street to call him a quack (personal communication). Now chiropractic doctors may receive patients directly as primary-contact practitioners. At times, they routinely refer patients to allopaths or other health-care providers.

The founder of chiropractic, Daniel David Palmer, was born in Port Perry, Ontario, in 1845 and moved to Davenport, Iowa, when he was 20. His work as a healer was based at first on what he thought were magnetic currents through the laying on of hands. His first success in spinal manipulation is said to have occurred in September 1895 when a deaf janitor in Palmer's apartment building dropped by to be examined. After discovering that the man had been deaf for 17 years and that his deafness had begun when he had exerted himself and felt something give way in his back, Palmer manipulated the man's spine. This immediately restored his hearing (Langone, 1982). Encouraged by this remarkable healing, Palmer investigated the impact of vertebral displacements on human disease. He called the newly discovered technique "chiropractic," from a combination of two Greek words, "cheir" and "practikas," meaning "done by hand" (Salmon, 1984).

Palmer campaigned for the legitimation and popularization of this new method of healing. He founded the Palmer School of Chiropractic, whose only admission requirement was a $450 fee. In 1906 Palmer was charged with practising without a licence and put in jail. It was not until 1913 that the first state, Kansas, passed licensing laws to allow the practice of chiropractic.

Palmer's most important pupil was his own son, Bartlett Joshua, or B.J. For 50 years or so, B.J. was able to popularize chiropractic to such an extent that he died a multi-millionaire. He was a gifted salesman who developed mail-order diplomas and advertising strategies that spread chiropractic around the world. B.J. advertised extensively for students, emphasizing the lack of exams or other requirements, lectured on business psychology, and wrote books with titles such as *Radio Salesmanship*. He was fond of making up slogans and having them engraved on the school's walls. One such slogan was, "Early to bed, early to rise; work like hell and advertise" (Weil, 1983, p. 130). B.J.'s sense of humour was also exhibited in the following question and answer, included in his book, *Questions and Answers About Chiropractic*, published in 1952. "Q. What are the principal functions of the spine? A. (1) to support the head; (2) to support the ribs; (3) to support the chiropractor" (quoted in Weil, 1983, p. 130).

B.J. Palmer believed that vertebral subluxation (misalignment) was the cause of all disease, and thus that chiropractic was a complete system that could cure everything and prevent disease from occurring. His belief that chiropractic was adequate to deal with all problems led to a major schism in 1924, when he introduced an expensive new piece of equipment—the neuro-calometer—and insisted that all chiropractic offices rent one from the Palmer School at $2,500 per annum. The major dissenter was an Oklahoma City lawyer who had become a chiropractor. In response to the unilateral dictate to buy this equipment, he established his own school of chiropractic. Within a few years he developed the theory that chiropractors should use other methods, such as nutrition and physical therapy, as well as spinal adjustment. Such a combination is called "mix," and this chiropractic philosophy is called "Mixer"; B.J. Palmer's philosophy, in contrast, is called "Straight." The schism continues today. However, Mixers are in the majority.

Chiropractic Theory and the Possible Future of Chiropractic

Two patterns of practice are based on spinal manipulation: osteopathy, founded in 1894 by Andrew Taylor Still, and chiropractic, founded by Daniel David Palmer in 1895. Osteopaths, who now include surgery and chemotherapy among their treatments, have achieved considerable legitimation around the world. Chiropractic has now achieved a good deal of legitimation in Britain, Europe, Australia, and Canada. In 2012 there were 75,000 chiropractors working in the US, 7,250 in Canada, 4,250 in Australia, and 3,000 in the UK, according to a report by the World Federation of Chiropractic (WFC) for the World Health Organization (World Federation of Chiropractic, 2013). According to CIHI the figure for Canada may have been an underestimate as they recorded 7,615 in 2008, 8,745 in 2013, and 8,571 in 2017. In addition, chiropractors work in more than 100 countries. But as recently as 1971 the AMA established a Committee on Quackery whose purposes included the containment and eventual elimination of chiropractic (Wardell, 1988, pp. 174–84). It had become a significant competitor to allopathic doctors. By

the 1960s, 3 million Americans were visiting over 20,000 chiropractors and spending $300 million annually. In spite of the efforts of the AMA, today chiropractic has undisputed if limited legitimacy in many parts of the world for the many people who believe in their treatments. Chiropractors are still included (up to a limit) under Medicaid, veterans' services, and military hospital systems in the US and are covered by various insurance companies and HMOs. Chiropractic education receives federal funds. Chiropractic is now the major healing occupation in competition with allopathic medicine throughout the world. The cost-effectiveness of chiropractic for head and neck pain, both of which are enormously prevalent, compare positively with allopathic care (World Federation of Chiropractic, 2013).

The theory of chiropractic is based on the idea that vertebral misalignment, by interfering with the patterns of the nervous system, can cause a wide variety of disorders. According to chiropractic, anything that can be said to result from or to develop out of the context of a depressed immune system can be treated or prevented by chiropractic. Chiropractic theory has been distinguished from allopathic theory along three lines (Caplan, 1984). In the first place, allopathic medicine views the symptoms as evidence of the disease and as a result of a simultaneously occurring disease process. The removal of symptoms is tantamount to the removal of disease for the allopath. Chiropractic, on the other hand, theorizes that symptoms are the result of a long-term pathological functioning of the organism via the spinal and the muscle systems. Disease precedes symptoms for a long period of time, perhaps years. The correction of the spinal subluxation by chiropractic allows the body to heal itself.

The second distinction lies in the competing views of the role of pathogens in disease. The allopathic understanding is that pathogens of a specific type and frequency invade the body and begin any of a number of different disease processes. Killing the pathogens thus becomes a goal of treatment and the basis of scientific medicine. All practitioners not subscribing to this view are by definition "unscientific" and have been derogatorily referred to as cultists and quacks (Caplan, 1984, p. 84). Chiropractic says that pathogens are a necessary but not a sufficient condition for the initiation of a disease process. Before pathogens can take effect, the body must be vulnerable. While a number of factors can enervate the body, including genetic defects, poor nutrition, and stress, vertebral subluxation is also an important factor.

The third distinction rests in the fact that allopathic doctors, even when they grant chiropractic some legitimacy, limit it to specific musculoskeletal conditions. Chiropractors, on the other hand, view their work as holistic, preventive care.

There are several alternative future scenarios for chiropractic in Canada. First, chiropractic could remain, as it is now, a marginal occupation in terms of state support, only partially financed through medicare. Second, allopathic physicians could adopt chiropractic techniques to use themselves in addition to the traditional surgical and chemotherapeutic techniques and thus usurp the sovereignty of the increasingly legitimated and regulated occupation. Third, chiropractors could be subjugated, as nurses and pharmacists have been, to work only under the jurisdiction of allopathic doctors. Fourth, chiropractic could increase in status, regulation, and legitimacy and become an equal competitor with allopathic medicine for funding as an alternative to allopathy.

Current Status of Chiropractic in Canada

In Canada, the Canadian Chiropractic Association is an association of Mixers only, as its description of chiropractic indicates:

> Chiropractic is a healing discipline firmly grounded in science. Although its main focus is the relationship between the skeleton (particularly the spine) and the nervous system that runs through it, chiropractic is concerned with the care of the entire body. (www.ccachiro.org/GENQA)

The number of chiropractors has grown from about 100 in 1906 to more than 100,000

around the world as of 2012 (World Federation of Chiropractic, 2013). Chiropractors constitute the third largest group of primary medical care practitioners in Canada, after physicians and dentists. The number of chiropractors in Canada increased rapidly after World War II when the Canadian Memorial Chiropractic College was established in 1945. The Department of Veterans Affairs gave an early impetus to the development of chiropractic when it funded the education of 250 veterans who desired training in chiropractic. Now the Université du Québec à Trois-Rivières also offers a Doctor of Chiropractic degree.

Still, chiropractic care is unevenly supported by provincial health plans across Canada. Since 2004, chiropractic care has not been covered by the Ontario Health Insurance Plan. Other provinces, such as Manitoba and Quebec, provide partial coverage. However, chiropractic care is covered by many extended health insurance plans across Canada and about 70 per cent of the population has membership in one or another of these privately financed plans, albeit that only a limited number of visits per year are covered by governments and insurance companies. The relative cost of chiropractic services as a proportion of the total expenditures on health is negligible compared to the proportion of the health-care budget currently expended on allopathic practitioners.

The standards for admission to chiropractic colleges are comparable to those for other health occupations such as dentistry, pharmacy, optometry, and medicine. To enter, a student must have a minimum of three years of university in any discipline, preferably including a full course with labs in organic chemistry and biology, a half-course in introductory psychology, and at least one and a half courses in the humanities or the social sciences (see www.ccachiro.org/cdninfo). The chiropractic program is usually four years based on studies of human anatomy and related basic sciences, including X-rays, diagnostic skills, and clinical studies. Graduates see themselves as part of a health-care team and, around the world, chiropractors increasingly work in concert with other health-care providers. Modern chiropractors neither claim nor want to promote the view that their type of health care is the only useful model.

The practice of chiropractic in Canada today is largely limited to musculoskeletal disorders such as headaches, neck and back pain, and soreness in the limbs. Approximately 4 million Canadians use chiropractic services annually (Lahave River Chiropractic and Health Centre, 2018). This is a higher percentage than for those who indicate that they use any other CAMs. Most people report using chiropractors for lower back pain (Lawrence & Meeker, 2007). In addition, a wide range of functional and internal disorders are believed to be caused fully or in part by spinal dysfunction. Some recent studies have demonstrated but not explained the superiority of chiropractic in treating neck and back injuries. There is some evidence to suggest the efficacy of chiropractic in treating a broader spectrum of disorders, including epilepsy, asthma, and diabetes (Caplan, 1984). Nonetheless, a few critics still claim that chiropractic is not only useless but often dangerous (Benedetti & MacPhail, 2002).

The future prospects for the development and spread of chiropractic, according to the perspectives of leaders in the field, must include a new focus on (1) peer-reviewed research publications; (2) increased monitoring to establish standards of practice; (3) improvement in the quality of chiropractic education and increased intra-group cohesion (Verhoef et al., 2006). Still, many conventional practitioners and their leaders continue to show resistance to the full support and inclusion of chiropractic into the mainstream (Kelner et al., 2004).

Naturopathy

Naturopathy is a form of holistic health care considered by its practitioners to be relevant to all the disabilities and diseases that might bring a patient to a doctor's office. It is "a system of primary care that uses natural methods and substances to support and stimulate the body's inherent self-healing processes" (Verhoef et al., 2006, p. 409). The term "naturopath" was first adopted in 1901 at a convention of drugless practitioners in the US (Gort, 1986, cited in Boon, 1996, p. 16). It is based on the assumption that health and illness both are natural components of a total human being—spirit, body, and mind. Just as individuals are unique, this philosophy proposes each individual's sickness is unique to him or her. Healing depends on the activation of the normal healing processes of the human body.

Naturopathy has its philosophic roots in Greek medicine and in the work of Hippocrates, who emphasized the body's own healing powers. Naturopathic medicine is a distinct system of primary health care that addresses the root causes of illness and promotes health and healing using natural therapies. It supports the body's own healing ability using an integrated approach to disease diagnosis, treatment, and prevention. Naturopathy includes a number of different healing modalities and research streams, including botanical medicine, clinical nutrition, traditional Chinese medicine and acupuncture, hydrotherapy, lifestyle counselling, naturopathic manipulation, and homeopathy (Verhoef et al., 2006). There are six accredited schools of naturopathic medicine in North America. Two are in Canada, one in Toronto (see www.ccnm.edu/) and the other in British Columbia.

In this text we will look further at only one of these components of naturopathic medicine, homeopathy. Homeopathy was first established by Samuel Hahnemann (1755–1843). A few years after he graduated from medical school in Vienna, because of disillusionment with the therapies available at the time, he left the practice of medicine to be a writer and translator of texts into German. The translation of a text by a Scottish physician, William Cullen, led Hahnemann into developing the theory of homeopathy. What stimulated Hahnemann was Cullen's description of why the bark of the cinchona tree, containing quinine, was able to treat the fever and malaise of malaria. It was already known that quinine was a treatment for malaria. The explanation, however, was unknown. Cullen taught that it was due to its bitterness and astringent qualities. Hahnemann, having translated many other medical treatises, knew that many substances of greater bitterness and astringency were not effective against malaria. Thus began the homeopathic career of Hahnemann, the scientist who used the following method: (1) observation, (2) hypothesis, and

(3) experiment. His first experiment was on himself. Knowing that quinine was not toxic in small doses, he ingested some. He developed the symptoms of malaria—chills, malaise, and headaches. He knew he did not have malaria and asked what had happened. Consulting Hippocrates, he found the idea that what causes a condition would also cure it. He rediscovered the old Hippocratic principle—"like cures like." The substances that cause symptoms in a healthy person are able to relieve symptoms in an unwell person. Intuitively, this finding reminds us of the notion of balance—of a natural force. "What homeopathy does is to treat the individual according to his or her own discomforts by pushing the organism in the same direction the vital force is trying to go" (Rothouse, 1997, p. 224).

Homeopathy, from the Greek words *homoios pathos*, which mean "similar sickness," is based on a number of principles that are in opposition to allopathic medicine. These include the following (Coulter, 1984):

- The key to the cure of illness is embodied in the principle of similars, i.e., minute dosages of a natural substance known to cause similar symptoms to those indicative of the disease are administered as treatment.
- Different people react differently to the same illness because each person is unique.

- The body should receive only one remedy at a time; otherwise the body's healing powers will be divided. The physician looks for the "most similar" remedy, not those that just seem superficially to be similar.
- The physician should administer the minimum dosage required by the patient. This minimum dose will provide the same curative powers as a larger dose.

Sickness is thought of as a message from the body rather than a biological pathology. Sickness provides a crisis through which the person can re-evaluate his or her own life (body, mind, and spirit). Thus, symptoms are not viewed as signs of disease, nor is the goal to eradicate symptoms through heroic measures such as surgical removal or chemical destruction. Rather, symptoms are indications of a healing crisis to be enhanced by the administration of minimum doses of a substance that causes the same symptoms. Naturopathic or homeopathic diagnosis is based on knowledge, not of the disease's normal or standard course, effects, and treatment, but rather of the unique and idiosyncratic characteristics of the interaction of the individual person and the particular patterning of symptoms. Naturopathic medicine, therefore, does not treat diseases but stimulates the individual's vital healing force.

Homeopathy originated at a time when conventional medicine was "primitive and brutal in

CRITICAL THINKING

Box 13.5 • Homeopathy

The premier medical journal in Great Britain, read throughout the world, *The Lancet*, published a meta-analysis of 119 clinical trials that examined the efficacy of homeopathic medicine. The purpose of the analysis was to investigate the published research reports on homeopathy and its usefulness for particular conditions. In the eternally pessimistic language of the "null hypothesis," the study found that "the results of our meta-analysis are not compatible with the hypothesis that the clinical effects of homeopathy are completely due to placebo" (Linde et al., 1997, p. 834). In fact, the combined odds ratio for the 89 studies entered into the main meta-analysis was 2.45 (95 per cent, CI 2.05–2.93) in favour of homeopathy. That is, homeopathy was approximately two and a half times as likely to work as not. This finding is contrary to the beliefs of some that the positive results from homeopathy can be explained by the fact that people believe in homeopathy—the placebo effect.

form, and frequently lethal for the patient" (May & Sirur, 1998, p. 169). Conventional medical treatments, which might involve the application of purgatives, bloodletting, or cupping, were basically the same as had been used for several centuries. However, because its development paralleled the therapeutic revolution based on the highly visible reactions characteristic of allopathic medicine and often originating in the chemistry lab, many saw homeopathic medicine's longer-term, less obvious results as ineffectual. Because homeopaths, many of whom were trained physicians, continued to focus on the uniqueness of the individual experiences of illness and on relatively benign, virtually invisible treatments and did not develop a theoretical foundation for their therapies that could compete with the "supra-molecular chemistry of the nineteenth century," they were unable to develop legitimacy in the competitive medical marketplace of North America.

Nevertheless, homeopathy is considered a legitimate alternative (and is evidently growing in legitimacy) in many Western countries. In Britain, for example, it had maintained a degree of acceptance among a minority until there was a steep decline from 134,000 to 16,359 prescriptions for homeopathic medications via the National Health Service during the years 2000–10. Four homeopathic hospitals, at Liverpool, London, Glasgow, and Bristol, were incorporated into the National Health Service in Britain at its inception in 1947, although one has since closed and another has been incorporated into the mainstream conventional care. Indeed, some members of the British royal family have always preferred homeopathic medicines. More recently, adopting the blind randomized control trial, homeopathic remedies have been found to be effective in the treatment of respiratory disease (Ferley et al., 1989, cited in May & Sirur, 1998) and pollen allergies (Reilly et al., 1986, cited in May & Sirur, 1998). However, in 2010 a House of Commons report in the UK found that homeopathic remedies were no more effective than placebos. At present, it is fairly popular in France. About 10,000 physicians in France were practising homeopathy over 20 years ago, and in that country 25 per cent of pharmacies were homeopathic. Other countries,

too, have a history of greater open access to homeopathic medicine. In Britain, half of all conventional physicians used or recommended homeopathy. And in India, homeopathy is taught in almost all medical and pharmacy schools (Rothouse, 1997).

There are numerous and complex methodological difficulties in comparing the efficacy of allopathic and homeopathic remedies, not least of which is that homeopathy is based on designing a unique treatment for each individual whereas evidence-based standards of allopathic practice compare the same treatment over a group of individuals diagnosed with a specific disease. Homeopathy is also based on a holistic model of the person, and a part of the treatment involves spending time with patients and offering psychosocial care whereas conventional medicine looks for one diagnosis at a time. One interesting finding, based on the study of the overall efficacy of homeopathic versus regular hospitals during the nineteenth-century cholera epidemics in America, is that the death rates in regular hospitals were five times greater than in homeopathic hospitals. Similarly, in London, England, in 1854, a Parliament-mandated study found that 59 per cent of those in regular hospitals died, while only 16 per cent died in homeopathic hospitals. Homeopathy treated cholera's symptoms of headache, malaise, diarrhea, anorexia, chills, convulsions, and so on with mild homeopathic remedies—camphora or veratrum album.

Current Status of Naturopathy and Homeopathy

Homeopathy arrived in the United States in 1825. By 1844, some of the most prominent allopathic physicians had adopted its principles and established the American Institute of Homeopathy, the country's first medical association. The allopaths were threatened by this move and in 1846 founded a competing organization, the American Medical Association (AMA). Professional contact between allopaths and homeopaths was prohibited by the AMA's newly established Code of Ethics (Coulter, 1984).

The formal system of naturopathic treatment, which incorporated homeopathic medicine, was established by Benedict Lust (1872–1945), who founded the first naturopathic college in 1900 in New York City. Lust's primary method of treatment was hydrotherapy, but this was enhanced by a variety of other techniques, including homeopathy, botanical remedies, nutritional therapy, psychology, massage, and manipulation (Weil, 1983).

Hostility persisted between allopaths and naturopaths until the number of naturopaths began to decline dramatically and they no longer posed a threat. Since then, naturopathy has never constituted a well-organized occupational group, but rather a loose assortment of holistic practitioners providing a variety of healing modalities. Until recently, most naturopaths were also chiropractors.

In Ontario, the Drugless Practitioners Act of 1925 can be seen as the starting point for the formal recognition by the province of naturopathy as a distinct healing occupation. By this Act a Board of Regents, composed of five appointees of the lieutenant-governor and made up of allopathic and chiropractic practitioners, was set up to regulate chiropractors and naturopaths. While naturopaths were allowed to practise, they were not formally included under this Act until 1944. In 1948, chiropractors were limited to "hands only, spine only" (Gort, 1986, p. 87). In the following year, 1949, the Ontario Naturopathic Association was formed by chiropractors who had been deprived of the right to the full range of practice (i.e., including homeopathic medicines) by the 1948 decision. By 1952 each form of drugless therapy was allowed to govern itself because it had become increasingly difficult for one board to regulate practitioners with diverse education, training, and practice modalities.

Naturopathy in Canada

Almost 500 naturopaths were practising and licensed in Canada by 2000 (Verhoef et al., 2006). They are not covered by medicare but operate under provincial jurisdiction. A number of provinces—including British Columbia, Saskatchewan, Manitoba, Ontario, and Alberta—have regulated naturopathic medicine (https://www.cand.ca). Today, one recognized

English-Canadian training institution, the Canadian College of Naturopathic Medicine, is located in Toronto; it began in 1978 as the Ontario College of Naturopathic Medicine. Another is in British Columbia—the Boucher Institute of Naturopathic Medicine (see www.cand.ca/index.php?36). At first, the Toronto program offered a post-graduate program to allopaths, chiropractors, and naturopaths to help them upgrade their qualifications. In 1982 the Ontario Ministry of Health appointed a Health Professions Legislative Review Committee to determine which occupations needed regulation for the protection of the public interest. This committee decided that naturopathy should not be regulated by the state but by its own members. The argument was that since (1) naturopathy was not scientific and (2) there was no standardization of practice, it posed a risk of harm to the patients and should not be regulated and thereby given official sanction.

The naturopaths responded in a brief titled *Naturopathic Medicine and Health Care in Ontario*, delivered in July 1983 to Keith Norton, the provincial Minister of Health at the time. The brief justified the value and efficacy of naturopaths as well-educated and trained healers, and made it clear that they believed the allopaths were trying to exclude them from practice. It levied a series of sharp criticisms at the costliness and narrowness of allopathic medicine, its mechanistic fallacy, and its negative social consequences. The final statement highlighted and summarized their critique of allopathic medicine: "We find little cause to applaud allopathy's near monopoly of the medical services of this province" (Ontario Naturopathic Association, 1983, p. 21).

Among the naturopaths' recommendations were: the establishment of a separate Act to regulate naturopathic medicine; granting of the right to use the title "doctor"; the right to use the terms "naturopathic medicine" and "naturopathic physician"; the elimination of the term "drugless practitioner" in favour of "naturopathic physician"; the right to hospital privileges; the right to refer to various laboratory and X-ray services; and the right to authorize medical exemptions and to sign medical documents. A number of provinces—including

British Columbia, Manitoba, Saskatchewan, Ontario, and Nova Scotia—have moved forward with regulation (see www.cand.ca/index.php?36).

In the same year, 1983, the Ontario College of Naturopathic Medicine became the first Canadian institution to offer a complete education in naturopathy, having devoted the five years since its founding in 1978 to fundraising and offering single stand-alone courses. By 1986 the planned deregulation, in spite of the organized opposition of the Ontario Naturopathic Association, was passed by the Ontario government. Despite signs of the resurgence of naturopathy—rising numbers of practitioners and the presence of colleges to provide training—it seems that naturopathy in Ontario is unable to expand because of deregulation.

One of the most difficult issues faced by naturopathic medicine in its struggle for legitimacy lies in the nature of its science. Allopathic medicine claims to be scientific because it is modelled on physics, the prototypical science of the nineteenth century. The goal of this model of research is the establishment of universally true causal laws. Individual differences are ignored in favour of generalizations. Alternatives included in naturopathic medicine such as homeopathy and traditional Chinese medicine, on the other hand, are based on different models of science. These models assume a universally true set of principles that are applied differentially to each individual. By contrast, allopathic scientific doctrine changes considerably over time as the result of new research findings (among other things). With each new discovery some aspect of allopathic medicine is nullified.

In a study of all licensed naturopathic practitioners in Canada, Boon (1998) observed two distinct paradigms of naturopathic practice. One she calls a "scientific world view," the other, "holistic." Those in the first category appear to emphasize physical and structural treatments and to be more practical, concrete, reductionistic, and objective. Those in the second category are more subjective, spiritual, abstract, intuitive, and likely to emphasize treatment at an emotional level.

In Canada, naturopathic doctors are highly trained, including three years of undergraduate work and four years of full-time studies in naturopathic medicine. They have extensive scientific and clinical knowledge of natural remedies, including their use, contraindication, possible adverse reactions, and toxicities (see www.naturopathicas-soc.ca/dr.html). As the holistic health movement grows, naturopathy may become increasingly accepted as legitimate. Claims of malpractice against chiropractors, massage therapists, and acupuncturists for 1990–6 were compared with those made against conventional doctors (Studdert et al., 1998). CAM practitioners were sued less frequently than conventional doctors and when they were sued the injury at issue was less severe. This might suggest that the safety records of CAM practitioners are better than those of allopathic practitioners. Nevertheless, there are sometimes serious and even fatal results from CAM practice, as there are in allopathic medicine, and more research needs to be done.

According to Verhoef et al. (2006), naturopathic medicine likely faces an uphill battle in efforts to become a fully regulated profession. The reasons for this are several and include: (1) the view that naturopathic medicine does not have a unique body of knowledge; (2) significant overlaps between naturopathic medicine and other healing modalities and practitioners who are also competing for regulation; (3) a lack of cohesion within the naturopathic medical community; and (4) a lack of vacancies (a glut on the market of trained naturopaths in some locations so there is no room for new graduates to open practice). Table 13.4 portrays the wide variety of types of treatment included under naturopathic medicine.

Historically, homeopathic practitioners were self-regulating in Canada. A slight increase in homeopathy in Canada has occurred recently. It is difficult to determine the exact number of homeopaths practising in Canada, although the number appears to be small (Kelner et al., 2006). According to a recent survey, about 2 per cent of Canadians seek the services of homeopaths (Statistics Canada, 2005). As early as 1845, homeopathic doctors began practising in Quebec, and shortly after that homeopaths were at work in Toronto. They became

Table 13.4 Types of Modalities Provided by Naturopathic Practitioners

	Provided to More Than 50% of Patients (%)	Provided to Less Than 50% of Patients (%)	Never Provided (%)	Total η
Nutritional supplementation	9.9	89.5	0.7	294
Nutritional counselling (e.g., macrobiotics)	10.2	89.2	0.7	295
Botanical medicine	20.5	78.5	1	293
Homeopathy	28.9	69.5	1.7	298
Laboratory testing	55.1	34.3	10.6	292
Novel assessment methods: VEGA testing, dark field microscopy	23	32.3	43.6	291
Psychological counselling	61.6	31.1	7.3	289
Traditional Chinese medicine	52.4	21.4	26.2	290
Naturopathic manipulation	40.8	15.8	43.4	292
Parenteral therapy, including injections	37.6	14.1	48.3	290
Acupuncture	48.7	13.7	34.2	284
Applied kinesiology	23.3	13.3	61.7	287
Meditation/visualization	64	10.8	25.2	286
Hydrotherapy	65.2	10.8	24	296
Electro-acupuncture	24.4	10.5	65.2	287
Massage	47.8	7	45.3	287
Iridology	23.4	6.5	70.1	291
Acupressure	37.3	5.6	57	268
Fasting	59.8	5.2	35.1	291
Lymphatic drainage	42.5	4.8	52.7	292
Craniosacral therapy	35.3	4.6	60.1	283
Ultrasound	20.5	3.4	76	292
Yoga	32.1	3.1	64.8	287
Colon therapy	14.6	2.8	82.6	281
Reflexology	12.2	1.7	86.1	287

Table 13.4 *Continued*

	Provided to More Than 50% of Patients (%)	Provided to Less Than 50% of Patients (%)	Never Provided (%)	Total η
Biofeedback	12.7	1.7	84.9	284
X-ray testing	27.5	1.4	71.1	287
Ayurvedic medicine	24.7	1.4	73.9	283
Natural childbirth	17.4	1.1	81.5	281
Magnetic therapy	22.8	1	76.2	290
Polarity therapy	4.2	0.3	95.5	286
Minor surgery	7.6	0	92.4	290
Hypnosis	7.2	0	92.8	293
Alexander technique	2.3	0	97.5	284

Source: Verhoef et al. (2006). Reprinted with permission from Elsevier.

regulated in Canada West (Ontario) in 1859 and in Montreal in 1865. They were represented in the College of Physicians and Surgeons of Ontario from 1869 to 1960. In British Columbia regulation began in 1889. There was a homeopathic hospital in Montreal in 1894; in Toronto, a homeopathic dispensary opened in 1888 and a homeopathic hospital in 1890. Ontario was the first province to regulate homeopathy—as of 1 April 2015—amid a great deal of controversy. For example, the headline of an article on this news by André Picard (2015), the highly respected health and medicine columnist of the *Globe and Mail*, read: "We're Aiding and Abetting Homeopathic Quackery."

If the trends in the United States are any indication of the future for naturopathic treatments in Canada, then it looks bright. From its heyday in the nineteenth century, when there were 15,000 practitioners, 14 training schools, dozens of periodicals, and organized groups in every state and large city (Coulter, 1984, p. 72), naturopathy declined to a low of about 100 practitioners in 1950. In the 1960s, however, this trend was reversed, and today thousands of mainstream practitioners (allopaths, chiropractors, nurses, and clinical psychologists) use at least some homeopathic methods. In Canada about 1,350 naturopathic doctors practise as such (see www.cand.ca/index.php?36). As well, a number of firms manufacture and export homeopathic remedies, and a number of governments have adopted licensing laws for the practice of naturopathic medicine.

Therapeutic Touch

One other alternative healing modality is quickly being incorporated into the practice of allopathic medicine via the nursing profession. This method is therapeutic touch. According to Michael Lerner in *Choices in Healing*, in which he critically reviews the research literature on the value of a wide variety of complementary and alternative medicines, therapeutic touch is a promising healing modality.

> The implications of therapeutic touch for medicine and science are—if the scientific studies of its efficacy are valid—truly awesome. Something is happening in these studies, if they are correct, that medicine should attend to and science cannot yet account for. (Lerner, 1994, p. 362)

Therapeutic touch has become established as a modern and empirically studied practice. It is now widely used in and out of hospitals, usually by nurses, across Canada and the US. It was started by Delores Kreiger, a nursing professor at New York University, and was based on her observations of and her collaboration with a renowned healer, Dora Kuntz, who believed that healing could be systematized, taught, and studied. Therapeutic touch does not involve touch (at least not primarily) but rather the movement of "energy" along the outside of the body (for about 15–20 minutes) a number of inches from the body in order to balance and restore energy where it is lacking. Research on the efficacy of therapeutic touch has found it to: (a) raise hemoglobin levels, (b) elicit the relaxation response, and (c) heal wounds, among other benefits.

Summary

1. Complementary and alternative medicines are growing in significance, rates of use, and public acceptance at a rapid pace. CAMs are even growing in legitimacy in the minds and referral practices of allopathic practitioners.
2. Daniel David Palmer founded chiropractic in 1895. Attempts to legitimate and popularize this method of healing were stunted by allopathic practitioners. Distinguishing features of chiropractic are: through the corrective manipulation of spinal subluxation the body is able to heal itself; the goal is not to kill germs but to make the body less vulnerable to germs; the work is viewed as holistic, preventive care.

Although chiropractic in Canada today is limited to musculoskeletal disorders, its legitimacy continues to grow.
3. Naturopathy is based on the assumption that health and illness are both natural components of a total but unique human being—spirit, body, and mind. Healing depends on the activation of the normal healing processes of the human body. Initially it was met with opposition by most allopaths. More and more mainstream practitioners use at least some naturopathic methods today.
4. Therapeutic touch is a CAM that is widely accepted and frequently studied.

Key Terms

acupuncture
allopathic medicine
chiropractic
complementary and alternative medicine (CAM)
herbalism
holistic health care

naturopathy
reflexology
rolfing
shiatsu
therapeutic touch

Questions for Study and Discussion

1. Why is complementary and alternative medicine becoming more acceptable to Canadians?
2. Why are allopathic doctors changing their views regarding chiropractors?

3. Assess the view that naturopathic and chiropractic medicines are non-scientific whereas allopathic medicine is based on scientific evidence.

4. What do you think the medical marketplace will look like in 25 years?

5. Examine a popular magazine or newspaper for its coverage of CAM over a period of time.

Suggested Readings

April, K.T., & Gaboury, I. (2013). A survey of Canadian regulated complementary and alternative medicine schools about research, evidence-based health care and interprofessional training. *BMC Complementary and Alternative Medicine, 13*, 374–81. An empirical article on the views of CAM schools regarding medical research and work.

Benedetti, P., & MacPhail, W. (2002). *Spin doctors: The chiropractic industry under examination.* Toronto: Dundurn. An empirical examination and critique of chiropractic.

Dossey, L. (1982). *Space, time and medicine.* New Science Library.

_____. 1991. *Meaning and medicine.* Bantam Books. Popular interpretations of philosophical principles behind some complementary and alternative medicine.

Liu, F., Li, Z.M., Jiang, Y.J., & Chen, L.D. (2014). A meta-analysis of acupuncture use in the treatment of cognitive impairment after stroke. *Journal of Alternative and Complementary Medicine, 20*(7), 535–44. A study of the effectiveness of acupuncture.

Qureshi, N.A., & Al-Bedah, M. (2013). Mood disorders and complementary and alternative medicine: A literature review. *Neuropsychiatric Disease and Treatment, 3*(9), 639–65. A literature review of a wide variety of complementary and alternative medicines and their impact on mood disorders.

Weil, A. (2011). *Spontaneous happiness.* Little, Brown and Company. A popular book on how to be happy.

The Pharmaceutical Industry and the Medical-Industrial Complex

14

Chapter Overview

- The medical-industrial complex includes many different organizations, products, and services.
- The pharmaceutical industry is one of the largest and most profitable and influential of these.
- Pharmaceutical use is affected by the socio-demographic characteristics of users.
- Pharmaceutical use is affected by the style of medical practice, the involvement of drug salespersons, and pharmaceutical company initiatives among other things.

- Pharmacists' interests also affect patterns of drug purchases and usage.
- The pharmaceutical industry retains its position through a number of powerful and effective marketing, regulating, pricing, and other business strategies.
- The cases of DES and thalidomide illustrate two of the historical problems in the regulation of the drug industry in Canada. That unsafe drugs continue to be placed in the Canadian marketplace is evidenced by the cases of HRT, Vioxx, and Diane-35.

- Many similar cases of the misuse by the pharmaceutical industry of drug markets in the developing world have been documented.

- The Health Protection Branch of the Canadian federal government has an ambiguous record with regard to protecting the health of Canadians from dangerous, ineffective, or questionable drugs.

Introduction

The **medical-industrial complex** is a large and growing network of private and semi-public corporations engaged in the business of providing medical care and medical care products, supplies, and services for a profit. Included in the medical-industrial complex are, among other things, hospitals and nursing homes, home-care services, diagnostic services, including expensive CT scanners and MRIs, hemodialysis supplies and equipment, pharmaceutical companies, medical tools and technology, and even laundry and food-packaging companies that supply hospitals and other health-care organizations. This complex is global and is a part of a new world order (Usher & Skinner, 2012) under neo-liberalism. The pharmaceutical industry, an important component of the medical-industrial complex, will be discussed in detail in this chapter.

When do you decide to go to the pharmacy for over-the-counter medication? Some of you try to become aware of the side effects of various over-the-counter and other medications. Some of you ask the doctor about long-term effects. Some of you take your prescribed medication exactly as directed—over the length of time suggested and at the prescribed intervals. Most of us assume that all the drugs available in Canada have been adequately tested and are safe. However, this assumption is not true (Canadian Foundation for Health Care Improvement, 2010). Many of you will have heard of thalidomide, Vioxx, Ritalin, Diane-35, or DES. Do you know some of the devastating results of their use? You may have considered the question of the extent to which the pharmaceutical, medical device, and biotechnology companies are reliant on and motivated by making a profit as compared to serving those suffering sickness and pain. Have

you ever thought about the effects of pharmaceuticals on the environment? They may be excreted from our bodies (our bodies only absorb a portion of the drugs we routinely administer to ourselves) or flushed as tablets or syrups down a drain when we no longer think they are of use. After a person dies, as the body decomposes, the drugs (or chemicals) leech from the body and are absorbed by the earth. These are among the issues that will be addressed in this chapter.

Drug Use

Any discussion of the pharmaceutical industry and the use of drugs in contemporary Canadian society must be fairly wide-ranging because this topic involves a large number of sociological issues. The drug industry is a major actor in Canadian medical care, and its share of health spending in Canada grew from 9.8 per cent in 1983 to 12.6 per cent in 1990. In 2019, according to the Canadian Institute for Health Information, 15.3 per cent of the total Canadian health-care budget was spent on pharmaceuticals (CIHI, 2019; see Figure 14.1). Prescribed drugs make up the largest component at 84.6 per cent and over-the-counter drugs comprise 15.4 per cent. There is evidence of the flattening of this upward trend line because several "blockbuster" drugs used to treat the high-prevalence conditions of hypertension and high cholesterol have moved off patent and thus are now available in the much less costly generic form. Still, drugs continue to be the second largest expenditure in the health-care system after that spent on hospitals. Although the proportion spent on physicians has been growing lately, as doctors' salaries and numbers have both grown, it is still somewhat less than that spent on drugs. While the Canada Health Act covers all necessary hospital, physician, surgical-dental, and a

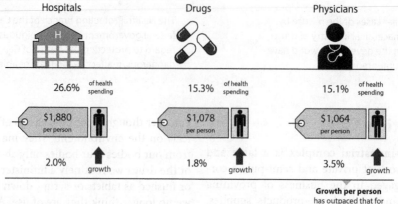

Figure 14.1   Where Is Most of the Money Being Spent in Health Care in 2019?

Note: These three line items account for 57 per cent of total annual health expenditures. The other 43 per cent is directed to such other expenses/costs as other health-care personnel (e.g., nurses, orderlies, paramedics, technicians), ambulance services, technology, and testing and research laboratories.

Source: CIHI (2019).

portion of long-term care services, it does not include prescription drugs outside of hospital. Thirty-one per cent of prescription drug costs are covered by private insurance plans, often associated with the workplaces of Canadians, 33 per cent of costs are paid for out of pocket, and 36 per cent by government programs (for Indigenous people, older people, and those in the military). The costs to consumers who either lack drug insurance altogether or have limitations in respect to drug coverage have grown more quickly than the overall health budget. This relative cost of pharmaceuticals constitutes another element of mounting privatization in health care in Canada. The proposal for universal pharmaceutical coverage (Morgan et al., 2015) paid through taxation seems to be gaining support. According to OECD data, Canada is near the top of the OECD countries with respect to the out-of-pocket cost of pharmaceuticals (see OECD, 2018).

In the latest figures, more than 15.3 per cent of Canada's health budget went for out-of-hospital drugs, or $1,078 per person. Slightly less was spent on physicians—$1,064 per person or 15.1 per cent (CIHI, 2019). Hospital expenditures amounted to 26.6 per cent or $1,880 per person, which included in-hospital pharmaceutical spending. The amount

spent reflects the growing reliance on drugs for treatment and for prevention. It also represents the adoption of new and thus more expensive drugs, according to CIHI's *National Health Expenditure Trends*. Greater spending includes an increase in cost for newer anti-psychotics and the uptake of prevalent anti-anxiety and anti-depression drugs. Drug cost increases constitute another element of mounting privatization in health care in Canada, and, needless to say, drug coverage varies by socio-economic and socio-demographic groups in Canada.

A significant cause of the increase in drug expenditures is the development of new and often me-too drugs. In the last few years these have been drugs to treat hepatitis C and macular degeneration (CIHI, 2018). Drugs designed to mitigate the inflammation of diseases such as arthritis and Crohn's disease reflected the highest proportion of expenditure for the sixth year in a row. These are newer, more expensive drugs marketed and used for the same conditions in the place of older, less expensive pharmaceuticals (Canadian Health Coalition, 2006). The new drugs may or may not be better than the older versions and they may or may not be safe (Canadian Foundation for Health Care Improvement, 2013).

The increase in drug expenditures is also due to aggressive advertising both to physicians and to consumers. This advertising is global and highly influential, especially in the presence of the World Wide Web (Usher & Skinner, 2012); plus, in Canada, televised drug commercials from American networks and cable channels have become ubiquitous. Drug "scandals" are frequent. Hormone replacement therapy (HRT) was prescribed to millions of women for a number of years. Then, epidemiological research demonstrated that it caused an increase in strokes, heart attacks, breast cancer, blood clots, and gallstones. It is now to be used only in exceptional circumstances (Canadian Health Coalition, 2006). Another prescription drug for women, Yasmin or YAZ is suspected to have caused at least 23 deaths in Canadian women (*CBC News*, 2013). Possibly the most widely prescribed drug class in Canada is a cholesterol-lowering statin called Lipitor for which there were many millions of prescriptions per year (*CBC News*, 2013). This drug is intended for basically healthy people to prevent high cholesterol, despite the fact that its value as a preventive is not clear and is hotly debated. In addition, it does have side effects. About 450,000 prescriptions of Diane-35, a drug marketed for acne and sometimes used for birth control, were sold to Canadian women annually. This drug was responsible for the deaths of 11 young women and over 200 adverse reactions reported to the *Toronto Star* (Zlomislic & Teotonio, 2013). Diane-35 was removed from sale in France because it was considered unsafe after four girls apparently died as a result of taking it. Such a finding may point to the relative weakness of the Canadian government in the face of the pharmaceutical industry (Zlomislic & Teotonio,

2013) and the difficulties in removing a drug from the market once it has been approved.

It may be helpful to begin our discussion in this chapter with a pictorial representation of the various levels of analysis that will be considered in our explanation and description of pharmaceutical use in Canada (see Figure 14.2).

At the first level the discussion will focus on how the socio-demographic characteristics of patients—age, gender, class—correlate with their legal drug-taking habits. The social characteristics of physicians, too, influence drug prescription—such as the form of medical practice (e.g., solo as compared with group practice), the amount of continuing education, and the size of the practice.

Pharmacists and the pharmaceutical industry, of course, are important forces in drug use as well. Cost, availability, advertising, pharmaceutical company websites, perks and benefits offered by pharmaceutical companies, and special pricing arrangements are among the factors known to influence physicians' decisions on what to prescribe and pharmacists' decisions on what to stock. Drug payment schemes—whether government-controlled, those offered by private insurance, or individual payment alternatives—also affect drug use. Much of the recent sociological research on drug use in Canada has focused on the pharmaceutical industry, its organization and structure, and especially on the fact that under capitalism and global neo-liberalism it must be guided by the profit motive, which at times conflicts with the goal of promoting health. The power of the pharmaceutical industry in negotiating with the Canadian government and in determining how drugs are regulated, brought onto the market, and monitored after they are on the market must be

Figure 14.2 Factors Affecting Drug Use in Canada

examined, too. All of these play a role in the safety, efficacy, and side effects related to the prevalence of drug use by Canadians.

Rates of Drug Use and Patient Variables: Age, Gender, and Class

Considerable evidence suggests that drugs are frequently over-prescribed in Canada. For example, it has been estimated that about half of the antidepressants prescribed do not work except as placebos (Smith, 2012). Today at least 14.3 per cent of children in Canada and 16.7 per cent of children in the US have been diagnosed with one mental illness or another, and if addictions are added then the number jumps to 25.6 per cent in the US (a comparable figure for Canada is not available) (Perou et al., 2013). The majority of these children are prescribed medications. Different drugs may be used together, and because many of the drugs prescribed are used "off-label" (not for the condition for which they have been approved) they are tried in the hope that they might work. Some argue that this experimenting essentially violates the human rights of children. This practice and others related to diagnosing and treating children with mental health and developmental issues have been said to contribute to "surplus suffering" (Clarke, 2013). Between 5 per cent and 23 per cent of hospital admissions result from drug-related illnesses. Approximately a third of all emergency room visits among people over 65 are due to adverse drug reactions (Budnitz et al., 2011). Inappropriate prescribing or prescribing a number of medications at one time (polypharmacy) leads to additional expense to the health system because of hospitalization resulting from drug reactions (Votova et al., 2013). Aside from children, two groups, the elderly and women, are particularly vulnerable to mis-prescribing and over-prescribing (Votova et al., 2013; Rachlis & Kushner, 1994). It is very difficult to accurately estimate the effects of mis-prescribing or over-prescribing because of the lack of systematic community-based follow-up and measurement. Nevertheless, a long history of evidence from a variety of types of studies shows that women are especially likely to be over-prescribed or mis-prescribed psychotropic drugs or sedatives (Harding, 1994; Currie, 2004). Women are also likely to become addicted at an earlier age and tend to show quicker movement to drug addiction with opioids (Unger et al., 2010), and they are more likely to be prescribed pain medications such as opioids that can become addictive. Men, on the other hand, are more likely to turn their addiction to licit opioid use to illicit street-sourced use (Gerum & Choo, 2015).

Medication errors are relatively common in Canada and can be life-threatening. Approximately 24 per cent of all adverse health events (caused by medical treatment) may be due to medication errors (CIHI, 2007, citing Baker et al., 2002). Moreover, this figure is likely to represent under-reporting. The most frequent causes of these medication errors include inappropriate prescribing, incorrect use by patients, and the lack of a follow-up monitoring system by regulatory bodies. The proportion of seniors who have been and continue to be incorrectly prescribed drugs has been such a problem that an online list regularly updates prescribed drugs that are internationally recognized to be inappropriate for seniors (the Beers list, named after Mark H. Beers, the geriatrician who first published the criteria for evaluating the safety of pharmaceuticals for aging bodies in 1991). Provincially, of four provinces with available records, the prescription errors among seniors range from 18.8 per cent in New Brunswick to 12.9 per cent in Alberta. Concerted efforts are now being made to reduce these numbers (Butt, 2010) as a part of the new focus on the reduction of all medical errors since the 1999 publication, by the Institute of Medicine Committee on Quality of Health Care in America, of *To Err Is Human: Building a Safer Health Care System.*

About 9 million people in the US, or 4.3 per cent of the adult population, are using prescription sleeping pills, and most of these people are white, educated women over 50, according to a survey by the Centers for Disease Control and Prevention (Chong et al., 2013). Market research has reported a tripling of the use of sleep aids from 1998 to 2007. Some have linked this rising rate of insomnia to the increasing stress of modern life, while others point to the marketing successes of the pharmaceutical industry. This incidence of medication use does not include the many over-the-counter sleep aids or those sold as health products or teas through health food stores. Moreover, because stigma is associated with sleeping pill use, these figures are probably underestimates. Sleeping medications may be especially problematic because they are addictive and can cause impaired cognition, memory, and balance. Women also are more likely to be prescribed such sleep aids for longer periods of time and they may be more likely to be prescribed for "problems in living," such as grief and adjusting to new motherhood.

Addiction is especially acute among women over 60. Benzodiazepines are often prescribed for elderly adults with sleep or anxiety problems, for longer periods of time, and at levels that may be unsafe. Benzodiazepines are especially associated with falls and hip fractures, motor vehicle accidents, accidental poisoning, hospitalization for depression, and other psychiatric problems resulting from their chronic use (CIHI, 2010). Moreover, the incidence of multiple drug use, including sleeping pills and other "hypnotics" among women and the elderly (who are more likely female), is well substantiated in the literature. In 2005 a national

survey of medication use found that almost all seniors (97 per cent) living in long-term care institutions had taken prescription medications in the past two days, as had 76 per cent of those living in private households (Ramage-Morin, 2009), as compared to 14 per cent of all Canadians. Further, more than half (53 per cent) of those in institutions and 13.5 per cent in private households reported taking multiple medications. In Canada, 39 per cent of people in long-term care are prescribed an anti-psychotic (Acosta et al., 2017). At times they may be effective with the delirium that sometimes accompanies dementia but they have serious side effects, too, including strokes, kidney failure, and heart disease, and may lead to earlier mortality (Elmi et al., 2015). Older people in the community generally do not need these drugs, yet those in long-term care institutions apparently do, which may raise serious questions about over-medicating in institutions and possibly other institutional practices.

Multiple drug use increases as Canadians age. One-quarter of all potentially inappropriate drug combinations results from overlapping and similar prescriptions prescribed by two doctors for one patient. There are many potential sources of problems in drug use, especially if a person is at home alone and has been prescribed more than one medication. Table 14.1 outlines inappropriate drug use and inappropriate prescribing. You

Table 14.1 Inappropriate Drug Use and Inappropriate Prescribing

Inappropriate Drug Use	Inappropriate Prescribing
• Not having a prescription filled or refilled. • Taking too much or too little of the drug prescribed. • Erratic dosing, such as altering time intervals or omitting doses. • Stopping the drug too soon. • Combining prescription drugs with over-the-counter products or illicit drugs. • Combining prescription drugs with alcohol.	• Under-prescribing or not specifying sufficient quantities or correct intervals of dosage. • Over-prescribing or going beyond the maximum therapeutic dosage. • Prolonged use that results in iatrogenic effects and adverse reactions. • Prescribing that is contraindicated by the medical condition. • Contraindicated combinations that produce an undesirable effect.

Source: Senate of Canada (2001).

may be able to add to this list of potential problems with some that you are aware of. I, for example, remember talking with a student a while ago who had received anti-depressants from the health services at the university. She mentioned that she just took them a few at a time when she was depressed. This was despite the fact that they were to be taken daily and that the level necessary for an effective dose level was not usually reached until a person had taken them for about one month. What makes this story all the more telling is that this was a bright, relatively well-educated, and healthy young woman who was taking a potentially dangerous drug casually and on her own whim.

Social as well as medical explanations contribute to our understanding of drug use—including the more and the less dangerous of these sleeping pills, tranquilizers, pain medications, heart and blood pressure medications, stomach remedies, and laxatives. Opioid drug use is a particular case in point. It is often prescribed first for pain relief in cases of intractable and serious pain. Often, however, these drugs become addictive and people may move into an addiction that can only be satisfied by the non-medical use of such drugs. The non-medical (street) use of opioid analgesics is considered an epidemic in Canada today and has resulted in many deaths, particularly among young people (Shield et al., 2011). The government even has a website dedicated to the opioid crisis in Canada.

Taking more than one drug at a time can lead to unpredictable problems whether the drug is non-prescription, prescribed, or a vitamin (or other "healthy" drug). Drug interactions can affect the absorption rate, distribution throughout the body, metabolism, and the elimination of a drug, and one drug can diminish or exacerbate the pharmacological effects of another drug. Drug effects are known to be somewhat different among the elderly as well as among people of different weights and overall health, among other things. Pharmaceuticals are routinely tested and prescribed on the assumption that the average user is a male in his thirties. The elderly, on average,

differ significantly from the average 30-year-old male. They are more likely to be female, to have slower metabolic rates, to weigh less, and to have some cognitive deficits. For those reasons alone, aside from multiple medication use, the elderly are more likely to experience drug reactions than younger adults.

The use of **over-the-counter drugs**, including supplements and natural health products, often exacerbates the problems noted above. One study found that as many as 70 per cent of the elderly take over-the-counter medication without discussing this with their physicians. Incidences of medication errors by the elderly have been well documented and many of them are in addition to the standard problems elucidated in Table 14.1. These include: forgetting to take medication, taking a smaller or larger dose than that prescribed, taking medication for the wrong reasons, being unable to read labels, having difficulty opening containers, and having impaired memory. Consequences of such drug misuse include falls, dizziness, various illnesses, hospitalization, and even death. If current trends continue, drug use will increase because the rate of drug use for those over 65 is higher than for any other age group, and this part of the population is growing the most quickly.

Females are consistently heavier prescription drug users than males. This pattern of greater use of prescription drugs among females is true of a wide variety of drugs. Those in lower-income groups spend a greater percentage of their incomes on prescription drugs. They also spend a higher percentage of income on food and shelter. In regard to prescription drugs, however, this may be the result of more expensive drugs, as there is some evidence that prices for the same drug can vary considerably, depending on the location where it is sold. It bears mention that pharmacies are essentially competitive businesses and are governed, therefore, by market principles. People in poorer, rural, or isolated neighbourhoods tend to lack the mobility (e.g., automobile transportation) required for comparison shopping and are thus more apt to pay whatever the going rate in the local pharmacy happens to be—or to not use the drug.

All provinces have introduced drug programs to subsidize medication purchases by low-income families (Lexchin, 1996; Dewa et al., 2005; Esmail, 2015). However, these programs vary widely from one province to another. The income level at which coverage begins varies. The deductible varies, and the premium varies. Everywhere there is coverage for catastrophic illness for low-income Canadians. People on social assistance also have universal access to drugs at a very reduced cost with low premiums and low deductibles. While efforts are being made, the cost of drugs for a low-income person may be significant relative to discretionary income. Moreover, the presence of a deductible, a premium, or a required out-of-pocket payment from a person with lower income can decrease the likelihood that the prescription will be filled (Law et al., 2019). In this context there are calls for pharmacare or universal drug coverage similar to medicare.

There is a high correlation between the number of visits to a physician and the number of prescriptions. In the US, 76.1 per cent of doctor visits result in a prescription for a medication (Centers for Disease Control and Prevention, 2019). The figures in Canada may be somewhat lower because we tend to have a slightly less interventionist/aggressive system. On the other hand, a sizable proportion of Americans do not go to the doctor at all because they lack medical insurance. Thus, it is difficult to estimate the correlation between doctor visits and prescription receipt. In Chapter 10 we saw that the number of physicians in a society affects the degree of medicalization. Physicians in general have a tendency towards medical intervention (e.g., to prescribe drugs) when confronted with a patient exhibiting a problem. Various social characteristics and conditions of patients affect the rates at which doctors prescribe drugs just as they affect other aspects of medical care.

Research has documented significant deficiencies in doctors' knowledge about drugs (Tannenbaum & Tsuyiki, 2013). Commercial sources of information, including drug advertising and salespersons, are significant influences on doctors' prescribing habits: the more heavily a drug is promoted the more it is prescribed, despite the fact that doctors themselves believe that "they used scientific sources and shunned commercial ones" (Mintzes, 2010). This may be a growing problem as physicians and patients come to rely more and more on the Internet, where health sites are frequently funded by the pharmaceutical industry even though this link may be invisible or obfuscated in one way or another (Usher & Skinner, 2012). One study, for example, found that more than 70 per cent of physicians made claims about particular drugs that reflected the claims made in drug advertisements even though these claims were diametrically opposite to those in the scientific literature (Mintzes, 2010). Doctors have tended not to be critical of drug advertising. They have tended to trust it and it has been incorporated into medical education through textbooks and guest speakers. Medical schools have just recently begun to develop policies limiting the potential for conflict of interest in medical education among both students and faculty (Glauser, 2013). Still, numerous studies have found that when patients go to doctors asking for particular drugs they have seen advertised, they are more likely to get them (including the particular brand requested) than not.

Good prescribing by physicians involves maximizing effectiveness, minimizing risks, minimizing costs, and respecting the choices of patients (Lexchin, 1988, p. 254). In the context of widespread **direct-to-consumer advertising**, this list now needs to include patient education because patients are often demanding drugs they have seen advertised on television, in magazines, or online, such as anti-depressants that may be of less help and that may be harmful. Even though there are very few studies of appropriate drug prescribing in Canada, those that do exist do not suggest that the values elucidated above are often realized. Drugs may be prescribed when less invasive options such as diet change should be tried first, as is the case in many of the cholesterol-reducing drugs that are so widely prescribed. Even if drugs are prescribed when needed, there may still be problems in drug administration such as dose, rate of absorption, and duration. Studies of elderly people have examined and confirmed the potential of inadequate prescribing. For instance, a study of prescribing in Alberta found that over 2,600 of the elderly population (1.1 per cent) had prescriptions for two or more non-steroid anti-inflammatory drugs (NSAIDs) dispensed on the same day, despite the fact that there is little, if any, rationale for such a practice. In addition, with respect to one of the mood-altering drugs—diazepam—a detailed study found that 14,000 elderly people (3.7 per cent of the province's elderly) received a potentially inappropriate prescription—often from a single physician, i.e., this over-prescription was not entirely or largely the result of seniors visiting more than one doctor at a time for the same problem. Adverse drug reaction is one of the top 10 causes of death in Canada today (Canadian Foundation for Health Care Improvement, 2010; Talmazan, 2017). This problem is exacerbated by the uptake of higher-cost newer drugs designed to replace older drugs, which thus increases the profit for pharmaceutical companies. In fact, one in five such new drugs will likely be found to be unsafe or will be withdrawn from the market (Canadian Foundation for Health Care Improvement, 2010), despite the fact that new drugs have to have regulatory approval after having gone through clinical trials to ensure their safety and effectiveness. This problem is exacerbated by the difficulty that Canada faces in removing drugs from the market once they have been approved.

"Safe" is a relative term, as there are virtually always some side effects and some of these may be more or less severe for users. Moreover, clinical trials are not absolutely perfect. As with all research, there are limitations. For example, women have long been excluded because of the possibility of pregnancy and because of the known cyclical and changing nature of their biochemistry through their reproductive cycles. The elderly have often been excluded for convenience or because of the (presumed) possibility that they may be suffering from another disease other than the one whose treatment is being evaluated. Also, while clinical trials may ensure the new drug is being used explicitly and exactly for the problem for which it is designed, off-label use and prescription are endemic. In fact, clinical trials are able, for a variety of reasons, to predict only about half of all serious adverse effects. In addition, all adverse effects are never known because reporting is voluntary and many people either do not know to or know how to report adverse effects (Canadian Foundation for Health Care Improvement, 2010).

The typical Canadian doctor prescribes only a very limited number of the many thousands of drugs presently on the Canadian market. Doctors in different specialties tend to have different drugs that they typically prescribe. Sometimes these go-to drugs are the new drugs that have been recently been developed and aggressively advertised. At times any given patient goes to more than one doctor, including different specialists, because of having different chronic or acute conditions. This can lead to polypharmacy. If each doctor prescribes medications for discreet issues but does not know that the patient is taking a number of pharmaceuticals a patient can end up taking too many drugs or drugs that interact with one another. Also, some or many practising doctors, even though they know that reliable sources of information about prescribing include continuing medical education, peer-reviewed journals (many of which are now easily available online), and association meetings, rely largely on pharmaceutical company sales representatives. These sales reps, as a rule, avoid discussing the side effects and contraindications of their medications, or their efficacy as compared to other drugs. Drug salespeople are incentivised to make only positive and, thus sometimes, incorrect statements about the drugs they are promoting.

Research has repeatedly shown that the more frequently physicians see drug sales representatives:

- the more likely they are to prescribe drugs even when not using drugs is the best option;
- the more often they adopt the commercial view of a given medicine;
- the more likely they are to prescribe inappropriately;
- the less likely they are to prescribe generically;
- the more likely they are to use more expensive medications when equally effective but less costly drugs are available.

CRITICAL THINKING

Box 14.1 • Prescription Drug Abuse

Prescription drug abuse is a significant problem in Canada today. Although almost any drug can be abused, the pharmaceuticals with psychotropic and pain elimination effects are most often subject to abuse. Probably the most worrisome type involves various opioid-based drugs for pain relief, followed by mood-altering and energy-changing drugs such as tranquilizers, stimulants, and amphetamines, along with sedatives and barbiturates. Anabolic steroids and asthma inhalers are also used (unsafely) for non-medical purposes at times.

Available evidence regarding legal prescriptions indicates that Canadians are among the highest users of psychotropic drugs in the world. Although it is difficult to get good comprehensive national data on either prescribed or illegally used psychotropics, a study by the Centre for Addiction and Mental Health (www.ccsa.ca) found that 11 per cent of their admissions to substance abuse treatment programs were among people with dependencies on these drugs.

How and why does prescription drug abuse occur? The Canadian Centre on Substance Abuse suggests the following factors:

- "Double-doctoring" or "doctor shopping"—obtaining multiple prescriptions from different physicians.
- Prescription-pad theft and tampering, resulting in forged or altered prescriptions.
- Physician fraud—fraudulent prescriptions written by doctors in return for money.
- Purchases from friends, relatives, or dealers for whom the drug has been legitimately prescribed.
- Diversion of drugs from substance abuse treatment programs (for example, methadone).
- Diversion from supplies intended for patients in health-care facilities.
- Break-ins and theft from homes, doctors' offices, pharmacies, manufacturers, wholesalers, courier companies, clinics, and hospitals.
- Purchase of drugs on the Internet.

Monitoring any of the above reasons for prescription drug abuse is difficult and ranges into the jurisdiction of the law rather than medicine. What prescription drugs are used illegally on your campus? For what purposes are they used? What are some of the detrimental side effects and long-term effects of their use?

Pharmaceutical firms are a major source of information for doctors and now patients and consumers about to become patients. The pharmaceutical industry works to control information about its products in a variety of ways. This influence is increasingly powerful in the context of globalization, the Internet, and Internet advertising (Usher & Skinner, 2012). Drug companies fund researchers to test their new products (and have been known to contractually prohibit publication of any but positive results from such research (Mather, 2005). Further, industry-sponsored research has a far greater likelihood of generating positive responses from physicians and the public than non-company-supported

research, because the drug companies have the money to advertise their research and corporate involvement in research leads to a greater likelihood of positive results than non-company-sponsored research. The industry also financially supports medical conferences, clubs in medical schools and hospitals, and continuing education events. Numerous gifts are given directly to physicians, including free drug samples, wall charts and posters, three-dimensional models, pen sets, and notepads. They serve to influence doctors to use their drugs. Unfortunately, many sources of information provided by industry to doctors have been found to be in error or misleading (Mather, 2005).

Nonetheless, many doctors learn much of what they know about medicines and their "appropriate" use from drug firms. There is no lack of evidence to document that the drug company representatives who call on physicians regularly with brochures, samples, and gifts are a major source of information about drugs for doctors. If expenditures by drug companies on promotion and advertising are any indication—they spend twice as much on pushing their products as they do on research and development—then these activities have an important impact on prescribing (Rachlis & Kushner, 1994; Gagnon & Lexchin, 2008). In the United States, pharmaceutical companies spend more on advertising than does, for example, the alcoholic beverage industry. Drug advertisements have repeatedly been criticized as misleading and incomplete, and as portraying people in stereotypical ways. For instance, the elderly may be seen engaging in passive activities wearing depressed faces or acting childishly (Foster & Huffman, 1995). Advertisements recommend drugs for such a variety of everyday, "normal" concerns that drugs seem to be suggested as useful to everyone at least some of the time. Drug prescribing, then, is often a symptom of the tendency towards the expanding medicalization of social issues.

Another major source of information for most Canadian doctors is the regularly updated *Compendium of Pharmaceuticals and Specialties* (CPS), a Canadian Pharmaceutical Association publication. Although the *Canadian Medical Association Journal* has recommended this as a source of information (Lexchin, 1984), it may be inadequate in a number of ways. It may not be comprehensive, and it is known to have continued recommending certain drugs long after research documenting dangerous side effects had been published in medical journals. The most thorough study of its value, done over 30 years ago, found that 46.3 per cent of the drugs listed by the *Compendium* were "probably useless, obsolete, or irrational mixtures" (Bell & Osterman, 1983). Well-known risks and negative effects were ignored for over 60 per cent of the drugs listed. Scientific errors regarding the biochemical effects of nearly 40 per cent of the entries were evident. Bell and Osterman were led to conclude that the CPS at that time was basically a tool to promote the interests of drug companies. More recent critiques of pharmaceutical regulation suggest ongoing reasons for skepticism and caution in assuming drug safety (e.g., Stelfox et al., 1998; Whitaker, 2010; Lexchin, 2012) and effectiveness even when drugs are used for the purposes officially intended.

Spotlight on Ethics

Box 14.2 • Conflict of Interest: Doctors and the Pharmaceutical Industry

There is clear and repeated documentation of conflict of interest in publications in medical journals. This means that at times medical publications are or may be biased because of the personal interests of one of the authors or editors. Financial investment in a particular product is one example. A study in the *New England Journal of Medicine* about publications regarding the safety of calcium blockers in the treatment of cardiovascular disorders is a case in point. The researchers went through the English-language medical literature to find articles concerning the safety of calcium-channel antagonists. Articles were categorized as neutral, supportive, or critical of calcium blockers. The authors of the articles were surveyed about their financial relationships with the manufacturers of the calcium-channel blockers. The findings revealed that authors who supported the use of calcium-channel blockers were significantly more likely than neutral or critical authors to have financial relationships with manufacturers of these products (Stelfox et al., 1998: 102). Conflicts of interest are a continuing problem among Canadian doctors today (Glauser, 2013). Many schools and medical journals have introduced policies to prevent and to openly acknowledge such conflicts of interest and to eliminate them where possible.

What other factors influence doctors' decisions about prescribing drugs? Freidson (1975) distinguishes between client-dependent and colleague-dependent forms of medical practice. His argument is that regulation is more effective in colleague-dependent than in client-dependent practices. When doctors have to account to other doctors for the diagnoses they make and the treatments they choose, they are likely to exhibit higher medical standards than when primarily seeking to satisfy the patient. Following this line of reasoning, it can be predicted that doctors who are involved in medical networks or in some form of group practice are more likely to have appropriate prescribing habits.

Surprisingly, perhaps, especially as it contradicts the common perception, physicians who see fewer patients may spend more time with them but also prescribe more medications. A Canadian study compared a group of doctors who worked on the basis of fee-for-service with a group of doctors who worked on salary (Lexchin, 1988). Approximately one-half of the doctors in private clinics, as compared to one-quarter in community health centres, prescribed drugs inappropriately. Doctors in private clinics spent less time per patient. Salaried physicians were more likely to warn patients of side effects and other potential problems. The researchers explained that because salaried physicians had more time per patient, they were able to take the time to prescribe appropriately and to explain when and how to use the drug, as well as potential side effects.

Several studies (e.g., Lexchin, 1994b) have shown that both drug advertisements and drug detail men and women (pharmaceutical company representatives who visit doctors with samples and information about drugs) significantly affect the drug-prescribing habits of doctors. Lexchin (1994b) indicates that much of the over-prescription of antibiotics, stomach ulcer medications, and antihypertensives results from drug advertising. The Canadian Medical Association and its journal historically defend the pharmaceutical industry and support its viewpoints (Lexchin, 1994a). Given the amount of money involved, perhaps this is not surprising. The drug industry is also heavily involved in supporting medical education. Apparently almost 56 per cent of the medical residency programs in the US received monies from the pharmaceutical industry (Kondro, 2010a, 2010b). The pharmaceutical industry also is heavily involved in the publication of medical journals and in medical research (Insel, 2010).

Robert Whitaker, who makes the case in *Anatomy of an Epidemic* that the rise of mental illness in the US is the result of pharmaceuticals, cites evidence of the biased trials of psychotropics funded by pharmaceutical companies (Whitaker, 2010, pp. 299–300); of the rescinding of an appointment to the University of Toronto of a researcher for having exposed his findings that suicidal thoughts are caused by SSRIs (pp. 305–6); of the suppression of the results of research studies (pp. 307–11); of inappropriate acceptance of money by academic psychiatrists (pp. 322–5); and of the invention of psychiatric categories of illness to "cover" the conditions created in children by the effects of drugs unnecessarily prescribed (pp. 325–6). The psychiatric profession routinely emphasizes to schizophrenic patients "the importance of remaining on medications as prescribed"; however, the spectrum of outcomes in schizophrenia patients has been shown at times to be superior when they are off antipsychotic medications (p. 117).

Another powerful influence on the prescribing habits of doctors is direct-to-consumer (DTC) advertising. Although this form of advertising is illegal in Canada, Canadians view television from the US and read newspapers and magazines published in the United States. One study found that 87.4 per cent of Canadian patients reported seeing DTC advertising (Mintzes et al., 2003). Interestingly, physicians were likely to give patients drugs that the patients, having seen advertisements, had requested (between 72 and 78 per cent of patient requests were filled). These figures compare to a rate of 12.4 per cent of prescriptions given to patients who had not specifically requested them. Direct-to-consumer advertising has been shown to be effective in increasing the sales of particular drugs (Mintzes et al., 2002). According to a cross-sectional survey of primary care physicians in Vancouver and Sacramento, there is a significant likelihood, regardless of the patient's health status, drug payment method, or gender, or of the medical specialty of the physician or number of years in practice, that patients who request a particular drug will be given it. Furthermore, physicians indicated that in at least 40 per cent of the cases in which they prescribed a drug at the request of the patient the physicians were ambivalent about the prescription of the particular drug. Clearly, patients' requests for certain drugs are a powerful factor in the prescribing habits of physicians, despite their possible professional reluctance. There is a direct link between the amount of advertising for a particular drug and the rate of its prescription (Mintzes et al., 2003).

This evident lack of respect for good and systematic knowledge about the efficacy and safety of drugs is exacerbated by the fact that there is no routine, ongoing monitoring of drug effects on an individual or population level in Canada. It is impossible, then, to link specific health outcomes to specific pharmaceutical interventions. It also is impossible to determine whether the use of newer and more expensive drugs results in better outcomes. As Zitner says, "auto repair shops, computer service technicians, and many other industries routinely contact people to learn if service was satisfactory" (Zitner, 2002, p. 2). By comparison, he argues, it would seem to be a good thing if our health-care system provided more systematic follow-up. Furthermore, Health Canada apparently has no record of what drugs have been withdrawn (or why) because of safety concerns (Lexchin, 2005). As Lexchin (2009, p. 3) writes, "Health Canada has explicitly rejected the development of quantitative standards for evaluating its post-marketing pharma-surveillance system." The present methods of monitoring the effects of drugs, once they are on the market and used by the public, are very weak. The post-market surveillance system is underfunded and understaffed. As a consequence, there is a significant level of under-reporting of adverse effects both by the public and by health professionals (Fuller, 2010).

Pharmacists

There were approximately 42,500 licensed pharmacists working in Canada in 2019, according to the Canadian Pharmacists Association. This number

represents a substantial rate of growth over the past decade or so. Little sociological analysis exists of the role of pharmacists with respect to prescription and non-prescription drugs. Unquestionably, however, they have considerable discretionary influence in making recommendations both to doctors and to individuals who shop for prescribed drugs as well as for over-the-counter drugs. Consumers frequently ask the pharmacist for advice on over-the-counter medications for a cough, sleeplessness, pain, or anxiety. The pharmacist may suggest a particular brand-name drug or a range of suitable products of different brand names. A number of factors will affect the pharmacist's recommendation. Discussion about legally broadening pharmacists' scope of practice beyond these limited tasks has been ongoing for some time. Among the reasons given for altering their present legal status are the following:

1. The accessibility of pharmacists to the public is greater than that of physicians, and pharmacists already have been advising and monitoring patients in regard to drug therapy for decades.
2. Pharmacists may have a professional relationship with patients that is legislated and that encompasses ethical and professional responsibilities.
3. Usually, the pharmacist is expected to assess prescriptions independently. Frequently, the pharmacist questions the patient to ensure that the need for and the use of the drug are fully understood.
4. Physicians often lack sufficient and appropriate information regarding the drugs they prescribe for patients.
5. Pharmacists already give a significant amount of advice on over-the-counter medications to patients.

Pharmacists do have discretionary power when presented with a drug prescription. Unless the physician has written "no substitution" on it, pharmacists are free to dispense any company's brand of a particular drug. They are also now able to renew prescriptions, refuse to fill prescriptions, initiate drug therapy for a number of self-limiting conditions, and substitute prescriptions (Tannenbaum & Tsuyiki, 2013). Depending on the province in which they work, pharmacists can order and interpret the findings of lab tests. Further, there is evidence of the effectiveness of an expanded role for pharmacists in the management of a number of chronic diseases such as diabetes and in avoiding or predicting adverse drug events.

The Pharmaceutical Industry

The Canadian drug industry has always been divided into domestically owned companies, the first one founded by E.B. Shuttleworth in Toronto in 1879, and foreign-owned subsidiaries, the first of which was established in Windsor by Parke, Davis and Company (Lexchin, 1984, p. 331). The industry grew slowly (the foreign-owned companies stayed in Canada because they could obtain tariff and tax advantages) until the 1940s. The antibiotic revolution and the development of medications to control patients in mental hospitals spurred the rapid growth of the industry. Economies of scale became possible in the manufacture of these drugs, and production was centralized. Centralization, plus the increasing openness of world trade—globalization—meant the small Canadian companies could not compete with the larger foreign-owned companies.

After World War II, only one Canadian company of any consequence—Connaught Laboratories—was left, but today Canada's domestic drug manufacturing industry is significant. Indeed, the pharmaceutical industry is one of the more profitable manufacturing activities in Canada. The median rate of return for shareholders of large pharmaceutical companies is about twice the median for all manufacturing: 20.1 per cent as compared to 9.8 per cent (Lexchin & Wiktorowicz, 2009). High profitability and the probability of consistent growth due to long-term demographics (e.g., the aging of the population) provide reasons for the likely continuation of this trend. What strategies do the drug companies use to maintain their profitability? What is the impact of the great financial success of the multinational drug companies on the health of Canadians and on the health of the people in less-developed countries? In what way do the profit-making strategies of the

drug companies affect health negatively? These three questions will be discussed here.

The pharmaceutical industry has been successful in maintaining its position as one of the most profitable industries through a variety of strategies, including: (1) the absence of a link between manufacturing cost and price; (2) patent protection; (3) competition and drug development focused on drugs with widespread potential for use (and thus profit) rather than on drugs for rare conditions; (4) production of brand-name rather than generic products; (5) drug distribution (dumping) in less-developed countries; (6) the change in the availability of many drugs from prescription only to over-the-counter consumer purchase; (7) drug shortages; and (8) advertising and providing select information to physicians and consumers

One of the major reasons for the high profits in the drug industry is that *the selling price of drugs is not directly related to drug production costs* (Lexchin, 1984, pp. 41–8). Manufacturers are free to determine prices in the interest of maximizing their profits. Variations in the cost to the consumer bear little or no relationship to manufacturing costs. Instead, prices reflect Canada's patent system, the relationship between Health Canada and the industry, the types and costs of research and development undertaken, and advertising costs, among other things (Lexchin & Wiktorowicz, 2009). This is intended as a profit-making industry. It is not dedicated to service or the well-being of the citizenry. It is accountable to its stockholders. While high profitability is the case in the pharmaceutical industry worldwide, it appears to be particularly so in Canada. Individual Canadians have the fifth highest expenditures on pharmaceuticals among countries in the OECD. The average per capita expenditure in the United States is $1,162, followed by Switzerland at $982, Japan at $798, Germany at $766, and then Canada at $756 per capita. There is wide variation in pricing for drugs from country to country. This is also reflected in the fact that, in recent years, some US citizens from border states have regularly crossed into Canada to buy prescription drugs with Canadian dollars in order to save, and others have bought online using the relative advantage of today's American dollar. In the recent past, though, when the Canadian dollar was about at par with the US dollar, Canadians could sometimes save by crossing the border (virtually and actually) to fill prescriptions in the US. Online purchasing of pharmaceuticals may save money for the consumer and it is expanding. However, it challenges all of the patenting and safety concerns discussed. Errors and adverse effects will be even less likely to be monitored when purchases are across borders through the Internet and the global pharmaceutical industry. Moreover, the future ability of individual countries to regulate drug costs and availability is threatened today by the accessibility of online pharmaceuticals.

Patent protection is the second technique used to maintain the high level of profits. Patents limit competition. Once the company has invented a new drug, patent protection gives the company an exclusive right to manufacture and distribute

the drug for a period of years. Determining the length of time that a new drug is protected from competition is a difficult matter. It depends on the relative power of the industry as compared to the governmental options. Industry pays taxes, offers jobs, and employs workers who also pay taxes. Canada provides patent protection for a minimum of seven years but generally 10 years for new drugs before generic drugs are marketed (Lexchin & Wiktorowicz, 2009). This period can be extended if the company takes out additional patents on associated drugs. Drug companies claim that patent protection allows them to pay for the research and development involved in the invention of new drugs. However, critics challenge this idea because much of the research done in any drug company is directed towards developing imitative medicines that can compete with products already successfully developed and marketed.

Highlighted Issues

Box 14.3 • Antibiotic Resistance

In the 1940s antibiotics were introduced. They were viewed as "miracle" drugs. They were able to keep people alive who would have died from pneumonia, tuberculosis, infections in wounds, and sexually transmitted diseases. Now, however, antibiotic resistance (or ineffectiveness) is growing (Branswell, 2002). The US Centers for Disease Control has confirmed that one of the most common and difficult of infections is becoming resistant to vancomycin, the strongest antibiotic presently available. The presence and spread of vancomycin-resistant staph aureus (VRSA) may herald a day when there is no antibiotic solution for the many bacterial diseases whose treatments, since the 1940s, we have come to take for granted (Branswell, 2002). Bacterial diseases have again become a serious threat to health here and around the globe (Ventola, 2015)

The major reasons for the growth of antibiotic resistance appear to be their inappropriate use for treating infections in people, animals, and plants. Sometimes antibiotics are prescribed when they are not necessary because the presence of bacterial rather than viral infection has not been documented. Sometimes people fail to take antibiotics as they have been prescribed. Bacteria are able to constantly adapt to survive. When antibiotics are used inappropriately bacteria have opportunities to change. When antibiotics are used in animals and plants they enter the human food chain and the water, land, and even air (Batt, 2010). Dumping of excess antibiotics and their excretion via the human body are other processes that increase the growth of antibiotic resistance in populations. The popular use of anti-bacterial soap and alcohol-based hand sanitizer is also associated with the development of resistance (Batt, 2010).

The third strategy is that the *drug companies rarely do research or attempt to develop medicines in areas where there is unlikely to be a large market* or with a view to addressing the needs of people with less-than-common diseases or when the materials for the medication are not subject to patent (Lexchin & Wiktorowicz, 2009). Rather, they tend to develop and produce new drugs based on similar existing drugs, thus maintaining patent protection for large markets that have already been developed. As an example, numerous anti-inflammatory (anti-arthritis) and benzodiazepine (minor tranquilizer) and anti-depressant drugs are currently on the market in Canada (Lexchin, 1988a; Lexchin & Wiktorowicz, 2009). Such a wide choice is of virtually no therapeutic or medical value; indeed, the value of benzodiazepine and of anti-depressants (Whitaker, 2010, pp. 126–47, 149–71) is open to question. However, because of the huge market for these two drugs, most every pharmaceutical company has a similar product. The development and introduction of "new" drugs sometimes appears to have more to do with profitability than with medical value.

Fourth, *the use of brand-name rather than generic products contributes significantly to the profits of the pharmaceutical companies.* (The generic name is the scientific name for a particular drug, while the brand name is the name given to, and advertised by, the drug by the pharmaceutical company that produces it.) On average, generics cost considerably less than the most expensive brand-name equivalents. It is clearly to the advantage of the pharmaceutical industry to promote brand-name products. Although when brand-name products are prescribed, the pharmacist may substitute a generic if it is available (unless otherwise directed by a physician). Paradoxically, however, that may not always be done because the economic viability of the pharmacies selling drugs is an important part of the pharmaceutical industry and another source for profit potential.

Fifth, the history of the pharmaceutical industry is replete with stories of drug-related illness and death. *The dumping of out-of-date drugs in the developing countries* is one example. The health-destroying side effects of many drugs, whether they are taken alone or in combination with other drugs, are an ongoing problem. The industry sometimes markets drugs for a wide variety of symptoms when they are appropriate for only a limited number of purposes.

Many countries in the developing world face serious problems in relation to pharmaceuticals. One problem is a lack of drugs, including vaccines that have come to be considered essential in the developed North. Other drugs known to extend or improve the quality of life in a chronic and potentially fatal disease, such as AIDS, are much too expensive for the vast majority of the world's population. For instance, while protease inhibitors could lengthen the lifespan of people diagnosed with HIV/AIDS, they are completely out of financial reach for most people in many countries where people cannot even afford a condom. Aside from the costs and the lack of availability, there are other equally serious problems in less-developed countries: at times, drugs are used inappropriately because they lack directions for use or these directions are written in a foreign language (i.e., English), or the consumer lacks literacy, or they are to be taken with water that may be unsafe or lacking. Sometimes drugs banned in one country are shipped to and sold in a different country that lacks the regulatory infrastructure to protect its population (Ollila & Hemminki, 1997, p. 309).

Sixth, a number of *drugs that were formerly available only by prescription are now available as over-the-counter* (OTC) *purchases.* This may increase the sales of such medications. Emergency contraception (the so-called "morning-after" pill) is one example (http://www.planb.ca/where.php). Now that this emergency contraception can be purchased over the counter it may be more widely used in a situation of fear of pregnancy. This trend to over-the-counter medications may seem a progressive step in that it promotes self-care, but the availability of OTC medications that formerly had to be gotten by prescription also boosts sales. In addition, this move saves medical insurance companies money because they do not pay for any but prescription drugs, and this increases the size of the private health-care system and the out-of-pocket expenses for many Canadians.

It is incorrect to assume that a drug licensed in one country is necessarily appropriate for another group because populations may differ in "metabolism, weight, and nutrition—and these are known to affect the efficacy, safety, occurrence of side effects, and acceptability of a drug" (Ollila & Hemminki, 1997, p. 323). For example, the World Health Organization found that schizophrenics had a better outcome in the less-developed world, presumably because they were far less likely to be drugged and because their social policies and cultural values for the mentally ill were more supportive (Whitaker, 2010, pp. x–xi).

Drug licensing is important for ensuring safety and efficacy. National governments are responsible for drug regulation. This inevitably means that prescription drug regulation is uneven around the world. Even in the industrialized world conflicts of interest are faced by pharmaceutical companies and their scientists regarding the need for licensing and regulation. Because a patent gives a drug company the exclusive right to manufacture and sell a particular drug for a limited period of time—and because patented drugs are much more profitable to drug companies—it is in their interest to speed a newly patented drug through the approval and regulatory boards in order to have the longest time possible to gain from the patent status (Abraham, 1995).

The Dalkon Shield IUD (an intrauterine device for birth control) is one example of the great health costs of a profit-driven industry (Vavasour & Mennie, 1984). The Dalkon Shield went on the market in 1971 in the United States. By early 1972 there were numerous reports of adverse reactions, such as pelvic inflammatory disease, blood poisoning, and tubal pregnancies. By 1974, 17 people had died from its use. Because the US market began to look very poor, the manufacturer offered the Dalkon Shield to developing nations at a discounted price of 48 per cent of the original price. The shields were distributed to the developing nations even though they were un-sterilized and nine out of 10 lacked the necessary inserter. Furthermore, only one out of 1,000 was distributed with any instructions for insertion (and their insertion is a delicate and potentially dangerous procedure). In 1975, the United States banned the Dalkon Shield, while continuing to sell them to the developing world (Miller, 1996).

A seventh strategy for maximizing pharmaceutical profits is the intentional creation of *drug shortages of particular drugs in Canada and around the world in order to increase prices*, even though such shortages can potentially be life- and health-threatening. Several different policy options to prevent drug shortages are being considered (Gagnon, 2012).

The eighth profit strategy is to *provide only select information to doctors and consumers about the efficiency and safety of various drugs*. On average, drug companies in Canada invested about $10,000 per physician in advertising as long ago as the early nineties (Williams et al., 1993). The advertisements are frequently presented as information. In the event that doctors are very busy with their practices they may be willing to rely on such advertising for information. Drug industry contacts with physicians are systematic and persistent and often include "perks" such as meals, stationery, conference fees, travel expenses, and computer equipment (physicians who prescribe most are most likely to receive these additional perks) (Williams et al., 1993). There is also considerable evidence that pharmaceutical companies restrict the information resulting from research studies that could inform doctors and the public, if the research is not supportive of the companies' bottom lines (Olivieri, 2010; Whitaker, 2010).

Fifteen general practitioners in Australia were asked to audiotape three encounters with pharmaceutical representatives (Roughead et al., 1998). Seven of these GPs agreed to take part. They asked 24 pharmaceutical representatives to participate; 16 agreed to do so. They were informed that they were being taped. A total of 64 medicines were described ("detailed") in the recordings. The interpretations averaged 2.75 minutes per drug. However, the information provided by the pharmaceutical company representatives bore very little similarity to the Australian Approved Product Information categories. Thus, there was very little correspondence between the information provided by the drug company representatives and the views and position of the Australian government in respect to indications (for use), pharmacology, pharmacokinetics, side effects, precautions, warnings, interactions, use in special groups, dosage and administration, and availability. Despite the fact that the Australia Pharmaceutical Manufacturers' Code of Conduct is in place to regulate the marketing of drugs and "includes standards for printed promotional material, pharmaceutical representatives' activities, competitions, gifts, samples, trade displays, and symposia" (Roughead et al., 1998, p. 270), the results of this study indicate that pharmaceutical company representatives do not comply with standards outlined in their codes of conduct. As recently as 2017, the Ontario government enacted legislation that would have forced doctors to disclose payments from pharmaceutical representatives and companies. Under the Health Sector Payment Transparency Act, passed in December 2017, the province would have developed an online database wherein patients could search to see whether or not their physicians demonstrated a conflict of interest. The implementation of this legislation was delayed pending further consultation with the health sector after the Conservatives took power in 2018.

In its policy on "Physicians and the Pharmaceutical Industry," updated in 2007, the Canadian Medical Association has expressed its concern about the conflict of interest that may confront physicians in their dealings with the pharmaceutical industry. The policy contains separate sections on industry-sponsored research, industry-sponsored surveillance studies, continuing medical education and development, electronic continuing development, advisory consultation boards, clinical evaluation packages, gifts, medical students and residents, and other considerations. While the Pharmaceutical Manufacturers Association of Canada is among the many organizations that have developed codes of ethics similar to those of the CMA, the enforcement of these codes remains somewhat uneven and unreliable.

In sum, the pharmaceutical industry invests in "educating" doctors because this has proven to be an effective strategy for sales in the developed and developing worlds, particularly as direct-to-consumer advertising is illegal in most of the world with the exceptions of the US and New Zealand. If the industry did not know from experience that marketing to doctors and consumers is effective, it would not have spent billions of dollars annually in recent years on this marketing.

The Case of Thalidomide

Just as the pharmaceutical companies have shown that their marketing strategies in developing countries take health less seriously than profits, so, too, have profits come first in Canada at times, and with deleterious consequences. Probably the incident with the most visibly tragic consequences was the **thalidomide** disaster, which resulted in the birth of over 100 babies in Canada with phocomelia (the absence of limbs and the presence of seal-like flippers instead).

A West German company developed thalidomide in 1954. It was called GRIPPEX, and was initially recommended for the treatment of respiratory infections, colds, coughs, flu, nervousness, and neuralgic and migraine headaches. It was widely available without prescription, quite cheap, and, therefore, very accessible. It was manufactured in West Germany, Canada, Great Britain, Italy, Sweden, and Switzerland under 37 different brand names (Klass, 1975, p. 92). Later it was marketed in Germany as the "safest" sleeping pill available because it was impossible to take enough at any time to commit suicide. It was advertised in Great Britain (where it was called Distavel) as so safe that the picture accompanying an advertisement was of a little child in front of a medicine chest. The caption read, "This child's life may depend on the safety of Distavel."

CRITICAL THINKING

Box 14.4 • Debate about New Reproductive Technologies

Among the most controversial of medical interventions available today are the new reproductive technologies. Largely unheard of before the birth of the first "test-tube baby," Louise Brown, in 1978, these technologies fall roughly into four groups: (1) those concerned with fertility control (conception prevention); (2) labour and delivery "management" (high-tech deliveries in hospital by obstetricians/gynecologists); (3) pre-conception and prenatal screening (and treatment) for abnormalities and sex selection (ultrasound, amniocentesis, genetic screening); and (4) reproductive technologies per se (conception, pregnancy, and birth management via technical, pharmaceutical, and medical intervention) (Eichler, 1988, p. 211). This discussion will be limited to the last category.

New reproductive technologies have separated gestational, genetic, and social parenthood for both men and women. They have eliminated the need for intercourse between a man and a woman for reproduction. They enable men and women to reproduce without an opposite-sex social parent through surrogate mothering arrangements or sperm banks. With the new reproduction technologies, conception, gestation, and birth can be entirely separated from social parenting.

Approximately 16 per cent (or one in six) of heterosexual Canadian couples experience infertility (Government of Canada, 2019). Infertility is defined variably by age and sex but basically refers to failure to conceive after regular intercourse for a period of about one year if under 35 and a period of six months if over 35. In the case of infertility the first medical intervention is fertility drugs. If a course of pharmaceutical treatment is not successful the next options, according to the government website (Government of Canada, 2019), include surgery, for example, to unblock the fallopian tubes or retrieve eggs or sperm; intrauterine insemination (IUI) whereby a thin catheter delivers sperm directly to the woman's uterus;

in-vitro fertilization (IVF), i.e., fertilization of the ovum outside the woman's body; and, finally, an embryo transfer. While cost estimates are difficult to assess, anecdotally, each IVF (in-vitro fertilization) costs more than $10,000. The cost of the drugs taken to enhance fertility and the anxiety and recurrent disappointment until fertilization occurs make this a very trying medical intervention for someone who is otherwise healthy. This figure is a significant underestimate of the overall costs. Moreover the psychosocial costs are not considered in this estimate.

This immensely complex issue has extensive ramifications. Sociologists have long been concerned to understand the relationships between technological innovation and social change. In particular, they have sought to understand the social organization and social control of technological innovation. Some fundamental questions are: In whose interest are the new reproductive technological developments? Whose interests should they serve? To what extent has the availability of these new technologies reinforced and even exacerbated a pronatalist philosophy? What are the effects of such a philosophy on men and women, particularly those who are infertile? What are the long-range physical, emotional, and social effects on children who have been produced by these technologies?

With respect to just one new intervention, in-vitro fertilization, there may be costs for the mother, father, and the fetus/embryo. For the mother and the fetus/embryo, these costs include significant short- and long-term health effects. The treatments can be very invasive and involve the administration of hormonal drugs at extraordinary levels. In the short run, the mother's body may experience pregnancy/non-pregnancy symptoms in turn, causing numerous minor side effects such as nausea, headaches, cramping, and the like. In the long run, these drugs (like DES, discussed below) may lead to a greater vulnerability to cancers—particularly of the reproductive system. As long-term studies have yet to be completed, the expectations for health or for side effects are now only speculative.

In addition to the biological costs are the social and emotional costs of being preoccupied with bodily functioning, with motherhood, and with the experience of repeated failure to conceive. Women have likened the experience of being involved with IVF to a roller coaster of recurrent hope and despair. Even when fertilization is successful, the offspring

have higher than average neonatal and perinatal mortality rates. There are much higher incidences of multiple births. The findings are inconclusive about other risks but, according to the Mayo Clinic, they may include ovarian cancer in the mother and birth defects in the offspring.

Given these side effects and the ethical issues, it is no wonder that new reproductive technologies have been the subject of widespread and ongoing debate about the various options and about whether or not they should be privately funded or covered by medicare. What do you think?

Spotlight on Ethics

Box 14.5 • Sperm Donor Fiasco

The story of Dr Norman Barwin illustrates just one of the numerous serious problems that happen in an environment in which the use of biomedical technologies is not regulated (Payne, 2018). In 1973, Ottawa General Hospital hired Dr Barwin to manage a high-risk fertility clinic. Dr Barwin established numerous initiatives, including a sperm bank at the hospital. He left the hospital about a decade later to establish his own practice, where he continued to offer fertility treatments and associated medical services. In 1995, Dr Barwin was sued by a lesbian couple for (allegedly) using the wrong sperm to inseminate one of the couple as they built their family. This lawsuit was settled out of court in 1998. This suit had little impact on the doctor's practice or reputation. In 1997, before the lawsuit was even resolved, he was awarded the Order of Canada for his work in the field of sexual health and fertility. But in 2013, Dr Barwin was again accused of mixing up sperm. In this case, three families lodged complaints. He was disciplined by the College of Physicians and Surgeons and banned from practice

for two months. In response, he resigned from his position as a recipient of the Order of Canada.

There is now a class action lawsuit against Dr Barwin, signed on by over 150 former patients and their families. The suit originated when one of the plaintiffs, Rebecca Dixon, became suspicious of her parentage after developing celiac disease, a hereditary disease that neither of her parents had. Dixon and her parents investigated further through blood testing, which indicated that her father could not be her biological father even though his sperm was supposed to have been used to inseminate her mother. This was confirmed by a DNA test (Motluk, 2017). Another young woman, Kat Palmer, was searching online for half-siblings after learning that she had been conceived using sperm from a donor. Using an ancestry website, she traced her DNA to a relative of Dr Barwin, who she knew was the fertility doctor who had inseminated her mother. Palmer contacted the clinic to arrange a paternity test, which confirmed that Dr Barwin was her biological father. Palmer was

continued

then introduced to Rebecca Dixon, and further genetic testing showed that the women were half-sisters, confirming that Dixon had also been conceived using Dr Barwin's sperm (Motluck, 2017).

At least 150 people have been in contact with the lawyers for the class action lawsuit against Barwin because of what they feel were harmful effects of his practices (Payne, 2018). Some people who were conceived through Barwin's treatments claim that they are the offspring of the wrong sperm donor. In some cases, the doctor was supposed to have used the sperm of the child's father, but the DNA results indicate that the sperm belonged to an unknown person. This means that the wishes of people who clearly chose sperm from a specific sperm donor for any of a variety of reasons were ignored. In several cases, the mother had chosen a sperm donor because he was willing to meet with the child once the child was 18 years of age, if the child desired. This violation of patient consent also meant that people had no knowledge of the particular genetic history and therefore had no forewarning of potential health issues, such as Dixon's celiac disease. There are numerous possible problematic issues raised by Dr Barwin's ethical violations in his work. Sixteen people have now come forward saying that DNA testing has confirmed they are the offspring of Dr Barwin (College of Physicians and Surgeons of Ontario, 2019).

Dr Barwin was revered and called the "baby god" because of his focus on infertility and hormone treatments for trans people long before such interventions were commonplace (DiManno, 2013). However, despite his apparently progressive stance on LGBTQ+ rights, he grossly violated patient consent throughout his career, raising questions about the true motivations for his work. And his disregard for rules extended beyond his clinics. In 2000, Dr Barwin was censured by the race director of the Boston Marathon for taking shortcuts during the race and was barred from running it again. Just a year later, he was caught cheating at the National Capital Marathon in Ottawa.

It is important to note that Dr Barwin is not the only fertility doctor with such a record. In recent decades some fertility doctors in the US have been found to be the biological fathers of many dozens of children. Even while the fertility industry is growing there are many more examples of calamitous mistakes and/or malfeasance (Kirkey, 2016). In the absence of adequate regulation and oversight, such incidents will continue. Beyond fertility treatments, medical error is a significant cause of death and is estimated to be the third highest cause of death in hospitals in the US (Makary & Daniel, 2016). In Canada preventable error causes more deaths annually than stroke, diabetes, Alzheimer's, and kidney disease combined (Weeks, 2017). But were Dr Barwin's actions error or malfeasance? Although his actions are considered medical error, that idea serves to obfuscate the fact that this likely was much more than carelessness. It appears that he intentionally and knowingly used his own sperm in many cases. What, if any, regulatory strictures would you suggest be placed on fertility clinics to prevent such "errors" from occurring?

By the summer of 1959 a number of reports in Germany, Australia, and Britain had noted serious side effects. These indicated that the drug caused nerve damage, affected balance, and caused tingling in the hands and feet. This should have been a warning about the potency of the drug and its effects on the central nervous system (Winsor, 1973). But the manufacturer continued to market the drug in Germany and licensed another company to produce and market the drug in Canada and the US. The drug was tested briefly in the US and then samples were distributed. It was manufactured, beginning 1 April 1961, under the name KEVADON in Canada. A warning was included in the package about peripheral neuritis. It was distributed in Canada under a number of different names.

By 1 December 1961 two representatives of the German companies reported to Ottawa that a number of babies with congenital deformities had been born in Germany and that the mothers of these babies had taken thalidomide. Rather than contacting the research centres in Germany, England, and Australia directly, the Canadian government relied on the ambiguous and evasive reports presented by the pharmaceutical companies involved. It was not until three months later, on 2 March 1962, that the Food and Drug Directorate of National Health and Welfare decided to withdraw the drug, claiming that, until then, the evidence for its removal was "only statistical" (Winsor, 1973). Removing the drug was complicated. Unlike France, Belgium, the US, and Britain, Canada did not require the drug manufacturers to label the drug with its international name—thalidomide—under which its side effects were being publicized (*Kitchener-Waterloo Record*, 1972). As a result, a number of pharmacists were not aware that their shelves contained the drug in question. By the time it was removed the damage had been done.

Approximately 125 babies were born in Canada with phocomelia (Peritz, 2010). Other external defects included small ears, eye defects, depressed noses, and facial tumours. Internal problems were found in the cardiovascular system and the intestinal tract. There were several cases of missing organs, such as gall bladder or liver. These physical anomalies meant emotional traumas for those born with health and body-function problems, as well as for the mothers, fathers, siblings, other family members, and anyone who was involved with the "thalidomide babies." In some communities the birth of the deformed children made local newspaper headlines, and townspeople "flocked" to the hospital to see for themselves. Some people blamed the mothers for having taken the drug. Whole families were stigmatized. There were approximately 3,000 disabled babies in West Germany and 500 in Great Britain. When Belgium, Sweden, Portugal, and other affected countries are included, the number of babies reached more than 10,000 (Dove, 2011).

Very few cases ever occurred in the US. Dr Frances Kelsey, the medical officer who reviewed safety data for the Food and Drug Administration, was skeptical and critical of the drug. She had, by chance, read a letter to the editor in a medical journal, which presented negative information about the drug (*Kitchener-Waterloo Record*, 1972). She was dissatisfied with the available information on the safety of the product and did not allow it to be marketed. In particular, she was concerned that the drug could cross the placenta of the mother. In the US, only the few samples of the drug given to doctors were ever used. Apparently, Dr Kelsey resisted extraordinary pressure from the drug company, which made "no less than 50 approaches of submissions to the FDA" (Winsor, 1973). (Kelsey, who was a Canadian doctor, died in August 2015 at the age of 101.)

The drug companies had used a number of tactics to increase the sales of thalidomide. One involved planting an article in the June 1961 issue of the *American Journal of Obstetrics and Gynecology*, allegedly written by Dr Ray Neilson of Cincinnati. The article said that the drug was safe for pregnant women (Winsor, 1973). Later, Dr Neilson admitted that the article had been written by the medical research director for the manufacturer and was based on incomplete evidence, i.e., on evidence only that the drug was harmless when taken in the last few months of pregnancy, when, of course, the limbs had already developed. Nevertheless, it was advertised as safe for pregnant women when it was clearly known to be unsafe if ingested in the early months. Canadians were reminded of this tragedy, and of the outcome for the people who suffered physical anomalies and emotional and social scars as a result, when the Canadian Broadcasting Company aired a documentary, *Broken Promises*, on the events and their aftermath. This documentary revealed the culpability of the Canadian government in failing to keep the drug out of Canada. The *Globe and Mail* (1989) reported on the program as follows: "the most striking impression left by 'Broken Promises' is that a number of pharmaceutical companies, druggists, doctors and prosthesis manufacturers have callously exploited the victims of thalidomide with the crudest and most obvious motive—profit." In addition, the Canadian government was criticized for failing to provide compensation. It has subsequently compensated and continues to compensate those who were directly affected by thalidomide. An additional class action lawsuit was pursued by others who could not prove their disabilities were caused by thalidomide, i.e., they were unable to provide 60-year-old prescription receipts or affidavits from long-deceased doctors. A hearing for approval of a Settlement Agreement was held in Federal Court in late February 2020 (Koskie Minsky, 2020). However, financial compensation can never be a completely satisfactory conclusion to such a life-changing mishap.

The *Globe and Mail* reported in February 2010 that many of those affected by thalidomide at birth have numerous health problems and have aged prematurely. As of that date, only 96 people of the estimated 125 born with phocomelia—or rather, those who could prove their mothers had taken thalidomide—were still alive. Some were shunned by their parents throughout their lives. Some now live alone and in poverty. According to the spokesperson for the survivors, "Today, some of Canada's 'thalidomiders,' as they call themselves, live fulfilling lives, with jobs, spouses and children. Most, however, are struggling" (Peritz, 2010).

The Case of DES

From the 1940s through the 1960s, many physicians prescribed the synthetic estrogen hormone **DES (diethylstilbestrol)**, also called simply stilbestrol, to pregnant women who had histories of miscarriage, diabetes, or toxemia during pregnancy. More than 4 million women worldwide took DES over this period. In the US, approximately 2 million male and 2 million female children of these women were exposed to DES in utero; there are approximately 400,000 children

of "DES mothers" in Canada. The girl children have developed a number of health difficulties, including a rare vaginal cancer, adenocarcinoma, and a variety of apparently benign structural changes of the uterus, cervix, and vagina. As many as 97 per cent of the DES daughters have cervical abnormalities. Adenosis, the most common problem, is estimated to occur in 43 to 95 per cent of the women. About one-half of DES daughters have had or may have problems with pregnancy, including primary infertility (difficulty in becoming pregnant), premature births, stillbirths, and ectopic pregnancies (gestation outside the uterus). Ectopic pregnancies, which may be dangerous to the mother as well as the fetus, appear to occur in five times as many DES daughters as in other women. Problems have been seen in DES sons as well. About 30 per cent have genital tract and semen abnormalities, including cysts and extremely small and undescended testicles. The impact of DES has become evident only over the past three decades or so. There may be links between DES exposure in mothers and testicular and prostate cancers in sons. However, all of the long-term effects may not yet be known.

DES is one of a series of hormone-based drug interventions developed in the last century for women. For more than a decade women had been advised to take hormone replacement therapy (HRT) to prevent the "symptoms" of menopause such as hot flashes and night sweats. Millions of women responded and began to take various admixtures of HRT despite the ongoing questioning of the severity of the side effects by the women's health movement (O'Grady, 2003). Hormone replacement therapies were widely prescribed before research by the National Heart, Lung, and Blood Institute of the National Institutes of Health in the US, with large and significant collaboration of the Women's Health Initiative, was complete. In the middle of the research on the effects and safety of hormone replacement therapy—three years before all the data were collected—the study was abandoned because HRT was found to be associated with an increased risk of breast cancer, stroke, and blood clots (O'Grady, 2003). After the publication of these results in 2002, the prescription of HRT decreased and, at the same time, the prescription of anti-depressants increased, and it appears that anti-depressants are sometimes being prescribed for the same symptom presentation as HRT (McIntyre et al., 2005).

Remembering Our History

Box 14.6 • The Discovery of the DES Problem in Canada

In 1982, Harriet Simard was a healthy 21-year-old philosophy student at McGill University in Montreal. Suddenly, after what was supposed to be a routine medical examination, Harriet was diagnosed with a rare cancer: clear cell adenocarcinoma of the cervix and vagina. She had to have a hysterectomy. She was given an 85 per cent chance of survival after five years. Later she discovered that the cancer was linked to DES, a "wonder" drug marketed between 1941 and 1971 to prevent miscarriage. Harriet's mother had tried unsuccessfully to carry a baby to term eight years before becoming pregnant with Harriet. To prevent another miscarriage, the doctors prescribed DES.

At the time DES was prescribed for a variety of "female conditions," including irregular bleeding and spotting and menopause, and as a "morning-after pill" to prevent successful implantation after conception. In fact, it was prescribed as a morning-after pill to numerous college and university students who had engaged in unprotected sexual intercourse and did not want to get pregnant.

Approximately one out of every thousand daughters of women prescribed DES will develop cancer. DES daughters also have an increased risk of contracting a precancerous condition called cervical dysplasia, of giving birth prematurely, of miscarriage during the second trimester, of ectopic pregnancy, of genital organ malformations, and perhaps of breast cancer.

When Harriet Simard learned that she had this rare form of cancer, she began to read up on the subject and to ask questions. She discovered that American medical journals had already published a number of papers on some of the results of DES. Harriet was shocked to discover that the Canadian government was not taking action to inform people of the potential long-term intergenerational effects of DES, even though early screening is known to have beneficial effects on the outcome of the disease. Partly because of the lobbying efforts of women's groups in the US, the American federal government had sponsored screening clinics for DES daughters and sons, as well as a widespread information campaign. Doctors were encouraged to inform the government of patients who had ever been prescribed DES.

None of this had happened in Canada. Yet Harriet and her mother Shirley, working together, found DES-related cancers in Quebec and in Ontario, and discovered that approximately 100,000 people had been exposed to the drug.

In response, the Simards founded DES Action Canada. They set up an office and initially received a $50,000 annual grant from the federal government. Numerous newspaper and magazine stories publicized their concerns, and many doctors volunteered to help in screening DES daughters and in contacting patients who had taken the drug. The National Film Board produced a film on the subject, and nine chapters of the organization were established across the country.

DES Action Canada is one example of a highly successful grassroots movement. Harriet and Shirley Simard helped to show what individual people can do to increase awareness and effect change.

Box 14.7 • Purdue Pharma and the Opioid Crisis

The opioid crisis gripping the US and Canada is leading to a decrease in life expectancy across both countries for the first time in many years. Opioids are not new. They have been used both recreationally and medically or therapeutically for thousands of years. They derive from sap inside the common poppy. Famous early physicians such as Hippocrates and Galen both mentioned opioids and their powerful effects. Canada's William Osler called opium-derived medications "god's own medicine" (Golden, 2009). Related drugs, including laudanum, morphine, codeine, and even heroin until it was banned in Canada by the Opium and Narcotic Drug Act of 1929, were all used for medicinal purposes throughout the nineteenth and twentieth centuries. However, the current crisis was precipitated by the widespread manufacturing of synthetic opioid drugs and their development into slow-release drugs in the 1990s, which were marketed by pharmaceutical companies as a treatment not just for acute, short-term pain, but also for chronic pain (Van Zee, 2009).

In 1995, Purdue Pharma, an American pharmaceutical company privately owned and operated by the Sackler family, released a new, slow-release version of oxycodone that they called OxyContin, which was approved by the US Food and Drug Administration (Mariani, 2015). The marketing of OxyContin was widespread and aggressive (Van Zee, 2009). By the late 1990s, Purdue had doubled its sales force and its total physician call list. They offered a patient starter coupon program that provided a free, limited-time prescription for a 7–30-day supply of OxyContin (Van Zee, 2009). Purdue advertised directly to doctors through branded personal items like fishing hats, stuffed plush toys, and music compact discs ("Get in the Swing with OxyContin"). They rewarded their salespeople with generous bonuses for selling OxyContin. In physician-targeted marketing campaigns, printed pamphlets and videos for patients, and its very popular website featuring tools to help patients measure their pain, Purdue consistently normalized pain as endemic, and in turn claimed that OxyContin was highly effective, risk-free, and unlikely to lead to addiction. Sales representatives were directed to say that opioids were only addictive in 1 per cent of the cases in which they were used. This figure was based primarily on two studies in which patients were not using the opioids for long-term or chronic pain. Rather, they were founded on opioid prescription for specific, time-limited conditions, such as burn therapy (Van Zee, 2009).

By the late 1990s, partially fuelled by Purdue's aggressive marketing, about one-third of the American population reported suffering from serious and chronic pain (Van Zee, 2009). Governments and insurance companies looked for a solution to this widespread suffering. Both insurance companies and governments tended to favour pain medications, which are much cheaper and act more quickly than alternatives such as surgery. Physicians increasingly prescribed their patients opioids such as fentanyl and oxycodone under names such as Percocet and OxyContin. An estimated 5–6 per cent of patients who were prescribed opioids for the first time became addicted to them. Many studies document an addiction rate between 3 and 16 per cent when the drugs are used over time for chronic conditions (Van Zee, 2009). Some doctors refused to continue to prescribe opioids after they felt the appropriate treatment time was up. Other physicians continued to prescribe opioids to their patients upon request. As these addictions were allowed to go unchecked, patients would develop a higher tolerance level and required more and more opioids to maintain normal functioning. When doctors refused to continue to prescribe indefinitely, some of their patients suffering with an addiction caused by their legal medical treatment would turn to illegal opioids such as heroin.

Even as a significant percentage of patients developed opioid addictions through their supposedly safe product, Purdue continued its extensive advertising campaign. It was effective. Purdue offered numerous national pain-management and speaker-training conferences at resorts in the Florida, Arizona, and California. More than 5,000 physicians, pharmacists, and nurses attended these all-expenses-paid symposia, where they were recruited and trained for Purdue's national speaker bureau. Purdue's marketing plan also included the use of sophisticated "prescriber profiles" on individual physicians across the US, allowing the pharmaceutical giant to precisely target the highest and lowest prescribers of particular drugs in a single zip code, county, state, or the entire country (Van Zee, 2009). Internal communications from Purdue revealed that the company was aware that OxyContin was addictive, but continued to sell the drug and approve marketing plans that dismissed those suffering from addiction as "junkies" and "criminals" (Willmsen, 2019). Eight members of the Sackler family, along with nine board members or company executives, have been indicted for continuing to market and sell OxyContin long after they knew that it was addictive and was causing thousands of deaths across the US (Willmsen, 2019).

Opioid addiction is now widespread across Canada. The rate of hospitalization due to opioid poisoning is high, and there were 13 hospitalizations per day in 2014–15. The rates of addiction and use are highest in the West and the North, with the prevalence highest among Indigenous people. There were 2,861 deaths in Canada as a result of opioids in 2016. Approximately 82 per cent of opioid-related deaths from January 2016 to June 2017 also involved one or more non-opioid substances. Deaths are highest among the homeless and among males and those between the ages of 30 and 39 (Belzak & Halverson, 2018). The increase in use, addiction, and death over the years has been due to a combination of legal and illegal drug use.

Today, a new crisis is afoot. Illegal fentanyl is being imported from overseas as a street drug and, with hundreds of thousands of people suffering from opioid addiction in the US and Canada, it is "flooding the market." Fentanyl is an extremely strong opioid, and carries a much higher risk of overdose than oxycodone or heroin, even for individuals with a high tolerance for opioids. Deaths from fentanyl have increased by 540 per cent across the United States since 2015. This accounts for almost "all the increase in drug overdose deaths from 2015 to 2016" (Dowell et al., 2017). Fentanyl is often manufactured in China and processed and packaged in Mexico before being smuggled into the US. A large amount of fentanyl is also purchased online and shipped through the US mail service. Carfentanyl, a much more highly concentrated drug than fentanyl, commonly used as a tranquilizer for elephants, is available through many outlets in China and readily shipped overseas (Rath, 2017).

Other Negative Effects of the Pharmaceutical Industry

Finally, the pharmaceutical industry must also be challenged for being part of a larger set of industries causing ill health. Harding (1987), for example, suggests, "the pharmaceutical industry is an outgrowth of the interlocking petrochemical industry, which also produces pesticides, herbicides and fertilizers." Toxins from the petrochemical industry have been responsible for environmental health calamities. Sharon Batt (2010) has documented the difficulties we face because of how the drugs we use and those that we throw out unused become a part of our natural world and pollute it in untold ways. For example, there are already trace amounts of pharmaceuticals to be found in the streams, rivers, lakes, and tap water that Canadians rely on. Remember, as you think about this, that pharmaceutical manufacturing is a relatively new phenomenon and thus the effects of long-term and increasing "dumping" of drugs into the environment are not yet known. Chemicals from food and personal products, such as those for cleaning, hygiene, shampooing, and food additives, and new genetic and biological chemicals have all been found in the ecosystem. Just as the methods for detecting such chemicals are improving, so is the growing inventory of the pollutants being uncovered. Although the short-term and the long-term consequences of this pollution are not known, a few cases for concern are already evident. The deleterious consequences for birds and fish of the excess of estrogen products in the water are beginning to be documented. For example, fish living downstream from sewage treatment plants have been found to be feminized and to have lost interest in spawning. Trace amounts of antibiotics, painkillers, anti-inflammatory drugs, hormones, tranquilizers, chemotherapy drugs, and drugs for cholesterol and epilepsy have been observed. Without knowing much about the specific effects of such pollutants, it is easy to imagine possibilities. Drinking water, too, has been found to carry personal care and pharmaceutical products. Some of these chemicals are persistent and do not dissolve or breakdown. The precautionary principle declares that we should not act until we know the consequences of the action. Clearly, the evidence is in that we are already causing harm to the ecosystem by the use of medical, cosmetic, and cleaning and health products. The public health dangers of these industries are potentially widespread and serious.

Issues in Drug Regulation

Governments can have an important role in the regulation of the drug industry and ultimately in the drug-related health of their citizens. However, most government regulations are inadequate. As a result, in Canada: (1) half the drugs now on the Canadian market have never passed modern tests regarding safety or effectiveness; (2) even where regulations are in place in the industrialized world, substandard drugs are being marketed and distributed overseas; (3) drug companies have a monopoly on the information available to doctors

as well as on the side effects of various drugs. One reason that the safety and effectiveness of drugs in Canada may even be declining is that responsibility for testing new drugs is increasingly being given over to the industry that manufactures and sells drugs for profit (Armstrong & Armstrong, 2003; Silversides, 2010). The balance of power between the Health Products and Foods Branch and the industry has been moving towards the industry as Canadian government policies have generally moved to the ideological right, with an emphasis on relying on market principles and globalization. In practical terms, this means that the pharmaceutical industry "is now providing a substantial fraction of the money needed to run the drug regulatory system" (Lexchin, 2012, p. 285). Since 1994, pharmaceutical companies have been charged a fee every time they submit a new drug for approval. In return, they have asked for a speedier approval process for new drugs (Lexchin, 2012). "Greater public scrutiny of the drug approval process is essential" (Silversides, 2010, p. 138).

A study of drug withdrawals from the Canadian market between 1963 and 2004 because of safety concerns is instructive in regard to the historical safety of the drugs introduced (Lexchin, 2005). Lexchin undertook a systematic study of drugs that had been removed from the market over a period of more than 20 years. He found it very difficult to get the information because Health Canada "does not maintain a comprehensive list of drugs that have been removed from Canada because of safety concerns" (p. 765). In addition, he notes that even asking the question about withdrawals led to further questions and concerns, such as the fact that drugs tend to be tested for a short period of time on a highly select group of patients, including "those with clear evidence of disease, who are not taking other products and who do not have other conditions that might interfere with an analysis of the efficacy of the product being tested" (p. 765). By contrast, many patients have multiple conditions and unknown conditions, and many use the drugs over a long period of time. In conclusion, Lexchin, who has been studying issues related to the pharmaceutical industry for many years, states that "the current safety system is inadequate" (p. 767).

However stringent the laws, the government cannot guarantee that any drug is safe for all the uses to which it may be put. It is not difficult to imagine a situation in which a drug is prescribed for one use or for one person, and is then used again by the same person on another occasion when the symptoms seem to be similar or is passed on to a friend or a family member who seems to have the same problem. People often regulate their drug use, ignoring the specific directions given by the physician and/or the pharmacist. In addition, people have been known to develop drug allergies very suddenly and unpredictably.

While the government can insist that patients be told about drug interactions, it cannot regulate the actual mixture of drugs taken by any one individual. Some drugs react negatively when taken in conjunction with alcohol. One characteristic of many alcoholics or even people who now and then have a glass or two of wine or a couple of bottles of beer is that they may try to keep their drinking habit secret—even from their doctor. Untold problems result from drug–alcohol interactions. In addition, a number of drug-related problems or side effects are only discovered after long-term use. For these and other reasons, the drug regulations established by the government can only be considered as partial protection.

The Canadian government is also in a weak position because of the Canadian branch-plant economy in the pharmaceutical industry. Most drugs are developed and tested elsewhere. The Canadian government frequently relies on tests done abroad by other governmental bodies or by the drug firms' research departments. This raises complex problems of biased information from pharmaceutical companies and political problems of intergovernmental relations. Moreover, as Lexchin documents, in spite of the fact that Canadian drug laws are among the strictest in the world, there are still major gaps that may jeopardize people's health.

Medical Devices and Bioengineering

Medical devices range from contact lenses to CT scanners, MRI machines, knee and hip replacement parts, prosthetics, and beyond. Companies that produce and sell various medical devices, such as artificial heart valves, artificial limbs, kidney dialysis machines, anaesthesiology equipment, surgical equipment, and heart pacemakers, are all medical device companies and are among the largest growth industries in the world. The regulations controlling the industry are uneven, especially under globalization and in the context of free trade. Health Canada has a continuous list of advisories, warnings, and recalls for all sorts of health-related products that are often used by people before they are found to cause death, disability, or disease.

Among the responsibilities of biomedical engineers are the evaluation and testing of equipment, the investigation and explanation of the causes of accidents, and the supervision of the repair of biomedical equipment. There is, however, a shortage of such personnel in Canada, owing in part to the lack of training programs as well as the lack of adequate government investment in monitoring and surveillance. From what limited information is available, it is clear that the whole issue of medical devices and **bioengineering** needs a great deal of research and more thorough and systematic regulation. At present, the Health Products and Foods Branch of Health Canada does not generally require adequate evidence concerning the potential for harm or benefit, or assurance of the safety of the various devices. The exceptions are for tampons, condoms, contact lenses, and devices implanted in the body for more than 30 days (see the website of the Health Protection Branch of the federal government: www.hc-sc.gc.ca/ahc-asc/branch-dirgen/hpfb-dgpsa/index-eng.php). These are accepted for marketing only after the government has examined the evidence—provided by the manufacturing firm itself—as to the safety of the device.

Spotlight on Ethics

Box 14.8 • Patenting Genetic Material: What Are the Ethical Issues?

The patenting of genetic material has been accepted in the US since 1980, when the US Supreme Court decided, in a 5–4 split, that it was legal to patent bacteria that had been modified to break down oil spills. Since the mapping of the human genome this decision has become very controversial. One of the debates concerns the recently "discovered" genes for breast cancer, the BRCA1 and BRCA2. A private laboratory, Myriad Genetics Laboratories, discovered them in the early 1990s. Myriad then claimed a patent on future testing of the presence of these genes.

Tests for the presence of the BRCA1 or BRCA2 are sometimes advised for or requested by women with a high risk of breast cancer because of family history. The presence or absence of one of the genes can help women decide what sorts of prophylactic action they might take. Because of the costs to Canada's healthcare system of the testing of patented genes, there have been many debates about whether testing should be covered by medicare or should be an out-of-pocket expense for those seeking such testing.

Regardless of who was to pay, Myriad declared in 2001 that hospitals in several provinces were violating its patent on the genetic susceptibility to breast cancer because they were testing for the genes but not paying Myriad. Myriad demanded that all tests were to be done in their US labs. This would cost about five times the current costs in Canada.

One province, Ontario, decided to challenge Myriad with respect to its right to control and to profit from diagnostic and medical tests using its patent. In 2013, many years after Myriad Genetics Laboratories "patented" the newly discovered BRCA1 and BRCA2 genes, the Supreme Court in the US struck down its right to patent, claiming that genes were a "product of nature" and could not therefore be patented (McVeigh, 2013).

What do you think? Should human genes be able to be patented for the profit of the individual or company who discovers the gene? What are the possible consequences of this decision?

Source: Willison & MacLeod (2002).

Summary

1. There is a correlation between people's socio-demographic characteristics and their drug-taking habits.

2. Psychoactive drugs are among the most heavily prescribed and often misprescribed drugs in Canada. Females, the elderly, and the unemployed are high users. Frequently, chronically ill patients are prescribed two or more psychoactive drugs simultaneously. Often, these mood-modifying drugs are given for social and personal reasons and not for medical problems.

3. Large differences exist in rates of prescription from doctor to doctor and even from one geographic area to another. Doctors receive much of their "information" about drugs from pharmaceutical companies. Other factors in the rate at which doctors prescribe drugs include education, type of practice, and method of remuneration.

4. Pharmacists may tend to recommend drugs that will maximize their profit. Pharmacists may often choose between a brand-name (more expensive) and a generic drug for a customer when filling a prescription. Pharmaceutical companies offer incentives to ensure that the pharmacist will choose their brand.

5. Multinationals control the vast majority of the Canadian prescription drug market. Pharmaceutical manufacturing is one of the more profitable manufacturing activities in Canada. Some of the reasons for this are: the absence of a link between manufacturing cost and price, the presence of patent protection, price-fixing, discount pricing, advertising, and drug distribution (dumping) in the less-developed countries.

6. In several Canadian instances, drug company profits have come before health. One is the case of thalidomide, which resulted in the birth of an untold number of babies in Canada with phocomelia. DES is another drug that was used by pregnant women with disastrous consequences. It is now known that it has caused cancer and many other many abnormalities in the reproductive systems of the offspring of these mothers.

7. The government has not adequately regulated the use of pharmaceuticals in Canada. After-market surveillance continues to be weak. Drug companies control much of the information available to doctors regarding various drugs, including the side effects.

8. The medical devices industry is a profitable and growing industry. Government regulation and monitoring of this industry needs improvement.

Key Terms

bioengineering
DES (diethylstilbestrol)
direct-to-consumer advertising

medical-industrial complex
over-the-counter drugs
thalidomide

Questions for Study and Discussion

1. Explain antibiotic resistance.
2. Discuss the reasons for and the consequences of multiple drug use among seniors in Canada.
3. What factors influence the prescribing patterns of doctors?
4. What are some of the reasons for the high profitability of the pharmaceutical industry?

5. Name and discuss three continuing problems in regard to drug promotion in the developing world.
6. Could a drug with the devastating effects of DES be marketed in Canada today?
7. Explain the challenges to adequate post-market surveillance of pharmaceuticals.

Suggested Readings

Abraham, J. (2010). Pharmaceuticalization of society in context: Theoretical, empirical and health dimensions. *Sociology, 44*(4), 603–22.

An examination of health and pharmaceuticals in the context of an increasing reliance on medication.

Barker, K. (2011). Pharmaceutical determinism. *Social Science and Medicine, 73*, 833–42. An argument that the existence of a drug aids in legitimating a contested disorder.

Eban, K. (2019). *Bottle of lies: The inside story of the generic drug boom.* Ecco. A critical analysis of the generic drug industry.

Macy, B. (2018). *Dopesick: Dealers, doctors, and the drug companies.* Little, Brown and Company. Description and analysis of a medical culture in which treatment with painkillers became routine and normative.

Meier, B. (2018). *Pain killer: An empire of deceit and the origin of America's opioid crisis.* Random House. Discussion of how the opioid addiction crisis originated and then exploded.

Metzl, J.M., & J. Angel, J. (2004). Assessing the impact of SSRI antidepressants on popular notions of women's depressive illness. *Social Science and Medicine, 58*, 577–84. An analysis of the gendered portrayal of anti-depressant medications.

Murray, E., Lo, B., Pollack, L., Donelan, K., & Lee, K. (2003). Direct-to-consumer advertising: Physicians' views of its effects on quality of care and the doctor–patient relationship. *Journal of the American Board of Family Practice, 16*(6), 513–24. A study of what doctors say about how prescribing is altered by advertising.

Whitaker, Robert. (2010). *Anatomy of an epidemic: Magic bullets, psychiatric drugs, and the astonishing rise of mental illness in America.* Crown. A thorough and highly readable critique by an investigative journalist of how psychoactive drugs—a-pharmaceutical "best-seller"—have negatively affected individuals and populations.

Globalization and Health-Care Systems

15

Chapter Overview

- Health care and changes in health care around the world must be considered in the context of globalization.
- Globalization presents challenges and benefits to health care.
- Globalization has meant the spread of conventional allopathic medicine throughout the world. This has been accompanied by both increased equality and inequality.
- Globalization also has meant the potential for the rapid spread of infectious disease around the globe, as happened in 2020 with the novel coronavirus disease, COVID-19.

- The changes in health in South Africa since democratization are a case in point.
- The first significant policy initiative regarding standardizing worldwide health using the conventional medical model occurred at Alma-Alta, Kazakhstan, and resulted in an accord in 1978 that essentially declared "Health for All by 2000."
- Arguably, the most important policy development of the accord was widespread propagation of primary health care (PHC), which involves a modern epidemiological approach to health along with medicalization.

- PHC involves such facets as prevention, social determinants of health, maternal and infant care, and direct clinical care offered by a various providers.
- The World Health Organization (WHO) monitors, encourages, funds, and supports PHC and other specific initiatives with the help of 194 member nations.
- Traditional medicine is still prevalent worldwide although it is threatened in various places.
- In the US, health care is largely composed of a wide variety of competing, for-profit, expensive, high-tech services. After the introduction of President Barack Obama's Affordable Care Act the number of uninsured Americans had apparently

decreased to 11.4 per cent by 2015 (although this is likely an underestimate of those who are uninsured).
- In the UK, health-care coverage is comprehensive and universal, with a small parallel private sector. Concerns are expressed about waiting times, the lack of coverage for some procedures, and deterioration in some of the state-supported infrastructure such as hospitals.
- In Brazil, a universal system, begun with the constitution of 1988, has not yet been fully implemented. There is a thriving parallel private system and large inequities in service provision based on race, income, and region.

Introduction

We discussed disease and death around the world in Chapter 2. We noted that the people in the developing world experience many different diseases than those living in the developed world. With a lower life expectancy, people in the developing world on average do not live long enough to experience the "diseases of civilization." The rates of under-five mortality and maternal mortality are very high, often from preventable diseases. In this chapter we are going to look briefly at some of the diverse health-care organizations for providing for some of the different health-care needs around the world.

Interest in global health has expanded in the past few decades and has been reflected in the powerful and dramatic pictures broadcast around the world about such events as the war in Syria and the multitude of refugees from that conflagration; widely reported famines in Ethiopia, Somalia, and Sudan; the devastating civil wars in Bosnia and Rwanda; natural disasters such as the 2010 earthquake in Haiti and the 2004 tsunami in Asia; and the Ebola epidemic of 2014–15 in sub-Saharan Africa that threatened to become a global pandemic. In fact, Canadians' concern for those affected by such crises sometimes has been so strong

that the Red Cross on occasion has had to refuse donations because they had received more money than they could use.

If these crises impacting public health were not enough, the global coronavirus pandemic of 2020 surely was more than enough. Our television and computer screens showed emergency hospitals in China built in little more than a week, field hospitals for overflow patients soon sprouting like spring flowers across the United States, satellite images of mass graves being dug in Iran, Italians in nationwide lockdown singing from apartment balconies with their neighbours across the way, and the eerily empty streets of major cities throughout the world. And when the massive North American professional and university sports world ended all competitions on the same day in mid-March just as the Canadian prime minister's wife tested positive for the virus after returning from a trip abroad, we knew, if we had not fully acknowledged so before, that public health truly is a global issue.

It is hard to think of these global issues without thinking of the celebrities who are attached to the various organizations supporting global public health. Our culture, in certain ways, is celebrity-driven, and numerous celebrities use their public recognition in the interests of health and development or humanitarian aid. For example, among the many goodwill ambassadors used to raise funds and awareness for the health and well-being of people around the globe for UNICEF are Katy Perry, Lang Lang, Orlando Bloom, Susan Sarandon, Mia Farrow, and Whoopi Goldberg. OXFAM has Meryl Streep, Colin Firth, and Michelle Dockery ("Lady Mary" from the popular television series *Downton Abbey)*. Some of you may be familiar with pop musicians such as Bob Geldof and his Band Aid concert of 1984, which was then a revolutionary way to raise money for the famine in Ethiopia. His co-written song "Do They Know It's Christmas?" is one of the best-selling singles of all time. Band Aid was followed by other concerts to raise funds for international aid, such as Live Aid and Live 8. In the United States, Farm Aid, organized and led by Willie Nelson, John Mellencamp, and Neil Young, which held its first concert to assist family farmers threatened with mortgage foreclosures in 1985, continues today to hold large outdoor concerts to assist farmers. Bono, of the stadium rock band U2, is perhaps one of the most widely renowned global music stars to dedicate concerts to global humanitarian efforts.

This celebritization points to the increasing prominence of global health concerns and to the increase in funds raised in the private sector for various issues under the constraints and possibilities of neo-liberalism and privatization. There are critiques of such efforts, though. Kapoor (2012) argues that the celebritization of international aid is often self-serving, promoting the brand of a particular celebrity, advancing consumerism, and depoliticizing the underlying causes of inequity and injustice throughout the world. But in March 2020, when award-winning actor Tom Hanks and his wife Rita Wilson, in Australia for a film shoot, posted on social media that they had contracted the coronavirus and called on people to be calm but to follow the advice of medical experts, millions of followers and many news organizations heard them, in a way and to a degree that otherwise might not have been possible.

The neo-liberal project is a global one. Major institutions have promoted global economic amalgamation and co-ordination since just after World War II. Called the Bretton Woods system, this institutional integration included the International Monetary Fund, the World Bank, and the General Agreement on Tariff and Trade (GATT), which evolved into the more institutionalized World Trade Organization in 1995 (De Vogli, 2011). The interlocking system was primarily intended to provide a regulatory framework for the maintenance of peace and economic stability following the disruptions of the two world wars of the twentieth century. It was designed to provide global stability and state intervention in several areas such as exchange rates, capital control, and welfare and employment policies. However, in the early 1970s the Bretton Woods system began to change dramatically when, with the so-called "Nixon Shock" of August 1971, the US backed away from the gold standard, whereby American dollars had been guaranteed to be backed by gold held by the US Treasury so that foreign holders of American dollars could convert their holdings to gold at the fixed price of $35 an ounce. This meant stability in the international monetary system with fixed exchange rates. After August 1971, however, national currencies were free-floating and fluctuated, and the focus shifted away from state intervention in the economy in favour of neo-liberalism and market independence or market fundamentalism. This essentially meant that markets were to be independent of state interference except for the role of the state in property rights and ensuring the freedom of capital. These changes in international economic policy occurred shortly before the conservative governments of Margaret Thatcher in the UK and Ronald Reagan in the US came to power. Their policies of privatization, the reduction in state responsibilities, trade expansion, and the deregulation of markets were hallmarks of neo-liberalism. Through these processes markets and transnational companies began to hold sway even over national governments, all the while spreading the view that such policies would develop wealth that would then trickle down from the rich to the poor nations around the globe, and from the wealthy to the less well-off within countries. These processes of neo-liberalism dominate today's economies around the world and have had mixed impacts on equality, health, and health care.

Unfortunately, just as trickle-down economics never really worked, the hoped-for upward trends in health and life expectancy have not consistently materialized despite the many pockets of improvements in health and well-being. If we look at the trends in life expectancy across regions of the world over the last 50 years or so we see that there have been health improvements in East and South Asia. However, the effects of these neo-liberal policies have been disastrous in sub-Saharan Africa. The poorest continent in the world has experienced a decrease in life expectancy and increasing poverty along with economic stagnation. Although HIV/AIDS has certainly been a significant factor in the economic and health problems confronted by Africa, that the spread of HIV/AIDS is linked to poverty cannot be overlooked. In many countries in sub-Saharan Africa the under-five mortality rate has also grown, especially in the decade of the 1990s.

Not only is there increasing inequality in some areas of the globe, but there is also increasing inequality within many highly developed countries such as Canada and the United States as a result of neo-liberalism. One dramatic and memorable example of the effects of global neo-liberalism can be found in the fact that the average CEO in the US had an income about 40 times that of the average worker in 1980 but by 2001 this difference had increased to about 350 times (Frydman & Saks, 2005, cited in De Vogli, 2011). In 2017, as shown in Figure 15.1, the CEOs of the top 350 US firms averaged 312 times the annual income of the average worker (Mishel & Schieder, 2018; also see Hodgson, 2015).

Many interventions made by international organizations, however, are of obvious assistance, at least in the short run. One small but important example addresses the seemingly simple fact that about one in 10 girls in Africa has to miss school during menstruation or drop out completely once menses begins because they do not have sanitary pads or tampons available. Instead of hygienic sanitary products women use leaves, paper, old clothes,

and rags. They are thus vulnerable both to infections and to humiliating leakage. This uncertainty can challenge their self-confidence about being in public. It can also prevent a girl from attending school in fear of embarrassment and discomfort. Although menstrual pads are available in the cities in some places, they are often very expensive. One young Canadian woman who was in Uganda to do volunteer work struggled to find pads to buy for herself and realized that her problem was an ongoing one for most of the women of the country. She and her partner decided to make reusable cloth pads for sale at an affordable cost. They hired a tailor, rented a small room and two sewing machines, and have now provided 3.2 million young women across 30 countries with a sustainable means to manage their menstrual periods. Afripads has now been running for about a decade and its value has spread to include hiring local workers, conducting reproductive health classes, and in general offering numerous additional positive results. "Every day we are demonstrating the power of a simple innovation to transform lives," says the founder (Fallon, 2013, p. 162). The website indicates that Afripads has employed more than 150 young women and expects to employ 500 more in rural Uganda when this new firm's current plans come to fruition. Global celebrities have become involved. The founders won a social entrepreneurship award. Reflecting the celebritization of international health causes, the award was supported by names such as Stella McCarthy, Yves Saint Laurent, and Gucci.

Canadians, more generally, have watched the changes in South Africa with great hope and enthusiasm. Nelson Mandela became an honorary citizen of Canada in 2001. Under Mandela's presidency, from 1994 to 1999, South Africa became a democracy and sought to eradicate inequality in health. However, the striking contrasts in health care offered to whites in South Africa as compared to the vast majority of black and coloured people continue today in spite of the goals originally set by Mandela's government. Unfortunately, the hope that accompanied the democratization of South Africa under the leadership of Nelson

Figure 15.1 CEO-to-Worker Compensation Ratio, Top 350 US Firms, 1965–2017

Notes: The top 350 American firms accounted for in this figure are ranked by annual sales. "Typical worker" compensation is the average annual compensation of the workers in the key industry of the firms in the sample.

Source: Adapted from Mishel & Schieder (2018, Figure C).

Mandela and the African National Congress (ANC) has been stalled by political and economic realities at both the global and national levels. Also, it certainly didn't help that Mandela's successor, Thabo Mbeki (1999–2008), was a leading voice in HIV/AIDS denialism and created a government that refused pharmaceutical treatments and encouraged superstitious and herbal remedies for the disease, which led to the unnecessary death of estimated hundreds of thousands of South Africans.

Over the years, the health inequalities in South Africa have worsened. In 1994, under Mandela, a number of policies were put in place supporting equity across the races and geographic areas. Health care became enshrined in the Constitution, and over the next few years the government constructed health-care facilities, provided free maternal and child care, and developed programs to make clean water available, improve nutrition for the poor, and provide welfare. These policies should have improved the social and health situations of the people of South Africa. However, these

plans for state intervention in welfare came at a time when the major economic institutions of the world were embracing neo-liberalism and decrying state intervention.

Until the late 1980s apartheid, whereby different racial groups were legally treated differently and unequally, held sway and extreme racial discrimination and segregation were legalized and normalized. Severe racial inequalities in all areas of life resulted. Thus, among black people the mortality and morbidity rates were excessively high, while white rates tended to mirror those of the West. Indeed, white South Africa was known globally for its highly successful medical care system (Sanders & Chopra, 2006). Dr Christiaan Barnard pioneered the first heart transplant in 1967 while the world looked on in awe. South African researchers also contributed critical insights into understanding such important public health issues as child malnutrition. They were also known for health system innovation, particularly a model of community-oriented primary care (Sanders & Chopra, 2006). But these signs of wealth and scientific expertise belonged only to the white population, whose health needs continued to be well served.

Despite the promise of the end of apartheid and the beginning of democracy hoped for when Mandela became president, the health status of the country did not improve and in the context of the spread of HIV/AIDS is, in many ways, substantially worse. From 1995 to 2002 life expectancy declined by about 16.3 per cent, from 61.4 years to 51.4 years. It is now about 62.7 years for the whole country. That figure obscures the great disparity between the wealthy and the poor (World Bank Group, 2017) and it reflects a dramatic difference of about 20 years of life expectancy with a country such as Canada.

Great disparities in health based on race remain. Even in 2001 the life expectancy of black people was 18 years less than that of whites. Furthermore, the average infant mortality rate of 59 per 1,000 observed in 2007 is similar to that in the late 1990s. This, too, supports the argument that the health benefits of the end of apartheid have not been realized (Sartorius et al., 2011). Life expectancy rates are also extremely varied across the country: people living in the formerly segregated Transkei Homeland of the Eastern Cape have an infant mortality rate of 99 per 1,000 live births as compared to urban black people, whose infant mortality rate is about 28 per 1,000 live births. Diseases among the white population are similar to those in Canada and the US, but the diseases experienced by black South Africans reflect the diseases of development discussed in Chapter 2. Violence and traffic accidents are also rampant in the black population. The rate of violence in Cape Town a city that is one of the premier tourist destinations in the world, is among the 10 highest in the world, with 65.53 homicides per 100,000 people (Business Tech, 2016).

Post-apartheid South Africa demonstrates many of the difficulties facing the world and, in particular, the World Health Organization's goal of health for all. Despite the formal intentions and the policies designed to equalize opportunity and health outcomes, there have been many barriers. Chief among them is perhaps what is called the "absorptive" capacity. This essentially means that investment in primary, secondary,

and tertiary health care depends on the available infrastructure. Thus, the already rich and mostly private health-care sector was poised to receive investment because it already had trained personnel, roads, clinics, hospitals, and the like (McIntyre & Gilson, 2000). Regions with the greatest capacity to spend funds, extend their services, and create more infrastructure received more funding than those without such capacity. This has created an "infrastructure inequality trap" characterized by the greatest distribution of funds going to those with the greatest "absorptive capacity." This "trap" perpetuates and even exacerbates the inequalities already in existence (Stuckler et al., 2011). According to the latest statistics, Africa, including Southern and South Africa, is home to many of the world's most extremely poor (World Bank, 2018, p. 29).

Globalization, Medicalization, and Health Care

Health-care systems around the world must be seen in the context of the powerful effects of political and economic globalization, which alters and eliminates the boundaries that separate societies and people from one another. The consequences of the neo-liberal philosophy that undergirds economic globalization are complex and contradictory, with effects that are both detrimental and beneficial to health and health care. Globalization is changing the relative importance of the sovereignty of nation-states and their geographic and governing structures as compared to huge multinational corporations. Under neo-liberalism the need to make a profit supersedes state-level regulations regarding equity, an adequate standard of living, health, and safety for workers. The environmental sustainability of communities and countries is challenged. Globalization is also linked to the spread of various diseases such as SARS and the various strains of influenza, as well as the appearance of Ebola in Europe and North America in 2014 and the coronavirus (COVID-19) pandemic of 2020 (see Garrett, 1995). Global development has already been associated with climate change and the spread of diseases such as malaria, encephalitis, and dengue fever. This rapid transmission of new infectious diseases represents one of the many potential negative consequences of the global movement of people and capital.

Simultaneously, along with neo-liberalism, globalization supports the extension of particular types of mainly Western knowledge and new technologies of health, prevention, medical care, and epidemiology through powerful global organizations such as the **World Health Organization (WHO)**, travel and tourism, academic and medical research, and so on. The processes of global change are homogenizing medical cultures, values, knowledge, technologies, and beliefs; in other words, they have assisted in expanding medicalization and diffusing the Western biomedical model. They have also led to increases in life expectancy and decreases in infant mortality around the globe as well as, at times, the reverse.

The World Health Organization has done extensive research to assess the state of health care globally. In consequence, the WHO's *World Health Report* has listed the most important failures of biomedical care systems around the world (Shah, 2011):

- **Inverse care** whereby the richest consume the greatest amount of the health care available around the world.
- **Impoverishing care** whereby millions of people around the world are still completely impoverished as the result of trying to pay for medical care resulting from a catastrophic personal health-care crisis.
- **Fragmented and fragmenting care** whereby the excessive specialization of providers and services threatens the routine care of the whole person and marginalizes some of the sick and suffering.
- **Unsafe care** whereby the provision of health care can be unsafe and unsanitary, leading to medical error and hospital-acquired infections.
- **Misdirected care** whereby the emphasis on secondary and tertiary care obscures the potentially greater benefits of primary care.

Thus, there are significant barriers to achieving health and health care for all, both in an unequal world and in unequal societies.

A Brief History of the Worldwide Concern for Health

The concerted effort to improve the health of people around the world predates the intensive globalization of the past two plus decades or so. One beginning marker of this effort was the international forum on health held at Alma-Alta (now called Almaty), Kazakhstan, in 1978, which included 134 governments and 67 international organizations. The Alma-Alta Accord, a unanimous resolution calling for "Health for All by 2000" (Seear, 2007), was to be based on the worldwide expansion of primary health care (PHC) as defined by the ethical principles of equity, community participation, intersectoral co-ordination, and the use of appropriate technology. The aims and goals encompassed medical care, essential drug provision, immunization, maternal and child care, disease control, local epidemiological research, and prevention efforts through improved education, sanitation, and nutrition (Seear, 2007). In addition, Alma-Alta reinvigorated the efforts to prevent and treat such prevalent diseases as malaria and tuberculosis through specific disease-related initiatives. Although it has been uneven in its operation, the resultant expansion of PHC has been linked to significant declines in maternal and infant mortality as well as to increases in life expectancy evident today in some parts of the developing world.

COVID-19

The World Health Organization and other international bodies have long been expecting another pandemic such as the flu of 1918–19. It arrived in the West in early 2020. COVID-19 is a new respiratory virus that became a global pandemic. Within a few months of its emergence, it spread around the world, causing hundreds of thousands of cases of serious illness and death. The first case was traced to Wuhan, China, a city of more than 11 million people in the province of Hubei, on 17 November 2019 (Davidson, 2020). It was a few weeks before the government of China publicly acknowledged the existence of the very contagious new type of difficult-to-treat pneumonia. Apparently 266 people had been identified with the virus like illness before the end of 2019. But when doctors who had first observed this had tried to warn the public about what appeared to be a new and fearsome threat, they were silenced, even fined, and made to recant their observations. Several professors, journalists, and doctors disappeared after sharing information with outsiders (Woodward, 2020).

Then, on 8 December 2019, the Chinese government announced the presence of the disease along with the first case. From that point Chinese officials took swift, decisive, and effective action, albeit with major costs to individual human rights and freedoms.

By the middle of February, China had reported more than 80,000 cases. By the middle of March, the case numbers there had dropped significantly. On 15 March 2020 only 27 new cases were reported in China (Brueck et al., 2020). China had all but eradicated the threat of the virulent disease in that country, but in the meantime it had spread globally and become pandemic, according to the head of the World Health Organization; but even then, the WHO had dragged its heels for weeks before officially labelling the COVID-19 outbreak with the dreaded word "pandemic." By the end of April 2020, some 200,000 people around the world were known to have died from the disease.

The virus likely started as a cross-species transfer of pathogens in a "wet market," that is, a live wild animal market. Preliminary analysis of the genome of the virus suggests that it likely originated in bats and possibly could have been transferred to pangolins as the intermediate hosts or "middlemen" that brought it to humans (Breiman, 2020). (Pangolins, a critically endangered species of anteater with scales, are sold illegally as a luxury food and for their scales, which are used in some Chinese traditional medicines.) Now, however, the virus is spreading among humans through respiratory droplets or close contact (Durrani, 2020). It also can live and be passed on via hard surfaces. Apparently, it can live on cardboard for at least 24 hours and for 72 hours on plastic and stainless steel. Such findings render the possibility that both the social and the material worlds can offer threats to our health. These threats changed our way of life.

Canada's first case of COVID -19 was identified on 25 January 2020 in a 51-year-old man in Toronto. That case was easy to explain. He had recently travelled to China and when he developed minor symptoms soon after arrival home, he called 911, was tested, and later was found to have COVID -19. His wife was soon diagnosed, too. In the ensuing months the virus spread all across the country. The first cases were of people who had travelled outside the country. Very soon it began to be spread invisibly through contacts with unknown people and objects, what we soon came to know as "community spread." Schools, universities, libraries, churches, restaurants, bars, clubs, and offices were closed across the country. People were advised to self-isolate and to practice "social distancing" (see Box 15.1). Groups of more than 50, then 10, then 2, were prohibited from meeting. Governments across the country declared states of emergency, and by 31 July 2020 there were 115,785 confirmed cases in Canada and 8929 deaths from the coronavirus. 100,862 people had recovered. Those numbers would grow. All but essential businesses were closed, and the Canadian and global economies experienced nearly unprecedented contraction. People were told to stay home. Online communications and commerce ballooned. Some people hoarded products such as toilet paper. Hand sanitizer was impossible to find. At the same time, medical personnel and researchers in Canada and around the world explored treatment protocols and sought to develop a vaccine.

Italy and Spain, in Europe, were especially overwhelmed by the pandemic, while in the United States the pandemic appeared even worse. Medical personnel in some locales ran out of adequate personal protective equipment (PPE), and critically needed hospital ventilators were in short supply. By 31 July 2020 there were 4,452,275 confirmed cases in the United States. There were 148,539 deaths and 1,414,155 people had recovered from the coronavirus. The numbers of cases are still rising around the world and especially in the United States and in Brazil.

The high rate of infection in the US was a result of a lack of leadership from the federal government, a hollowing out of global and national health offices within the US during the Trump administration, a failure in preparedness, the uneven and sometimes lax response of state and local governments, and, not least, a profit-oriented health-care system that saw hospitals, states, and cities competing in bidding wars for basic supplies and equipment with one another and with the federal government. Indeed, the tragic American failure in fair part could be attributed to an American ethos of "rugged individualism" and to the value many Americans have placed on individual freedom over caring for the collective good. This could be seen in young people flocking to Florida beaches for their annual spring break bacchanalia, in some state governors initially flaunting social distancing and shelter-in-place recommendations even while nursing homes and meatpacking plants became local hot beds of disease and death, and in some churches insisting on holding worship services of 1,000 and more parishioners in the midst of catastrophe. The risks inherent in living in a risk society had become greater than anyone might have imagined.

As with other diseases, the novel coronavirus is disproportionately distributed across society and occurs most often in people who are already vulnerable because of underlying health issues (the incidence of which varies by social class and racism, among other social factors) and/or because they are older, poor, unsheltered, or precariously housed (Durrani, 2020). The incidence of disease and death among people of colour, which in some locales was threefold greater than their proportion of the population, clearly indicated broad social and health inequities.

Canada in a Global Context

Box 15.1 • Dictionary of a Pandemic

The COVID-19 pandemic changed our lives in countless ways. The economic and social basis upon which we live together crashed and working from home—or not working—became the new normal for most people, at least for a time. Our language has become infused with new terms. Here is a brief list of words and phrases for which many of us now know the meaning.

- **boomer remover:** Facetious phrase suggesting that the virus was somehow designed to rid the world of the baby boomer generation.
- **community spread:** The transmission of a contagious disease within a population when the vector(s) of transmission or direct source of

contagion for an individual case can no longer be identified.

- **contact tracing:** Identifying persons who have come into close contact with an infected person and isolating and monitoring them for symptoms over a period of days or weeks in an effort to halt ongoing transmission and spread of the contagion.
- **doubling time:** The time, measured in days, that it takes for the number of cases in a population to double.
- **epicentre:** A geographic location with an especially high concentration of activity, such as disease and death.

continued

- **flattening the curve**: The need expressed by public health officials to slow the daily/weekly growth rate of an infectious disease in a population by flattening an ascending line on a graph that portrays the spread of infection in a population.
- **herd immunity**: Those within a population who have contracted and recovered from an infectious disease and who therefore have developed antibodies to prevent their re-infection—the larger the "herd," the greater the protection for the entire community, and those who have recovered can become front-line workers in health care and other sectors of the economy.
- **high-risk groups**: Those groups at greatest risk of contracting a disease, such as the elderly, those with underlying health problems, and people in compromised social positions, including the poor, the racialized, the poorly sheltered, and those living in densely populated communities and overcrowded homes.
- **intubation**: Insertion of a plastic tube or tubes into a patient's body, often both into the trachea when the patient can't breathe without mechanical ventilation and into the stomach as a feeding tube.
- **lethality**: The percentage probability of death from the virus, as measured by the total population that has contracted the disease or by a particular age group within that population.
- **morgue truck**: A refrigerated trailer truck used to hold a surplus of dead bodies.
- **novel coronavirus**: A particular type of viral infection among people that is new, so that no one on earth is immune when it first is identified in the human population; many common colds are caused by a coronavirus that has been in the global population for millennia.
- **PPE**: Personal protective equipment, especially as needed for first responders and health-care workers, such as masks, gloves, gowns.
- **self-isolation**: Self-quarantine, i.e., keeping oneself apart from other people; for COVID-19, for at least 14 days to determine if disease symptoms develop.
- **shelter in place**: Staying at home.
- **social distancing**: Maintaining a physical distance at all times of at least two metres between self and any other people to avoid the spread of airborne contagion.
- **triage**: In health facilities, the process of determining which patients get attention in what order based on the severity of symptoms, injury, need, and/or ability of health-care personnel to help; in some instances with COVID-19 as hospitals become overrun with desperately sick patients, those who are deemed least valuable to the economy/society, such as the elderly, or those deemed unlikely to survive.
- **ventilator**: An expensive ($25,000–$50,000) type of hospital equipment used in intensive care units for patients who are unable to breathe on their own; the ventilator forces oxygen into the lungs and draws carbon dioxide from the lungs.
- **wet markets**: Open street markets where trade in live animals is conducted.

Health-Care System Differences around the Globe

The most useful way to understand the globalization of health and medical care is to use data and analysis from the World Health Organization. We discussed core, periphery, and semi-periphery countries in Chapter 2. These terms reflect the theoretical perspective of dependency theory (Wermuth, 2003) and are important to bear in mind in the context of this discussion. The World Health Organization distinguishes among countries for comparative and statistical purposes based on related ideas: geographic region and level of income. The regions, representing the 194 WHO member states, are Africa, the Americas, Southeast Asia, Europe, Eastern Mediterranean, and Western Pacific. Countries are also divided into income categories: low income, lower-middle income, upper-middle income, and high income. The six major regions, classified according to what the WHO calls its Global Burden of Disease regional system, are roughly equivalent to the world's geographical regions or continents. They are comprised of 14 sub-regions differentiated by income, health outcomes and resources, and epidemiological factors. Thus, for example, countries in North Africa are classified as Eastern Mediterranean, as are some countries in the Horn of Africa, while other Horn of Africa countries are classified in the African region. Likewise, former Soviet republics in Central Asia are classified as part of Europe, and while South Korea falls in the WHO's Western Pacific region, North Korea is considered part of the Southeast Asia region, though clearly, in geographical terms, the Democratic People's Republic of Korea is not situated geographically in what we generally consider to be Southeast Asia.

The WHO has documented the direct link between the spread of Western biomedicine and income level of the countries in a region. Thus, on average, there are 2.8 physicians per 10,000 people in low-income countries, 10.1 per 10,000 in lower-middle-income countries, 22.4 per 10,000 in upper-middle-income countries, and 28.6 per 10,000 in high-income countries. The findings are consistent—the richer the country, the more entrenched is allopathic or conventional Western medicine—and the same is true in regard to male and female life expectancy, i.e., the poorest health outcomes are in the poorest countries. Among them are Swaziland, Angola, Botswana, and most of the rest of the continent of Africa (see Figures 15.2, 15.3, and 15.4). These findings are mirrored in the under-five mortality rates of the United Nations' 10 Millennium Development Goal regions (Figure 15.5).

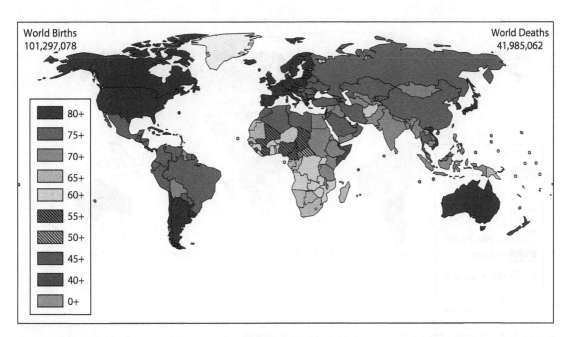

Figure 15.2 World Life Expectancy, Female, 2018

Source: World Life Expectancy, https://www.worldlifeexpectancy.com/world-life-expectancy-map

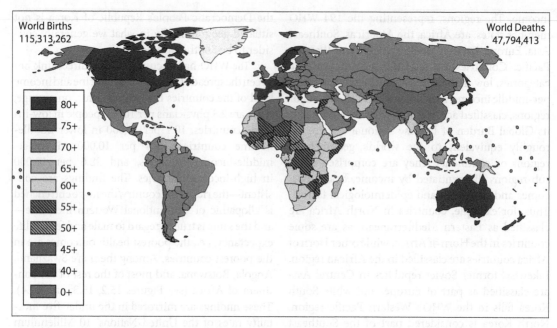

Figure 15.3 World Life Expectancy, Male, 2018

Source: World Life Expectancy, https://www.worldlifeexpectancy.com/world-life-expectancy-map

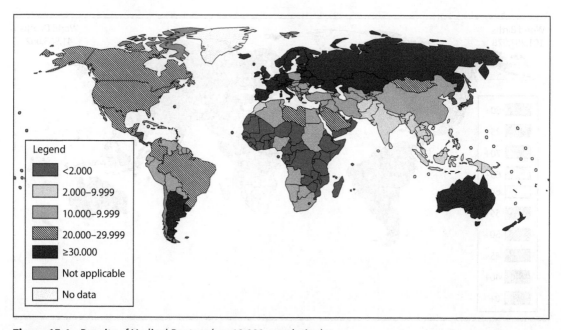

Figure 15.4 Density of Medical Doctors (per 10,000 population)

Source: World Health Organization (2019), https://www.who.int/gho/health_workforce/doctors_density/en

Northern Africa **114**
Caucasus and Central Asia **62**
Oceania **13**
Developed regions **80**
Western Asia **117**
Latin America and the Caribbean **196**
Eastern Asia **194**
Southeastern Asia **331**
Sub-Saharan Africa **2,947**
Southern Asia **1,891**

Figure 15.5   Under-Five Mortality by Millennium Development Goal Region, 2015 (thousands)

Source: Based on UNICEF. *Levels & Trends in Child Mortality: Report 2011.*

Traditional Medicines in Global Context

The discussion so far has been focused on allo-pathic or conventional Western biomedicine. However, a parallel type of medicine sometimes called traditional medicine (TM) or folk heal-ing (Helman, 2007) is widespread throughout the world. In the developed world it is known as complementary and alternative medicine (CAM). TM is not really a system but refers to a group of disparate methods of healing and health care incorporating herbal medicines, spiritual prac-tices, use of animal parts, manual treatments, acupuncture, and Indigenous medicines, among other things (WHO, 2002, 2008; Helman, 2007). Although traditional medicine is widespread, valid information is not available about the extent to which it is practised or its effectiveness across cultures or even in many particular situ-ations. However, researchers and governments estimate that about 80 per cent of the population in Africa and India rely on TM, as do about 40 per cent of the population in China (WHO, 2008, p. 12). In Uganda it is projected that the ratio of TM practitioners to the population is in the range of 1 to 200 or 1 to 400. By comparison, the ratio of allopathic doctors to the population is about 1 to 20,000 or less (WHO, 2008, p. 12). Some

traditional medicines may very well be danger-ous, some innocuous, and some others may be beneficial to healing and health. From a modern scientific perspective, little is known about the benefits and costs of various treatments (see, for instance, Patwardhan, 2005).

The World Health Organization, its member countries, and other interested groups are work-ing to develop an international strategy for evalu-ating and monitoring TM. To this end, objectives have been developed for integrating TM/CAM into allopathic care. These objectives set goals in relation to overseeing the impacts of policy, safety, efficacy, quality, accessibility, and con-sistent and rational use of TM. They are being monitored and studied.

Research on some types of traditional medi-cine is extremely difficult. TM practices range from more standardized systems to the highly secretive, mystical, and subjective procedures that may be linked to the particular abilities, skills, and beliefs of individual practitioners. TM often has a spiritual and/or non-visible compon-ent. Standardized traditional methods such as Chinese medicine, which includes acupuncture, moxibustion, and herbs, and Indian Ayurvedic medicine are well-developed and entrenched systems. They have been in use for centuries and are much easier to assess. They are taught in many medical schools in China and India, re-spectively (Helman, 2007). The most universally accepted aspect of TM is the **traditional birth attendant (TBA)**. TBAs attend the majority of the births worldwide and have played a signifi-cant role in the decreases in infant and maternal mortality.

Many traditional medical practices are not standardized but based on local cultural beliefs, actions, and charismatic healers such as John of God, who for decades had been an internation-ally popular Brazilian healer, attracting many thousands of sick people. Recently, however, he was indicted for rape and sexual abuse of hun-dreds of women (Castano, 2018). Frequently, such healers are trained through apprenticeship and/or chosen at birth, through inheritance, or

Spotlight on Ethics

Box 15.2 • Medical Tourism

"Medical tourism" is a relatively new term that reflects an industry that is growing rapidly as a result of globalization. It involves travelling away from one's home country to seek conventional Western medical treatment and also receiving global travellers to one's home country for treatment. Thus, travel for medicine goes both to and from the developed and the developing parts of the world. Among the most popular places for North Americans to seek health care internationally are Mexico, India, Singapore, Thailand, Malaysia, and the Philippines. The rich in poorer countries also travel to the US and Canada and to other developed nations to acquire modern allopathic care when they are ill or just want particular medical treatment.

People from the US often travel because they are uninsured or underinsured (the specific medical interventions they seek are not covered by their insurer or they lack money for the co-payment). At times, US insurance companies and even state governments encourage their clients to go abroad for cheaper care. They may offer rewards such as five-star hotel rooms, flat-screen televisions, and holidays to tourist destinations because such care may be relatively inexpensive (Turner, 2007). Health insurance companies in the US and Canada and other Western nations benefit from this as it boosts their profits or lowers their expenses. Patients from the developing world travel to the US because of the prestige and the perceived safety and effectiveness of gaining treatment in world-renowned and branded institutions such as the Mayo Clinic, Johns Hopkins, and the Cleveland Clinic.

More than 63,000 Canadians travelled abroad for medical care in 2016 (*CTV News*, 2017). At times, this was due to the wait times for particular discretionary surgeries or other treatments. Sometimes it was because the treatment wanted was not available or not covered in Canada. Some provincial governments have supported medical tourism with websites clearly indicating the process through which hopeful medical tourists must go to seamlessly re-enter the healthcare system back in Canada for follow-up care. This

becomes especially important in cases where there are problematic side effects from the offshore treatment. Some Canadian hospitals are also working to attract wealthy patients from around the world. Many health policy-makers and politicians are promoting the value to the Canadian economy of welcoming medical tourists from outside of the country (Turner, 2012). They argue that expending unused capacity on weekends and in the nights could increase revenues for Canadian hospitals and provinces. Opponents argue that there is no unused capacity and if there were it should be used for Canadians. An opposition to medical tourism is also mounted by those who reject it on the principle that it will lead to the privatization of Canadian health care.

Table 15.1, from the website of an organization that arranges medical treatments, travel, and accommodations for US patients seeking less expensive hospital procedures abroad, demonstrates the advertising and the relative costs of popular treatments. As you can see, there is a significant difference in the cost of surgical procedures between the US and India and Costa Rica.

For the lower-income countries medical tourism is a source of income. Reliance on medical tourists by poorer countries, however, may be detrimental to citizens seeking care in their own countries. If doctors and hospitals are busy with tourists, they may not have the time and resources to care for their own citizens. As a result, the "best" care, reflecting the Western biomedical model, is often only available to the richest within these developing countries. Nevertheless, this global industry is flourishing and is considered an important source of revenue by governments in developing countries.

One example is the Bumrungrad International Hospital in Bangkok, Thailand. It is one of the top destinations for medical tourism in the world today (Finch, 2014a). The hospital can be compared to an upscale shopping plaza or a five-star hotel. It includes 21 VIP suites. The commercial floors host both Starbucks and McDonald's restaurants. Thailand's

Table 15.1 Costs of Particular Medical Treatments in the United States, India, and Costa Rica, 2014

Type of Procedure	US Retail Price Range	India: Average Overall Package Price	Costa Rica: Average Overall Package Price
Laparoscopic gastric bypass	$35,000–$45,000	$17,800	$20,700
Laparoscopic sleeve gastrectomy	$30,000–$40,000	$15,500	$18,700
Hip replacement, unilateral	$40,000–$55,000	$17,000	$22,300
Hip replacement, bilateral	$80,000–$100,000	$25,000	$35,500
Knee replacement, unilateral	$35,000–$50,000	$16,000	$20,600
Knee replacement, bilateral	$70,000–$95,000	$23,000	$33,400
Knee arthroscopy*	$9,000–$16,000	$8,900	$9,300
ACL repair	$25,000–$35,000	$11,500	$11,800
Shoulder replacement	$35,000–$45,000	$17,500	$19,400
Shoulder arthroscopy*	$10,000–$18,000	$9,000	$10,400
Rotator cuff repair	$19,000–$28,000	$15,000	$14,400
Hysterectomy	$16,000–$27,000	$14,700	$16,500
Hernia repair*	$10,000–$20,000	$10,200	$12,400
Spinal fusion (1-level)	$90,000–$120,000	$19,500	–
Spinal fusion (2-level)	$120,000–$160,000	$24,500	–
Spinal fusion (3-level)	$150,000–$200,000	$29,500	–
Spinal disc replacement (1-level)	$160,000–$380,000	$20,500	–
Spinal disc replacement (2-level)	–	$25,500	–
CABG (heart bypass)	$120,000–$170,000	$17,500	–
Single heart valve replacement	$150,000–$200,000	$21,000	–
Double heart valve replacement	$170,000–$240,000	$23,000	–

*Package costs shown for these outpatient procedures do not include the companion travel benefit due to the relatively low levels of cost savings.

Note: The combined package pricing for India and Costa Rica includes all customary costs associated with the hospital stay, operating room/ICU/recovery charges, doctors' fees, anesthesiologist fees, pre/post-surgical consultations and diagnostics, medications, nursing care, physical therapy and rehabilitation services, as well as all costs associated with case management, expedited passport processing fees, applicable visas and permits, air travel, travel insurance, local transportation, consultations, communications, and hotel stay and meals for the patient and an accompanying companion.

Source: Adapted from IndUShealth, http://www.indushealth.com/pricing.

Ministry of Public Health estimates that Thailand hosts about 2.5 million people for medical tourism. Others say this is an overestimate. Regardless, it is a highly sought-after destination because it is affordable and offers advanced high-quality medical care. Singapore and India are next in line in popularity.

Unfortunately, medical tourism may be initiating and exacerbating health-care disparity among the citizens of Thailand (Finch, 2014b). It may be adding to the brain drain of doctors to other countries and the shortage of physicians as well as the increased costs for Thai and other citizens of developing countries.

Sources: Herrick (2007); Turner (2007); Finch (2014a, 2014b).

by revelation. They may incorporate families and communities into a combination of spiritual, relationship, community, and bodily care. Some traditional healers are working to organize and professionalize to become included in state-sponsored medical care. The law, in most countries of the world, upholds allopathic medicine. Successful parallel systems of TM and Western medicine are practised in many countries. In China, for example, traditional Chinese and Western medical schools, hospitals, and practitioners coexist, showing that co-operation is possible. People tend to prioritize one or the other healing mode depending on their medical problems. However, the medicine with the most cachet in the developing world is usually Western or allopathic medicine. It also tends to be the medicine to which the rich around the world turn when ill. It is the medical model most likely to be supported through international development dollars.

Although traditional medicines and medical practices tend to be less expensive than allopathic medicine and treatment, they can be very costly. It is thought that herbal medicines alone are generating many billions of dollars annually. In Europe, yearly revenues averaged about $5 billion by 2003–4; in China, sales of products reached $14 billion in 2005; and in Brazil, herbal medicines alone generated $160 million in 2006 (Castano, 2018). The revenues from herbs and botanicals apparently constituted $33 billion around the world in 2010, and the sector is growing rapidly (Dennis, 2012). By 2018 the revenues from botanicals and herbal medicines were expected to reach $129 billion according to industry analysts (Market Research Future, 2019). Besides herbs and botanicals, various traditional medicines are often more accessible, particularly in the developing world where allopathic medicine may be largely unavailable to rural residents and those lacking in income. Western medicine may be culturally unacceptable, at times, because of such widespread beliefs as that illness is the result of spiritual rather than physical malfunctioning.

Spotlight on Ethics

Box 15.3 • Health as a Human Right

The World Health Organization advocates that health is a human right. Thus, we owe it to one another as members of the same species to ensure that at least the following conditions, which would allow for the possibility of health for all, are universally fulfilled. These conditions include:

- safe drinking water and sanitation;
- safe food and adequate nutrition;
- adequate housing;
- safe working and living conditions;
- health-related education and knowledge;

- gender equality;
- timely access to such medical services as are available;
- free health care;
- prevention, treatment, and control of disease;
- essential medicines;
- child and maternal care.

Do you think health care and the other precursors to the possibility of a healthy life should be international human rights?

Health Care in the United States

We turn now to look at medical care in three countries—the US, the UK, and Brazil. Many studies of medical care in the US have found that although it is the most expensive medical care system in the world it consistently underperforms in terms of five key indicators of health system performance: quality, access, efficiency, equity, and healthy lives (Davis et al., 2010). Table 15.2 tells this story in data from the highly respected Commonwealth Fund. The US continues to rank poorest overall among 11 leading developed nations even though it spends considerably more per person. The US not only underperforms other developed countries but also spends the highest proportion of its **gross domestic product (GDP)** on health care. According to the World Bank data, expenditures per capita for health care in the US have continued to climb, from $8,299 per capita in 2010 to $9,146 in 2013. The US expenditures for 2016 were $9,892 per capita (OECD, 2017a). This is despite the fact that a substantial proportion of the population does not have access to any health care.

How can the discrepancy between cost and value be explained? Whereas elsewhere in the world health is considered a human right, in the US it is treated as a commodity to be traded in the marketplace. One of the first and most notable features of American health care is that no universal, federal system exists, but rather a patchwork of competitive systems and corporations. Health-care reform and the development of a universal system have been a priority for Democratic Party governments for many years. The Obama administration managed to shepherd the Patient Protection and Affordable Care Act (PPACA) through Congress to allow some reform and extension of insurance across the country. However, due to fierce opposition from Republicans, Democrats were only able to pass the Act as a watered-down version of the proposed legislation. The changes they were able to make were further threatened by President Donald Trump when the Republicans won the presidential election in 2016. However, Trump was unable to carry out his plans to scrap the medical insurance scheme, as the majority of Americans did not want to lose the benefits they had gained under what became known as "Obamacare."

Besides Obamacare, there are a few specialized government and tax-based programs, such as Medicaid and Medicare for the elderly, military families, the disabled, and the very poor, but these are piecemeal. The Children's Health Insurance Program (CHIP) created in 1997 is government supported, but is still unevenly available, and about 15 per cent of children remain uninsured (Weiss & Lonnquist, 2012). Millions of people in the US—about 28.9 million people under 65—remain uninsured and at risk of being unable to pay for routine medical care, early detection technologies, or treatment for catastrophic illnesses (Centers for Disease Control and Prevention, 2017). Many others are underinsured and have insurance for only some medical procedures, plus, much of this insurance involves "co-pays," where the individual must pay a significant sum in addition to the insured coverage for numerous diagnostic and surgical procedures. In addition, it is essential to remember that these figures may under-represent the numbers of people without health care because many of the people without coverage are those who are not counted in various censuses because they are homeless or insecurely housed, are illegal immigrants, or in a number of other ways are among the invisible, powerless, and poor. Thus, this is likely an underestimate of the percentage of people not covered under the new Act. It is also important to remember that statistics are not necessarily objective and can be influenced by politics.

Historically, health care in the US has been provided by a conglomeration of fee-for-service physicians, mostly private (for-profit) hospitals, and insurance companies. Most Americans who have insurance obtained it as a benefit of their employment. For the most part, only certain larger organizations include health insurance for their employees. Other people have to pay individually and privately. Many others lack the means to buy insurance. Currently, approximately 1,300 private insurance companies offer medical care insurance and compete against one another for subscribers to their plans. In this context of competition, insurance companies have turned to **managed care**. Health maintenance organizations (HMOs) are one type of insured managed care, which involves a group of physicians and hospitals who agree to provide services in return for premium payments from enrollees. However, as the majority of managed-care organizations are for-profit companies, they are motivated to provide fewer services and services that are less expensive in order to maximize profits. This "system," led by the insurance industry and HMOs, results in disparities in health-care services and outcomes across social classes. It takes place among a myriad of diagnostic, early detection, and prevention technologies. The result is substantial inequity between the poorer, underinsured, uninsured, and insured members of society—and the rich. This system also leads patients to seek health care in cheaper jurisdictions Some insurance companies even give their enrollees financial bonuses in return for their willingness to travel overseas for health care, particularly for discretionary surgery (see Table 15.1). Corporations use figures such as these to decide where to send their patients for specific interventions.

Another notable feature of medical care in the US is that it supports and develops extensive innovative medical research, leading-edge technologies, and experimental drug and other trials, as well as expensive and sophisticated medical devices such as CT scanners and magnetic resonance imaging machines (MRIs). These advances are often picked up by health-care systems elsewhere. In a sense, then, the US investment in original research and technologies subsidizes their use in the rest of the world, although there is no doubt that the US also profits from this investment. Many would argue that the US system is overly developed in high-technology and tertiary care procedures and capabilities at the expense of primary care. Comparisons with regard to just two relatively new and very expensive technologies, CT scanners and MRIs, are illustrative of this point. Canada,

according to the latest figures available, had 15.2 CT scanners per million people, whereas the US had 42.6 scanners per million (OECD, 2017b). The disparity was even greater with respect to MRIs, with 9.9 per million Canadians versus 37.5 per million Americans (OECD, 2017c).

Despite the great successes in innovation and development, hospital-acquired infections and medical mistakes are a leading cause of illness, disability, and death in the US. Medical error is estimated to be the third leading cause of death in the US, according to a 2016 report (Makary & Daniel, 2016).

As Weiss and Lonnquist (2012) indicate, US health care is very expensive for a number of reasons. The *first* and most important is the tremendous power and prevalence of the profit-making corporations such as the managed-care organizations, the pharmaceutical and medical device industries, most hospitals, and a variety of other health services. *Second* is the reliance on tertiary care, high-technology solutions, and medical testing rather than on primary care. *Third* is the aging of the population combined with the medicalization of aging. Most people in the US die in hospital in old age, often after being subjected to heroic and very expensive medical interventions that may extend their lives for only a few days, weeks, or months. *Fourth*, the administrative costs of managing the mélange of insurance and managed care and the numerous other medical institutions are significant—about 20–30 per cent of the total. *Fifth* is physician conflict of interest, when physicians prescribe drugs, tests, and other services for which they may have partial ownership. *Sixth*, some corporations such as pharmaceutical companies are among the highest profit-making businesses in the US. As an illustration, some top executives of pharmaceutical, medical testing, and medical device companies make millions of dollars in annual salary or compensation. *Seventh*, Weiss and Lonnquist note that medical fraud is a substantial problem—medical fraud is estimated to add about $470 billion annually to the US health-care costs. Finally, *eighth*, doctors' salaries in the US are relatively higher than elsewhere and the reliance on specialty medicine pushes doctors' average total income even higher.

Table 15.2 Health-Care System Performance Rankings

	Australia	Canada	France	Germany	Netherlands	New Zealand	Norway	Sweden	Switz.	UK	US
Overall Ranking	2	9	10	8	3	4	4	6	6	1	11
Care Process	2	6	9	8	4	3	10	11	7	1	5
Access	4	10	9	2	1	7	5	6	6	3	11
Administrative Efficiency	1	6	11	6	9	2	4	5	6	3	10
Equity	7	9	10	6	2	8	5	3	4	1	11
Health-Care Outcomes	1	9	5	8	6	7	3	2	4	10	11

Source: Schneider et al. (2017).

Many Americans are unhappy with their health care. Costs are rising more quickly than inflation. Almost half of personal bankruptcies result from the inability to pay medical bills. Increasing costs are unsustainable, particularly in the face of the lack of effectiveness and the financial crisis of 2008–9, and the unprecedented public health and economic upheaval caused by the 2020 coronavirus pandemic only worsened an already difficult health and financial situation for many people. About one-quarter of Americans surveyed are dissatisfied with their health care (Reinhart, 2018). Although the US has emphasized allopathic or conventional medicine, there has been a substantial increase in the use of CAM (Nahin et al., 2009). Such care, as we saw in Chapter 13, tends to be less expensive than Western, allopathic medical care.

Canada in a Global Context

Box 15.4 • Selected Facts Regarding Globalization and Health Today

The Good News

1. Life expectancy around the world has improved more in the last 40 years than in the previous 4,000 years.
2. Smallpox, once a major cause of mortality, has been (almost) eradicated.
3. Child and maternal mortality have declined significantly around the world and by more than 90 per cent in some places.
4. Widespread use of oral rehydration therapy and improvements in sanitation have contributed to a substantial decline in deaths from diarrhea.
5. Disease surveillance is more widely available and helped prevent the spread of SARS in 2003 and to end the Ebola crisis in West Africa from 2013 to 2016, which could easily have spread around the world.
6. The spread of gender rights and equality has improved numerous health outcomes.
7. Information for health promotion and prevention is diffusing.

More to Be Done

1. Tobacco use is spreading and with it the diseases it causes. By 2020 it was expected to be the largest health problem in the world and responsible for 8.5 million deaths annually.
2. HIV/AIDS continues to cause death, disability, and suffering around the world, particularly in sub-Saharan Africa.
3. More than 10 million children die every year from preventable diseases. Most of these deaths occur in low-income countries.
4. Malaria continues to cost lives and health despite the availability of preventative measures and treatment.
5. The global pandemic of a novel coronavirus that began in Wuhan, China, in late 2019 and spread across the world in 2020 has shown governments and their citizens that drastic public health measures must be pursued at once to stop the spread of disease.
5. The gap in income between the high-income and the low-income countries and between people within these countries continues to widen.
6. Environmental destruction of the earth, air, and water, and climate change are spreading rapidly along with development.
7. Obesity, and with it diabetes, is spreading.
8. The overuse of natural resources threatens the viability of the planet.

Sources: Adapted and updated from WHO, www.who.int/en; Canadian Society for International Health, "Facts and Figures: Global Health," www.csih.org

Health Care in the United Kingdom

The United Kingdom is comprised of England, Scotland, Wales, and Northern Ireland. The total population is approximately 63 million and is 90 per cent urban. Founded in 1948, the health-care system is called the **National Health Service (NHS)**. It is a nationalized, tax-supported, and government-run system that provides universal coverage, although the health system of each part of the country differs in some ways and thus there may be some discrepancies from area to area. Formally, the government covers necessary services for all people ordinarily resident in the UK. General practitioners (GPs) usually have the right to add an individual or family to their roster simply by filling out a form. In this way, refugees and immigrants frequently are included in health-care provision. Emergency service is provided to anyone needing it. All other necessary health-care services, such as tests, physician visits, and hospitalization costs are covered. Certain procedures such as cosmetic surgery or highly expensive or experimental medical interventions may not be covered in the public system. There is a small out-of-pocket co-payment for some services or products. This revenue amounts to about 4 per cent of the NHS budget and includes such things as out-of-hospital drugs, eyeglasses, dentures, and pharmaceuticals. Particular groups of people, such as the elderly, pregnant women, children, and people with certain medical conditions, may be exempt from the user fees.

In the UK, doctors are paid a base salary plus capitation (per patient on a fixed patient load); they are also paid for additional services rendered, such as vaccinations. Patients have a choice of their primary care provider or GP. Also, physicians receive a supplement for caring for some categories of people, such as the poor and the elderly. The majority of the budget is paid to primary care physicians. Referral is necessary from GPs to specialists or consultants, and specialists are paid for through hospital budgets. Hospitals bill the government for their costs. The country is divided into 191 Clinical Commissioning Groups (CCGs) for service delivery in their local areas. They are led by elected governing bodies, including GPs, nurses, care consultants, and lay citizens. CCGs are responsible for about two-thirds of the NHS budget and charged with making decisions on the basis of the specific local needs of their respective communities (NHS Clinical Commissioners, 2019). There has been a move to increased flexibility and independence that would allow some competition between hospitals and other health-care facilities in order to improve service, decrease wait times, and lower costs.

As in other European countries, there is a parallel private system into which people can choose to pay and from which they can then seek services. Generally, the private system offers shorter waiting time, private hospital room provision, and some superior hospital services such as better food. About 4 million people in the British population pay for, or have through their places of work, private insurance to improve on the guaranteed coverage (Collinson, 2017). Nevertheless, the NHS is the fifth largest employer in the world, with 1.7 million employees. Only Walmart, McDonald's, the Chinese People's Liberation Army, and the US Department of Defense directly employ more individuals (Alexander, 2012).

A wide variety of CAM or TM is practised in the UK. Herbalism, reflexology, massage, aromatherapy, and acupuncture are among the most popular services. Homeopathy has been withdrawn as a source of universal funding by the NHS. A 2010 report of the effectiveness of homeopathy concluded that it performed "No better than placebos" (National Health Service, 2017). However, despite recent research critical of the effectiveness of homeopathy, the attachment of members of the influential royal family to this mode of treatment may still have some influence and there is a court homeopath (Rainey, 2013). That this finding contrasts with what is described in Box 13.5 is interesting and difficult to understand without recognizing that homeopathic treatments are individualized rather than generalized and thus are very difficult to study or to compare with other treatments. Further, the impact of the political economy of research and the role of the pharmaceutical companies in supporting both certain research and certain findings (Whitaker, 2010) cannot be overlooked as we try to understand differences in findings.

Considering what might appear to be a health-care regime in competition with itself, the UK's hybrid system works fairly well. People have a lot of choice as to health-care providers and are allowed to supplement their tax-supported service level. This system ranks very well on the Commonwealth Fund indicators (Table 15.2) for quality, access, efficiency, and equity. On the other hand, OECD statistics place the UK as about average among developed countries in regard to quality of care (Table 15.3).

Although the cost of the NHS has doubled as a fraction of the overall United Kingdom economy in the years since 1948 (Roberts et al., 2012), it is still relatively inexpensive. Some users and commentators are critical of wait times as well as the restrictions with regard to what services are considered necessary. Some citizens and health-care policy writers argue that this system is underfunded and has not maintained its physical infrastructure (e.g., many hospitals are deteriorating). According to the Commonwealth Fund, the NHS does relatively poorly in terms of health-care outcomes or supporting long, healthy, and productive lives, with the UK ranking next to last and just ahead of the US among the 11 developed countries shown in Table 15.2. Part of this poor showing in life expectancy relates to inequality in the various social determinants of health.

Health Care in Brazil

The acronym BRIC, coined in 2001, refers to four developing countries: Brazil, Russia, India, and China. In 2010 the acronym changed to **BRICS** to include South Africa in this growing block of economies, whose leaders meet for an annual summit. Some analysts have believed the BRICS countries were about to capture the balance of economic power thought to have been lost by the OECD countries in the wake of globalization and exacerbated by the financial crisis of 2008

(O'Neill et al., 2005). BRICS populations are huge and growing, as are their domestic economies and international trade. Investors around the world are paying close attention to these economies and many believe they are critical to future financial growth and world prosperity. For the purposes of this chapter, we will confine this discussion to Brazil, although many of the lessons evident there are also true elsewhere in the developing world. By 2010 the Brazilian economy was worth US$2.09 trillion as compared to the UK economy, which had a GDP of US$2.25 trillion. It continued to grow until 2015 and since then has experienced a serious slump. The economy began to rebound in 2017 and 2018, but its growth has been very slow (World Bank, 2019).

Brazil, the sixth most populous nation in the world with an estimated population in March 2020 of 217 million (Countrymeters, 2020), has dramatically improved its health services and outcomes through a combination of social, political, and medical reforms. Throughout the world, the most important improvements in the health of populations have occurred as the result of changes in the social and ecological systems. Brazil provides an example, with a significant increase in sanitation and infrastructure. In 1970 only approximately one-third of the population had water piped to their houses; by 2010 slightly more than 93 per cent did and by 2015 the figure had increased to 97 per cent. In 1970 about 17 per cent of the households had access to sewage systems to dispose of household waste; in 2010 about 60 per cent of houses were connected to municipal sewerage systems. No households had garbage collection in 1980 but by 2010 almost 90 per cent did (Table 15.4). The federal government in 2013 pledged 100 per cent coverage by 2023. These improvements must be seen as the bedrock of the changes in health outcomes. In addition, there has been a rapid increase in vaccinations, with no record of vaccinations until after the country's **Sistema Único de Saúde (SUS)**, or Unified Health System, was established in 1988. For example, in 1990 less than 9 per cent of the population had

Table 15.3   Quality of Care, Selected OECD Countries

	Asthma and COPD Hospital Admissions (age/sex standardized rate per 100,000 population)	Antibiotics Prescribed (defined daily dose per 1,000 population)	Acute Myocardial Infarction Mortality (age/sex-standardized rate per 100,000 population)	Colon Cancer Survival* (age-standardized survival rate in %)	Obstetric Trauma: Instrument (crude rates per 100 vaginal deliveries)*
OECD	236	20.6	7.5	62.8	5.7
Australia	371 (X)	23.4 (¤)	4.0 (√)	70.6 (√)	7.2 (X)
Canada	247 (¤)	20.8 (¤)	5.1 (√)	67.2 (¤)	16.9 (X)
Denmark	333 (¤)	16.1 (¤)	4.0 (√)	61.6 (¤)	10.9 (X)
France	150 (¤)	29.9 (X)	5.6 (¤)	63.7 (¤)	—
Germany	284 (¤)	14.4 (√)	7.7 (¤)	64.8 (¤)	6.4 (¤)
Israel	259 (¤)	21.4 (¤)	6.7 (¤)	71.7 (√)	1.9 (√)
Japan	58 (√)	—	11.7 (X)	67.8 (¤)	—
Netherlands	202 (¤)	10.7 (√)	5.4 (¤)	63.0 (¤)	3.2 (¤)
United Kingdom	303 (¤)	20.1 (¤)	7.1 (¤)	60.0 (¤)	6.8 (¤)
United States	262 (¤)	—	6.5	64.9 (X)	9.6 (X)

√ Better than OECD average
¤ Close to OECD average
X Worse than OECD average
— Missing data

*Canada is excluded from the calculation of the standard deviation.

Note: All data refer to 2015 or nearest year.

Source: Adapted from OECD (2017a).

Highlighted Issues

Box 15.5 • Global Clinical Trials Industry

Before new drugs and other medical interventions are introduced into the marketplace they must be tested for safety, efficacy, side effects, acceptability, and other characteristics. Most often, the testing begins in the lab and on animals. When sufficient success has been proven on animals, they are tested on humans. People are enrolled in a clinical trial in which they may be randomized either to test the new treatment or to receive the standard treatment or a placebo. This process goes on around the world and has become an enormous industry. In 2007 alone in the US, clinical trial expenditures reached 40 per cent of the research and development budget of pharmaceutical companies, or about $18 billion. It is estimated to cost $2.6 billion to develop and bring a new drug to market in the United States (Glover, 2015).

Due to the size of the pharmaceutical industry and the concomitant need for huge samples of people to test new drugs, clinical trials have become globalized so that participants can be paid much less in poorer countries than in the countries where the research usually originates. According to the most recent data available, from 2013, there are now more than 23,000 clinical trials annually (Viergever & Keyang, 2015). A large part of the expansion of this industry, because of the less stringent regulations regarding patient safety and the cheaper costs, has been in lower-income countries in Asia, Latin America, and Eastern Europe. This strategy sometimes leads to death, side effects, long-term problems, and permanent residual effects for the people who enrol in clinical trials to earn money.

Source: Petryna (2009).

Canada in Global Context

Box 15.6 • Worldwide Violence against Women Is a Major Cause of Harm and Death

The World Health Organization (2017) states that violence is a significant cause of both mental and physical health threats and even death for women around the globe. More than one in three women around the globe experience violence in their lives. This figure includes only physical and sexual violence—not emotional abuse. The human costs for women directly and for their children indirectly are enormous and challenge all aspects of their everyday life. The high levels of violence experienced by women worldwide breed fear and anxiety, which can limit the lives and contributions of women in both private and public spaces. As women are forced to restrict their lives due to fear, violence has profound effects on women's levels of education, employment, and income, whether or not they are experiencing violence in their own lives.

As a result of this data the World Health Organization, with a number of partners around the world, has established a campaign against violence against women called Respect. Respect stands for seven initiatives:

Relationship skills strengthened
Empowerment of women
Services Ensured
Poverty reduced
Environments made safe
Child and adolescent abuse prevented
Transformed Attitudes, Beliefs, and Norms

These changes and challenges are pertinent to the Canadian context. They are also relevant to university and college campuses. Consider what changes your university might (or ought to) make to eliminate violence against women students.

Women are the chief recipients of violence globally, but it is essential to note that other groups also are targeted. Among the most significant are racialized minorities, including Indigenous students and those with minority gender identities and sexual preferences. Consider what your university or college could do to protect people from this kind of targeted violence. What overlapping and different proposals would be relevant to as many intersections as possible?

received immunization for hepatitis B, but 98 per cent had by 2010. Similarly, prior to the formation of SUS, only the wealthy few who could afford health care sought it privately, whereas now well over half of population are served by community health workers (60.4 per cent) and family health teams (49.5 per cent), and more than 45 per cent are cared for, as well, by oral (i.e., dental) health teams.

The Brazilian health system is relatively new. Thus, one of the reasons that coverage is not wider is that about 20 per cent of the population live in remote rural areas and it will take time for access to health services to permeate the countryside. Public health and medical coverage is much greater in the cities than in the rural areas, the mountains, and the rainforest. Nevertheless, as Table 15.5 shows, the infant mortality rate has declined dramatically, from 113 per 1,000 in 1975 to 19 per 1,000 in 2010. Life expectancy has climbed from 52.3 to 72.8 years over the past four decades. Functional illiteracy has declined from 36.9 in 1990 to 20.3 in 2010. Education, literacy, and employment have increased dramatically over this period, and significant increases in prevention efforts have

Table 15.4 Sanitation and Utility Infrastructure, Brazil, 1970–2010

	1970	1980	1990	2000	2010	2015
Households with piped water	32.8%	79.6% (1981)	90.7%	91.6% (2001)	93.1% (2007)	97%
Households with sewerage	17.5%	39.8% (1981)	48.0% (1992)	52.8%	59.5%	86%
Households with refuse collection	n.a.	n.a.	64.5%	83.2%	88.4%	n.a
Households with electricity	48.6%	67.4%	88.8% (1992)	96.0%	98.5%	n.a
Households consuming firewood (10^3 thermoelectric power units)	19,070	14,974	7,960	6,325	5,713	n.a
Households with basic sanitation						86%

n.a. = not available

Source: Reprinted from Paim et al. (2011), with permission from Elsevier.

been realized. Table 15.5 indicates that improvements in health and life expectancy outcomes are associated with the dramatic changes in the provision of health care from 1970 to 2010.

Brazil's health-care system, the SUS, was initiated with the passage of the constitution in

1988, which proclaims health as the right of all citizens and the duty of the state to protect and maintain. Other health- and equity-related changes in Brazil have been particularly dramatic since the defeat of the military dictatorship in free elections in 1985. In fact, universal health

Table 15.5   Demographic, Social, and Macroeconomic Indicators, Brazil, 1970–2010

	1970	1980	1990	2000	2010
Population	95,993,400 (1971)	121,611,375	147,593,859	170,143,121	190,732,694
Urban population	55.9%	67.5%	75.5%	81.2%	83.8%
Infant mortality (per 1,000 live births)	113.9 (1975)	69.1	45.2	27.4	19 (2007)
Life expectancy (years)	52.3	62.6	66.6	70.4	72.8 (2008)
Men	n.a.	59.7	63.1	66.71	68.7
Women	n.a.	65.7	70.9	74.35	76.4
Female-headed households (% of families)	13.0%	15.4% (1977)	22.7% (1993)	27.3% (2001)	33.0% (2007)
Functional illiteracy*	n.a.	n.a.	36.9% (1992)	27.3% (2001)	20.3% (2009)
Health spending per capita (purchasing power parity, $US)	n.a.	n.a.	$473 (1995)	$572	$771.56 (2008)
Proportion of GDP spent on health	n.a.	n.a.	6.7%	7.2%	8.4% (2007)
Proportion of health spending in the private sector	n.a.	n.a.	56.9%	60.6%	57.1% (2007)

n.a. = not available

*Individuals aged 15 or older with less than four years of formal education.

Source: Reprinted from Paim et al. (2011), with permission from Elsevier.

care for the people had been one of the most important rallying cries of the protest movements organized to topple the dictatorship. Today the SUS is a federally sponsored system enshrined in the constitution but decentralized into the 26 states and 5,563 municipalities and dedicated to, among other things, improving the health of the Brazilian population. SUS care is divided into regional groups for administration, and a primary health-care model and services are offered through about 32,000 family health teams and 240,000 community health workers who focus on the poor and, as much as possible, those living in rural and remote areas (see Gragnoloti et al., 2013).

Despite the vast improvements in coverage, the number and spread of public health interventions, and improved health outcomes, problems remain (Paim et al., 2011). One is the disproportionate concentration on the provision of care in urban areas. Another is underfunding of the public sector. Care provision is inequitable so that the poorer and racialized people (Brazil is about half brown- or black-skinned, and this group suffers stigma and discrimination) receive less care and inferior care. A parallel private and for-profit health sector, into which individuals can pay and for which they can also buy insurance as individuals, groups, or through their workplace, thrives. This sector is growing rapidly, and both international and national investments are quickly being made in the large and growing pharmaceutical, medical testing, and medical devices industries. About 26 per cent of the population have private insurance and are able to buy the best care available. The public sector supports the private sector in that it sometimes purchases care from private hospitals and clinics. Secondary and tertiary care is disproportionately provided through the private sector and is more available to the wealthiest. The public sector struggles with long waiting lists and crowded hospitals and clinics. Furthermore, the public infrastructure is deteriorating and the disjointed public/private system is in crisis (Paim et al., 2011). Traditional medicine plays an important role in Brazil, among both the rich and others. Its origins are African and Portuguese, and it is the predominant means of health care along the northeast coast, including the Amazon River and rainforest.

Brazil is one of the most popular medical tourism destinations in the world and provides such popular services as cosmetic surgery at competitive prices. Most of the hospitals are in the private sector as is most of the sophisticated technology. For example, only about 24 per cent of the CT scanners and 13 per cent of the MRIs are available in the public system; the rest are available only privately. In addition, with the rapid growth of the private sector (Couttolenc & Alexandre, 2007), private medical practitioners, specialists, and diagnostic clinics tend to offer more select and speedier service. There are approximately 6,500 hospitals and 70 per cent are private (Export.gov, 2018). Brazil's health system stands on the brink of becoming more like that of either the US or the UK. The forces of global development and investment will play a significant role in its future.

Indicators of health-care effectiveness and costs in Brazil compare favourably relative to the UK and the US. As shown in Table 15.6, although infant and maternal mortality rates are still significantly higher than in the more developed countries, the overall life expectancy at 74 years, has become quite similar to that of the US (80 years) and the UK (81 years). The health expenditures per person in the public sector are decidedly smaller in Brazil, at about US$875. Brazilian government spending on health as a percentage of total public and private health expenditures is slightly lower than in the US, at 44 per cent as compared to 47.8 per cent, but is substantially lower than in the UK. Proportionally, Brazil has fewer doctors and hospital beds, but the country now offers almost complete coverage by birth attendants.

Table 15.6   Comparative Health Expenditures, Health Workforce, and Demographic Characteristics: Brazil, UK, and US

Indicator	Year(s)	Brazil	United Kingdom	United States
Programs, funding, and financing				
Health expenditure per capita	2008	$875	$3,222	$7,164
Government health expenditure as per cent of total public and private health costs	2008	44.0%	82.6%	47.8%
Private expenditure on health	2008	56.0%	17.4%	52.2%
Out-of-pocket expenditure on health	2008	57.1%	63.7%	24.4%
Health workforce and capacity				
Physicians per 10,000*	2015	18.5	28.1	25.5
Births attended by skilled health personnel*	2017	98%	n.a.	99%
Hospital beds per 10,000*	2017	23	29	31
Demography				
Infant mortality rate per 1,000 live births*	2017	17.5	4.3	5.8
Maternal mortality rate per 100,000*	2015	44	9	14
Life expectancy, years at birth*	2017	74	80.8	80

Sources: WHO, www.who.int/medicines/areas/policy/world_medicines_situation/WMS_ch18_wTraditionalMed.pdf; *Index mundi, https://www.indexmundi.com/g/g.aspx?v=29&c=uk&l=en

Summary

1. The process of globalization is advancing rapidly around the world.
2. There are health benefits and costs to globalization.
3. The mortality rates of low-income and high-income countries differ substantially.
4. The coronavirus global pandemic (Coronavirus disease 2019 or COVID-19) renewed the awareness of governments and people of just how globalized economies and public health have become.
5. South Africa provides an excellent example of health disparities within a country.
6. The World Health Organization monitors global mortality and morbidity by maintaining up-to-date statistical profiles of the health and health-care systems of nations and by working to improve health around the globe.
7. Both Western and traditional medicine are used worldwide. Many more studies document the effects of Western medicine than of traditional medicine.
8. Health care in the US is a patchwork of mostly for-profit medicine that is relatively expensive and frequently unavailable to a significant minority of people.

9. Health care in the UK is a universal and comprehensive system that is relatively inexpensive and effective.
10. Health care in Brazil is in a transitional state; it encompasses a mixture of the universally provided UK system and the American free-enterprise system. The public infrastructure is deteriorating and the disjointed public/private system is in crisis; its future will depend on investment.

Key Terms

BRICS
fragmented and fragmenting care
gross domestic product (GDP)
inverse care
impoverishing care
managed care

misdirected care
National Health Service (NHS)
Sistema Único de Saúde (SUS)
traditional birth attendant
unsafe care
World Health Organization (WHO)

Questions for Study and Discussion

1. Information about health care and health-care outcomes around the world is uneven and sometimes difficult to obtain. Can you explain why reliable and valid information and statistics are not always available?
2. Global development has produced a tension between improvements in living standards and consequent health, on the one hand, and the potential to spread illness and illness-causing behaviours, such as cigarette smoking, on the other. Discuss.
3. The US health-care "non-system" is a patchwork that does not provide free health care to all of its citizens and results in some very poor health outcomes, particularly for those Americans who are at the bottom of the social hierarchy. Discuss.
4. Investigate what simple things could be done to eradicate malaria and tuberculosis, two of the most challenging diseases worldwide.
5. Tobacco smoking has increased in parts of the developing world, such as China, even while it has decreased in the developed world. Explain.

Suggested Readings

Davies, S.E. (2010). *Global politics of health*. Polity Press. An overview of a political and economic understanding of global health.

De Vogli, R. (2011). Neoliberal globalisation and health in a time of economic crisis. *Social Theory & Health, 9*, 311–25. A paper about the growth of inequality under globalization.

Finch, S. (2014). Medical tourism driving health care disparity in Thailand. *Canadian Medical Association Journal, 186*(1), 11. A discussion of some of the negative effects of health-care tourism on Thailand.

Kapoor, I. (2012). *Celebrity humanitarianism: The ideology of global charity*. Routledge. A critical look at the impact of celebrity fundraising for global development.

Appendix
Websites for Sociological Research on Health and Medicine

https://www.marxists.org/archive/marx/works/1848/communist-manifesto
This site includes *The Communist Manifesto*.

www.cihi.ca
The Canadian Institute for Health Information site is full of useful information for understanding health and medicine in Canada.

https://www.statcan.gc.ca/eng/start
The Statistics Canada website includes daily news, census materials, Canadian statistics, and so on.

https://www.apc.org/
Association for Progressive Communications provides international communication links for activists. It includes many progressive publications from around the world in English, French, and/or Spanish.

www.networklobby.org
The Catholic Social Justice Lobby promotes economic and social justice, including welfare reform, anti-poverty efforts, and health-care reform.

www.worldbank.org/publications
The World Bank site includes ordering details for various publications related to international development, such as *World Development Indicators*, *World Bank Atlas*, and *Global Development Finance*, and complete text for such sources as the *World Bank Annual Report*.

www.who.org
The World Health Organization offers the biggest collection of current news stories about global health issues. The site includes information on diseases, the environment and lifestyle, family and reproductive health, health policies, statistics, and systems.

www.csih.org
The Canadian Society for International Health is the leading Canadian health and development organization.

www.paho.org
The Pan-American Health Organization's bilingual English/Spanish site contains lots of publications and links to useful documents.

www.idrc.ca
The International Development Resource Centre is a Canadian, government-based organization dedicated to helping communities in the developing world find solutions to social, political, economic, environmental, and health problems.

www.iwh.on.ca
The Institute for Work and Health is an independent, not-for-profit organization that conducts and disseminates research related to the underlying factors that contribute to workplace health and disability.

www.ccohs.ca
The Canadian Centre for Occupational Health and Safety offers information and research related to the promotion of safe and healthy working environments.

www.iglhrc.org
The International Gay and Lesbian Human Rights Commission seeks to protect and advance the human rights of all people and communities who experience discrimination and abuse on the basis of sexual orientation, gender identity, or HIV/AIDS status.

www.wilpf.org
The Women's International League for Peace and Freedom, founded in 1915, works on issues including, but not limited to, women's rights, disarmament, ending US overseas intervention, and racial justice.

www.cwp-csp.ca
The national anti-poverty organization, Canada without Poverty, offers news, information about research, and activist advocacy.

www.ccsd.ca
The Canadian Council on Social Development site includes information about poverty and child poverty in Canada, welfare, and income.

www.hc-sc.gc.ca
Health Canada provides a wide variety of information on topics such as Indigenous health, alcohol and drug use, HIV/AIDS, diabetes, the Great Lakes environment, family violence, and other related health issues.

www.cmaj.ca
The Canadian Medical Association provides information about many current issues facing the medical profession in Canada, as well as the *Canadian Medical Association Journal*. It includes its own internal search engine.

www.ama-assn.org
The American Medical Association site includes journal articles, links, and discussion of many timely concerns related to international medicine. The *Journal of the American Medical Association* (*JAMA*), one of the most influential medical journals, is available online via this site.

www.cna.ca
The Canadian Nuclear Association provides information about nuclear energy, safety, and security.

https://www.cna-aiic.ca
The Canadian Nurses Association site includes news related to health and nursing, and weekly updated articles from the magazine *Canadian Nurse*.

https://nccih.nih.gov
The National Center for Complementary and Integrative Health of the NUS National Institutes of Health provides information on health topics and current news features.

www.drweil.com
The website of one of America's best-known natural health advocates, Dr Andrew Weil, includes an interactive component, updated daily, in which the user can ask Dr Weil questions.

https://www.chiropractic.ca
The Canadian Chiropractic Association site includes health tips and information on chiropractic.

www.naturopathicassoc.ca
The Canadian Association of Naturopathic Doctors site includes links to related Canadian and international resources relevant to naturopathy.

www.phac-aspc.gc.ca/index-eng.php
At the website of the Public Health Agency of Canada you can find up-to-date information about chronic disease, public health emergencies, influenza outbreaks, vaccines, and various topics constantly under surveillance by this agency.

www.oecd.org
The website for the Organisation for Economic Co-operation and Development publishes comparative health and social indicators for a number of countries.

www.fnhc.ca
The First Nations Health Council represents and accounts to the BC First Nations. The site includes updated information and news related to Indigenous health in British Columbia and beyond.

www.seniorsinfo.ca
This Ontario government site provides examples of and links to statistics and research related to seniors and their health needs.

Glossary

absolute homelessness The condition of those who have no home and spend their nights either in homeless shelters or on the streets.

accessibility One of the five principles of medicare: that health care is accessible to all Canadians, regardless of where they live.

acupuncture Such practices as the insertion of fine needles into particular places on the body, moxibustion (burning of leaves on the skin), and other techniques based on Chinese medicine, designed to stimulate the flow of chi (energy) through the body to maximize the ability of the body to heal.

administration One of the five principles of medicare: that it is administered on a not-for-profit basis.

allopathic doctors Doctors practising within the Western paradigm of medicine who use the conventional methods of their training to oppose disease. Typical methods of opposing the disease process include removing it surgically, burning it through radiation, and killing, diminishing, or controlling it through pharmaceuticals.

allopathic medicine Medical practice based on the assumption of a division between the body and the mind, and an approach to the treatment of disease by opposing it through surgery, drugs, and radiation.

aspirational health The use of medicine to change one's identity and improve or enhance the self.

attachment process The process whereby more and more of social life becomes medicalized as medicine expands its jurisdiction in four different ways related to technology, living the good life, and the sovereignty of the individual body.

barber-surgeons Early surgeons who were also barbers and limited their cutting to external parts of the body and to limbs.

BBC chain Biography, body, and self-conception: an approach to understanding how people cope with chronic illness affecting the body by modifying or "rewriting" their personal biographies and their conceptions of self.

bioengineering Applying the techniques of engineering to biological processes, in areas ranging from organ transplants, joint replacements, and prosthetics to in-vitro fertilization.

biomedicalization The intensification of medicalization over the past 20–30 years through such technoscientific processes as computer programming, genomization, molecular biology, developments in transplant medicine, and new, expensive diagnostic technology.

birth rate The number of babies born in a given place over a given period of time expressed as a function of the total population.

BRICS Brazil, Russia, India, China, and South Africa: five countries believed to be on the verge of becoming economic superpowers, whose leaders meet annually for a summit. Formed in 2001 as BRIC, with the addition of South Africa in 2010 the group became the BRICS.

capitation A method of physician payment through which the doctor receives a set fee for managing a particular number of patients annually.

chiropractic Health care concerned primarily with the well-being of the spine, based on the idea that disease results from partial spinal dislocation or subluxation.

climate change Changes in temperature and weather patterns resulting from the emission of greenhouse gases into the atmosphere. Consequences include rising sea levels, alterations in regional precipitation, heat waves, flooding, thawing of the tundra, and other extreme events.

clinical experience A dominant value in the profession of medicine that much of medical practice is an art of joining accumulated knowledge to the interpersonal relationship with the patient, the nature of the disease, and appropriate treatment.

commodification A view of health and the provision of health care as a commodity to which cost–benefit analyses can be applied, as espoused by many health administrators and by those in the for-profit health services sector.

complementary and alternative medicine (CAM) A broad range of health and medical care that falls outside of the practice of conventional or allopathic medicine, including acupuncture, traditional Chinese medicine, homeopathy, and chiropractic; often conceptualized as preventative, holistic, and focusing on health rather than on disease.

comprehensive coverage One of the five principles of medicare: that coverage should be for an extensive range of conditions.

conflict theory A foundational sociological theory based on Marxian belief that the social classes are in fundamental conflict with one another. The social world is understood in terms of opposing/conflictual forces.

core, periphery, and semi-periphery countries A schema that differentiates nation-states on the basis of their stages of economic development and governance stability.

critical anti-racist theory A theoretical approach that views racialization and racism as a cause of much social inequality.

cumulative advantage theory A theory that points to the importance of early life experiences of advantage (generally, of socio-economic advantage).

cumulative effects The accumulation of advantage or disadvantage over a lifetime and how this affects the subsequent probability of health or illness as the person ages.

dependent variables The presumed effect of other, independent variables that must precede the dependent variables in a study of human social behaviour, i.e., the observed results of independent variables. For example, in seeking a cause of diabetes, a diet high (or low) in sugars and starches would be an independent variable, while the rate of diabetes within a population would be the dependent variable.

DES (diethylstilbestrol) Also called stilbestrol, a synthetic estrogen hormone given to pregnant women from the 1940s through the 1960s that led to assorted medical complaints. Its use by pregnant mothers in Canada led to numerous cancers in their sons and daughters as they matured and may have affected the third generation as well.

diarrheal disease A leading cause of infant death in the developing world; caused by polluted water, poor hygiene, and inadequate sanitation.

digitized medicine Medical care and information provided online.

direct-to-consumer advertising Advertising for various sorts of drugs to the public through the mass media.

"dirty work" of physicians Routine tasks such as monitoring blood pressure, setting up intravenous infusions, and giving medications that have largely been taken over by nurses.

discourse Ways of conceiving and talking about issues, such as medicine, so that reality is defined in particular terms by the power of language.

disease A medical diagnosis pertaining to ill health.

disease-mongering The idea that corporations such as pharmaceutical companies sometimes market a new disease after they have developed a new and relevant treatment.

diseases of civilization Diseases that result from lifestyle behaviours and social determinants of health rather than from the lack of clean water, ample food, and the like. They tend to occur later in life.

doctrine of specific etiology The idea that each disease is the result of a particular pathogen or organ malfunction.

downstream model Interventions to cure the illness that occur after disease has started.

drapetomania A "disease" prevalent in the nineteenth century, which was said to cause slaves to run away from their masters.

dysaethesia aethiopis A "disease" discovered among slaves in the nineteenth century, which referred to poor work habits.

environmental illness A painful and sickening sensitivity to the environment; also called "twentieth-century disease."

epidemiology The field of study that focuses on patterns of disease and disease outbreak.

essentialized The assumption made that there is an essential or basic biologically driven gender, race, sexuality, and so on. This notion ignores the powerful effects of the social on these categories.

ethnicity Characteristics of a group of people because of a shared cultural background, including such factors as religion, family patterns, and language.

evidence-based medicine (EBM) A relatively new development in medical practice that aims to provide clinicians with information based on the best and the latest scientific research for their decision-making.

e-waste All of the waste that results from the rapid obsolescence of electronic equipment such as computers, cell phones, and associated products.

exclusion A process used by an occupational group to deny the legitimacy of its practice by a different occupational group.

fee-for-service A method of paying physicians based on a set fee for a particular diagnosis and intervention.

female circumcision Surgical procedures (performed without anaesthetic by folk practitioners) such as circumcision, where the hood of the clitoris is cut; excision, where the clitoris and all or part of the labia minora are cut out; and infibulation, which includes cutting the clitoris, labia minora, and at least part of the labia majora and suturing the two sides of the vulva, leaving only a minuscule opening.

feminist theory A theoretical approach that views patriarchal structures in society, including in the family, the workplace, and other social institutions, as the cause of a lack of gender equality and, consequently, of numerous social problems.

Flexner Report An evaluation of medical schools across North America in the early part of the last century, which led to radical reforms in medical education and an emphasis on science as the basis for medicine.

food insecurity A situation, either chronic or acute, in which people do not have access to enough safe, nutritious, and culturally acceptable food.

fragmented and fragmenting care Excessively specialized care that mitigates the provision of basic primary care for all.

fundamental cause The first or fundamental cause of illness.

global ecosystem The ecosphere, where environmental policies and actions in one region or country can affect aspects of the environment in other parts of the world.

Grange Inquiry An Ontario commission chaired by Justice Grange that examined the actions surrounding suspicious infant deaths at the Hospital for Sick Children in 1980 and 1981.

greenhouse gases (GHGs) Gases emitted on earth—mostly due to the burning of fossil fuels and the methane resulting from intensive or "factory" farming of animals—that absorb and reflect radiation, trapping heat in the atmosphere to cause global warming.

gross domestic product (GDP) The value of the goods and services produced within a particular country during a specified period of time.

health in all policies (HiAP) The assertion that all social policies have consequences for the health of a population.

health indicators Rates of occurrence of activities or conditions used by governments to assess the levels of health of the population or of subpopulations, including such factors as smoking, obesity, alcohol consumption, clean water supply, diabetes, influenza, and infant mortality rates.

healthism A focus on health as a source of life's meaning.

healthy immigrant effect The tendency of immigrants upon arrival in the receiving country and for some period of time afterwards to be healthier than non-immigrants of the same ages.

herbalism The use of plants for healing and in preventive medicine.

holistic health care Health care that attempts to consider the body/mind and spirit as integrated and, thus, in need of integrated treatment.

home health-care work Work in the home, most often done by women, that involves providing healthy conditions, nursing the sick, teaching about health, and mediating with those in the medical care system on behalf of family members with health problems.

homeopathy A type of health care based on the principle of "similars" or the idea that "like treats like." Rather than opposing disease, as in allopathic medicine, highly diluted traces of botanical, mineral, and other natural substances are used to stimulate the body's self-healing abilities and to build the body's defences to promote health.

hyperkinesis Disability, especially among young boys, "discovered" and diagnosed in the past century and now called attention deficit disorder (ADD), attention deficit hyperactivity disorder (ADHD), or dyslexic syndrome, and characterized by such traits as reversals of letters in words and words in sentences, difficulty ordering objects and activities, mood swings, hyperactivity, intermittent attention span, restlessness, and poor co-ordination (clumsiness).

iatrogenesis Illness or disability that results from a medical intervention.

illness The experience of feeling not well.

illness candidate Someone in remission from a life-threatening condition.

illness iceberg The notion that, just as most of an iceberg is under water and unseen, much of illness, individually or within society as a whole, is undetected or not acknowledged.

impoverishing care The circumstance in which people become impoverished because of their need for and the high cost of medical care.

incidence The rate or number of new cases of disease (either diagnoses or deaths) in a population in a given period of time.

independent variables The presumed causes of a change that must precede the changes observed in a study of human social behaviour.

infant mortality rates Measurements of the number of deaths of infants (usually infants of less than one year) in a given year as a function of the total number in the cohort, usually presented as deaths per 1,000 live births.

interpretive/social constructionist theory Sociological approach derived from the work of Max Weber that, according to Weber, "attempts the interpretive understanding of social action in order thereby to arrive at a causal explanation of its course and its effects"; in other words, this theoretical approach focuses on the reality of the beliefs and behaviour of human subjects from the subjects' perspectives.

intersectionality A theoretical understanding that individuals and groups of people cannot be defined and understood by only one characteristic of their identity, such as gender, "race," or income status, but that various identities are dynamically entwined.

inverse care Where the richest consume the greatest proportion of the medical care.

Kyoto Accord A 1997 agreement among most countries, using 1990 emissions as a baseline, to cut greenhouse gas emissions in order to control climate change. Although Canada ratified the agreement in 2002, pledging by 2008–12 to lower emissions by 6 per cent from 1990 levels, Canadian emissions soon thereafter exceeded the target by more than 20 per cent, and in late 2011 the Conservative government officially reneged on the Canadian commitment to Kyoto.

latency effects The long-term health impacts on individuals of early developmental characteristics, such as premature birth or being underweight or overweight at birth.

life course approach The perspective on the social determinants of health that focuses on the additive or cumulative effects of inequity or equity on the life chances and health of individuals.

life course transitions Changes in status over a lifetime such as beginning and ending different levels and types of schooling, getting married or divorced, being widowed, and so on.

life expectancy The average age to which people born in a given year in a particular country or region of a country can expect to live.

limitation A process used by a dominant professional group whereby it limits the areas of work allowed to members of another occupational group.

machine metaphor The notion that the body is like a machine in that it has discrete parts operating together in order to function.

managed care Medical care provided through a health maintenance organization (HMO) in the US, whereby a person who enrols with an HMO and pays a premium to that organization has access to the physicians and hospitals who are participants within the plan of the HMO.

managerial ideology A viewpoint that organizes work into bureaucratic order and numerous specialty divisions.

materialist approach An approach to the social determinants of health that focuses on how health is impacted by the extent to which people can access such material things as adequate and nutritious food and good housing.

mediated Experiences of life often mediated or transformed through their presentation in the mass media.

medical errors The harmful results of the actions of doctors that do not fit within the norms worked out in practice and agreed on within the profession.

medical-industrial complex A large and growing network of private and public corporations engaged in the business of providing medical care and medical care products, supplies, and services for a profit, such as the pharmaceutical and medical device industries.

medicalization The tendency for more and more of people's lives to be encompassed by medical definitions of reality, for example, the drawing of birthing and dying into the purview of medical definitions of appropriate behaviour and care.

medical responsibility The sometimes onerous moral weight attached to making decisions that impinge on the life and death of the patient.

microaggressions Casual and seemingly minor slurs, slights, and interpersonal assumptions directed towards racialized people.

midwifery The long tradition of women trained and experienced in childbirth accompanying and assisting women during the birthing process.

mind–body dualism A philosophical assumption fundamental to the development of allopathic medicine that posits the separation of the mind or soul and the body; known as the Cartesian duality, after Descartes.

minority status A numerical under-representation of an identifiably different group within a population.

misdirected care An emphasis on secondary or tertiary care that limits the availability of primary care.

moral entrepreneur Someone who, through his/her position, intentionally or unwittingly imposes a personal moral paradigm on others, as when the work of the doctor involves moral decision-making and the patient can be coerced or unduly influenced into the doctor's way of thinking.

moral mistakes Mistakes, usually interpersonal, that call into question the physician's attitude, reliability, or responsibility to the patient, which is considered moral failure and, therefore, more egregious than a technical mistake.

morbidity Being or feeling sick to the point of being unable to do and accomplish all that one normally would on a daily or weekly basis.

mortality rate The number of people who die in a given year as a function of the total population of a designated region, usually calculated as the number of deaths per 1,000 people.

National Health Service (NHS) The nationalized, tax-supported, and government-run health-care system in the UK that provides universal coverage.

naturopathy The practice of a number of different, alternative methods, including homeopathy, acupuncture, and hydrotherapy, that employ natural methods and substances to support and stimulate the body's inherent healing processes.

neo-liberalism Political ideology that focuses on the primacy of the market and free enterprise in economic development and on social and political values that give priority to individual freedom rather than to group rights.

neo-materialist approach A view of inequality and health that considers the importance of adequate material resources but then acknowledges the importance of the relative distribution of material and social goods within a society as a critical factor in subsequent health outcomes.

non-disease The "non-existent" category in medical practice, because doctors diagnose disease, and their focus usually is not on health per se but on returning the patient to that condition where disease is not present.

occupational stress Work-related stress that can lead to a number of health problems, caused by such factors as unreasonable deadlines, interpersonal conflicts, lack of feedback, unclear job requirements, and lack of influence.

over-the-counter drugs Drugs available for purchase without a prescription from a doctor.

pathologized Conceptualized as problematic and/or needing medical treatment.

pathway effects Early experiences of equity or inequity that set a person on a course towards better or poorer health.

patient-in-waiting Someone living with the statistically or genetically predicted expectation of disease.

pharmacare Publicly funded prescription drug program for all of society or some segment of society.

pharmaceuticalization The increasing emphasis and reliance on drugs within the medical profession, and within society, to address issues of health and illness.

pharmaceuticals and personal care products (PPCPs) Cosmetics and over-the-counter medicines that can have a negative impact on the health of consumers and that are harmful to the environment in their production and/or disposal.

phenomenological Analytical and descriptive, focusing on direct personal experience and consciousness.

physical reductionism The notion that the smallest unit of observation and analysis is a microcosm of the whole.

political economy perspective A perspective on world development that considers the place of nations in respect to their economic and political condition, and that examines how national and international politics and economies feed off one another.

population pyramid A type of graph portraying a population by age and gender, with the younger ages at the bottom and, conventionally, males on the left half and females on the right half.

portability One of the five principles of medicare: that Canadian residents can take their coverage from province to province if they move or travel.

positivism A philosophy of science that holds valid such values as objectivity, observation, replication, experimental design, and numerical analysis. It has often been used in concert with structural-functional theory.

post-structuralism Theoretical stance emphasizing contingency and the shifting meanings and values of words, concepts, and identities, which rejects the validity of binary thinking and analysis, e.g., male or female, well or ill, sane or insane.

post-traumatic stress disorder (PTSD) A psychiatric term referring to anxiety, as well to psychological and physical suffering, that results from the experience of trauma.

practice norms Generally accepted beliefs and practices regarding the diagnosis and treatment of specific diseases and medical problems within a particular identifiable area, whether a hospital, a province or state, or a country.

precautionary principle The need for caution in regard to the introduction and acceptance of new technologies; "first, do no harm."

prevalence The extent to which a disease (diagnoses or deaths) occurs in a population at a particular time interval.

primary health care The essential and basic medical care that people and societies receive or should receive, including necessary drug provision, immunization, maternal and child care, disease control, local epidemiological research, and prevention efforts through improved education, sanitation, and nutrition.

principles of medicare Values that include universality, portability, comprehensive coverage, administration, and accessibility.

privatization A shift from the public sector to the private sector in the provision of health services, often with the assumption that the individual rather than the state must pay for these services.

profession as ideology The status of a profession based on its success in perpetuating a particular set of beliefs and values, such as, in the case of allopathic medicine, unemotional neutrality in dealing with patients, altruism, and placing the needs of others above one's own welfare.

profession as occupation The trait approach to defining occupation as an accumulation of more or less unique traits acquired through training and experience.

profession as process The acquisition by an occupational group of professional status over a period of time through fulfilling certain prerequisites, such as establishing its own criteria and institutions for education, licensing, practice, administration, ethics, and self-censure.

provisionally accommodated Those who live in a car, "couch surfers" who live with friends or family, and those in long-term institutions.

psychoneuroimmunology The theory in modern biological science that focuses on the body's immune response to psychological states.

psychosomatic Illnesses and diseases caused by psychological, mental, or emotional conditions.

"race" A social construction based on external physical characteristics, such as skin colour.

racialization The process whereby social distinctions are constructed by and about groups of people on the basis of skin colour and other perceived differences.

racism A process of evaluating and acting prejudicially and negatively towards people of a different social group and skin colour.

reflexology Natural healing therapy based on the principle that there are "reflex" points on the feet, hands, and ears that correspond to every part of the body. Stimulation of those areas is believed by practitioners and adherents to cause changes in related body tissues at a distance from the reflex points.

regimen and control The idea that the body is to be managed and controlled through eating, exercising, and so on.

remission society The social situation caused by the increase in people who are alive after a serious diagnosis, such as cancer, yet are continually on the lookout for the disease to return.

residential schools The result of a policy instituted by the Canadian government with the assistance of major religions whereby Indigenous children were (sometimes forcibly) removed from their homes to live in schools designed to assimilate the children into the dominant culture. The site of grievous harm to the children and their families resulting in trauma and other damage to generations of Indigenous people.

resilience Ability to respond to challenges, such as loss of a loved one or a serious accident or diagnosis, in ways that are helpful to one's well-being.

risk society Postmodern society characterized by ubiquitous risks, many of which are created in the process of manufacturing our supposed quality of life, ranging from the cars we drive to the medicines we take and various risky but pleasurable behaviours.

rolfing Deep manipulation of the muscles and connective tissue to shift the body into alignment; pressure is applied with the fingers and knuckles, etc.

secondary gains The "additional" benefits of feigning sickness.

secondary health care Health care directed towards disease treatment in hospital and community via various (usually Western-style) medical practitioners.

sense of coherence A belief that the world makes sense and that the individual knows how to achieve desired goals and cope with life's vicissitudes because of the confidence that, in the long run, things will work out well.

sequential stages of medicalization The idea that medicalization is a process that increases over time through sequential stages including the definition of a behaviour as deviant, prospecting, claims-making, legitimation, and institutionalization.

sex-mortality differential The difference between male and female mortality rates expressed as a percentage, proportion, or fraction of the population.

shiatsu A type of massage therapy in which the practitioner applies pressure to points on the body using fingers, palms, knees, or cushioned elbows to relax the body to promote its natural ability to heal.

sickness The behaviours engaged in by the person who feels ill, such as staying in bed or going to the doctor.

sick role A concept from structural functionalism that holds that sickness is a social role characterized by two rights and two duties.

Sistema Único de Saúde (SUS) Brazil's national health system, established in 1988.

"Sixties Scoop" A policy of the Canadian government begun in the 1960s whereby children were removed from Indigenous homes designated as inadequate to be placed in foster and adoptive homes

social capital The power and well-being—economic, relational, emotional, and spiritual—gained by individuals as members of social networks.

social cohesion The relational "glue" of interactions and shared activities that bind, integrate, and foster mutual interdependence of people into social life.

social determinants of health The social conditions of inequity based on such factors as income, gender, age, education, housing, and neighbourhood that lead to differences in health outcomes.

social inclusion Characteristics of communities, such as civic engagement, voter turnout, and the representation of people of diverse backgrounds in positions of power in local governments and community organizations, that allow people of different backgrounds and incomes to feel part of and to participate in the larger community.

Social Readjustment Rating Scale A scale that measures the amount of social change an individual has undergone in a given period of time. The results are said to predict the likelihood of subsequent illness.

social support Practical help, sympathetic understanding, and/or integration into social life offered to an individual.

stigma The "othering" or blaming of a person or group as a result of a particular characteristic, such as mental illness or ethnicity.

stress Adverse physiological and/or psychological manifestations that result from demands in the individual's environment—natural, work, family, interpersonal, financial, etc.—that are greater than one usually experiences or is able to cope with over an extended period of time.

structural functionalism A foundational sociological theory that views the social world as a system of interlocking parts working together to fulfill functions geared to the sustainability of the social order.

subordination A process used by a dominant occupational group to restrict the work of another group under its jurisdiction.

survivor Someone who has not succumbed to a deadly disease or accident and has been given a qualified or tentative "clean bill of health."

symbolic interactionist theory An approach to understanding society that focuses on meaning-making

and discourses of social life; similar to interpretive/social constructionist theory.

tautological Saying essentially the same thing twice using different words.

technical mistakes Medical mistakes that harm the patient, caused by error in using technology; considered not as important as moral mistakes.

technological imperative The concept that technological development precedes social change.

technologies of self Governing the self in the interests of the prevailing medical power/knowledges.

tertiary care Health care that occurs in a teaching hospital attached to a university, with a side emphasis on health promotion.

thalidomide A medication developed in Germany for the treatment of respiratory infections, colds, coughs, flu, nervousness, and neuralgic and migraine headaches that was given to some pregnant women in Canada in 1961–2 before it was withdrawn because it caused serious birth defects, including phocomelia (absence of limbs).

therapeutic touch A type of treatment based on the idea that that the body is surrounded by energy fields that are affected by disease and that can be manipulated. Treatment, in this perspective, can include the therapist's "smoothing" and otherwise working with the energy fields by moving the hands above the surface of the body.

traditional birth attendant Health-care provider specializing in reproduction issues.

twentieth-century disease Hypersensitivity to toxic chemicals in the environment; also known as "total allergy syndrome" and "environmental illness."

uncertainty Not knowing what the outcome of a diagnosis will be.

universality One of the five principles of medicare: its availability to the whole population.

unsafe care Health care causing illness or death.

upstream model Interventions that occur prior to disease occurrence, intended to prevent illness.

verstehen A term used by German sociologist Max Weber meaning "empathetic understanding," the desired approach to research.

World Health Organization (WHO) A United Nations organization comprised of 194 countries that administers and reports on global and regional health issues and concerns.

References

Chapter 1

Abedi, M. (2017, July). Raising the smoking age in Canada is inevitable: Advocate. *GlobalNews*. www.globalnews.ca/news/3620432/higher-minimum-legal-smoking-age/

BCBecky (2017, Apr.). Remissions society and mourning my fantasy future. *BCBecky Blog*. www.bcbecky.com/2017/04/remission-society-and-mourning-my-fantasy-future/

Beck, U. (1992). *Risk society: Towards a new modernity* (M. Ritter, Trans.). Sage Publications.

Becker, H.S. (1963). *Outsiders: Studies in the sociology of deviance*. Free Press.

Begley, S. (2014, June). WHO Urged to regulate e-cigarettes. *Globe and Mail*.

Boston Women's Health Collective. (2011). *Our bodies, our selves*, 25th anniversary edn. Simon & Schuster.

Branigan, A. (2018). Black Toronto residents are 20 times more likely to be killed by police: New report finds. *The Root*. www.theroot.com/black-toronto-residents-are-20-times-more-likely-to-be-1831012076

Breggin, P.R. (2014). The rights of children and parents in regard to children receiving psychiatric diagnoses and drugs. *Children & Society, 28*, 231–41.

Colen, C.G., & Ramey, D.M. (2016). Social science and medicine. *Social Science and Medicine, 109*, 55–65.

Connell, E., & A. Hunt. (2010). The HPV vaccination campaign: A project of moral regulation in an era of biopolitics. *Canadian Journal of Sociology, 35*(1), 63–82.

Crandall, C., & Moriarty, D. (1995). Physical illness stigma and social rejection. *British Journal of Social Psychology, 34*, 67–83.

Crossley, M.L. (2009). Breastfeeding as moral imperative: An autoethnographic study. *Feminism & Psychology, 19*(1), 71–87

Davis, D. (2007). *The secret history of the war on cancer*. Basic Books.

de Kok, I.M., van Lenthe, F.J., Avendano, M., Louwman, M., Coebergh, J.W., & Mackenbach, J.P. (2008). Childhood class and cancer incidence: Results of the globe study. *Social Science and Medicine, 66*(5), 1131–9.

De Vogli, R. (2011). Neoliberal globalisation and health in a time of economic crisis. *Social Theory & Health, 9*(4), 311–25.

Dunkel-Schetter, C., & Wortman, C. (1982). Interpersonal dynamics of cancer: Problems in social relationships and their impact on the patient. In H.S.F. Friedman & M. Robin DeMatteo (Eds), *Interpersonal issues in health care*, (pp. 69–117). Academic Press.

Ehrenreich, B. (2009). *Bright-sided: How the relentless promotion of positive thinking has undermined America*. Henry Holt.

Engels, F. (1985) [1845]. *The condition of the working class in England*. Stanford University Press.

Epstein, S.S. (1998). *The politics of cancer revisited*. East Ridge Press.

Flurey, C., White, A., Rodham, K., Kirwan, J., Noddings, R., & Hewlett, S. (2018). "Everyone assumes a man to be quite strong": Men, masculinity and rheumatoid arthritis: A case-study approach. *Sociology of Health & Illness, 40*(1), 115–29.

Fortune Global. (2019). Search Global 500. *Fortune Global 500*. www.fortune.com/global500/list/

Foucault, M. (1964). *Madness and civilization: A history of insanity in the age of reason*. Vintage Books.

———. (1978, 1984) *The history of sexuality*. Éditions Gallimard.

———. (1994) [1973]. *The birth of the clinic: An archeology of medical perception* (A.M. Sheridan Smith, Trans.). Vintage Books.

Frank, A. (1991). *At the will of the body*. Houghton Mifflin.

Friedan, B. (1963). *The feminine mystique*. W.W. Norton and Co.

Gartland, A. (2018, Sept.). The Guardasil controversy: As reports of adverse effects increase, cervical cancer rates rise in HPV vaccinated age groups. *Changing Times*. www.changingtimes.media/2018/09/13/the-gardasil-controversy-as-reports-of-adverse-effects-increase-cervical-cancer-rates-rise-in-hpv-vaccinated-age-groups/

Gerry, V. (2017). Black, white, black and white: Mixed race and health in Canada. *Ethnicity & Health*.

Goddeferis, R. (2010). Precarious beginnings: Gendered risk discourses in psychiatric research literature about postpartum depression. *Health, 14*(5), 451–66.

Goffman, E. (1963). *Stigma: Notes on the management of spoiled identity*. Prentice-Hall.

Graham, H. (1984). *Women, health and the family*. Wheatsheaf Books.

Hankivsky, O., de Leeuw, J., Lee, S., Vissandjee, B., & Khanlou, N. (2011). *Health inequities in Canada: Intersectional frameworks and practices*. University of British Columbia Press.

Haynes R., Jones A., Reading, R., Daras, K., & Amon, A. (2008). Neighbourhood variations in child accidents and related child and maternal characteristics: Does area definition make a difference? *Health & Place, 14*(4), 693–701.

Heisz, A. (2015) Trends in income inequality in Canada and elsewhere. In D.A. Green, W.C. Riddell, & F. St. Hilaire (Eds), *Income inequality: The Canadian story*. Institute for Research on Public Policy.

Johnson, C. (2016, Feb.). The breastfeeding story is more complicated than you think. *Washington Times*. www.washingtonpost.com/news/wonk/wp/2016/02/23/what-youve-read-about-breastfeeding-may-not-be-true/?utm_term=.4a8789403551

Johnson, C.S., Bacsu, J., McIntosh, T., Jeffery, B., & Novik, N. (2017). *Home care in Canada: An environmental scan.* Saskatchewan Population Health and Evaluation Research Unit, University of Regina and University of Saskatchewan.

Jung, C. (2008). *Lactivism: How Feminists and fundamentalists, hippies and yuppies, and physicians and politicians made breastfeeding big business and bad policy.* Basic Books.

Kaufert, P.A., & Gilbert, P. (1987). Medicalization and the menopause. *Health and Canadian society,* 172–84.

Kaufman, K.J. (1998). A history of Ontario midwifery. *Journal of Obstetrics and Gynaecology Canada, 20*(10), 976–81.

Kerr, A., Ross, E., Jacques, G., & Cunningham- Burley, S. (2018). Sociology of cancer: A decade of research. *Sociology of Health and Illness, 40*(3), 552–76.

King, S. (2006). *Pink Ribbons, Inc.: Breast cancer and the politics of philanthropy.* University of Minnesota Press.

Kronenfeld, J.J., Reiser, M., Glik, D.C., Alatorre, C., & Jackson, K. (1997). Safety behaviors of mothers of young children: Impact of cognitive, stress and background factors. *Health, 1*(2), 205–25.

Kuhn, T. (1962). *The structure of scientific revolutions.* University of Chicago Press.

Laing, R.D., & Esterson, A. (1970) [1964]. *Sanity, madness and the family.* Penguin.

Lippman, A., Melnychuk, R., Shimmin, C., & Boscoe, M. (2007). Human papillomavirus, vaccines and women's health: Questions and cautions. *Canadian Medical Association Journal (CMAJ), 177*(5).

McClean, J., & Cribb, R. (2018, Nov.). Faulty and unproven medical devices implanted in Canadian patients despite known risks. *Toronto Star.* www.thestar.com/news/investigations/2018/11/25/faulty-and-unproven-medical-devices-from-vaginal-mesh-to-hip-replacements-implanted-in-canadian-patients-despite-known-risks.html

McCrea, F.B. (1983). The politics of menopause: The discovery of a deficiency disease. *Social Problems, 31*(1), 111–23.

Markowitz, F.E. (1998). The effects of stigma on the psychological well-being and life satisfaction of persons with mental illness. *Journal of Health and Social Behavior, 39*(4), 335–47.

Martindale, D. (1960). *The nature and types of sociological theory.* Houghton Mifflin.

Matei, M.C., Chirica, V., & Azoicai, D. (2015). A review on cancer research funding. *Social Research Reports, 27,* 9–11.

Navarro, V. (1976). Social class, political power and the state and their implications for medicine. *Social Science and Medicine,10,* 437–57.

Nestel, S. (2012). Colour coded health care: The impact of race and racism on Canadians' health. *Wellesley Institute.* www.wellesleyinstitute.com/wp-content/uploads/2012/02/Colour-Coded-Health-Care-Sheryl-Nestel.pdf

Nicklett, E. (2011).Socioeconomic status and race/ethnicity independently predict health decline among older diabetics. *BMC Public Health, 11,* 684.

Oakley, A. (1984).*The Captured womb: A history of the medical care of pregnant women.* Basil Blackwell.

O'Connor, J. (1973). *The fiscal crisis of the state.* St Martin's Press.

O'Connor, J.M., Sedghi, T., Dhodapkar, M., Kane, M.J., & Gross, C.P. (2018). Factors associated with cancer disparities among low-, medium-, and high-income US counties. *JAMA Network Open, 1*(6).

Parsons, T. (1951). *The social system.* Free Press.

Pirie, Marion. (1988). Women and the illness role: Rethinking feminist theory. *Canadian Review of Sociology and Anthropology, 25* (4), 628–48.

Ryan, J. (2019, Jan.). WHO declares the anit-vax movement a global threat in 2019. *Cnet,* www.cnet.com/news/world-health-organization-declares-anti-vax-movement-global-health-threat-in-2019/

Schneider, J., & Conrad, P. (1983). *Having epilepsy: The experience and control of illness.* Temple University Press.

Shepherd, L., & Turner, H. (2018). The over-medicalization and corrupted medicalization of abortion and its effect on women living in poverty. *Journal of Law, Medicine and Ethics, 9.* Oct.

Seale, C. (2001). Sporting cancer: Struggle language in news reports of people with cancer. *Sociology of Health and Illness, 23*(3), 308–29.

Sefa Dei, G.J. (1999). Knowledge and politics of social change: The implication of anti-racism. *British Journal of Social Education, 20*(3), 395–409.

Strohschein, L., & Gauthier, A. (2017). Poverty dynamics, parenting and mental health in Canada. *Society & Mental Health, 8*(3), 231–47.

Szasz, T.S. (1974) [1961]. *The myth of mental illness.* Harper and Row.

——. (1997) [1970]. *The manufacture of madness.* Syracuse University Press.

Turner, B.S. (1987). *Medical power and social knowledge.* Sage Publications.

Ubelacker, S. (2018, Dec.). Updated breast cancer screening guidelines in Canada consider women's preference. *Toronto Star.* www.thestar.com/life/health_wellness/2018/12/10/updated-mammography-guidelines-in-canada-consider-womans-preference-not-only-age.html

Walters, V. (1991). Beyond medical and academic agendas: Lay perspectives and priorities. *Atlantis, 17*(1), 28–35.

Weber, M. (1947). *The theory of social and economic organization* (A.M. Henderson & T. Parsons, Trans.). Free Press.

Weber, M. (1968). *Economy and society: An outline of interpretive sociology* (E. Fischoff, Trans., G. Roth & C. Witlich, Eds). Bedminster Press.

Weeks, C. (2014, June). The double standards of Canada's tobacco control. *Globe and Mail.* www.theglobeandmail.com/life/health-and-fitness/health/the-double-standards-of-canadas-tobacco-control/article19202446

Weiss, R. (2019, 29 July). Yes, boys should get the HPV vaccine: 5 things to know. *Health Central.* https://www.healthcentral.com/article/hpv-vaccine-boys-recommendations

World Health Organization (WHO). (2018). Tobacco. https://www.who.int/news-room/fact-sheets/detail/tobacco

Yerman, M.G. (2011, Nov.). An interview with Dr. Diane M. Harper, HPV expert. *Huffington Post*. www.huffingtonpost.com/marcia-g-yerman/an-interview-with-dr-dian_b_405472.html

Chapter 2

Adams, P. (2015, May). Migration: Are more people on the move than ever before? *BBC News*. www.bbc.com/news/world-32912867

Anderson, C. (2016, Mar.). Drinking culture at university: Are students taking their health for granted too young? *Independent*. https://www.independent.co.uk/student/student-life/health/drinking-culture-at-university-are-students-taking-their-health-for-granted-too-young-a6921151.html

Arnup, K. (2018, May). *Family perspectives: Death and dying in Canada*. Vanier Institute for the Family. http://www.virtualhospice.ca/Assets/2018-05-07_FP_DeathDying-2018_20180607111418.pdf

Benoit, C., Shumka, L., Phillips, R., Kennedy, M., & Belle-Isle, L. (2015). Issue brief: Sexual violence against women in Canada. *Status of Women Canada*. www.cfc-swc.gc.ca/svawc-vcsfc/issue-brief-en.pdf

BBC News. (2016, Nov.). Who are Nigeria's Boko Haram Islamist group? www.bbc.com/news/world-africa-13809501

Begley, S. (2014, June). WHO urged to regulate e-cigarettes. *Globe and Mail*.

Belzak. L., & Halverson, J. (2018). Evidence synthesis: The opioid crisis in Canada: A national perspective. *Health Promotion and Chronic Disease Prevention in Canada: Research, Policy and Practice, 38*(6), 224.

Boulos, D., & Zamorski, M.A. (2013). Deployment-related mental disorders among Canadian forces personnel deployed in support of the mission in Afghanistan 2001–2008. *CMAJ, 185*(11), 545–52.

Boutilier, A., & Campion-Smith, B. (2015). Canada's military suffers "sexualized culture," report says. *Toronto Star*. https://www.thestar.com/news/canada/2015/04/30/canadasmilitary-suffers-sexualized-culture-report-says.html

Business Week. (1979, Apr.). A boycott over infant formula. 137–40.

Canadian Cancer Society (2019). Childhood cancer statistics. www.cancer.ca/en/cancer-information/cancer-101/childhood-cancer-statistics/?region=on

Canadian Centre on Substance Use and Addiction. (2018). Heavy episodic drinking among post-secondary students. https://www.ccsa.ca

Canadian Institute for Health Information. (2018). Amount of opioids prescribed dropping in Canada; prescriptions on the rise. www.cihi.ca/en/amount-of-opioids-prescribed-dropping-in-canada-prescriptions-on-the-rise

Canadian Press. (2009, Oct.). Teens buying more black market cigarettes: Study. *CTV News*. www.ottawa.ctvnews.ca/teens-buying-more-black-market-cigarettes-study-1.443470

——. (2017, June). Health Canada approves three safe injection sites in Toronto. *CBC News*. www.cbc.ca/news/canada/toronto/toronto-injection-sites-1.4144096

CATIE. (2018). Fast facts: Sexually transmitted infections in Canada. www.catie.ca/en/pif/fall-2018/fast-facts-sexually-transmitted-infections-canada

Centers for Disease Control and Prevention (CDC). (2015). Thimerosal in vaccines. www.cdc.gov/vaccinesafety/concerns/thimerosal/index.html

——. (2018). Breastfeeding. www.cdc.gov/breastfeeding/faq/index.htm#benefits

——. (2019a). Preventing sexual violence. www.cdc.gov/violenceprevention/sexualviolence/consequences.html

——. (2019b). Fast facts. https://www.cdc.gov/tobacco/data_statistics/fact_sheets/fast_facts/index.htm

——. (2019c). Outbreak of lung injury associated with the use of e-cigarette, or vaping, products. https://www.cdc.gov/tobacco/basic_information/e-cigarettes/severe-lung-disease.html

Circumcision Reference Library. (2008). Canada circumcision statistics. www.cirp.org/library/statistics/Canada/

Cure Search. (n.d.). Childhood cancer statistics. www.cure-search.org/Childhood-Cancer-Statistics

D'Aliesio, R. (2017). Nearly half of soldiers who killed themselves in 2016 were dealing with loved one's suicide. *Globe and Mail*. www.theglobeandmail.com/news/national/nearly-half-of-soldiers-who-killed-themselves-in-2016-were-dealing-with-loved-ones-suicide/article37122431/

Decady, Y., & Greenberg, L. (2014). Ninety years of change in life expectancy. *Statistics Canada: Health at a Glance*.

De Vogli, R. (2011). Neoliberal globalisation and health in a time of economic crisis. *Social Theory & Health, 9*(4): 311–25.

Doidge, N. (2015). *The brain's way of healing: Remarkable discoveries and recoveries from the frontiers of neuroplasticity*. Viking.

Elliott, C.D., Carruthers, R., Hood, D., & Conlon, M.J. (2013). Food branding and young children's taste preferences: A reassessment. *Canadian Review of Public Health, 104*(5), 364–8.

Eyer, J. (1984). Capitalism, health and illness. In J.B. McKinley (Ed.), *Issues in the political economy of health care* (pp. 23–59). Tavistock.

Food and Agriculture Organization (FAO), International Fund for Agricultural Development, UNICEF, World Food Programme, & WHO. (2017). The state of food security and nutrition in the world 2017: Building resilience for peace and food security. www.fao.org/3/a-i7695e.pdf.

Flegel, K. (2013). Big alcohol catches up with adolescent girls. *CMAJ, 185*(10), 859.

Frank, J. (1996). 15 Years of AIDS in Canada. *Canadian Social Trends* (Summer), 4–7.

Gartland, A. (2018). The Gardasil controversy: As reports of adverse effects increase, cervical cancer rates rise in HPV-vaccinated age groups. *Changing Times*. www.changingtimes.media/2018/09/13/the-gardasil-controversy-as-reports-of-adverse-effects-increase-cervical-cancer-rates-rise-in-hpv-vaccinated-age-groups/

Ghosh, S. (2002). HIV/AIDS: One generation's story. *Voices, 9*, 10.

Goldscheider, C. (1971). *Population, modernization and social structure.* Little, Brown.

Government of Canada. (2016). Vaccine coverage in Canadian children: Highlights from the 2013 childhood National Immunization Coverage Survey. www.canada.ca/en/public-health/services/publications/healthy-living/vaccine-coverage-canadian-children-highlights-2013-childhood-national-immunization-coverage-survey.html

———. (2017). Human papillomavirus (HPV) prevention and HPV vaccines: Questions and answers. www.canada.ca/en/public-health/services/infectious-diseases/sexual-health-sexually-transmitted-infections/hpv-prevention-vaccines-questions-answers.html

———. (2018). Tackling obesity in Canada: Childhood obesity and excess weight rates in Canada. www.canada.ca/en/public-health/services/publications/healthy-living/obesity-excess-weight-rates-canadian-children.html

———. (2019a). Supervised consumption sites: Status of applications. www.canada.ca/en/health-canada/services/substance-use/supervised-consumption-sites/status-application.html

———. (2019b). "Opioid-related harms in Canada." https://health-infobase.canada.ca/substance-related-harms

Grant, M. (2018, Dec.). Medical student's rape conviction first of its kind in Calgary. *CBC News.* www.cbc.ca/news/canada/calgary/prachur-shrivastava-guilty-sex-assault-third-option-calgary-1.4960875

The Guardian. (2019, Jan.). Editorial: View of crank arguments: Such talk costs lives. www.theguardian.com/commentisfree/2019/jan/18/the-guardian-view-of-crank-arguments-such-talk-costs-lives

Guttmacher Institute. (2018) Induced abortion worldwide: Fact sheet. www.guttmacher.org/fact-sheet/induced-abortion-worldwide

Haque, A. (2019, 26 Mar.). Breast ironing awareness "needed in school." *BBC News.* www.bbc.com/news/education-47695169

Harbarger, M. (2019, Feb.). What will it take to tighten vaccination laws in Oregon, Washington? A measles outbreak might help. *The Oregonian.* Retrieved from www.oregonlive.com/business/2019/02/what-will-it-take-to-tighten-vaccination-laws-in-oregon-washington-a-measles-outbreak-might-help.html

Hamo, C.E., & Bloom, M.W. (2015). Getting to the heart of the matter: An overview of cardiac toxicity related to cancer therapy. *Clinical Medicine Insights: Cardiology, 9.* https://doi.org/10.4137/CMC.S19704

Index Mundi. (2018). World fertility rate. www.indexmundi.com/world/total_fertility_rate.html

Koss, M.P., Heise, L., & Russo, N.F. 1994. The global health burden of rape. *Psychology of Women Quarterly,18*, 509–37.

McDonald, C. (2018, May). Patient abused by Toronto doctor upset his medical license won't be revoked. *Global News.* https://globalnews.ca/news/4186086/javad-peirovy-court-of-appeal-decision/

McKeown, T. (1976). *The role of medicine: Dream, mirage or nemesis.* Neufeld Provincial Hospitals Trust.

McKinlay, J.B., & McKinlay, S.M. (1977). The questionable contribution of medical measures to the decline of mortality in the United States in the twentieth century. *Milbank Memorial Fund Quarterly* (Summer), 405–28.

——— & ———. (1981). Medical measures and the decline of mortality. *Sociology of Health and Illness, 4.*

Makin, K. (2018). How Canada's sexual assault laws violate rape victims. *Globe and Mail.* www.theglobeandmail.com/news/national/how-canadas-sex-assault-laws-violate-rape-victims/article14705289/

Mecredy, G.C., Diemert, L.M., Callaghan, R.C. & Cohen, J.E. (2013). Association between use of contraband tobacco and smoking cessation outcomes: A population-based cohort study. *CMAJ, 185*(7), 287–94.

Meier, B. (2018, May). Origins of an epidemic: Purdue pharma knew its opioids were widely abused. *New York Times.* www.nytimes.com/2018/05/29/health/purdue-opioids-oxycontin.html

Metraux, S., Clegg, L.X., Daigh, J.D., Culhane, D.P., & Kane, V. (2013). Risk factors for becoming homeless among a cohort of veterans who served in the era of the Iraq and Afghanistan conflicts. *American Journal of Public Health, 103*(suppl. 2), 255–61.

Mudle, L. (2015). Chinese men outnumber women by 33 million after decades of gender bias. *Radio Free Asia.* www.rfa.org/english/news/china/gender/01222015125826.html

National Institute on Drug Abuse. (2016). Drug and alcohol use in college age adults in 2016. https://www.drugabuse.gov/related-topics/trends-statistics/infographics/drug-alcohol-use-in-college-age-adults-in-2016

Novotny, T.E. (2013). Irreconcilable conflict: The tobacco industry and the public health challenge of tobacco use. *PLOS Medicine, 10*(5).

Olya, G. (2018). Here's how much the average person makes in 30 countries around the world. *Go Banking Rates.* www.gobankingrates.com/making-money/wealth/average-person-income-around-world/

Omran, A.R. (1979). Changing patterns of health and disease during the process of national development. In G. Albrecht and P.C. Higgins (Eds), *Health, Illness and Medicine* (pp. 81–93). Rand McNally.

Osterholm, M.T., Kelley, N.S., Sommer, A., & Belongia, E.A. (2012). Efficacy and effectiveness of influenza vaccines: a systematic review and meta-analysis. *The Lancet: Infectious Diseases, 12*(1), 36–44.

Patel, V., & Kleinman, A. (2003). Poverty and common mental disorders in developing countries. *Bulletin of the World Health Organization, 81*, 609–15.

Poland, G., & Jacobson, R. (2012). The re-emergence of measles in developed countries: Time to develop the next-generation measles vaccines? *Vaccine, 30*(2), 103–4. www.ncbi.nlm.nih.gov/pmc/articles/PMC3905323/

Rabin, R. (2006, June). Breast-feed or else. *New York Times.* www.nytimes.com/2006/06/13/health/13brea.html?ex=1307851200anden=34fe96e9a

Reitzel, L.R., Regan, S.D., Nguyen, N., Cromley, E.K., Strong, L.L., & Wetter, D.W. (2014). Density and proximity of fast food restaurants and body mass index among African Americans. *American Journal of Public Health, 104*(1), 110–16.

Rotermann, M. (2012). Sexual behaviour and condom use of 15- to 24-year-olds in 2003 and 2009/2010. *Health Reports, 23*(1), 1–5.

Scheifele, D.W., Halperin, S.A., & Bettinger, J.A. (2014). Childhood vaccination rates in Canada are too low. *Pediatrics Child Health, 19*(50), 237–8. www.ncbi.nlm.nih.gov/pmc/articles/PMC4029243/

Schoeppe, S., Alley, S., Van Lippevelde, W., Bray, N.A., Williams, S.L., Duncan, M.J., & Vandelanotte, C. (2016). Efficacy of interventions that use apps to improve diet, physical activity and sedentary behaviour: A systematic review. *International Journal of Behavioral Nutrition and Physical Activity, 13*(1), 127.

Sheppard, A.J., Shapiro, G.D., Bushnik, T., Wilkins, R., Perry, S., Kaufman, J.S., . . . & Yang, S. (2017). Birth outcomes among First Nations, Inuit and Métis populations. *Health Reports, 28*(11), 11–16.

Sorokan, S.T., Finlay, J.C., Jefferies, A.L., Canadian Paediatric Society, Fetus and Newborn Committee, & Infectious Diseases and Immunization Committee. (2015). Newborn male circumcision. *Paediatrics & Child Health, 20*(6), 311–15.

Statistics Canada. (2015). Trends in mortality rates, 2000 to 2011. https://www150.statcan.gc.ca/n1/pub/82-625-x/2014001/article/11897-eng.htm

———. (2016). Health fact sheets: Heavy drinking, 2016. https://www150.statcan.gc.ca/n1/pub/82-625-x/2017001/article/54861-eng.htm

———. (2018). Physical activity, self-reported, adult, by age group. www150.statcan.gc.ca/t1/tbl1/en/tv.action?pid=1310009613

Syre, T.R., & Martino-McAllister, J.M. (1997). Alcohol and other drug use at a university in the southeastern United States: Survey findings. *College Student Journal, 31*(3), 373–81.

Tallman, L. (2011). *Hemispheric integration and the ears: A scientific and inclusive paradigm of human behaviour including the mild and severe forms of mental illness.* Northern Light Books.

Tamburri, R. (2012, 29 Aug.). Heavy drinking a problem at most Canadian universities: Report. *University Affairs.* www.universityaffairs.ca/heavy-drinking-a-problem-at-most-canadian-campuses-report.aspx

Twells, L.K., Gregory, D.M., Reddigan, J., & Midodzi, W.K. (2014). Current and predicted prevalence of obesity in Canada. *Canadian Medical Association Open Access Journal, 2*(1):18–26.

UNFPA. (2011). United Nations Population Fund. www.unfpa.org/public/home/factsheets/pid/3856.

United Nations (UN). (2000). 17 goals to transform our world. www.un.org/sustainabledevelopment/

———. (2015). We can end poverty. UN development goals and beyond 2015. https://www.un.org/millenniumgoals/2015

United Nations High Commissioner for Refugees (UNHCR). (2017). Global trends: Forced Displacement in 2017. www.unhcr.org/globaltrends2017/

———. 2019. Figures at a glance. https://www.unhcr.org/ph/figures-at-a-glance

United Nations Office on Drugs and Crime (2018). Global Study on homicide: Gender-related killings of women and girls. www.unodc.org/documents/data-and-analysis/GSH2018/GSH18_Gender-related_killing_of_women_and_girls.pdf

UN Women. (n.d.). In focus: Orange the world, #HearMeToo. www.unwomen.org/en/news/in-focus/end-violence-against-women

———. (2017). New IPU and UN women map shows women's representation in politics in stagnating. Retrieved from www.unwomen.org/en/news/stories/2017/3/press-release-new-ipu-and-un-women-map-shows-womens-representation-in-politics-stagnating

Wainberg, M.L., Scorza, P., Shultz, J.M., Helpman, L., Mootz, J.J., Johnson, K.A., . . . & Arbuckle, M.R. (2017). Challenges and opportunities in global mental health: A research-to-practice perspective. *Current Psychiatry Reports, 19*(5), 28.

Walters, J. (2018, June). Opioid lawsuit targets rich family behind drug that fueled US crisis. *The Guardian.* https://www.theguardian.com/us-news/2018/jun/12/massachusetts-opioid-lawsuit-sackler-family-oxycontin

Webster, P.C. (2012). Aboriginal health programming under siege, critics charge. *Canadian Medical Association.*

Wermuth, L. 2003. *Global Inequality and Human Needs.* Allyn & Bacon.

Wheeler, R. (2016). The vape debate: What you need to know. *WebMD.* www.webmd.com/smoking-cessation/features/vape-debate-electronic-cigarettes#1

Wilkinson, R., & Pickett, K. (2010). *The spirit level: Why equality is better for everyone.* Penguin UK.

Wiltshire, G., Lee, J., & Williams, O. (2019). Understanding the reproduction of health inequalities: Physical activity, social class and Bourdieu's habitus. *Sport, Education and Society, 24*(3), 226–40.

Wodon, Q.T., & De La Briere, B. (2018). Unrealized potential: The high cost of gender inequality in earnings. *The World Bank.* www.elibrary.worldbank.org/doi/abs/10.1596/29865

World Economic Forum. (2018). *The global risks report, 13th edition.* www.weforum.org/reports/the-global-risks-report-2018

World Health Organization (WHO). (n.d. a). Life expectancy. www.who.int/gho/mortality_burden_disease/life_tables/situation_trends/en/

———. (n.d. b). Global Health Observatory data: Under five mortality. www.who.int/gho/child_health/mortality/mortality_under_five_text/en/

———. (n.d. c) Breastfeeding. www.who.int/topics/breastfeeding/en/

———. (n.d. d). Violence and injury prevention. www.who.int/violence_injury_prevention/en/

———. (n.d. e). Global Health Observatory data: Suicide rates.www.who.int/gho/mental_health/suicide_rates_male_female/en/

———. (n.d. f). Migration and health: Key issues. www.euro.who.int/en/health-topics/health-determinants/migration-and-health/migrant-health-in-the-european-region/migration-and-health-key-issues

———. (n.d. g). Tobacco. www.who.int/health-topics/tobacco

———. (1981, May). *International code* (Article 1).

———. (2017a). Diarrhoeal disease. www.who.int/news-room/fact-sheets/detail/diarrhoeal-disease

———. (2017b). Human papillomavirus (HPV). www.who.int/immunization/diseases/hpv/en/

———. (2018a). Female genital mutilation (FGM). www.who.int/reproductivehealth/topics/fgm/prevalence/en/

———. (2018b). Mental disorders. www.who.int/en/news-room/fact-sheets/detail/mental-disorders

———. (2018c). Obesity and overweight. www.who.int/news-room/fact-sheets/detail/obesity-and-overweight

———. (2019a). Violence against children. www.who.int/news-room/fact-sheets/detail/violence-against-children

———. (2019b). Immunization coverage. www.who.int/news-room/fact-sheets/detail/immunization-coverage

Young, L. (2017, July). Statistics Canada report finds sexual assault rates steady over 10 years. *Global News*. www.globalnews.ca/news/3590345/statistics-canada-report-finds-self-reported-sexual-assault-rates-steady-over-10-years/

Zabolai-Csekme, E. (1983). *Women, health and development*. WHO.

Zhang, M. (2018, Mar.). Legal marijuana is a boon to the economy, study finds. *Forbes Magazine*. www.forbes.com/sites/monazhang/2018/03/13/legal-marijuana-is-a-boon-to-the-economy-finds-study/#71a60022ee9d

Zlotozynska, M., Wood, E., Montaner, J.S., & Kerr, T. (2013). Supervised injection sites: Prejudice should not trump evidence of benefit. *CMAJ, 185*(15), 1303–4.

Chapter 3

Albin, M., Rylander, L., Mikoczy, Z., Lillienberg, L., Höglund, A.D., Brisman, J., . . . & Nielsen, J. (2002). Incidence of asthma in Swedish hairdressers. *Occupational and Environmental Medicine, 59*(2), 119–23.

Asbestos.com. (2019). Asbestos facts & statistics. https://www.asbestos.com/asbestos/statistics-facts/

Association of Workers' Compensation Boards of Canada. (n.d.). 2017 lost time claims in Canada. http://awcbc.org/?page_id=14

Batt, S. (2004). Pharmaceuticals in our water: A new threat to public health? *Facts to Act on from Women and Health Protection*. www.whp-apsf.ca/en/documents/phrmWater.html

———. (2010). Full circle: Drugs, the environment, and our health. In A.R. Ford & D. Saibil (Eds), *The push to prescribe: Women and Canadian drug policy* (pp. 185–206). Women's Press.

Bhattacharya, S. (2003, Oct.). European heatwave caused 35000 deaths. *News Scientist*. www.newscientist.com/article/dn4259-european-heatwave-caused-35000-deaths/

Bjerga, A. (2017, Aug.). Bees are bouncing back from colony collapse disorder. *Bloomberg*. https://www.bloomberg.com/news/articles/2017-08-01/good-news-for-bees-as-numbers-recover-while-mystery-malady-wane

Bone, R.M. (2016). *The Canadian North: Issues and challenges*, 5th edn. Oxford University Press.

Brauer, M., Reynolds, C., & Hystad, P. (2013). Traffic-related air pollution and health in Canada. *CMAJ, 185*(18), 1557–8.

Brown, M.R., Agyapong, V., Greenshaw, A.J., Cribben, I., Brett-MacLean, P., Drolet, J., . . . & Kitching, D. (2019). After the Fort McMurray wildfire there are significant increases in mental health symptoms in grade 7–12 students compared to controls. *BMC Psychiatry, 19*(1), 18.

Burnett, R.T., Cakmak, S. & Brook, J.R. (1998). The effect of the urban ambient air pollution mix on daily mortality rates in 11 Canadian cities. *Canadian Journal of Public Health, 89*(3), 152–5.

CBC News. (2006). CBC News: Year in review. www.cbc.ca/news/background/yearinreview2006/2006

Clark D. (2010, Sept.). The surprisingly complex truth about planes and climate change. *The Guardian*.

Commissioner of the Environment and Sustainable Development. (2011, 4 Oct.). *2011 Report of the Commissioner of the Environment and Sustainable Development*. Office of the Auditor General.

Conference Board of Canada. (2020). Gender wage gap. https://www.conferenceboard.ca/hcp/provincial/society/gender-gap.aspx?AspxAutoDetectCookieSupport=1

Council of Canadians with Disabilities. (2019). Employment equality for Canadians with disabilities. http://www.ccdonline.ca/en/socialpolicy/employment/Employment-Equality9June2014

Cross, A. (2012, June). More than half of Canadians think banning plastic bags a good idea: Poll. *National Post*. https://nationalpost.com/news/more-than-half-of-canadians-think-banning-sale-of-plastic-bags-a-good-idea-poll

Crouse, D.L., Balram, A., Hystad, P., Pinault, L., van den Bosch, M., Chen, H., . . . & Martin, R.V. (2018). Associations between living near water and risk of mortality among Canadians. *Environmental Health Perspectives, 126*(7), 077008.

The Daily. (2016). Vehicle registrations, 2016. https://www150.statcan.gc.ca/n1/daily-quotidien/170629/dq170629d-eng.htm

Dallas, M. (2011, Oct.). Shift work may put teens at risk for multiple sclerosis. *Healthy Day*. https://consumer.healthday.com/diseases-and-conditions-information-37/misc-diseases-and-conditions-news-203/shift-work-may-put-teens-at-risk-for-multiple-sclerosis-657873.html

Driving.ca. (2018). Canada's 10 best-selling vehicles in the first three quarters of 2018. https://driving.ca/ford/f-150/auto-news/news/canadas-10-best-selling-vehicles-in-the-first-three-quarters-of-2018

Dumit, J. (2006). Illnesses you have to fight to get: Facts as forces in uncertain, emergent illnesses. *Social Science and Medicine, 62*(3), 577–90.

Environmental Defense Fund. (2019). Methane: The other important greenhouse gas. https://www.edf.org/climate/methane-other-important-greenhouse-gas

Environment Canada. (2017). The Canadian Environmental Protection Act, 1999 and hazardous waste and hazardous recyclable materials. https://www.canada.ca/content/dam/eccc/migration/main/lcpe-cepa/2a241d76-e45b-4ee3-8fee-d52838fc4b77/fs_fi-hzrwaste-decdang.pdf

Evans, L.B., & McInturff, K. (2016). *Making women count: The unequal economics of women's work*. Canadian Centre for Policy Alternatives/Oxfam Canada.

Finlay, K. (2015). Preventable medical error is Canadian healthcare's silent killer. *Huffington Post*. https://www.huffingtonpost.ca/kathleen-finlay/medical-error-deaths_b_8350324.html

Firth, M., Brophy, J., & Keith, M. (1997). *Workplace roulette: Gambling with cancer*. Between the Lines.

Galloway, G. (2014, June). Government mum on asbestos policy. *Globe and Mail*.

Geran, L. (1992). Occupational stress. *Canadian Social Trends* (Autumn), 14–17.

Glauser, W. (2013). Delhi's dumps are "public health time bombs." *CMAJ, 185*(8), 319–20.

GMO-free Europe. (n.d.). GMO-free regions. http://www.gmo-free regions.org/gmo-free-regions.html

Government of Canada. (2018a). Data blog: Asthma and chronic obstructive pulmonary disease (COPD). https://www.canada.ca/en/public-health/services/publications/diseases-conditions/asthma-chronic-obstructive-pulmonary-disease-canada-2018.html

———. (2018b). Yearly food-borne illness estimates for Canada. https://www.canada.ca/en/public-health/services/food-borne-illness-canada/yearly-food-borne-illness-estimates-canada.html#ov

———. (2018c). Concussions in sport. https://www.canada.ca/en/public-health/services/diseases/concussion-sign symptoms/concussion-sport-infographic.html

———. (2019a). Extreme heat waves. https://www.canada.ca/en/health-canada/services/sun-safety/extreme-heat-heat-waves.html

———. (2019b). About the air quality health index. https://www.canada.ca/en/environment-climate-change/services/air-quality-health-index/about.html

Hague, M. (2019). Is it possible to live truly plastic-free? *Globe and Mail*. https://www.theglobeandmail.com/life/article-can-one-truly-live-plastic-free

Hausfather, Z. (2018). Fact check: How global warming has increased US wildfires. *Carbon Brief*. https://www.carbonbrief.org/factcheck-how-global-warming-has-increased-us-wildfires

Hochschild, A. (2012) [1983]. *The managed heart: The commercialization of human feeling*. University of California Press.

Hystad, P., Brauer, M., Demers, P.A., Johnson, K.C., Setton, E., Cervantes-Larios, A., Poplawski, K., McFarlane, A., Whitehead, A., & Nichol, A.M. (2014). Geographic variation in radon and associated lung cancer risk in Canada. *Canadian Journal of Public Health, 105*(1), 4–10.

Institute for Work & Health. (2010). Shift work and health. https://www.iwh.on.ca/summaries/issue-briefing/shift-work-and-health

Israel, S. (2017, Mar.). StatsCan on gender pay equity: Women earn 87 cents to men's dollar. *CBC News*. https://www.cbc.ca/news/business/statistics-canada-genderpay-gap-1.401495

Jamal, S. (2018). Right to know: Exposing toxic fragrance in beauty personal care and cleaning products. *Environmental Defence*. https://environmentaldefence.ca/2018/09/26/exposing-toxic-fragrance-chemicals-products

Johnson, C. (2010, May). Pesticides linked to ADHD in children. *Globe and Mail*, L3.

Kardan, O., Gozdyra, P., Bratislav, M., Faisal, M.L., Paus, T. & Berman, M.G. (2015). Neighbourhood greenspace and health in a large urban area. *Scientific Reports, 5*, 11610.

Klauer, S.G., Feng Guo, B.G., Simons-Morton, M.C., Ouimet, S.E.L, & Dingus, T.A. (2014). Distracted driving and risk of road crashes among novice and experienced drivers. *New England Journal of Medicine, 370*(1), 54–9.

McInturff, K. (2013). *The gap in the gender gap: Violence against women in Canada*. Canadian Centre for Policy Alternatives. www.policyalternatives.com

McKenzie, T. (2016, July). Bang on! Canadians worst nation per capita for water consumption. *London Free Press*. https://lfpress.com/2016/07/07/bang-on-canadians-worst-nation-per-capita-for-water-consumption/wcm/f23ca177-d3c0-4a0320d6b080f7a3dacc

Makary, M.A., & Daniel, M. (2016). Medical error—the third leading cause of death in the US. *British Medical Journal, 353*, i2139.

Mayo Clinic. (2017). Domestic violence against men know the signs. https://www.mayoclinic.org/healthy-lifestyle/adult-health/in-depth/domestic-violence-against-men/art-20045149

Min, S.T., & Redelmeier, D.A. (1998). Car phones and car crashes: An ecologic analysis. *Canadian Journal of Public Health, 89*(3), 157–61.

Mohr, N. (2005, Aug.). A new global warming strategy. *EarthSave International*.

NASA Earth Observatory. (n.d.). World of change global temperatures. https://earthobservatory.nasa.gov/world-of-change/DecadalTemp

Nelson, K (2017). The Current: Thought asbestos was fully banned in Canada? Not until 2018. *CBC News*. https://www.cbc.ca/radio/thecurrent/the-current-for-december-15-2016-1.3896671/thought-asbestos-was-fully-banned-in-canada-not-until-2018-1.3896765

Ontario Campaign for Action on Tobacco. (2003). Health effects of second hand smoke. http://www.ocat.org/healtheffects/index.html#4

Ontario Nurses Association. (2018). Violence should not be part of our job. https://www.ona.org/wp-content/uploads/ona_flfeature_workplaceviolence_201505.pdf

Organic Trade Association. (2019). Organic market analysis. https://ota.com/resources/market-analysis

Paperny. A.M., & Bascaramurty, D. (2018). Ontario crash sheds light on plight of migrant workers. *Globe and Mail.* https://www.theglobeandmail.com/news/national/ontario-crash-sheds-light-on-plight-of-migrant-workers/article545533/

Paul, G. (2014, June). Local e-waste buyers capitalizing on disposable society. *The Record.* https://www.therecord.com/news-story/4591752-local-e-waste-buyers-capitalizing-on-disposable-society/

Raven, P.H., Berg, L.R., & Johnson, G.B. (1993). *Environment.* Saunders.

Redelmeier, D.A., & McLellan, B.A. (2013). Modern medicine is neglecting road traffic crashes. *PLOS Medicine.* http://www.plosmedicine.org/article/info%3Adoi%2F10.1371%2Fjournal.pmed.1001463.

Rundell, K.W., Caviston, R., & Hollenbach, A.M. (2006). Vehicular air pollution, playgrounds, and youth athletic fields. *Inhalation Toxicology, 18,* 541–7.

Schroeder & Schroeder. (2018). E-waste management in Canada. *Schroeder Inc.* https://www.schroeder-inc.com/2016/03/19/e-waste-management-in-canada/

Schwartz, D. (2014, Apr.). Workplace safety by the numbers. *CBC News.* http://www.cbc.ca/news/canada/workplace-safety-by-the-numbers-1.2622466.

Semenza, J.C., Rubin, C.H., Falter, K.H., Selanikio, J.D., Flanders, W.D., Howe, H.L., & Wilhelm, J.L. (1996). Heat-related deaths during the July 1995 heat wave in Chicago. *New England Journal of Medicine, 335*(2), 84–90.

Shields, M. (2003). *The health of Canada's shift workers.* Statistics Canada.

Sinha, M. (2013). Measuring violence against women statistical trends. Statistics Canada Catalogue no. 85-002-X.

Smith, J.N., Brown, R.M., Williams, W.J., Robert, M., Nelson, R., & Moran, S.B. (2015). Arrival of the Fukushima radioactivity plume in North American continental waters. *Proceedings of the National Academy of Sciences, 112*(5), 1310–15.

Statista. (2018). Number of hospitalizations due to injuries in Canada 2016–2017, by cause. Retrieved from https://www.statista.com/statistics/496420/canada-injury-hospitalization-by-causes/

———. (2019). Share of agricultural land used for organic farming in Canada 2000–2017. https://www.statista.com/statistics/707014/organic-farming-share-of-land-canada/

Statistics Canada. (2015). Current cigarette smoking rates, Canada and the provinces, 2015. https://www150.statcan.gc.ca/n1/daily-quotidien/161109/cg-b002-eng.htm

———. (2018). Statistics Canada. https://www.statcan.gc.ca/eng/start

Stastna, K. (2012, 8 Feb.). Canada's migrant farm worker system—what works and what's lacking. *CBC News.* http://www.cbc.ca/news/canada/canada-s-migrant-farm-worker-system-what-works-and-what-s-lacking-1.1142489

Tataryn, L. (1979). *Dying for a living.* Deneau and Greenberg.

ThinkInsure.ca. (2020, 24 Feb.). Texting and driving in Ontario. https://www.thinkinsure.ca/insurance-help-centre/texting-and-driving.html

Toronto Star. (2013, 25 Apr.). Bangladesh building collapse kills more than 230: Joe Fresh clothing, other brands made on site. https://www.thestar.com/news/world/2013/04/25/bangladesh_building_collapse_toll_nears_200_joe_fresh_clothing_other_brands_made_at_site.html

United States Environmental Protection Agency. (n.d.). Facts and figures about the Great Lakes. https://www.epa.gov/greatlakes/facts-and-figures

USA Today. (2003, 25 Sept.). Weather. https://usatoday30.usatoday.com/weather/news/2003-09-25-france-heat_x.htm

Weeks, C. (2010, May). Perfumes contain hidden harmful chemicals, an environmental group says. *Globe and Mail.* https://www.theglobeandmail.com/life/health-and-fitness/perfumes-contain-hidden-harmful-chemicals-environmental-groups-say/article4318688/

Weller, C. (2014). California Slaughterhouse indicted over known sale of cancerous beef to avoid high costs, regulations. *Medical Daily.* https://www.medicaldaily.com/california-slaughterhouse-indicted-over-known-sale-cancerous-beef-avoid-high-costs-298894

Wilson, E.O. (1991). Biodiversity, prosperity and value. In H.F. Brohman & S.R. Kellert (Eds), *Ecology, economics and ethics: The broken circle.* Special issue of *Society, 30*(1), (Nov.–Dec.), 90–3.

World Health Organization (WHO). (n.d. a). Ten chemicals of major public health concern. https://www.who.int/ipcs/assessment/public_health/chemicals_phc/en/

———. (n.d. b). How air pollution is destroying our health. https://www.who.int/air-pollution/news-and-events/how-air-pollution-is-destroying-our-health

———. (2014). Injuries and violence: The facts 2014. https://www.who.int/violence_injury_prevention/media/news/2015/Injury_violence_2014/en/

———. (2019). Drinking water. https://www.who.int/news-room/fact-sheets/detail/drinking-water

World Wildlife Fund. (2014). Newfoundland cod fishery announces milestone sustainability assessment. http://www.wwf.ca/newsroom/?14901/Newfoundland-cod-fishery-announces-milestone-sustainability-assessment

Chapter 4

Aday, L.A. (2005). *Reinventing public health: Policies and practices for a healthy nation.* Jossey-Bass.

Alzheimer's Society. (2019a). How Alzheimer's is diagnosed. https://www.alzheimers.net/how-is-alzheimers-diagnosed/

———. (2019b). Women and dementia: The overlooked majority. https://www.alzheimers.org.uk/blog/women-and-dementia-overlooked-majority

American Public Health Association. (2017). *Public health and early childhood education: Support for universal preschool in the United States: Policy statements and advocacy.*

Bell, N., & Hayes, M. (2012). The Vancouver area neighbourhood deprivation index vandix: A census-based tool for assessing small-area variations in health status. *Canadian Journal of Public Health, 103*(suppl. 2), 528–32.

Bourdieu, P. (1984). *Distinction: A social critique of the judgment of taste.* Harvard University Press.

Browning, C.R., & Cagney, K.A. (2003). Moving beyond poverty: Neighborhood structure, social processes, and health. *Journal of Health and Social Behavior, 44*(1), 552–71.

Buckingham, J., Wheldall, K., & Beaman-Wheldall, R. (2013). Why poor children are more likely to become poor readers: The school years. *Australian Journal of Education, 57*, 190–213.

Canadian Foundation for Health Care Improvement. (2011). *Myth: The aging population is to blame for uncontrollable health costs.* Mythbusters.

Canadian Observatory on Homelessness. (2016). The state of homelessness in Canada. https://homelesshub.ca/sites/default/files/SOHC16_final_20Oct2016.pdf

Centers for Disease Control and Prevention (CDC). (2012). Higher education and income are keys to better health, according to annual report on the nation's health. https://www.cdc.gov/media/releases/2012/p0516_higher_education.html

Chang, F., Patel, T., & Schulz, M.E. (2015). The "Rising Tide" of dementia in Canada. What does it mean for pharmacists and the people they care for? *Canadian Pharmacists Journal, 148*(4), 193–9.

Chang, V.W., & Lauderdale, D.S. (2009). Fundamental cause theory, technological innovation, and health disparities: The case of cholesterol in the era of statins. *Journal of Health and Social Behavior, 50*(3), 245–60.

Chenier, H. (2013). Older Canadians at risk of undernourishment. *CMAJ, 185*(10): 473.

Chetty, R., Friedman, J.N., Hilger, N., Saez, E., Schanzenbach, D.W., & Yagan, D. (2011). How does your kindergarten classroom affect your earnings? Evidence from Project STAR. *Quarterly Journal of Economics, 126*, 1593–1660.

Coburn, D. (2003). Income inequality, social cohesion, and the health status of populations: The role of neo-liberalism. In R. Hofrichter (Ed.), *Health and social justice: A reader on the politics, ideology, and inequity in the distribution of disease* (pp. 335–41). Jossey-Bass.

Conference Board of Canada. (2019). Child poverty. https://www.conferenceboard.ca/hcp/Details/society/childpoverty.aspx?AspxAutoDetecCookieSupport=1

Darmon, N., & Drewnoski, A. (2008). Does social class predict diet quality? *American Journal of Clinical Nutrition, 87*(5): 1107–17.

Doyal, L. (1979). *The political economy of health.* Pluto Press.

Eggertson, L. (2013). *Hospitalizations for self-harm higher in poorer neighbourhoods.* Canadian Medical Association.

Ehrenreich, B. (2001). *Nickel and dimed: On (not) getting by in America.* Metropolitan Books.

Engels, F. (1985) [1845]. *The condition of the working class in England.* Stanford University Press.

Epp, Jake. (1986). *Achieving health for all: A framework for health promotion.* Minister of National Health and Welfare.

Erickson, M. (2011). Capital and health implications for health. *Global Health Action, 4,* 10.3402/

Food Banks Canada. (2016). Hunger count, 2016. https://www.foodbankscanada.ca/getmedia/6173994f-8a25-40d9-acdf-660a28e40f37/HungerCount_2016_final_singlepage.pdf

Friendly, M. (2009). Early childhood education and care as a social determinant of health. In D. Raphael (Ed.), *Social determinants of health: Canadian perspectives* (pp. 128–42). Canadian Scholars' Press.

Fruh, S.M., Nadglowski, J., Hall, H.R., Davis, S.L., Crook, E.D., & Zlomke, K. (2016). Obesity stigma and bias. *Journal for Nurse Practitioners, 12*(7), 425–32.

Gore, D., & Kothari, A. (2012). Social determinants of health in Canada: Are healthy living initiatives there yet? A policy analysis. *International Journal for Equity in Health, 11*(1), 41.

Government of Canada. (2011). Obesity in Canada—determining and contributing factors. https://www.canada.ca/en/public-health/services/health-promotion/healthy-living/obesity-canada/factors.html

Jackson, A. (2009). The unhealthy Canadian workplace. In D. Raphael (Ed.), *Social determinants of health: Canadian perspectives* (pp. 99–113). Canadian Scholars' Press.

Latkin, C.A., & Curry, A.D. (2003). Stressful neighborhoods and depression: A prospective study of the impact of neighborhood disorders. *Journal of Health and Social Behavior, 44*, 34–44.

MacIntosh, N. (2020). *Minimum wages across Canada 2019–2020.* Monster.ca. https://www.monster.ca.career-aqdvice-advice/article/minimum-wages-across-canada-2019-2020

Martin, M.C., Seanna, E., Willows, N.D., Colman, I., & Ohinma, A. (2013). Diet quality and feelings of worry, sadness or unhappiness in Canadian children. *Canadian Journal of Public Health, 104*(4), 322–6.

Mikkonen, J., & Raphael, D. (2010). *Social determinants of health: The Canadian facts.* York University School of Health Policy and Management.

Mok, P.L., Antonsen, S., Pedersen, C.B., Carr, M.J., Kapur, N., Nazroo, J., & Webb, R.T. (2018). Family income inequalities and trajectories through childhood and self-harm and violence in young adults: A population-based, nested case-control study. *The Lancet Public Health, 3*(10), e498–e507. https://www.thelancet.com/journals/lanpub/article/PIIS2468-2667(18)30164-6/fulltext

Monaghan, L.F., Colls, R., & Evans, B. (2013). Editorial: Obesity discourse and fat politics: Research, critique and intervention. *Critical Public Health, 23*(3), 249–62.

Navarro, V., & Borrell, C. (2004). *The political and social contexts of health.* Baywood Publishing.

——— & Shi, V. (2003). The political context of social inequalities and health. *International Journal of Health Services, 31*(1), 1–21.

Organisation for Economic Co-operation and Development (*OECD*). (2015). In it together: Why less inequality benefits all. https://doi.org/10.1787/9789264235120-en

———. (2016). Income inequality update. https://www.oecd.org/social/OECD2016-Income-Inequality-Update.pdf

———. (2017). Health at a glance 2017. http://www.oecd.org/health/health-systems/health-at-a-glance-19991312.htm

———. (2019). Infant mortality rates. https://data.oecd.org/healthstat/infant-mortality-rates.htm

Payette, H., & Shatenstein, B. (2005). Determinants of healthy eating in community-dwelling elderly people. Canadian *Journal of Public Health, 96*(suppl. 3), S27–S31.

Piketty, T. (2014). *Capital in the twenty-first century* (A. Goldhammer, Trans.). Belknap Press of Harvard University Press.

Polanyi, M. (2004). Understanding and improving the health of work. In D. Raphael, *Social determinants of health: Canadian perspectives* (pp. 95–106). Canadian Scholars' Press.

Power, E.M. (2005). Determinants of healthy eating among low-income Canadians. *Canadian Journal of Public Health, 96*, S37–S42.

Raphael, D. (2002a). *Social justice is good for our hearts: Why societal factors—not lifestyles—are major causes of heart disease in Canada and elsewhere. CSJ* Foundation for Research and Education.

———. (2002b). *Poverty, income inequality, and health in Canada.* CSJ Foundation for Research and Education.

———. (2004). *Social determinants of health: Canadian perspectives.* Canadian Scholars' Press.

———. (2009). *Social determinants of health*, 2nd edn. Canadian Scholars' Press.

Ronson, B., & Rootman, I. (2009). Literacy and health: Implications for health and education professionals. In L.M. English (Ed.), *Adult education and health* (pp. 107–22). University of Toronto Press.

Peña, F.S. (2013). Health in all policies: The emperor's old clothes. Healthy Policies for a Healthier World. www.healthypolicies.com/2011/08/health-in-all-policies-the-emperor's-old-clothes

Penman-Aguilar, A., Carter, M., Snead, C., & Kourtis, A.P. (2013). Socio-economic disadvantage as a social determinant of teen childbearing in the *U.S. Public Health Reports, 128*(Suppl. 1), 5–22.

Schulz, R., & Sherwood, P.R. (2009). Physical and mental effects of family caregiving. *American Journal of Nursing, 108*(Suppl. 9): 23–7.

Scripps Research Institute. (2011, 3 Mar.). *Liver, not brain, likely source of Alzheimer's plaques.* Science Daily.

Spitzer, D.L. (2005). Engendering health disparities. *Canadian Journal of Public Health, 96*(2), S78–S96.

Trading Economics. (2019) Canada unemployment rate. https://tradingeconomics.com/canada/unemployment-rate

Velasco, S. (2013, Dec.). CEO versus worker pay: Walmart, McDonald's and eight other firms with the biggest gaps.

Christian Science Monitor. https://www.csmonitor.com/Business/2013/1212/CEO-vs.-worker-pay-Walmart-McDonald-s-and-eight-other-firms-with-biggest-gaps/AT-T

Wilkinson, R., & Pickett, K. (2010). *The spirit level: Why equality is better for everyone.* Penguin UK.

Williams, P.L., Johnson, C.S.J., Johnson, C.P., Anderson, B.J., Kratzmann, M.L., & Chenhall, C. (2006). Can households earning minimum wage in Nova Scotia afford a nutritious diet? *Canadian Journal of Public Health, 97*(6), 430–4.

Willson, A.E., Shuey, K.M., & Elder, G.H. (2007). Cumulative advantage processes as mechanisms of inequality in life course health. *American Journal of Sociology, 112*(6), 1886–1924.

World Health Organization (WHO). (n.d.). Mental health, poverty and development. https://www.who.int/mental_health/policy/development/en/

———. (2011). World health statistics 2011. http://www.who.int/whosis/whostat/EN_WHS2011_Full.pdf

Chapter 5

Abuya, B.A, Ciera, J., Kimani-Murage, E. (2012). Effect of mother's education on child's nutritional status in the slums of Nairobi. *BMC Pediatrics, 12*(80), doi:10.1186/1471-243112-80

Access Alliance Multicultural Community Health Centre. (2005). A literature review exploring poverty, housing, race-based discrimination and access to health care as determinants of health for racialised groups. In *Racialised groups and health status* (pp.1–16). AAMCHC.

Adelson, N. (2005). The embodiment of inequity: Health disparities in Aboriginal Canada. *Canadian Journal of Public Health, 96*(suppl. 2), S45–S61.

Alzheimer's Society of Canada. (2019). Dementia numbers. https://alzheimer.ca/en/Home/About-dementia/What-is-dementia/Dementia-numbers

American Psychological Association. (2017). Low birth weight babies at higher risk for mental health problems later in life: Increased risk runs from childhood into at least 30s, says study. *Science Daily.* www.sciencedaily.com/releases/2017/02/170213131

AMMSA. (2008). Government of Canada asks for forgiveness. https://ammsa.com/publications/windspeaker/government-canada-asks-forgiveness

Andermann, A. (2017). Outbreaks in the age of syndemics: New insights for improving Indigenous health. *Public Health Agency of Canada.* Volume 43-6: Indigenous Health. https://www.canada.ca/en/public-health/services/reports-publications/canada-communicable-disease-report-ccdr/monthly-issue/2017-43/ccdr-volume-43-6-june-1-2017/outbreaks-age-of-syndemics-new-insights-improving-indigenous-health.html

Anstey, K.J., Andrews, G., & Luszcz, M.A. (2001). Psychosocial factors, gender and late-life mortality. *Aging International, 27*(2), 73–89.

Barton, S.S., Thommasen, H.V., Tallio, B., Zhang, W., & Michalos, A.C. (2005). Health and quality of life of Aboriginal residential school survivors. *Social Indications Research, 73*(2), 295–312.

Beiser, M. (2005). The health of immigrants and refugees in Canada. *Canadian Journal of Public Health, 96,* S30–S44.

Boghani, P. (2015, June) When transgender kids transition medical risks are both known and unknown. *PBS Frontline.* https://www.pbs.org/wgbh/frontline/article/when-transgender-kids-transition-medical-risks-are-both-known-and-unknown/

Bone, R.M. (2016). *The Canadian North: Issues and challenges,* 5th edn. Oxford University Press.

Brook, R.H., Kanberg, C.J., Mayer Oakes, A., et al. (1989). *Appropriateness of acute medical care for the elderly.* Rand Corporation.

Bruser, D. (2020, 4 Apr.). Grassy Narrows signs deal for care home. *Toronto Star,* A2.

Canada Population. (2018). Population of Canada 2018. http://canadapopulation2018.com/

Canada Without Poverty (n.d.). Just the facts. http://www.cwp-csp.ca/poverty/just-the-facts/

Canadian Conference of Catholic Bishops. (n.d.). Apology on residential schools by the Catholic Church. http://www.cccb.ca/site/eng/media-room/files/2630-apology-on-residential-schools-by-the-catholic-church

Canadian Mental Health Association. (2019). Lesbian, queer and trans people mental health. https://ontario.cmha.ca/documents/lesbian-gay-bisexual-trans-queer-identified-people-and-mental-health/

Caring for Kids New to Canada. (2019). Tuberculosis. https://www.kidsnewtocanada.ca/conditions/tuberculosis

CBC News. (2015, Aug.). First Nations adults more than twice as likely to die from avoidable causes. https://www.cbc.ca/news/indigenous/first-nations-adults-more-than-twice-as-likely-to-die-from-avoidable-causes-1.3196496

CBC Sports. (2016, Dec.). Doping report details "institutional conspiracy" in Russia involving more than 1,000 athletes. https://www.cbc.ca/sports/olympics/mclaren-report-olympic-doping-russia-1.3888744

Chu, P.L., McFarland, W., Gibson, S., Weide, D., Henne, J., Miller, P., Partridge, T., & Schwarcz, S. (2003). Viagra use in a community-recruited sample of men who have sex with men, San Francisco. *Journal of Acquired Immune Deficiency Syndromes, 33*(2), 191–3.

Colour of Justice Network. (2007). Colour of poverty: Fact sheets. www.cop.openconcept.ca

Colpitts, E., & Gahagan, J. (2016). "I feel like I am surviving the health care system": understanding LGBTQ health in Nova Scotia, Canada. *BMC Public Health, 16*(1), 1005.

Contenta, S. (2018, 30 Sept.). Toronto is segregated by race and income. And the numbers are ugly. *Toronto Star.* https://www.thestar.com/news/gta/2018/09/30/toronto-is-segregated-by-race-and-income-and-the-numbers-are-ugly.html

Crawford, A. (2016). Suicide among Indigenous peoples in Canada. *The Canadian Encyclopedia.* https://www.thecanadianencyclopedia.ca/en/article/suicide-among-indigenous-peoples-in-canada

Crowe, K. (2014, Sept.). Grassy Narrows: Why is Japan still studying the mercury poisoning when Canada isn't? *CBC News.* https://www.cbc.ca/news/health/grassy-narrows-why-is-japan-still-studying-the-mercury-poisoning-when-canada-isn-t-1.2752360

Dennis, J.A., & Mollborn, S. (2013). Young maternal age and low birth weight risk: An exploration of racial/ethnic disparities in the birth outcomes of mothers in the United States. *Social Science Journal, 50*(4): 625–34.

Dickason, O.P. (2002). *Canada's First Nations: A history of founding peoples from earliest times,* 3rd edn. Toronto: Oxford University Press.

Doyal, L. (2003). Sex and gender: The challenges for epidemiologists. *International Journal of Health Services, 33*(3), 569–79

Ebley, E.M., Hogan, D.B. & Fung, T.S. (1996). Correlates of self-rated health in persons aged 85 and over: Results from the Canadian study of health and aging. *Canadian Journal of Public Health, 87*(1), 28–31.

Eichler, M., & Pederson, A. (2018). Marriage and divorce. *The Canadian Encyclopedia.* https://www.thecanadianencyclopedia.ca/en/article/marriage-and-divorce

Fantus, D., Shah, B.R., Qui, F., Hux, J., & Rochon, P. (2009). Injury in First Nations communities in Ontario. *Canadian Journal of Public Health, 100*(4), 258–63.

Fenge, T., & Penikett, P. (2014). Paper promises by avoiding treaty obligations, Canada undermines its own legal basis. http://reviewcanada.ca/magazine/2014/07/paper-promises/

Ferguson, J.A. (1990). Patient age as a factor in drug prescribing practices. *Canadian Journal of Aging, 9,* 278–95.

First Nations Health Authority. (n.d.). Our history, our health. http://www.fnha.ca/wellness/our-history-our-health

Fontaine, T. (2015, Oct.). Record 10 Indigenous MPs elected to the House of Commons. *CBC News.* https://www.cbc.ca/news/indigenous/indigenous-guide-to-house-of-commons-1.3278957

Frideres, J.S. (2020). *Indigenous peoples in the twenty-first century,* 3rd edn. Oxford University Press.

Galabuzi, G.E. (2001). Canada's creeping economic apartheid. *CSJ Foundation for Research and Education.* http://www.socialjustice.org

Giger, J., Davidhizar, R.E., Purell, L., Harden, J.T., Phillips, J., & Strickland, O. (2007). American Academy of Nursing expert panel report: Developing cultural competence to eliminate health disparities in ethnic minorities and other vulnerable populations. *Journal of Transcultural Nursing, 18*(2): 95–102.

Government of Canada. (2017). Canadian Community Health Survey. https://www.canada.ca/en/health-canada/services/food-nutrition/food-nutrition-surveillance/health-nutrition-surveys/canadian-community-health-survey-cchs.html

———. (2018). The Chief Public Health Officer's Report on the state of public health in Canada 2018: Preventing problematic substance use in youth. https://www.canada.ca/en/public-health/corporate/publications/chief-public-health-officer-reports-state-public-health-canada/2018-preventing-problematic-substance-use-youth.html

———. (2019). Measuring the impact of the opioid overdose epidemic on life expectancy at birth in Canada. https://www.canada.ca/en/health-canada/services/substance-use/problematic-prescription-drug-use/opioids/data-surveillance-research/harms-death/measuring-impact-on-life-expectancy.html

———. (2020, 5 Feb.). Ending long-term drinking water advisories. https://www.sac-isc.gc.ca/eng/1506514143353/1533317130660

Grenier, E. (2017). 21.9% of Canadians are immigrants, the highest in 85 years. *CBC News.* https://www.cbc.ca/news/politics/census-2016-immigration-1.4368970

Hartley, H. (2006). The "pinking" of Viagra culture: Drug industry efforts to create and repackage sex drugs for women. *Sexualities,* 363–78.

Hawkley, L.C., & Cacioppo, J.T. (2010). Loneliness matters: A theoretical and empirical review of consequences and mechanisms. *Annals of Behavioral Medicine, 40*(2), 218–27.

Health Council of Canada. (2013). *Canada's most vulnerable: Improving health care for First Nations, Inuit, and Métis seniors.* Health Council of Canada. http://www.metisnation.org/media/422632/senior_ab_report_2013_en_final.pdf.

Helman, C.G. (2007). *Culture, health and illness,* 5th edn. Hodder Arnold.

Indigenous and Northern Affairs Canada. (2011). Fact sheet—2011 National Household Survey, Aboriginal demographics, educational attainment and labour market outcomes. https://www.aadnc-aandc.gc.ca/eng/1376329205785/1376329233875

Indigenous Corporate Training Inc. (ICT). (2019, 26 Apr.). 8 key issues for Indigenous Peoples in Canada. https://www.ictinc.ca/blog/8-key-issues-for-aboriginal-people-in-canada

Joshi, R. (2017). Child poverty rate double for racialized children in Toronto area. *Social Planning Toronto.* https://www.socialplanningtoronto.org/new_report_child_poverty_rate_double_for_racialized_children_in_toronto_area

Kawachi, I., Kennedy, B.P., Gupta, V., & Prothrow-Stith, D. (1999). Women's status and the health of women and men: A view from the States. *Social Science and Medicine, 48,* 21–32.

Kennedy, S., Kidd, M.P., McDonald, J.T., & Biddle, N. (2015). The healthy immigrant effect: Patterns and evidence from four countries. *Journal of International Migration Integration, 16*(2), 317–32.

Keung, N. (2017, Oct.). Raising immigrant levels would benefit Canada, study finds. *Toronto Star.* https://www.thestar.com/news/immigration/2017/10/02/raising-immigration-levels-would-slow-aging-population-raise-gdp-study-finds.html

King, S. (2006). *Pink Ribbons, Inc.: Breast cancer and the politics of philanthropy.* University of Minnesota Press.

Kirkup, K. (2017). Canada's Indigenous population growing 4 times faster than rest of country. *Canadian Press.* https://globalnews.ca/news/3823772/canadas-growing-indigenous-population/

Koch, A., Brierley, C., Maslin, M., & Lewis, S.L. (2019). Earth system impacts of the European arrival and the great dying in the Americas after 1492. *Quaternary Science Reviews, 207*(1), 13–36.

Koenen, K.C., Lincoln, A., & Appleton, A. (2006). Women's status and child well-being: A state-level analysis. *Social Science and Medicine, 63,* 2999–3012.

Kreiger, N. (2011). *Epidemiology and the people's health.* Oxford University Press.

Levasseur, J., & Marcoux, J. (2015). Bad water: "Third World" conditions on First Nations in Canada. *CBC News.* https://www.cbc.ca/news/canada/manitoba/bad-water-third-world-conditions-on-first-nations-in-canada-1.3269500

McCallum, J. (2008). Steroids in America: The real dope. *Sports Illustrated.* sportsillustrated.cnn.com/2008/magazine/03/11/steroids1/index.html.

McCormick, R., Nedan, R., McNicoll, P., & Lynam, J. (1997). Taking back the wisdom: Moving forward to recovery and action. *Canadian Journal of Community Mental Health, 16*(2): 5–8.

McGibbon, E.A., & Etowa, J.B. (2009). *Anti-racist health care practice.* Canadian Scholars' Press.

Millar, W., Strachan, J., & Wadhera, S. (1993). Trends in low birthweight. *Canadian Social Trends, 28,* 26–9.

Mothers Against Drunk Driving (MADD). (2019). Alcohol or drugs among crash victims. https://madd.ca/pages/impaired-driving/overview/statistics/

Movember. (2019). *Annual report.* https://cdn.movember.com/uploads/files/2019/Financials/Annual-Report_2019.pdf

Moynihan, R. (2003). The making of a disease: Female sexual dysfunction. *British Medical Journal, 326*(7379), 45–7.

Mulé, N.J., Ross, L.E., Deeprose, B., Jackson, B.E., Daley, A., Travers, A., & Moore, D. (2009). Promoting LGBT health and wellbeing through inclusive policy development. *International Journal for Equity in Health, 8*(1), 18.

National Collaborating Centre for Indigenous Health. (2020). Welcome to the NCCIH. https://www.nccih.ca/en/

National Inquiry into Murdered and Missing Indigenous Women and Girls. (2019). *Reclaiming power and place: The final report of the National Inquiry into Missing and Murdered Indigenous Women and Girls.* http://www.mmiwg-ffada.ca/final-report/

Nault, F. (1997). Narrowing mortality gaps 1978 to 1995. *Health Reports, 9*(1), 35–41.

Nestel, S. (2012). *Colour-coded health care: The impact of race and racism on Canadians' health.* Wellesley Institute. http://www.wellesleyinstitute.com/wp-content/uploads/2012/02/Colour-Coded-Health-Care-Sheryl-Nestel.pdf

Ng, E., Wilkins, R., Gendron, F., & Berthelot, J. (2005). *The changing health of immigrants.* Statistics Canada Catalogue no.11-008.

Nikiforuk, A. (1991, Sept.–Oct.). The great fire. *Equinox, 59.*

Office of the Correctional Investigator. (2014). *Annual report of the Office of the Correctional Investigator 2013-2014.* http://www.oci-bec.gc.ca/cnt/rpt/annrpt20132014-eng.aspx#sIV

Oscanoa, T.J., Lizaraso, F., & Carvajal, A. (2017). Hospital admissions due to adverse drug reactions in the elderly: A meta-analysis. *European Journal of Clinical Pharmacology, 73*(6).

Paperny, A.M. (2014). Immigrant unemployment: The more education the bigger the gap. *Global News*. https://globalnews.ca/news/1074811/immigrant-unemployment/

Parkin, A. (2015). *International report card on public education: Key facts on Canadian education and equity*. The Environics Institute. http://education.chiefs-of-ontario.org/upload/documents/resources/research-reports/reports-education/environics-institute-parkin-internationa.pdf

Perreaux, L. (2018, Mar.). Canadian attitudes towards immigrants, refugees remain positive: Study. *Globe & Mail*. https://www.theglobeandmail.com/canada/article/canadian-attitudes-toward-immigrants-refugees-remain-positive-study/

Pinquart, M. (2001). Creating and maintaining purpose in life in old age: A meta-analysis. *Aging International, 27*(2), 90–114.

Phillips, C. (2009). Images, femininity and cancer: An analysis of an international patient education program. *Health: An Interdisciplinary Journal for the Social Study of Health, Illness and Medicine, 13*(1), 67–85.

Population Reference Bureau. (2011). The effect of girls' education on health outcomes: Fact sheet. https://www.prb.org/girls-education-fact-sheet/

Porter, J. (2015, June). Mercury levels still rising near Grassy Narrows First Nation, report says. *CBC News*. https://www.cbc.ca/news/canada/thunder-bay/mercury-levels-still-rising-near-grassy-narrows-first-nation-report-says-1.3109261

———. (2017, June). Ontario announces $85M to clean up mercury near Grassy Narrows, Wabaseemoong First Nation. *CBC News*. https://www.cbc.ca/news/canada/thunder-bay/ontario-mercury-cleanup-1.4180631

Purnell, L. (2000). A description of the Purnell model for cultural competence. *Journal of Transcultural Nursing, 11*(1), 40–6.

Rabson, M. (2018, Mar.). No apology for Canada's residential schools, Pope Francis says. *Global News*. https://globalnews.ca/news/4110276/canada-residential-school-pope-francis-church-apology/

Ranzijn, R. (2001). The potential of older adults to enhance community quality of life: Links between positive psychology and productive aging. *Aging International, 27*(2), 30–55.

Rennie, S. (2014, July). Supreme Court rules in Grassy Narrows logging dispute. *Maclean's*. https://www.macleans.ca/news/canada/supreme-court-rules-in-grassy-narrows-logging-dispute/

Robards, J., Evandrou, M., Falkingham, J., & Vlachantoni, A. (2012). Marital status, health mortality. *Maturitas, 73*(4), 295–9.

Robles, T.F., & Kiecolt-Glaser, J.K. (2003). The physiology of marriage: Pathways to health. *Physiology & Behavior, 79*(3), 409–16.

Rosenfeld, D., & Faircloth, C.A. (2006). *Medicalized masculinities*. Temple University Press.

Rutherford, R.D. (1975). *The changing sex differential in mortality*. International Population and Urban Research, University of California, Berkeley, Studies in Population of Urban Demography No. 1. Greenwood Press.

Sawchuk, J.A., Pederson V., David, M., & Koch, M.F. (2018). Social conditions of Indigenous peoples. *The Canadian Encyclopedia*.

Settlement Ontario. (2016). What are credentials? https://settlement.org/ontario/education/evaluate-my-credentials/credential-evaluation/what-are-credentials/

Shah, C.P. (2004). The health of Aboriginal People. In D. Raphael (Ed.), *Social determinants of health: Canadian perspectives* (pp. 267–80). Canadian Scholars' Press.

Shingler, B. (2013, 24 Nov.). Sarnia's Aamjiwnaang First Nation near Ontario's "Chemical Valley" exposed to pollutants. *Huffington Post*. http://www.huffingtonpost.ca/2013/11/24/aamjiwnaang-first-nation-chemical-valley_n_4333685.html.

Shkilnyk, A. (1985). *A poison stronger than love*. Yale University Press.

Shorr, R.I., Bauwens, S.F., & Landefeld, C.S. (1990). Failure to limit quantities of benzodiazepine hypnotic drugs for outpatients: Placing the elderly at risk. *American Journal of Medicine, 89*, 725–32.

Smylie, J., Crengle, S., Freemantle, J., & Taualii, M. (2010). Indigenous birth outcomes in Australia, Canada, New Zealand and the United States—an overview. *The Open Women's Health Journal, 7*(4).

Spitzer, D.L. (2005). Engendering health disparities. *Canadian Journal of Public Health, 96*(2), S78-S96.

Statista. (2018). Number of immigrants in Canada 2000–2018 (in 000s). https://www.statista.com/statistics/443063/number-of-immigrants-in-canada/

Statistics Canada. (2008). Gender differences in police-reported violent crime in Canada, 2008. https://www.150.statcan.gc.ca/n1/pub/85f0033m/85f0033m2010024-eng.htm

———. (2010). Study: Projections of the diversity of the Canadian population. *The Daily*. www.statcan.gc.ca/daily-quotidien/100309/dq100309a-eng.htm

———. (2011). Top ten causes of death male to female expressed as a ratio. http://themenscentre.ca/wp-content/uploads/2014/03/topten.jpg

———. (2015). Projected life expectancy at birth, by sex, by Aboriginal identity. https://www150.statcan.gc.ca/n1/pub/89-645-x/2010001/life-expectancy-esperance-vie-eng.htm

———. (2016). Deaths, causes of death and life expectancy, 2016. https://www150.statcan.gc.ca/n1/daily-quotidien/180628/dq180628b-eng.htm

———. (2019). Gender, diversity and inclusion statistics. https://www.statcan.gc.ca/eng/topics-start/gender_diversity_and_inclusion

———. (2020). Focus on Geography Series, 2016 Census: Aboriginal peoples. https://www.12.statcan.gc.ca/census-recensement/2016/as-sa/fogs-spg/Facts-CAN-eng.cfm?Lang=Eng&GK=CAN&GC=01&TOPIC=9

Sue, D.W. (2012). *Microaggressions in everyday life: Race, gender and sexual orientation*. Wiley.

Tamblyn, R.M., McLeod, P.J., Abrahamowicz, M., Monette, J., Gayton, D.C., Berkson, L., Dauphinee, W.D., Grad, R.M., Huang, A.R., & Isaac, L.M. (1994). Questionable prescribing for elderly patients in Quebec. *CMAJ, 150*(11), 1801.

TD Economics. (2013). A demographic overview of Aboriginal Peoples in Canada. https://www.td.com/document/PDF/economics/spcial/sg0513_aboriginal_nhs.pdf

———. (2015). The long and winding road towards Aboriginal economic prosperity. https://www.ccab.com/wp-content/uploads/2016/11/TDAboriginalEconomicProsperity.pdf

Thackrah, R.D., & Thompson, S.C. (2013). Refining the concept of cultural competence: Building on decades of progress. *Medical Journal of Australia, 199*(1), 35–8.

Thoits, P.A. (2011). Mechanisms linking social ties and support to mental and physical health. *Journal of Health and Social Behavior, 52*(2), 145–61.

Toronto Star. (2011, 12 Dec.). Ryan Braun's drug test "insanely high," source claims. https://www.thestar.com/sports/baseball/2011/12/12/ryan_brauns_drug_test_insanely_high_source_claims.html

Truth and Reconciliation Commission of Canada (TRC). (2015). *Honouring the truth, reconciling for the future: Summary of the final report of the Truth and Reconciliation Commission of Canada*. Truth and Reconciliation Commission of Canada. http://nctr.ca/assets/reports/Final%20Reports/Executive_Summary_English_Web.pdf

Tuck, I., Moon, M.W., & Allocca, P.N. (2010). An integrative approach to cultural competence education for advanced practice nurses. *Journal of Transcultural Nursing, 21*(4), 402–9.

UN Women. (2019) The Beijing Platform for action turns 20. http://beijing20.unwomen.org/en/in-focus/poverty#facts

Uppal, S., & Barayandema, A. (2018). Life satisfaction among Canadian seniors. Statistics Canada. https://www150.statcan.gc.ca/n1/pub/75-006x/2018001/article/54977-eng.htm

US Department of Transportation. (2017). Traffic safety facts 2016 data: Alcohol-impaired driving. www.crashstats.nhtsa.dot.gov/Api/Public/ViewPublication/812450

Vang, Z., Sigouin, J., Flenon, A., & Gagnon, A. (2015). The healthy immigrant effect in Canada: A systematic review. *Population Change and Lifecourse Strategic Knowledge Cluster Discussion Paper Series, 3*(1), 4.

Verbrugge, L.M. (1985). Gender and health: An update on hypothesis and evidence. *Journal of Health and Social Behavior, 26*, 156–82.

———. (1989). The twain meet: Empirical explanations of sex differences in health and mortality. *Journal of Health and Social Behavior, 31*(3), 282–304.

——— & Wingard, D. (1987). Sex differentials in health and mortality. *Women and Health, 12*(2), 103–45.

Vowel, C. (2016). *Indigenous writes: A guide to First Nations, Métis and Inuit Issues in Canada*. Highwater Press.

Waldron, I. (1981). Why do women live longer than men? *Journal of Human Stress, 2*, 19–30.

Wermuth, L. (2003). *Global inequality and human needs*. Allyn & Bacon.

Wotherspoon, T. (1994). Colonization, self-determination and the health of Canada's First Nations peoples. In B.S. Bolaria & R. Bolaria (Eds), *Racial minorities, medicine and health* (pp. 247–68). Fernwood.

Zwiers, A. (2009). LGBT people and mental health: Healing the wounds. *Visions: BC's Mental Health and Addictions Journal, 6*(2), 10–11.

Chapter 6

Antonovsky, A. (1979). *Health, stress and coping*. Jossey-Bass.

American Psychological Association. (2011). Stress and gender. https://www.apa.org/news/press/releases/stress/2011/gender.aspx

Baetz, M., & Toews, J. (2009). Clinical implications of research on religion, spirituality, and mental health. *Canadian Review of Psychiatry, 54*(5), 292–301.

Beckman, L.F. (1977). Social networks, host resistance and mortality: A follow-up study of Alameda County residents. PhD dissertation, University of California, Berkeley.

Benson, J.E. (2014). Re-evaluating the "subjective weathering hypothesis": Subjective aging, coping resources, and the stress process. *Journal of Health and Social Behavior, 55*(1), 73–90.

Best, M., Butow, P., & Olver, I. (2016). Doctors discussing religion and spirituality: A systematic literature review. *Palliative Medicine, 30*(4), 327–37.

Bieliauskas, L.A. (1982). *Stress and its relationship to health and illness*. Westview Press.

Brown, C.G. (2012). *Testing prayer: Science and healing*. Harvard University Press.

Burgmann, T. (2016). Internet meme for Suicide Squad film ridicules Amanda Todd's death, mom says: Carol Todd says she has shared the images to build awareness and discussion. *Canadian Press*. https://www.cbc.ca/news/canada/british-columbia/suicide-squad-amanda-todd-1.3712615

Cannon, W.B. (1932). *The wisdom of the body*. W.W. Norton.

Chuang, Y.C., Chuang, K.Y., &Yang, T.H. (2013). Social cohesion matters in health. *International Journal for Equity in Health*. https://equityhealthj.biomedcentral.com/articles/10.1186/1475-9276-12-87

Clarke, A.E., Mamo, L., Fishman, J.R., Shim, J.K., & Fosket, J.R. (2003). Biomedicalization: The technoscientific transformations of health, illness, and U.S. biomedicine. *American Sociological Review, 68*(2), 161–94.

Cobb, S. (1976). Social support as a moderator of life stress. *Psychosomatic Medicine*.

Cyranowski, D. (2016). CRISPR gene editing tested in a person for the first time. *Nature: International Weekly Journal of Science*. https://www.nature.com/news/crispr-gene-editing-tested-in-a-person-for-the-first-time-1.20988

Cornwell, E.Y., & Waite, L.J. (2012). Social network resources and management of hypertension. *Journal of Health and Social Behavior, 53*(2), 215–31.

Ellison, C. (1991). Religious involvement and subjective well-being. *Journal of Health and Social Behavior, 32*, 80–99.

Engel, G.L. (1971). Sudden and rapid death during psychological stress: Folklore or folk wisdom? *Annals of Internal Medicine, 74,* 771–82.

Ericksson, M., & Lindstrom, B. (2006). Antonovsky's sense of coherence scale and the relation with health: A systematic review. *Journal of Epidemiology and Community Health, 60,* 376–81.

Fancourt, D., Ockelford, A., & Belai, A. (2014). The psychoneurological effects of music: A systematic review and new model. *Brain, Behavior, and Immunity, 36*: 15–26.

Frankl, V. (1965). *Man's search for meaning* (I. Lasch, Trans.). Beacon Press.

Fuchs, M. (1974). Health care patterns of urbanized Native Americans. PhD dissertation, University of Michigan.

Galloway, G. (2017, Nov.). Census 2016: More Canadians than ever living alone, and other takeaways. *Globe and Mail.* https://www.theglobeandmail.com/news/national/census-2016-statscan/article35861448/

Griswold, M.G., et al. (2018). Alcohol use and burden for 195 countries and territories, 1990–2016: A systematic analysis for the Global Burden of Disease Study 2016. *The Lancet, 392*(10152), 1015–35.

Haig, T. (2017, Jan.). Quebec City man charged in Sunday mosque attack that killed six. *Radio Canada International.*

Hawthorne, G. (2006). Measuring social isolation in older adults: Development and initial validation of the friendship scale. *Social Indications Research, 77,* 521–48.

He, Y., Costa, P.L., Walker, J.M., Miner, K.N., & Wooderson, R.L. (2019). Political identity dissimilarity, workplace incivility, and declines in well-being: A prospective investigation. *Stress and Health, 35*(3), 256–66.

Helliwell, J.F., & Aknin, L.B. (2018). Expanding the social science of happiness. *Nature Human Behaviour, 2*(4), 248–52.

Holland, J.C., & Rowland, J.H. (Eds). (1989). *Handbook of psychooncology: Psychological care of the patient with cancer.* Oxford University Press.

Holmes, T.H., & Rahe, R.H. (1967). The social readjustment rating scale. *Journal of Psychosomatic Research, 11*(2), 213–18.

Kaplan, H.B. (1991). Social psychology and the immune system: A conceptual framework and review of the literature. *Social Science and Medicine,* 909–23.

Kiwanis Magazine. (2018). Stress test. https://kiwanismagazine.org/2018/02/22/stress-test/

Koenig, H.G. (2009). Research on religion, spirituality, and mental health: A review. *Canadian Journal of Psychiatry, 54*(5), 283–91.

———, McCullough, M., & Larson, D.B. (2001). *Handbook of religion and health: A century of research reviewed.* Oxford University Press.

Kravitz-Wirtz, N. (2016). Cumulative effects of growing up in separate and unequal neighborhoods on racial disparities in self-rated health in early adulthood. *Journal of Health and Social Behavior, 57*(4), 453–70.

Krucoff, M.W., Crater, S.W., Gallup, D., Blankenship, J.C., Cuffe, M., Guarneri, M., Krieger, R.A., Kshettry, V.R., Morris, K., Oz, M., Pichard, A., Sketch, M.H., Koenig, H.G., Mark, D., & Lee, K.L. (2005). Music, imagery, touch, and prayer as adjuncts to interventional cardiac care: The monitoring and actualisation of noetic trainings (MANTRA) II randomised study. *The Lancet, 366*(9481), 211–17.

Lane, R.D., Reis, H.T., Hsu, C.H., Kern, K.B., Couderc, J.P., Moss, A.J., & Zareba, W. (2018). Abnormal repolarization duration during everyday emotional arousal in long QT syndrome and coronary artery disease. *American Journal of Medicine, 131*(5), 565–72.

Lantz, P.M., House, J.S., Mero, R.P., & Williams, D.R. (2005). Stress, life events, and socioeconomic disparity: Results from the Americans' changing lives study. *Journal of Health and Social Behavior,46*, 274–88.

Last, J. (1963). The Iceberg: Completing the clinical picture in general practice. *The Lancet, 2*(729), 28–31.

Latkin, C.A., & Curry, A.D. (2003). Stressful neighborhoods and depression: A prospective study of the impact of neighborhood disorders. *Journal of Health and Social Behavior, 44*, 34–44.

Lazarus, R.S., & Delongis, A. (1983). Psychological stress and coping in aging. *American Psychologist, 38*, 245–54.

Lerner, M. (1994). *Choices in healing.* MIT Press.

Levin, J.S. (1993). Esoteric vs. exoteric explanations for findings linking spirituality and health. *Advances, 9*(4), 54–6.

—— & Schiller, P.L. (1987). Is there a religious factor in health? *Journal of Religion and Health, 26*(1), 9–36.

—— & Vanderpool, H.Y. (1989). Is religion therapeutically significant for hypertension? *Social Science and Medicine, 29*(1), 69–78.

Liebenberg, L., Ungar, M., & LeBlanc, J.C. (2013). The CYRM-12: A brief measure of resilience. *Canadian Journal of Public Health, 104*(2), 131–5.

McKenzie, K. (2003). Racism and health. *British Medical Journal, 326*(7380), 65–6.

McPherson, K., Kerr, S., McGee, E., Cheater, F., & Morgan, A. (2013). *The role and impact of social capital on the health and well-being of children and adolescents: A systematic review.* Glasgow Centre for Population Health.

Martire, L., & Franks, N. (2014). The role of social networks in adult health: Introduction to the special issue health psychology. *American Psychological Association, 33*(6), 501–504.

Maselko, J., & Kubzansky, L.D. (2005). Gender differences in religious practices, spiritual experiences and health: Results from the US general social survey. *Social Science and Medicine, 62*(11), 2848–60.

Mechanic, D. (1978). Sex, illness, illness behavior, and the use of health services. *Social Science and Medicine. Part B: Medical Anthropology, 12*, 207–14.

Miller, A. (2013). Incorporating theology into medical education. *CMAJ, 185*(1), 35–7.

Nausheen, B., Gidron, Y., Peveler, R., & Moss-Morris, R. (2009). Social support and cancer progression: A systematic review. *Journal of Psychosomatic Research, 67*(5), 403–15.

Newport, F. (2013, Apr.). How religion could lower health care costs in America. *Business Journal*.

Nittle, N.K. (2018, Dec.). Depression is serious effect of racism on children and youth. *ThoughtCo*. thoughtco.com/childhood-depression-serious-effect-of-racism-2834777

Nomaguchi, K., & House, A.N. (2013). Racial-ethnic disparities in maternal parenting stress: The roles of structural disadvantages and parenting values. *Journal of Health and Social Behavior, 54*(3), 386–404.

Panko, B. (2017). Racism harms children's health, study finds. *Smithsonian.com*. https://www.smithsonianmag.com/science-nature/racism-harms-childrens-health-180963167/

Patton, S. (2014, Nov.). In America, black children don't get to be children. *Washington Post*.

Paul, D. (2019, 12 Feb.). Pittsburgh lawmakers tried to get guns off the street. Now they are being treated like criminals. *Washington Post*. https://www.washingtonpost.com/nation/2019/02/12/pittsburgh-pushes-strict-gun-laws-after-synagogue-massacre-some-people-still-dont-want-them/?utm_term=.f831eafcfeba

Pearlin, L.I., Schieman, S., Fazio, W.M., & Meersman, S. (2005). Stress, health, and the life course: Some conceptual perspectives. *Journal of Health and Social Behavior, 46*, 205–19.

Phillips, D.P., & Feldman, R.A. (1973). A dip in deaths before ceremonial occasions: Some new relationships between social integration and mortality. *American Sociological Review, 38*, 678–96.

Picard, A. (2002, July). Wine lifestyle touted as promoting health. *Globe and Mail*.

Poortinga, W. (2006). Social relations or social capital? Individual and community health effects of bonding social capital. *Social Science and Medicine, 63*, 255–70.

Pridemore, W.A. (2014). The mortality penalty of incarceration: Evidence from a population-based case control study of working age males. *Journal of Health and Social Behavior, 55*(2), 215–33.

Rahe, R.H., Mahan, J.L., & Arthur, R.J. (1970). Prediction of near-future health change from subjects preceding life changes. *Journal of Psychosomatic Research, 14*(4), 401–6.

——— & Paasikivi, J. (1971). Psychosocial factors and myocardial infarction. II. An outpatient study in Sweden. *Journal of Psychosomatic Research, 15*(1), 33–9.

Riggio, R.E. (2012, Oct.). Don't let life's hassles become stressors. *Psychology Today*. http://www.psychologytoday.com/blog/cutting-edge-leadership/201210/don-t-let-life-s-hassles-become-stressors

Rocha, V., Ribeiro, A.I., Severo, M., Barros, H., & Fraga, S. (2017). Neighbourhood socioeconomic deprivation and health-related quality of life: A multilevel analysis. *PLOS One, 12*(12), e0188736.

Roy, B.C.R., & Sinha, R. (2018). Emotion regulation moderates the association between chronic stress and cardiovascular risk in humans: A cross-sectional study. *Stress, 21*(6), 548–55.

Selye, H. (1956). *The stress of life*. McGraw-Hill.

Shahidi, F.V., Ramraj, C., Sod-Erdene, O., Hildebrand, V., & Siddiqi, A. (2019). The impact of social assistance programs on population health: A systematic review of research in high-income countries. *BMC Public Health, 19*(1), 2.

Sheitle, C.P., & Adamczyk, A. (2010). High-cost religion, religious switching, and health. *Journal of Health and Social Behavior, 51*(3), 325–42.

Slater, J., & Perera, A. (2019, 22 Apr.). At least 290 killed in Easter Sunday attacks on churches and hotels. *Washington Post*. https://www.washingtonpost.com/world/coordinated-explosions-rock-three-churches-and-two-hotels-in-sri-lanka-on-easter-sunday/2019/04/21/a09002a0-63f6-11e9-9ff2abc984dc9eec_story.html

Spencer, B. (2014, July). Moderate drinking is bad for health: Just two glasses a day can cause problems. *Daily Mail*. http://www.dailymail.co.uk/health/article-2688161/Moderate-drinking-IS-bad-health-Just-two-glasses-wine-day-cause-problems.html.

Spiegel, D., Bloom, J., Kraemer, H., & Gotheil, E. (1989, Oct.). Effects of psychosocial treatment on survival of patients with metastatic breast cancer. *The Lancet, 15*.

Strayhorn, J.M., & Strayhorn, J.C. (2009). Religiosity and teen birth rate in the United States. *Reproductive Health, 6*(14).

Statistics Canada. (2011). Canadian households in 2011: Type and growth. http://www12.statcan.ca/census-recensement/2011/as-sa/98-312-x/98-312-x2011003_2-eng.cfm

Sternthal, M.J., Williams, D.R., Musick, M.A., & Buck, A.C. (2010). Depression, anxiety and religious life: A search for mediators. *Journal of Health and Social Behavior, 51*(3), 343–59.

Szreter, S., & Woolcock, M. (2004). Health by association? Social capital, social theory, and the political economy of public health. *International Journal of Epidemiology, 33*(4), 650–67.

Targ, E. (1997). Evaluating distant healing: A research review. *Alternative Therapies, 3*(6), 74–8.

Theorell, T., & Rahe, R.H. (1971). Psychosocial factors and myocardial infarction: I. An inpatient study in Sweden. *Journal of Psychosomatic Research, 15*(1), 25–31.

Thoits, P.A. (2010). Stress and health: Major findings and policy implications. *Journal of Health and Social Behavior, 51*(suppl. 1), 41–53.

———. (2011). Mechanisms linking social ties and support to mental and physical health. *Journal of Health and Social Behavior, 52*(2), 145–61.

Troyer, A. (2016). The health benefits of socializing. *Psychology Today*. https://www.psychologytoday.com/us/blog/living-mild-cognitive-impairment/201606/the-health-benefits-socializing

Tsitsika, A.K., Barlou, E., Andrie, E., Dimitropoulou, C., Tzavela, E.C., Janikian, M., & Tsolia, M. (2014). Bullying behaviors in children and adolescents: An ongoing story. *Frontiers in Public Health, 2*(7).

Turner, R.J., & Noh, S. (1983). Class and psychological vulnerability among women: The significance of social support and personal control. *Journal of Health and Social Behavior*, 2–15.

Vyncke, V., De Clercq, B., Stevens, V., Costongs, C., Barbareschi, G., Jónsson, S.H., Curvo, S.d., Kebza, V., Currie, C., & Maes, L. (2013). Does neighbourhood social capital aid in levelling the social gradient in the health and well-being of children and adolescents? A literature review. *BMC Public Health, 13*(1), 65.

Whitbeck, L.B., Hoyt, D.R., McMorris, B.J., Chen, X., & Stubben, J.D. (2001). Perceived discrimination and early substance abuse among American Indian children. *Journal of Health and Social Behavior*, 405–24.

Windle, G. (2011). What is resilience? A review and concept analysis. *Reviews in Clinical Gerontology, 21*(2), 152–69.

Yang, C., McClintock, M.K., Kozloski, M., & Li, T. (2013). Social isolation and adult mortality: The role of chronic inflammation and sex differences. *Journal of Health and Social Behavior, 54*(2), 183–203.

Zola, I. (1973). Pathways to the doctor: From person to patient. *Social Science and Medicine, 7*(9), 677–89.

Chapter 7

Abrams, D., & Weil, A. (2009). *Integrative oncology*. Oxford University Press.

American Society of Plastic Surgeons. (2017). Plastic surgery statistics report. https://www.plasticsurgery.org/documents/News/Statistics/2017/plastic-surgery-statistics-full-report-2017.pdf

Ansari, A. (2016, Sept.). First face transplant patient Isabelle Dinoire, dies at 49. *CNN*. https://www.cnn.com/2016/09/06/health/france-face-transplant-patient-dies/index.html

Barker, K. (2005). *The fibromyalgia story: Medical authority and women's worlds of pain*. Temple University Press.

———. (2011). Pharmaceutical determinism. *Social Science and Medicine, 73*, 833–42.

Beck, U. (1992). *Risk society: Towards a new modernity* (M. Ritter, Trans.). Sage Publications.

Bennett, M.P., & Lengacher, C. (2008). Humour and laughter may influence health: III. Laughter and health outcomes. *Evidence-Based Complementary and Alternative Medicine, 5*(1), 37–40.

Block, W.D., & Muradali, D. (2013). Breast cancer in men. *CMAJ, 185*(14), 1247.

Bluebond-Langer, M. (1978). *The private worlds of dying children*. Princeton University Press.

Breggin, P.R. (2014). The rights of children and parents in regard to children receiving psychiatric diagnoses and drugs. *Children & Society, 28*, 231–41.

Brown, K.L. (2013, Oct.). I can't believe I had a heart attack. *Chatelaine*, 146–50.

Bulow, P.H., & Hyden, L. (2003). Patient school as a way of creating meaning in a contested illness: The case of CFS. *Health: An Interdisciplinary Journal for the Social Study of Health, Illness, and Medicine, 7*(2), 227–49.

Burnfield, A. (1977, 12 Feb.). Multiple sclerosis: A doctor's personal experience. *British Medical Journal, 6058*, 435–6.

Centers for Disease Control and Prevention (CDC). (2020). Estimated influenza illnesses, medical visits, hospitalizations, and deaths in the United States—2018–2019 influenzaseason.https://www.cdc.gov/flu/about/burden/2018-2019.html

Charity Navigator. (2019). Susan G. Komen for the Cure. https://www.charitynavigator.org/index.cfm?bay=search.summary&orgid=4509

Charmaz, K. (1987). Struggling for a self: Identity levels of the chronically ill. *Research in the Sociology of Health Care, 6*, 283–321.

Chopra, A.K., & Doody, J.A. (2007). Schizophrenia, an illness and a metaphor: Analysis of the use of the term "schizophrenia" in U.K. national newspapers. *Journal of the Royal Society of Medicine, 100*(9), 423–6.

Chopra, D. (1987). *Creating Health*. Houghton Mifflin.

———. (1989). *Quantum healing: Exploring the frontiers of body medicine*. Bantam Books.

——— & Kafatos, M. (2017). *You are the universe*. Harmony Books.

Clarke, A.E., Mamo, L., Fishman, J.R., Shim, J.K., & Fosket, J.R. (2003). Biomedicalization: The technoscientific transformations of health, illness, and U.S. biomedicine. *American Sociological Review, 68*(2), 161–94.

Clarke, J.N. (1999). Prostate cancer's hegemonic masculinity, in select print mass media depictions (1974–1995). *Health Communication, 11*(1), 59–74.

———. (2006). Homophobia out of the closet in the media portrayal of HIV/AIDS 1991, 1996, 2001: Celebrity, heterosexism and the silent victims. *Critical Public Health, 6*(4), 317–30.

———, Amerom, G.V., & Binns, J. (2007). Gender and heart disease in mass print media: 1991, 1996, 2001. *Women & Health, 45*(1), 17–35.

——— & Everest, M. (2006). Cancer in the mass print media: Fear, uncertainty and the medical model. *Social Science and Medicine, 62*(10), 2591–600.

——— & Gawley, A. (2009). The triumph of pharmaceuticals: The portrayal of depression 1980–2006. *Administration and Policy in Mental Health, 36*, 91–101.

———, McClellan, L., & Hoffman-Goetz, L. (2006). The portrayal of HIV/AIDS in two popular African American magazines. *Journal of Health Communication: International Perspectives, 11*(5), 495–507.

——— & Robinson, J. (1999). Testicular cancer: Medicine and machismo in the media (1980–1994). *Health, 3*(3), 263–82.

Clements, F.E. (1932). Primitive concepts of disease. *Publications—American Archeology and Ethnology 32*(2), 182–252.

Cole, S., & Lejeune, R. (1972). Illness and the legitimation of failure. *American Sociological Review, 37*, 347–56.

Corbin, J., & Strauss, A. (1987). Accompaniments of chronic illness: Changes in body, self, biography and biographical time. *Research in the Sociology of Health Care, 6*, 249–81.

Cousins, N. (1979). *Anatomy of an illness as perceived by the patient*. Bantam Books.

———. (1983). *The healing heart*. W.W. Norton.

Culos-Reed, N.S., Carlson, L.E., Daroux, L.M., & Hately-Aldous, S. (2006). A pilot study of yoga for breast cancer survivors: Physical and psychological benefits. *Psycho-Oncology, 15*, 891–7.

Currie, D. (1988). Starvation amidst abundance: Female adolescence and anorexia. In B.S. Bolaria & H.D. Dickinson (Eds), *Sociology of health care in Canada* (pp. 198–216). Harcourt Brace Jovanovich.

——— & Raoul, V. (Eds). (1992). *Anatomy of gender: Women's struggle for the body*. Carleton University Press.

Dossey, L. (1982). *Space, time and medicine*. New Science Library.

———. (1991). *Meaning and medicine*. Bantam Books.

———. (2013). *One mind: How our individual mind is part of a greater consciousness and why it matters*. Hay House.

Dowbiggin, I. (2009). High anxieties: The social construction of anxiety disorders. *Canadian Journal of Psychiatry, 54*(7), 429–36.

Drew, S. (2003). Self-reconstruction and biographical revisioning: Survival following cancer in childhood or adolescence. *Health: An Interdisciplinary Journal for the Social Study of Health, Illness, and Medicine, 7*(2), 181–99.

Encyclopaedia Britannica. (2015, 18 Nov.). Andrew Weil, American physician. In *Encyclopædia Britannica online*.

Ehrenreich, B. (2009). *Bright-sided: How positive thinking is undermining America*. Metropolitan Books.

——— & English, D. (1979). *For her own good: 150 Years of the experts' advice to women*. Anchor Press/Doubleday.

Elliott, C. (2003). *Better than well: American medicine meets the American dream*. W.W. Norton.

Foucault, M. (1994) [1973]. *The birth of the clinic: An archeology of medical perception* (A.M. Sheridan Smith, Trans). Vintage Books.

Frank, A. (1997). *The wounded storyteller: Body, illness and ethics*. University of Chicago Press.

———. (2002). *At the will of the body: Reflections on illness*. Houghton Mifflin Harcourt.

Frith, H., Raisborough, J., & Klein, O. (2013). Making death "good": Instructional tales for dying in newspaper accounts of Jade Goody's death. *Sociology of Health and Illness, 35*(3), 419–33.

Gibson, V. (2019, Jan.). *Brampton, Ont., woman at the centre of brain death legal battle dies naturally. Globe and Mail*. https://www.theglobeandmail.com/canada/article-brampton-woman-at-centre-of-brain-death-legal-battle-dies-naturally/

Giddens, A. (1999). Risk and responsibility. *Modern Law Review, 62*, 1–10.

Goffman, E. (1961). *Asylums: Essays on the situation of mental patients and other inmates*. Anchor Press/Doubleday.

———. (1963). *Stigma: Notes on the management of spoiled identity*. Prentice-Hall.

Horwitz, A.V. (2013). *Anxiety: A short history of anxiety*. Johns Hopkins University Press.

——— & Wakefield, J.C. (2012). *All we have to fear: Psychiatry's transformation of natural anxieties into mental disorders*. Oxford University Press.

Hughes, C.C. (1967). Ethnomedicine. In D. Gills (Ed.), *International encyclopedia of social sciences* (pp. 87–92). Macmillan and Free Press.

Karp, D. 1996. *Speaking of sadness, depression, disconnection and the meanings of illness*. Oxford University Press.

King, Samantha. (2006). *Pink Ribbons, Inc.: Breast cancer and the politics of philanthropy*. University of Minnesota Press.

King, Sorrel. (2009). *Josie's story: A mother's inspiring crusade to make medical care safe*. Atlantic Monthly Press.

Klawiter, M. (1999). Racing for the cure, walking women, and toxic touring: Mapping cultures of action within the Bay Area terrain of breast cancer. *Social Problems, 46*(1), 104–26.

Kramer, P.D. (1993). *Listening to prozac*. Penguin Books.

Lockwood, N.L., & Yoshimura, S.M. (2014). The heart of the matter: The effects of humor on well-being during recovery from cardiovascular disease. *Health Communication, 29*, 410–20.

LeShan, L. (1978). *You can fight for your life*. M. Evans.

Li, S., & Arber, A. (2006). The construction of troubled and credible patients: A study of emotion talk in palliative care setting. *Qualitative Health Research, 16*(1), 27–46.

Lincoln, A. (2006). Psychiatric emergency room decision-making, social control and the "undeserving sick." *Sociology of Health & Illness, 28*(1), 54–75.

McCambridge, R. (2018). Another Komen chapter goes under amidst massive revenue losses. *Nonprofit Quarterly*.

MacDonald, S., Watt, G., & MacLeod, U. (2013). In search of the cancer candidate: Can lay epidemiology help? *Sociology of Health and Illness, 35*(4), 575–91.

McInerney, F. (2006). Heroic frames: Discursive constructions around the requested death movement in Australia in the late 1990s. *Social Science and Medicine, 62*(3), 654–67.

McKenzie, H., & Crouch, M. (2004). Discordant feelings in the lifeworld of cancer survivors. *Health: An Interdisciplinary Journal for the Social Study of Health, Illness, and Medicine, 8*(2), 139–57.

Makary, M., & Daniel, M. (2016). Medical error the third leading cause of death in the US. *British Medical Journal, 3*(353).

Mariotto, A.B., Rowland, J.H., Yabroff, K.R., Scoppa, S., Hachey, M., Ries, L., & Feuer, E.J. (2009). Long-term survivors of childhood cancers in the United States. *Cancer Epidemiology and Prevention Biomarkers, 18*(4), 1033–40.

Metzl, J.M., & Angel, J. (2004). Assessing the impact of SSRI antidepressants on popular notions of women's depressive illness. *Social Science and Medicine, 58*, 577–84.

Miller, L.E. (2014). Uncertainty management and information seeking in cancer survivorship. *Health Communication, 29,* 233–43.

Nordquist, G. (2006). Patient insurance status and do-not-resuscitate orders: Survival of the richest? *Journal of Sociology and Social Welfare, 33*(1), 75.

Orbach, S. (1986). *Hunger strike: An anorexic's struggle as a metaphor for our age.* W.W. Norton.

Paget, M.A. (1993). *A complex sorrow: Reflections on cancer and an abbreviated life* (M.L. Devault, Ed.). Temple University Press.

Perrow, C. (1999). Organizing to reduce the vulnerabilities of complexity. *Journal of Contingencies and Crisis Management, 7*(3), 150–5.

Pitts, V. (2004). Illness and Internet empowerment: Writing and reading breast cancer in cyberspace. *Health: An Interdisciplinary Journal for the Social Study of Health, Illness, and Medicine, 8*(1), 33–59.

Reissman, C.K. (1987). Women and medicalization: A new perspective. In H.D. Schwartz (Ed.), *Dominant issues in medical sociology,* 2nd edn (pp. 101–21). Random House.

Reynolds, C. (2012). B.C. teens, twenty-somethings turn to Botox for forever 21 look. *Vancouver Sun.* http://www.vancouversun.com/teens+twenty+somethings+turn+Botox+forever+look/7002991/story.html

Roth, J. (1963). *Timetables: Structuring the passage of time in hospital treatment and other careers.* Bobbs-Merrill.

Schneider, J., & Conrad, P. (1983). *Having epilepsy: The experience and control of illness.* Temple University Press.

Schofield, P., Carey, M., Bonevski, B., & Sanson-Fisher, R. (2006). Barriers to the provision of evidence-based psycho-social care in oncology. *Psycho-Oncology, 15,* 863–72.

Schwappach, D.L.B. (2010). Review: Engaging patients as vigilant partners in safety: A systematic review. *Medical Care Research and Review, 67*(2), 119–48.

Seale, C. (2006). Gender accommodation in online cancer support groups. *Health: An Interdisciplinary Journal for the Social Study of Health, Illness, and Medicine, 10*(3), 345–60.

Seow, H., Barbera, L., Sutradhar, R., Howell, D., Dudgeon, D., Atzema, C., Liu, Y., Husain, A., Sussman, J., & Earle, C. (2011). Trajectory of performance status and symptom scores for patients with cancer during the last six months of life. *Journal of Clinical Oncology, 29*(9), 1151–8.

Shoshana, A., & Teman, E. (2006). Coming out of the coffin: Life-self and death-self in six feet under. *Symbolic Interaction, 29*(4), 557–76.

Siirla, A. (1981). *The voice of illness: A study in therapy and prophecy,* 2nd edn. Edwin Mellen Press.

Simonton, C.O., Simonton, S.M., & Creighton, J.L. (1978). *Getting well again.* Bantam Books.

Sontag, S. (1978). *Illness as metaphor.* Random House.

Speigel D. (2012). Mind matters in cancer survival. *Psycho-oncology.* https://onlinelibrary.wiley.com/doi/full/10.1002/pon.3067

Steinem, G. (1983). *Outrageous acts and everyday rebellions.* Holt, Rinehart and Winston.

Strauss, A.L., & Glaser, B.G. (1975). *Chronic illness and the quality of life.* Mosby.

Strean, W.B. (2009). Laughter prescription. *Canadian Family Physician, 55*(10), 965–7.

Sudnow, D. (1967). *Passing on: The social organization of dying.* Prentice-Hall.

Timmermans, S. (1998). Social death no self-fulfilling prophecy: David Sudnow's *Passing On* revisited. *Sociological Quarterly, 39*(3), 453–72.

——— & Buchbinder, M. (2010). Patients-in-waiting: Living between sickness and health in a genomics era. *Journal of Health and Social Behavior, 51*(4), 408–23.

Turner, B.S. (1987). *Medical power and social knowledge.* Sage Publications.

Vagianos, A. (2018, June). Being transgender is no longer seen as a mental disorder by the World Health Organization. *Huffington Post.* https://www.yahoo.com/news/being-transgender-no-longer-considered-211437119.html

Weil, A. (2011). *Spontaneous happiness.* Little, Brown.

Whitaker, R. (2010). *Anatomy of an epidemic: Magic bullets, psychiatric drugs, and the astonishing rise of mental illness in America.* Crown.

Zborowski, M. (1952). Cultural components in response to pain. In E. Jaco (Ed.), *Patients, physicians and illness* (pp. 256–68). Free Press.

———. (1969). *People in pain.* Jossey-Bass.

Chapter 8

Australian Government. (2010). Hormone replacement therapy (HRT) and the risk of cancer. https://canceraustralia.gov.au/publications-and-resources/position-statements/hormone-replacement-therapy-hrt-and-risk-breast-cancer

Balshem, M. (1991). Cancer, control and causality: Talking about cancer in a working class community. *American Ethnologist, 18,* 152–72.

Bérard, G. (1993). *Hearing equals behavior.* Keats Publishing.

Bhattacharya, S. (2015, Jan.). Up to 140,000 heart attacks linked to Vioxx. *New Scientist.* https://www.newscientist.com/article/dn6918-up-to-140000-heart-attacks-linked-to-vioxx/

Boseley, S. (2008, 26 Nov.). Mbeki's AIDS denial "caused 300,000 deaths." *The Guardian.* http://www.theguardian.com/world/2008/nov/26/aids-south-africa

Bransen, E. (1992). Has menstruation been medicalized or will it never happen? *Sociology of Health and Illness, 14*(1), 98–110.

Butler, I. (1993). Premature adoptions and routinization of medical technology: Illustrations from childbirth technology. *Journal of Social Issues, 49*(2), 11–34.

Calnan, M., & Williams, S. (1992). Images of scientific medicine. *Sociology of Health and Illness, 14*(2), 233–54.

Chapman, E.N., Kaatz, A., & Carnes, M. (2013). Physicians and implicit bias: How doctors may unwittingly perpetuate health care disparities. *Journal of General Internal Medicine, 28*(11), 1504–10.

Cho, N., Boland, L., & McIsaac, D. (2019). The association of female sex with application of evidence-based practice recommendations for perioperative care in hip fracture surgery. *CMAJ, 191*(6), E151–E158.

Chow, S. (1998). Specialty group differences over tonsillectomy: Pediatricians versus otolaryngologists. *Qualitative Health Research, 8*(1), 61–75.

Clark, J.A., & Mishler, E.G. (1992). Attending to patients' stories: Reframing the clinical task. *Sociology of Health and Illness, 14*(3), 344–72.

——, Potter, D.A., & McKinlay, J.B. (1991). Bringing social structure back into clinical decision making. *Social Science and Medicine, 32*(8), 853–63.

Cornwell, J. (1984). *Hard-earned lives: Accounts of health and illness from East London.* Tavistock.

Dellorto, D. (2011, 31 May). WHO: Cell phone use can increase possible cancer risk. *CNN.* http://www.cnn.com/2011/HEALTH/05/31/who.cell.phones/index.html

Desai, N., Dole, E.J., Yeaton, S.T., & Troutman, W.J. (1997). Evaluation of drug information in an Internet newsgroup. *Journal of the American Pharmaceutical Association, 37*(4), 391–4.

Doidge, N. (2007). *The brain that changes itself: Stories of personal triumph from the frontiers of brain science.* Penguin.

——. (2015). *The brain's way of healing: Remarkable discoveries and recoveries from the frontiers of neuroplasticity.* Viking.

Donaldson, T., & Dunfee, T.W. (2002). Ties that bind in business ethics: Social contracts and why they matter. *Journal of Banking & Finance, 26*(9), 1853–65.

Dubos, R. (1959). *The mirage of health.* Doubleday.

Fahy, E., Hardikar, R., Fox, A., & Mackay, S. (2014). Quality of patient health information on the Internet: Reviewing a complex and evolving landscape. *Australas Medical Journal, 7*(1), 24–8. doi:10.4066/AMJ.2014.1900

Findlay, D. (1993). The good, the normal and the healthy: The social construction of medical knowledge about women. *Canadian Journal of Sociology, 18*(2), 115–33.

Finlay, K. (2016, 24 Oct.). Preventable medical error is Canadian healthcare's silent killer. *Huffington Post.* https://www.huffingtonpost.ca/kathleen-finlay/medical-error-deaths_b_8350324.html

Filopovic, Jill. (2014, Apr.). Inside a war on natural birth: C sections as status symbol and a "choice" as a myth. *The Guardian.*

Foucault, M. (1994) [1973]. *The birth of the clinic: An archeology of medical perception* (A.M. Sheridan Smith, Trans.). Vintage Books.

Foucault, M. (2006). *History of madness* (J. Khalfa & J. Murphy, (Eds and Trans.). Routledge.

Fox, N.J. (1993). Discourse, organization and the surgical ward round. *Sociology of Health and Illness, 15*(1).

Freund, P., McGuire, M.B., & Podhurst, L.S. (2003). *Health, illness and the social body: A critical sociology*, 4th edn. Prentice-Hall.

Fuller, C., & Saibil, D. (2005). Post-market surveillance of therapeutic drugs in Canada. *Women and Health Protection.* http://www.whp-apsf.ca/en/documents/adrBackground.html

Grant, K. (2019, 1 Apr.). Cesarian delivery associated with higher risk of severe complications for mothers aged 35 and older, study shows. *Globe and Mail.* https://www.theglobeandmail.com/canada/article-cesarean-delivery-associated-with-higher-risk-of-severe-complications/

Hadler, N.M. (2011). *Rethinking aging: Growing old and living well in an overtreated society.* University of North Carolina Press.

Hart, N., Grand, N., & Riley, K. (2006). Making the grade: The gender gap, ADHD, and the medicalization of boyhood. In D. Rosenfeld and C.A. Faircloth (Eds), *Medicalized Masculinities* (pp. 132–64). Temple University Press.

Helman, C.G. (2007). *Culture, health and illness*, 5th edn. Hodder Arnold.

Hochschild, A. (2012) [1983]. *The managed heart: The commercialization of human feeling.* University of California Press.

Hoffman-Goetz, L., & Clarke, J.N. (2000). Quality of breast cancer sites on the World Wide Web. *Canadian Journal of Public Health, 91*, 281–4.

Hollander, I. (2006). Viagra's rise above women's health issues: An analysis of the social and political influences on drug approval in the United States and Japan. *Social Science and Medicine, 62*, 683–93.

Humphries, K.H., Kerr, C.R., & Connolly, S.J. (2001). New-onset atrial fibrillation: Sex differences in presentation, treatment, and outcome. *Circulation, 103*, 2365–70.

Impicciatore, P., Pandolfini, C., Casella, N., & Bonati, M. (1994). Reliability of health information for the public on the world wide web: Systematic survey of advice on managing fever in children at home. *British Medical Journal, 314*, 1875–81.

Jeffcoate, T. (1957). *Principles of gynecology.* Butterworth.

Kafetsios, K., Anagnostopuolos, F., Lempesis, E., & Valindra, A. (2014). Doctors' emotion regulation and patient satisfaction: A social functional perspective. *Health Communication, 29*, 205–14.

Klarenbach, S., Sims-Jones, N., & Lewin, G. (2018). Recommendations on screening for breast cancer in women aged 40–74 years who are not at increased risk for breast cancer. *CMAJ, 190*(49), E1441–E1451.

Kuhn, T. (1962). *The structure of scientific revolutions.* University of Chicago Press.

Lakoff, A. (2004). The anxieties of globalization: Antidepressant sales and economic crisis in Argentina. *Social Studies of Science, 34*(2), 247–69.

Loe, M. (2006). The Viagra blues: Embracing or resisting the Viagra body. In D. Rosenfeld and C.A. Faircloth (Eds), *Medicalized Masculinities* (pp. 21–44). Temple University Press.

Lupton, D. (2012). M-health and health promotion: The digital cyborg and surveillance society. *Social Theory & Health, 10*(3), 229–34.

McKinlay, J.B., &. McKinlay, S.M. (1981). From promising report to standard procedure: Seven stages in the career of a medical innovation. *Milbank Memorial Fund Quarterly, 59*, 374–411.

Manning, P.K., & Fabrega, H. (1973). The experience of self and body: Health and illness in the Chipas Highlands. In G. Psathas (Ed.), *Phenomenological sociology*. John Wiley and Sons.

Martin, E. (1987). *The woman in the body: A cultural analysis of reproduction*. Beacon Press.

Meel, B.L. (2003). The myth of child rape as a cure for *HIV/AIDS* in Transkei. *Medicine, Science & the Law, 43*(1), 85–8.

Miles, N. (2005). South Africa's broken HIV promises. *BBC News*. http://news.bbc.co.uk/2/hi/africa/4482007.stm

Montini, T., & Slobin, K. (1991). Tensions between good science and good practice: Lagging behind and leapfrogging ahead along the cancer care continuum. *Research in the Sociology of Health Care, 9*, 127–40.

Moyer, A., Grenner, S., Beavis, J., & Salovey, P. (1994). Accuracy of health research reported in the popular press: Breast cancer and mammography. *Health Communication, 7*(1), 147–61.

Moynihan, R. (2006). Scientists find new disease: Motivational deficiency disorder. *British Medical Journal, 332*, 745.

———, Heath, I., & Henry, D. (2002). Selling sickness: The pharmaceutical industry and disease mongering. *British Medical Journal, 324*, 886–91.

Murphy, L. (2015, Nov.). Canada's C-section crisis: Why are rates so high? Today's Parent. https://www.todaysparent.com/pregnancy/giving-birth/canadas-c-section-crisis-why-are-rates-so-high/

Nettleton, S. (2004). The emergence of e-scaped medicine. *Sociology, 38*(4), 661–80.

Nischal, A., Tripathi, A., Nischal, A., & Trivedi, J.K. (2012). Suicide and antidepressants: What current evidence indicates. *Menssana monographs, 10*(1), 33.

Olivieri, N.F. (2003). Patients' health or company profits? The commercialisation of academic research. *Science and Engineering Ethics, 9*(1), 29–41.

Payer, L. (1988). *Medicine and culture: Varieties of treatment in the United States, England, West Germany and France*. Holt.

Pinto, A.D., Aratangy, T., Abramovich, A., Devotta, K., Nisenbaum, R., Wang, R., & Kiran, T. (2019). Routine collection of sexual orientation and gender identity data: A mixed-methods study. *CMAJ, 191*(3), E63–E68.

Rachlis, M., & Kushner, C. (1989). *Second opinion: What's wrong with Canada's health care system*. HarperCollins.

Regitz-Zagrosek, V., Petrov, G., & Lehmkuhl, E. (2010). Heart transplantation in women with dilated cardiomyopathy. *Transplantation, 89*, 236–44.

Rosenfeld, D., & Faircloth, C.A. (2006). Introduction: Medicalized masculinities: The missing link. In D. Rosenfeld and C.A. Faircloth (Eds), *Medicalized masculinities* (pp. 1–20). Temple University Press.

Sinyor, M., Schaffer, A., & Nishikawa, Y. (2018). The association between suicide deaths and putatively harmful and protective factors in media reports. *CMAJ, 190*(30), E900–E907.

Smith, G. (2009). The elderly and health care rationing. *Catholic University of America*. Columbus School of Law CUA Law Scholarship Repository.

Stanley, E.M.G., & Ramage, M.P. (1984). Sexual problems and urological symptoms. In S.L. Stanton (Ed.), *Clinical gynecological urology* (pp. 398–405). Mosby.

Stein, H.F. (1990). *American medicine as culture*. Westview Press.

Toronto Star. (2002, July). Week-old infant raped in S. Africa.

Tuller, D. (2014). ADHD and disease mongering. *Berkeley Wellness*. http://www.berkeleywellness.com/self-care/preventive-care/article/adhd-disease-mongering

Weijts, W., Houtkoop, H., & Mullen, P. (1993). Talking delicately: Speaking about sexuality during gynecological consultation. *Sociology of Health and Illness, 15*(4).

Wexler, D.J., Grant, R.W., & Meigs, J.B. (2005). Sex disparities in treatment of cardiac risk factors in patients with type 2 diabetes. *Diabetes Care, 28*, 514–20.

Whitaker, R. (2010). *Anatomy of an epidemic: Magic bullets, psychiatric drugs, and the astonishing rise of mental illness in America*. Crown.

Widman, L., & Tong, D.A. (1997). Requests for medical advice from patients and families to health care providers who publish on the world wide web. *Archives of Internal Medicine, 157*, 209–12.

World Health Organization (WHO). (n.d.). Caesarean sections should only be performed when medically necessary, says WHO. https://www.who.int/reproductivehealth/topics/maternal_perinatal/cs-statement/en/

Yeaton, W.H., Smith, D., & Rogers, K. (1990). Evaluating understanding of popular press reports of health research. *Health Education Quarterly, 17*, 223–34.

Young, L. (2018, Apr.). Canadian mothers increasingly giving birth through C-section. *Global News*. https://globalnews.ca/news/4155705/c-section-birth-statistics-canada/

Zlomislic, C., & Teotonio, I. (2013, 31 Jan.). Diane-35: Deaths of 11 Canadian women linked to acne drug, compared to four in France. *Toronto Star*. https://www.thestar.com/news/canada/2013/01/31/diane35_deaths_of_11_canadian_women_linked_to_acne_drug_compared_to_four_in_france.html

Chapter 9

Abraham, J. (2010). Pharmaceuticalization of society in context: Theoretical, empirical and health dimensions. *Sociology, 44*(4), 603–22.

Ayo, N. (2012). Understanding health promotion in a neoliberal climate and the making of health conscious citizens. *Critical Public Health, 22*(1), 99–105.

BBC News. (2019). Breast implants: France bans designs linked to rare cancer. https://www.bbc.com/news/world-europe-47824312

Beck, U. (1992). *Risk society: Towards a new modernity* (M. Ritter, Trans.). Sage Publications.

Blaxter, M. (1978). Diagnosis as category and process: The case of alcoholism. *Social Science and Medicine, 12*, 9–77.

Bullough, B., & Bullough, V. (1972). A brief history of medical practice. In J. Lorber and E. Freidson (Eds), *Medical men and their work: A sociological reader* (pp. 86–101). Aldone Atherton.

Centre for ADHD Awareness Canada (CADDAC). (2019) ADHD facts: Dispelling the myths. https://caddac.ca/adhd/understanding-adhd/in-general/facts-stats-myths/

Canadian Press. (2012, Sept.). Inquest into Ashley Smith's death begins again Thursday. *CBC News.* https://www.cbc.ca/news/canada/toronto/inquest-into-ashley-smith-s-death-begins-again-thursday-1.1226346

Canadian Institute for Health Information (CIHI). (2019). Health spending. https://www.cihi.ca/en/health-spending

Canadian Internet Registration Authority (CIRA). (2016). 2016 Internet factbook. https://cira.ca/factbook/domain-industry-data-and-canadian-Internet-trends/internet-use-canada

Clarke, A.E., Mamo, L., Fishman, J.R., Shim, J.K., & Fosket, J.R. (2003). Biomedicalization: The technoscientific transform-ations of health, illness, and U.S. biomedicine. *American Sociological Review, 68*(2), 161–94.

Clarke, J.N., & James, S. (2003). The radicalized self: The impact on the self of the contested nature of the diagnosis of chronic fatigue syndrome. *Social Science and Medicine, 57*(8), 1387–95.

Clendening, L. (Ed.). (1960). *Source book of medical history.* Dover.

Coburn, D., Rappolt, S., & Bourgeault, I. (1997). Decline vs. retention of medical power through rest ratification: An examination of the Ontario case. *Sociology of Health and Illness, 19*(1), 1–22.

Conrad, P. (1975). The discovery of hyperkinesis: Notes on the medicalization of deviant behaviour. *Social Problems, 23*(Oct.), 12–21.

———. (2005). The shifting engines of medicalization. *Journal of Health and Social Behavior, 46*(1), 3–14.

——— & Schneider, J.W. (1980). *Deviance and medicalization: From badness to sickness.* Mosby.

Crawford, R. (2006). Healthism and the medicalization of everyday life. *Health, 10,* 401–20.

Dickson, G.L. (1990). A feminist poststructural analysis of the knowledge of menopause. *Advances in Nursing Science* (Apr.), 15–31.

Dumit, J. (2006). Illnesses you have to fight to get: Facts as forces in uncertain, emergent illnesses. *Social Science and Medicine, 62*(3), 577–90.

Elliott, C. (2004). *Better than well: American medicine meets the American dream.* W.W. Norton.

Foucault, M. (1973). *The birth of illness.* A.M. Sheridan Smith (Trans.). Pantheon Books.

———. (1980). *Power/knowledge: Selected interviews and other writings, 1972–1977* (C. Gordon, Ed.). Pantheon Books.

———. (1991). Governmentality. R. Braidotti (Trans.), C. Gordon (Revised). In G. Burchell, C. Gordon, & P. Miller (Eds), *The Foucault effect: Studies in governmentality* (pp. 87–104). University of Chicago Press.

———. (2006). *History of madness.* J. Khalfa & J. Murphy (Ed. and Trans.). Routledge.

Fox, R.C. (1977). The medicalization and demedicalization of American society. In J.H. Knowles (Ed.), *Doing Better and feeling worse: Health in the United States* (pp. 9–22). W.W. Norton.

Freidson, E. (1970). *Professional dominance: The social structure of medical care.* Atherton Press.

———. (1975). *The profession of medicine: Study in the sociology of applied knowledge.* Dodd Mead.

Geise, R. (2013). The mainstreaming of mental health. *The Walrus* (Mar.), 30–9.

Giddens, A. (1999). Risk and responsibility. *Modern Law Review,62,* 1–10.

Grohol, J. (2018). DSM-5 released: The big changes. *PsychCentral.* https://psychcentral.com/blog/dsm-5-released-the-big-changes/

Hart, N., Grand, N., & Riley, K. (2006). Making the grade: The gender gap, ADHD, and the medicalization of boyhood. In D. Rosenfeld & C. Faircloth (Eds), *Medicalized masculinities* (pp. 132–64). Temple University Press.

Hesse, B.W., Nelson, D.E., Kreps, G.L., Croyle, R.T., Arora, N.K., Rimer, B.K., & Viswanath, K. (2005). Trust and sources of health information: The impact of the Internet and its im-plications for health care providers: findings from the first Health Information National Trends Survey. *Archives of Internal Medicine, 165*(22), 2618–24.

Howson, A. (1998). Surveillance, knowledge and risk: The embodied experience of cervical screening. *Health, 2*(2), 195–215.

Illich, I. (1976). *Limits to medicine.* McClelland & Stewart.

Kudlow, P. (2013). The perils of diagnostic inflation. *CMAJ, 185*(1), 25–6.

LaVigne, M., & Van Rybroek, G.J. (2011). Breakdown in the language zone: The prevalence of language impairments among juvenile and adult offenders and why it matters. *UC Davis Journal of Juvenile Law and Policy, 15*(1): 37–123. http://ssrn.com/abstract=1663805

Lett, D. (2010). Police launch criminal investigation into actions of emergency department. *CMAJ, 182*(18), 817.

Lewinsohn, R. (1998). Medical theories, science and the practice of medicine. *Social Science and Medicine, 46*(10), 1261–70.

Loe, M. (2006). The Viagra blues: Embracing or resisting the Viagra body. In D. Rosenfeld & C. Faircloth (Eds.), *Medicalized masculinities* (pp. 21–44). Temple University Press.

Lupton, D. (1993). Risk as moral danger: The social political functions of risk discourse in public health. *International Journal of Health Services, 23*(3), 425–35.

McCrea, F.B. (1983). The politics of menopause: The discovery of a deficiency disease. *Social Problems, 31*(1), 111–23.

Metzl, J. (2010). *The protest psychosis: How schizophrenia became a black disease.* Beacon Hill Press.

Metzl, J.M., & Angel, J. (2004). Assessing the impact of SSRI antidepressants on popular notions of women's depressive illness. *Social Science and Medicine, 58,* 577–84.

Miller, A.B., Wall, C., Sun, P., Baines, C.J., To, T., & Narod, S.A. (2014). Twenty-five year follow-up for breast cancer incidence and mortality of the Canadian national breast cancer screening study: Randomized screening trial. *British Medical Journal*, 348.

Myers, D.G. (2000). *A quiet world: Living with hearing loss*. Yale University Press.

Murray, E., Lo, B., Pollack, L., Donelan, K., Catania, J., Lee, K., Zapert, K., & Turner, R. (2003). The impact of health information on the Internet on health care and the physician–patient relationship: National US survey among 1.050 US physicians. *Journal of Medical Internet Research, 5*(3), e17.

Navarro, V. (1976). Social class, political power and the state and their implications for medicine. *Social Science and Medicine, 10*, 437–57.

O'Hagan, J., MacKinnon, N.J., Persaud, D., & Etchegary, H. (2009). Self-reported medical error in seven countries: Implications for Canada. *Health Quarterly, 12*, 55–61.

Rose, N. (2006). Disorders without borders? The expanding scope of psychiatric practice. *Biosocieties, 1*, 465–84.

Rosen, G. (1963). The evolution of social medicine. In H.E. Freeman, S. Levine, & L.G. Reader, (Eds), *Handbook of medical sociology* (pp. 23–50). Prentice-Hall.

Sadasivam, R.S., Kinney, R.L., Lemon, S.C., Shimada, S.L., Allison, J.J., & Houston, T.K. (2013). Internet health information seeking is a team sport: Analysis of the Pew Internet Survey. *International Journal of Medical Informatics, 82*(3), 193–200.

Stanford Health Care. (2019). Stanford medicine online second opinion program. https://stanfordhealthcare.org/second-opinion/overview.html

Thomas, L. (1985). *The youngest science: Notes of a medicine-watcher*. Oxford University Press.

Timmermans, S., & Buchbinder, M. (2012). *Saving babies: The consequences of newborn screening*. University of Chicago Press.

Tone, A. (2009). *The age of anxiety: A history of America's turbulent affair with tranquilizers*. Basic Books.

Underhill, C., & McKeown, L. (2008). Getting a second opinion: Health information and the Internet. Statistics Canada. http://www.statcan.gc.ca/pub/82-003-x/2008001/article/10515-eng.pdf

Williams, S.J., & Calnan, M. (1996). The limits of medicalization? Modern medicine and the lay population in "late" modernity. *Social Science and Medicine, 42*(12), 1609–20.

Wolf, N. (1991). *The beauty myth*. Vintage Books.

Zola, I. (1972). Medicine as an institution of social control. *Sociological Review, 20*, 487–504.

Chapter 10

Alter, D.A., Basinski, A.S., & Naylor, C.D. (1998). A survey of provider experiences and perceptions of preferential access to cardiovascular care in Ontario, Canada. *Annals of Internal Medicine, 129*(7), 567–72.

Barer, M.L., Evans, R.G., & Stoddart, G.L. (1979). *Controlling health care costs by direct charges to patients: Snare or delusion?* Occasional Paper No. 10. Ontario Economic Council.

Barua, B., & Globerman, S. (2018). Timely health care—there's an app for that! *The Fraser Forum: The Fraser Institute Blog*. https://www.fraserinstitute.org/blogs/timely-health-care-there-s-an-app-for-that

Bilson, G. (1980). *A darkened house: Cholera in nineteenth-century Canada*. University of Toronto Press.

Booth, G.L., Bishara, P., Lipscombe, L.L., Shah, B.R., Feig, D.S., Bhattacharyya, O., & Bierman, A.S. (2012, Aug.). Younger, low income Ontarians with risk of diabetes have higher risk of death than their high income counterparts. *ICES*.

Buckley, R.E., & Harasym, P.H. (1999). Level symptoms and causes of surgical residents' stress. *Annals, Royal College of Physicians and Surgeons of Canada, 324*(June), 216–21.

Budgell, A. (2018). *We all expected to die: Spanish influenza in Labrador, 1918–1919*. ISER Books.

Burke, M., & Stevenson, H.M. (1993). Fiscal crises and restructuring in medicine: The politics and political science of health in Canada. *Health and Canadian Society, 1*(1), 51–80.

Canadian Institute for Health Information (CIHI). (2014). *National health expenditure trends, 1975–2013*. https://secure.cihi.ca/free_products/NHEXTrendsReport_EN.pdf

———. (2017). *Physicians in Canada, 2016: Summary report*. https://secure.cihi.ca/free_products/Physicians_in_Canada_2016.pdf

———. (2019, Feb.). *Physicians in Canada, 2017*. https://secure.cihi.ca/free_products/Physicians_in_Canada_2017.pdf

Canadian Internet Registration Authority. (2016). 2016 Internet factbook. https://cira.ca/factbook/domain-industry-data-and-canadian-Internet-trends/internet-use-canada

CBC News. (2003, Dec.). In-depth SARS timeline. https://www.cbc.ca/news2/background/sars/timeline.html

Chan, A.O.M., & Huak, C.Y. (2004). Psychological impact of the 2003 severe acute respiratory syndrome outbreak on health care workers in a medium size regional general hospital in Singapore. *Occupational Medicine, 54*, 190–6.

Charles, C.A. (1976). The medical profession and health insurance: An Ottawa case study. *Social Science and Medicine, 10*, 33–8.

Closson, T.R., & Catt, M. (1996). Funding system initiatives and the restructuring of health care. *Canadian Journal of Public Health, 87*(2), 86–9.

Coburn, D., & Biggs, C.L. (1987). Chiropractic: Legitimation or medicalization? In D. Coburn, C. D'Arcy, & G. Torrance (Eds), *Health and Canadian society* (pp. 336–84). University of Toronto Press.

———, Torrance, G.M., & Kaufert, J.M. (1983). Medical dominance in Canada in historical perspective: The rise and fall of medicine? *International Journal of Health Services, 13*(3), 407–32.

Commission on the Future of Health Care in Canada (Roy Romanow, chairman). (2002). *Final report*. www.hc-sc.gc.ca/english/care/romanow/index1.html.

Dickin McGinnis, J.P. (1977). The impact of epidemic influenza: Canada 1918–1919. Canadian Historical Association, *Historical Papers*.

Gidney, R.D., & Millar, W.P.S. (1984). Origins of organized medicine, Ontario, 1850–1869. In C.G. Roland (Ed.), *Health, disease and medicine: Essays in Canadian history* (pp. 72–95). Hannah Institute for the History of Medicine.

Hamowy, R. (1984). *Canadian medicine: A study in restricted entry.* Fraser Institute.

Heagerty, J.J. (1928). *Four centuries of medical history in Canada,* 2 vols. Macmillan.

Holling, S.A. (1981). Primitive medicine among the Indians of Ontario. In S.A. Holling et al. (Eds), *Medicine for heroes.* Mississauga Historical Society.

ICES. (2011). Universal access to health care is not enough to ensure that Canadians get and stay healthy. https://www.ices.on.ca/Newsroom/News-Releases/2011/Universal-access-to-health-care-is-not-enough-to-ensure

Kasman, N.M., & Badley, E.M. (2004). Beyond access: Who reports that health care is not being received when needed in a publicly-funded health care system? *Canadian Journal of Public Health, 95*(4), 304–8.

Lalonde, M. (1974). *A new perspective on the health of Canadians.* Information Canada.

Lee, F.J., Stewart, M., & Brown, J.B. (2008). Stress, burnout and strategies for reducing them. *Canadian Family Physician, 54*(2), 234–5.

Locke, M., & Ray, J.G. (1999). Higher neonatal morbidity after routine early hospital discharge: Are we sending newborns home too early? *CMAJ, 161,* 249–53.

McLeod, T.H., & McLeod, I. (1987). *Tommy Douglas: The road to Jerusalem.* Hurtig.

Marks, G., & Beatty, W.K. (1976). *Epidemics.* Charles Scribner's.

Morgan, S.G., Martin, D., Gagnon, M.A., Mintzes, B., Daw, J.R., & Lexchin, J. (2015) Pharmacare 2020: The future of drug coverage in Canada. *Pharmaceutical Policy Research Collaboration, University of British Columbia.*

Naylor, C.D. (1982). In defense of medicare: Are Canadian doctors threatening the health care system? *Canadian Forum, 62*(Apr.), 12–16.

Organisation for Economic Co-operation and Development (OECD). (2014). OECD health statistics 2014—frequently requested data. http://www.oecd.org/els/health-systems/oecd-health-statistics-2014-frequently-requested-data.htm

——. (2017). *Health at a glance 2017.* OECD Indicators. OECD Publishing, Paris. http://www.oecd.org/health/health-systems/health-at-a-glance-19991312.htm

Owens, B. (2018). Telemedicine on the rise but lagging in Canada. *CMAJ, 190*(38), E1149.

Pettigrew, E. (1983). *The silent enemy: Canada and the deadly flu of 1918.* Western Producer Prairie Books.

Pharmacare 2020. (2015). Summary of recommendations: Moving from principles to policies. https://pharmacare2020.ca/assets/pdf/Moving_From_Principles_To_Policies.pdf

Quan, H., Fong, A., De Coster, C., Wang, J., Musto, R., Noseworthy, T.W., & Ghali, W.A. (2006). Variation in health services utilization among ethnic populations. *CMAJ, 174*(6), 787–91.

Pylypchuk, Y., & Sarpong, E.M. (2013). Comparison of health care utilization: United States versus Canada. https://www.ncbi.nlm.nih.gov/pmc/articles/PMC3626357/

Rutledge, R., & Robinson, L. (2004). Taking care of us. *Journal for Canadian Cancer Professionals: Oncology Exchange, 3*(5), 24–7.

Senate of Canada. (2002). *The health of Canadians: The federal role* (Kirby Report). https://www.canada.ca/en/health-canada/services/health-care-system/health-human-resources/strategy/kirby-report.html

Shackleton, D.F. (1975). *Tommy Douglas.* McClelland & Stewart.

Statistics Canada. (2011). Access to a regular medical doctor, 2010. https://www150.statcan.gc.ca/n1/pub/82-625-x/2011001/article/11456-eng.htm

Stoddart, G.L., & Labelle, R.J. (1985). *Privatization in the Canadian health care system: Assertions, evidence, ideology and options.* Health and Welfare Canada.

Thomas, D.J. (1982). *The experience of handicap.* Methuen.

Torrance, G. (1987). Socio-historical overview: The development of the Canadian health system. In D. Coburn. C. D'Arcy, & G. Torrance (Eds), *Health and Canadian society* (pp. 6–32). University of Toronto Press.

Tully, P., & Pierre, E. (1997). Downsizing Canada's hospitals, 1986/7 to 1994/5. *Health Reports, 8*(4).

Tyre, R. (1962). *Douglas in Saskatchewan: The story of a socialist experiment.* Mitchell Press.

Ubelacker, S. (2013, Jan.). MD's gross income $307,000. *Globe and Mail.* https://www.theglobeandmail.com/life/health-and-fitness/health/mds-gross-income-307000-report-finds/article7640498/

Walters, V. (1982). State, capital and labour: The introduction of federal–provincial insurance for physician care in Canada. *Canadian Review of Sociology and Anthropology, 19,* 157–72.

Chapter 11

Ansari, S. (2014, 5 Dec.). College of Physicians and Surgeons launches review of sexual abuse policy. *Toronto Star.* https://www.thestar.com/life/health_wellness/2014/12/05/physician_watchdog_launches_review_of_sexual_abuse_policy.html

Association of Faculties of Medicine of Canada (AFMC). (2016). *Canadian medical education statistics 2016,* vol. 38. https://afmc.ca/sites/default/files/CMES2016-reduced.pdf

——. (2017). Q3B: How much is tuition at a Canadian medical school? https://afmc.ca/node/247

Awareness, M. (1980). *Academic American encyclopedia.* Arete Publishing.

Barrera, J. (2019, Feb.). MP asks RCMP for criminal probe of coerced sterilization of Indigenous women. *CBC News.* https://www.cbc.ca/news/indigenous/ndp-rcmp-indigenous-women-coerced-sterilization-1.5028101

Barua, B., Palacios, M., & Emes, J. (2017). The sustainability of health care spending in Canada. *The Fraser Institute.* https://www.fraserinstitute.org/sites/default/files/sustainability-of-health-care-spending-in-canada-2017.pdf

Beck, U. (1961). *Boys in white: Student culture in medical school.* University of Chicago Press.

———. (1992). *Risk society: Towards a new modernity.* M. Ritter (Trans.). Sage Publications.

———. (1994). *Ecological politics in an age of risk.* Polity Press.

Blishen, B.R. (1969). *Doctors and doctrines: The ideology of medical care in Canada.* University of Toronto Press.

Bliss, M. (1982). *The discovery of insulin.* McClelland & Stewart.

———. (1984). *Banting: A biography.* McClelland & Stewart.

Bosk, C. (1979). *Forgive and remember: Managing medical failure.* University of Chicago Press.

Brenan, M. (2017, 26 Dec.). Nurses keep healthy lead as most honest ethical profession. *Gallup.* https://news.gallup.com/poll/224639/nurses-keep-healthy-lead-honest-ethical-profession.aspx

Broom, A. (2005). Medical specialists' accounts of the impact of the Internet on the doctor/patient relationship. *Health, 9*(3), 319–38.

Bunker, J. (1985, 25 Apr.). When doctors disagree. *New York Times Review of Books,* 7–12.

Buske, L. (1999). Our incredible shrinking medical schools. *CMAJ, 160,* 772.

Canadian Foundation for Healthcare Improvement (CFHI). (2004). Myth: We can eliminate errors in healthcare by getting rid of the "bad apples." https://www.cfhi-fcass.ca/SearchResultsNews/04-09-01/3e36e6e7-2120-49cd-98cb-d02395009483.aspx

———. (2006). Myth: Medical malpractice lawsuits plague Canada. https://www.cfhi-fcass.ca/SearchResultsNews/06-03-01/70e601b8-487a-44d0-b390-4e4a0a453493.aspx

Canadian Institute for Health Information (CIHI). (2007). *Quality of healthcare in Canada: A chartbook.* CIHI.

———. (2019). *Physicians in Canada, 2018.* https://secure.cihi.ca/free_products/physicians-in-canada-2018.pdf

Canadian Medical Association (CMA). (2018). *Code of ethics, 2018.* http://policybase.cma.ca/dbtw-wpd/PolicyPDF/PD04-06.pdf

Canadian Medical Protective Association (CMPA). (2013). *Annual report.* https://www.cmpa-acpm.ca/en/about/annual-report/archives

———. (2017). 2017 fee schedule. https://www.cmpa-acpm.ca/static-assets/pdf/membership/fees-and-payment/2017cal-e.pdf

Canadian Midwifery Regulators Council. (2018). Healthcare in Canada. https://cmrc-ccosf.ca/node/19

Castiglioni, A. (1941). *A history of medicine.* Knopf.

CBC News. (2004, June). Medical errors killing up to 24,000 Canadians a year. https://www.cbc.ca/news/technology/medical-errors--killing-up-to-24-000-canadians-a-year-1.514758

———. (2014, July). Refugee health care cuts: Doctors gave voice to the "most vulnerable." https://www.cbc.ca/news/canada/refugee-health-care-cuts-doctors-gave-voice-to-most-vulnerable-1.2696961

CBC Radio. (2018, 13 Nov.). Indigenous women kept from seeing their newborn babies until agreeing to sterilization, says lawyer. https://www.cbc.ca/radio/thecurrent/the%20current-for-november-13-2018-1.4902679/indigenous-women-kept-from-seeing-their-newborn-babies-until-agreeing-to-sterilization-says-lawyer-1.4902693

Charney, W. (2012). Do no harm? The epidemic of fatal medical errors in the US and Canada. *Canadian Dimension, 63*(3).

Clarke, A.E., Mamo, L., Fishman, J.R., Shim, J.K., & Fosket, J.R. (2003). Biomedicalization: The technoscientific transformations of health, illness, and U.S. biomedicine. *American Sociological Review, 68*(2), 161–94.

Coburn, D., Rappolt, S., & Bourgeault, I. (1997). Decline vs. retention of medical power through rest ratification: An examination of the Ontario case. *Sociology of Health and Illness, 19*(1), 1–22.

Cohen, D. (2002, 27 July). Ageism can be lethal: Undetected homicides in older people. *British Medical Journal, 325,* 181.

Colliers Encyclopedia, vol. 3. (1973). Crowell-Collier.

Conrad, P. (1998). Learning to doctor: Reflections on recent accounts of the medical school years. In W.C. Cockerham, M.Glassen, & L.S. Huess (Eds), *Readings in medical sociology (pp. 335–45).* Prentice-Hall.

Druzin, P., Shrier, I., Yacowar, M., & Rossignol, M. (1998). Discrimination against gay, lesbian and bisexual family physicians by patients. *CMAJ, 158*(5), 593–7.

Encyclopaedia Britannica, vol. 3. (1976). William Benton.

Elgie, B. (2014, Mar.). The science of harm: Eugenics in Canada past and present. *McGill Daily.* https://www.mcgilldaily.com/2014/03/the-science-of-harm/

Ferguson, S.J. (2016). Women and education: Qualifications, skills and technology. Statistics Canada. https://www150.statcan.gc.ca/n1/pub/89-503-x/2015001/article/14640-eng.htm

Flexner, A. (1910). *Medical education in the United States and Canada. A report to the Carnegie Foundation for the Advancement of Teaching.* Bulletin No. 4. Carnegie Foundation.

Ford, A.R., & Saibil, D. (2010). *The push to prescribe: Women and Canadian drug policy.* Women's Press.

Foucault, M. (1973). *The birth of illness* (A.M. Sheridan Smith, Trans.). Pantheon Books.

Fox, R.C. (1957). Training for uncertainty. In R.K. Merton, G.G. Reader, & P. Kendall (Eds), *The student-physician* (pp. 207–41). Harvard University Press.

Freidson, E. (1975). *The profession of medicine: Study in the sociology of applied knowledge.* Dodd Mead.

Giacomini, M., Rozee-Koker, P., & Pepitone-Arreola-Rockwell, F. (1986). Gender bias in human anatomy textbook illustrations. *Psychology of Women Quarterly, 10,* 413–20.

Glauser, W. (2017). Medical schools addressing student anxiety, burnout and depression. *CMAJ, 189*(50), E1569–E1570.

Goode, W.J. (1956, Apr.). Community within a community: The professions. *American Sociological Review, 22,* 194–200.

———. (1960). Encroachment, charlatanism and the emerging profession: Psychology. *Sociology Review, 25*(6), 902–14.

Gordon, S., & Allan, T. (1952). *The scalpel, the sword*. McClelland & Stewart.

Hamowy, R. (1984). *Canadian medicine: A study in restricted entry*. Fraser Institute.

Iedema, R., Flabouris, A., Grant, S., & Jorm, C. (2006). Narrativizing errors of care: Critical incident reporting in clinical practice. *Social Science and Medicine, 62*, 134–44.

Johnson, T. (1972). *The professions and power*. London: Macmillan.

———. (1977). Industrial society: Class, change and control. In R. Scase (Ed.), *The professions in the class structure* (pp. 93–110). Allen and Unwin.

———. (1982). Social class and the division of labour. In A. Giddens and G. Mackenzie (Eds), *The state and the professions: Peculiarities of the British* (pp. 182–208). Cambridge University Press.

Kersten, L. (2013, Sept.). British Columbia repeals the Sexual Sterilization Act. *Eugenics Archive*. http://www.eugenicsarchive.ca/discover/connections/5233c89f5c2ec50000000091

Kirkup, K. (2018, Dec.). Coerced sterilization reports sparking concern in Canadian medical community. *CBC News*. https://www.cbc.ca/news/canada/saskatchewan/coerced-sterilization-canadian-medical-association-1.4955056

McKinlay, J.B. (1996). Some contribution from the social system to gender inequality in heart disease. *Journal of Health and Social Behavior, 37*(1), 1–26.

McQuigge, M. (2 June). "If you ever do this again, we'll turn you in," pastor told killer nurse. *Toronto Star*. https://www.thestar.com/news/canada/2017/06/02/if-you-ever-do-this-again-well-turn-you-in-pastor-told-killer-nurse.html

Medical Council of Canada. (2019). Advancing medical education for physicians in Canada. https://mcc.ca/news/advancing-medical-education-for-physicians-in-canada/

Merton, R.K., Reader, G., & Kendall, P. (Eds). (1957). *The student-physician: Introductory studies in the sociology of medical education*. Harvard University Press.

Millman, M. (1977). *The unkindest cut*. William Morrow.

Mroz, J. (2011, 6 Sept.). One sperm donor, 150 offspring. *New York Times*. https://www.nytimes.com/2011/09/06/health/06donor.html?pagewanted=all&_r=0

Nettleton S. (2004). The emergence of e-scaped medicine. *Sociology, 38*(4), 661–80.

Paget, M.A. (1988). *The unity of mistakes: A phenomenological interpretation of medical work*. Temple University Press.

Parsons, T. (1951). *The social system*. Free Press.

Payne E. (2018, May). Barwin's babies: The remarkable story of a disgraced Ottawa fertility doctor and those who say they are his children. *Ottawa Citizen*. https://ottawacitizen.com/news/local-news/barwins-babies

Picard, A. (2016). Doctor payments rise 3.7 per cent in 2015 while incomes stall. *Globe and Mail*. https://www.theglobeandmail.com/news/national/doctor-costs-rise-37-per-cent-in-2015-while-incomes-stall/article31503411/

Rachlis, M., & Kushner, C. (1994). *Strong medicine: How to save Canada's health care system*. HarperCollins.

Ontario Government. (2018). Regulated Health Professions Act, 1991. Nov. 1., 2018 (e-laws currency date). https://www.ontario.ca/laws/statute/91r18

Revah, G., & Bell, C. (2007). Shopping for high-technology treatment in another province. *Healthcare Policy, 2*(4), 49–55.

Shapiro, M. (1978). *Getting doctored: Critical reflections on becoming a physician*. Between the Lines.

Shephard, D.A. (Ed.). (1982). *Norman Bethune—his times and legacy*. Canadian Public Health Association.

Sibbald, B. (1998). In your face: A new wave of militant doctors lashes out. *CMAJ, 158*, 1505–9.

Smoke, P. (2018, Dec.). UN committee recommends Canada criminalize involuntary sterilization. *CBC News*. https://www.cbc.ca/news/indigenous/un-committee-involuntary-sterilization-1.4936879

Stevenson, L. (1946). *Sir Frederick Banting*. Ryerson Press.

Stewart, R. 1977. *The mind of Norman Bethune*. Lawrence Hill.

Tortelli, B. (2016). The fear of discrimination in LGBT health care. *Institute for Public Health*. https://publichealth.wustl.edu/fear-discrimination-lgbt-healthcare/

Ubelacker, S. (2017, 8 Mar.). "Liberation therapy" ineffective for treating MS, Canadian study finds. *Toronto Star*. https://www.thestar.com/news/canada/2017/03/08/liberation-therapy-ineffective-for-treating-ms-canadian-study-concludes.html

Vogel, L. (2018, 29 Aug.). Doctors on their own when dealing with racism from patients. *CMAJ News*. https://cmajnews.com/2018/08/29/doctors-on-their-own-when-dealing-with-racism-from-patients-cmaj-109-5633/

Wahn, M. (1987). The decline of medical dominance in hospitals. In D. Coburn, C. D'Arcy, & G. Torrance (Eds), *Health and Canadian society* (pp. 422–41). University of Toronto Press.

Wennberg, J.E. (1984, Summer). Dealing with medical practice variations: A proposal for action. *Health Affairs, 4*, 6–32.

———, Buncker, J.P., & Barnes, B. (1980). The need for assessing the outcomes of common medical practice. *Annual Review of Public Health, 1*, 277–95.

Wertz, R.W., & Wertz, D.C. (1986). Notes on the decline of midwives and the rise of medical obstetricians. In P. Conrad & R. Kern (Eds), *The sociology of health and illness: Critical perspectives*. St Martin's Press.

Wilensky, H.L. (1964). The professionalization of everyone. *American Journal of Sociology, 70*, 137–58.

Williams, A.P., Dominick, K., & Vayda, E. (1993). Women in medicine: Toward a conceptual understanding of the potential for change. *Journal of the American Medical Women's Association, 48*(4), 115–23.

Willis, E. (1983). *Medical dominance: The division of labour in Australian health care*. George Allen and Unwin.

Woods, A. (2017, 17 June). No easy cure for left out medical school grads. *Toronto Star*. https://www.thestar.com/news/canada/2017/06/17/no-easy-cure-for-left-out-medical-school-grads.html

Woodward, C.A. (1999). Medical students' attitudes toward women: Are medical schools microcosms of society? *CMAJ, 160*, 347–8.

Zelek, B., Phillips, S.P., & Lefebre, Y. (1997). Gender sensitivity in medical curricula. *CMAJ, 156*(9), 1297–300.

Zingel, A. (2019, Apr.). Indigenous women come forward with accounts of forced sterilization, says lawyer. *CBC News*. https://www.cbc.ca/news/canada/north/forced-sterilization-lawsuit-could-expand-1.5102981

Chapter 12

Abbott, M. (1931). *The history of medicine in the province of Quebec*. McGill University Press.

Aiken, L.H., Clarke, S.P., Cheung, R.B., Sloane, D.M., & Silber, J.H. (2003). Educational levels of hospital nurses and surgical patient mortality. *Journal of the American Medical Association, 290*(12), 1617–23.

Amann, R., Chua, N., James, T., & Sanga, N. (2018). The benefits and barriers to nurses attending ward rounds. *Nursing Review*. http://nursingreview.co.nz/the-benefits-and-barriers-to-nurses-attending-ward-rounds/

Armstrong, P., Choiniere, J., & Day, E. (1993). *Vital signs: Nursing in transition*. Garamond Press.

Austin, W. (2007). The McDonaldization of nursing? *Health: An Interdisciplinary Journal for the Social Study of Health, Illness and Medicine, 11*(2), 265–72.

Barrington, E. (1985). *Midwifery is catching*. NC Press.

Biggs, C.L. (1983). The case of the missing midwives: A history of midwifery in Ontario from 1795–1900. *Ontario History, 75*, 21–35.

Bourgeault, I.L., Angus, J., & Fynes, M. (1998). Gender, medicine dominance and the state: Nurse practitioners and midwives in Ontario. Paper presented at International Sociological Association meeting.

Bull, A. (1985). *Florence Nightingale*. Hamish Hamilton.

Campbell, M. (1988). The structure of stress in nurses' work. In B.S. Bolaria & H.D. Dickinson (Eds), *Sociology of health care in Canada* (pp. 393–406). Harcourt Brace Jovanovich.

Canadian Health Infoway. (2017). National survey of Canadian nurses: Using digital health technology in practice. https://www.infoway-inforoute.ca/en/component/edocman/resources/reports/3320-2017-national-survey-of-canadian-nurses-use-of-digital-health-technology-in-practice

Canadian Institute for Health Information (CIHI). (2006). *The regulation and supply of nurse practitioners in Canada: 2006 update*. secure.cihi.ca/cihiweb/products/The_Nurse_Practitioner_Workforce_in_Canada_2006_Update_final.pdf

———. (2012). *Regulated nurses: A summary report*. https://secure.cihi.ca/free_products/RegulatedNurses2012Summary_EN.pdf

Canadian Nurses Association. (2010a). *Nurse fatigue and patient safety report*. http://cna-aiic.ca/~/media/cna/page-content/pdf-en/fatigue_safety_2010_summary_e.pdf

———. (2010b). 2010 workforce profile of registered nurses in Canada. https://www.cna-aiic.ca/-/media/cna/page-content/pdf/en/2010_rn_snapshot_e.pdf

———. (2011) A nursing call to action. https://www.cna-aiic.ca/~/media/cna/files/en/nec_report_e.pdf

———. (2017). Nursing statistics. https://www.cna-aiic.ca/en/nursing-practice/the-practice-of-nursing/health-human-resources/nursing-statistics

Cassidy, A., & McIntosh, B. (2014). The return of autonomy in nursing: The way forward. *British Journal of Nursing, 23*(11), 562–3.

Ceci, C. (2004). Nursing, knowledge and power: A case analysis. *Social Science and Medicine, 59*, 1879–89.

Conley, M.C., & Maukasch, H.O. (1988). Registered nurses, gender and commitment. In A. Statham, E.M. Miller, and H.O. Maukasch (Eds), *The worth of women's work: A qualitative synthesis*. State University of New York Press.

Devitt, N. (1977, Summer). The transition from home to hospital birth in the U.S. 1930–1960. *Birth and Family Journal*, 45–58.

Eberts, M. (1987). *Report of the Task Force on the Implementation of Midwifery in Ontario*. Ontario Ministry of Health.

Ehrenreich, B., & English, D. (1973). *Witches, midwives and nurses: A history of women healers*. Feminist Press.

Freidson, E. (1970). *Professional dominance: The social structure of medical care*. Atherton Press.

Growe, S.J. (1991). The nature and type of doctors' cultural assumptions about patients as men. *Sociological Focus, 24*(3), 211–23.

Holyoake, D.D. (2011). Is the doctor–nurse game still being played? *Nursing Times, 107*, 43.

Jeffries, K., Tamlyn, D., Aston, M., & Murphy, G.T. (2019). Promoting visible minority diversity in Canadian nursing. *Canadian Journal of Nursing Research, 51*(1), 3–5.

Kanter, R.M. (1977). *Men and women of the corporation*. Basic Books.

Kingma, M. (2001). Workplace violence in the health sector: A problem of epidemic proportion. *International Nursing Review, 48*(3), 129–30.

Krause, E.A. (1978). *Power and illness: The political sociology of health and medical care*. Elsevier.

Litoff, J. (1978). *American midwives: 1860 to the present*. Greenwood Press.

McGillis Hall, L., Doran, D., Baker, G.R., Pink, G.H., Sidani, S., O'Brien-Pallas, L., & Donner, G.L. (2003). Nurse staffing models as predictors of patient outcomes. *Medical Care, 41*(9), 1096–1109.

——— & Kiesners, D. (2005). A narrative approach to understanding the nursing work environment in Canada. *Social Science and Medicine, 61*, 2482–91.

May, J., & Wasserman, J. (1984). Selected results from an evaluation of the New Jersey diagnosis-related group system. *Health Services Research, 19*(5), 548.

Mojtehedzadeh, S. (2017, 5 Nov.). Violence against health care workers "out of control," survey finds. *Toronto Star*. https://www.thestar.com/news/gta/2017/11/05/violence-against-health-care-workers-out-of-control-survey-finds.html

Nicholson, G.W.L. (1967). *The white cross in Canada*. Harvest House.

Ontario Council of Hospital Unions. (2014). *Pushed out of hospital, abandoned at home: After twenty years of budget cuts Ontario's health system is failing patients*. http://www.ochu.on.ca/resources/Events/HOTLINE_REPORT_2014.pdf

Oppenheimer, J. (1983, Mar.). Childbirth in Ontario: The transition from home to hospital in the early twentieth century. *Ontario History, 75*, 36–60.

Peate, I. (2014). Compassion fatigue: The toll of emotional labour. *British Journal of Nursing, 23*(5), 251.

Potter, P., Barr, N., McSweeney, M., & Sledge, J. (2003). Collecting baseline patient outcome data should precede nurse staffing changes. *Nursing Economics, 21*(4), 158–66.

Priest, L. (2008, Jan.). Nursing and hospital violence. *Globe and Mail*. https://www.theglobeandmail.com/opinion/nursing-and-hospital-violence/article18441494/

Pruden, J. (2016). A history of nurses charged with killing patients. *Globe and Mail*. https://www.theglobeandmail.com/news/national/elizabeth-wettlaufer-history-of-nurses-charged-with-killing-patients/article32526085/

Punnett, L. (1976). Women-controlled medicine—theory and practice in 19th century Boston. *Women and Health, 1*(4), 3–10.

Rankin, J.M., & Campbell, M.L. (2006). *Managing to nurse: Inside Canada's health care reform*. University of Toronto Press.

Registered Nurses Association of Ontario. (1987). *The RNAO responds: A nursing perspective on the events at the Hospital for Sick Children and the Grange Inquiry*. RNAO.

Reverby, S.M. (1987). *Ordered to care: The dilemma of American nursing*. Cambridge University Press.

Romelis, S. (1985). Struggle between providers and recipients: The case of birth practices. In E. Lewin & V. Olesen (Eds), *Women, health and healing* (pp. 174–208). Tavistock.

Sinclair, M. (2000). *The report of the Manitoba Pediatric Cardiac Surgery Inquest: An inquiry into twelve deaths at the Winnipeg Health Sciences Centre in 1994*. Provincial Court of Manitoba.

Stein, L. (1987). The doctor–nurse game. In H.D. Schwartz (Ed.), *Dominant issues in medical sociology*, 2nd edn. Random House.

St Denis, V. (2017, July/Aug.). Perception of health technologies benefits increases with longer use. *The Canadian Nurse*. https://canadian-nurse.com/articles/issues/2017/july-august-2017/perception-of-health-technologies-benefits-increases-with-longer-use

Taunton, R.L., Klienbeck, S.V.M., Stafford, R., Woods, C., & Bott, M. (1994). Patient outcomes: Are they linked to registered nurse absenteeism, separation or workload? *Journal of Nursing Administration, 24*(45), 48–55.

Tencer, D. (2016, 30 May). Canada suffering nurse shortage, though other countries have it worse. *Huffington Post*. https://www.huffingtonpost.ca/2016/05/30/nurse-shortage-canada_n_10208080.html

Toronto Star. (2017, 5 Nov.). Violence against health-care workers "out of control," survey finds. https://www.thestar.com/news/gta/2017/11/05/violence-against-health-care-workers-out-of-control-survey-finds.html

Urban, A.M. (2012). Nurses and their work in hospitals: Ruled by embedded ideologies and moving discourses. PhD diss., University of Regina. http://ourspace.uregina.ca/bitstream/handle/10294/3553/Urban_Ann-Marie_188003945_PhD_EDUC_Spring2012.pdf?sequence=1

Wertz, R.W., & Wertz, D.C. (1977). *Lying-in: A history of childbirth in America*. Free Press.

Wilson, J. (1987, Mar.). Why nurses leave nursing. *The Canadian Nurse, 83*, 20–3.

Wood, C. (2014). Choosing the "right" people for nursing: Can we recruit to care? *British Journal of Nursing, 23*(10), 5.

Zelek, B., & Phillips, S.P. (2003). Gender and power: Nurses and doctors in Canada. *International Journal for Equity in Health, 2*, 1–7.

Chapter 13

April, K.T., & Gaboury, I. (2013). A Survey of Canadian regulated complementary and alternative medicine schools about research, evidence-based health care and interprofessional training, as well as continuing education. *BMC Complementary and Alternative Medicine, 13*, 374–81.

Barnes, P.M., Powell-Griner, E., McFann, K., & Nahin, R.L. (2004). Complementary and alternative medicine use among adults: United States, 2002. *Seminars in Integrative Medicine, 2*(2), 54–71.

Beck, C.S., Aubuchon, S.M., McKenna, T.P., Ruhl, S., & Simmons, N. (2014). Blurring personal health and public priorities: An analysis of celebrity health narratives in the public space. *Health Communication, 29*, 244–56.

Beck, U. (1992). *Risk society: Towards a new modernity* M. Ritter (Trans.). Sage Publications.

Benedetti, P., & MacPhail, W. (2002). *Spin doctors: The chiropractic industry under examination*. Dundurn.

Boon, H. (1996). Canadian naturopathic practitioners: Holistic and scientific world views. *Social Science and Medicine, 46*(9), 1213–25.

Boon, H.H., MacPherson, S., Fleishman, S., Grimsgaard, M., Koithan, A., Norheim, J., & Walach, H. (2007). Evaluating complex health care systems: A critique of four approaches. *eCAM, 4*(3), 279–85.

Caplan, R.L. (1984). Chiropractic. In J.W. Salmon (Ed.), *Alternative medicines: Popular and policy perspectives* (pp. 80–113). Tavistock.

Cooper, R.A., & Stoflet, S.J. (1996). Trends in the education and practice of alternative medicine clinicians. *Health Affairs, 15*(3), 226–38.

Coulter, H.L. (1984). Homeopathy. In J.W. Salmon (Ed.), *Alternative medicines: Popular and policy perspectives*, (pp. 57–9). Tavistock.

Crawford, R. (2006). Healthism and the medicalization of everyday life. *Health, 10*, 401–20.

Eddy, M.B. (1934). *Science and health with a key to the scriptures*. Published by the Trustees under the Will of Mary Baker Eddy.

Eisenberg, D.M., Davis, R.B., Ettner, S.L., Appel, S., Wilkey, S., Van Rompay, M., & Kessler, R.C. (1998). Trends in alternative medicine use in the United States, 1990–1997: Results of a follow-up national survey. *Journal of the American Medical Association, 280*(18), 1569–75.

Ferley, J.P., Zmirou, D., D'Adhemar, D., & Balducci, F. (1989). A controlled evaluation of a homoeopathic preparation in the treatment of influenza-like syndromes. *British Journal of Clinical Pharmacology, 27*(3), 329–35.

Frith, H., Raisborough, J., & Klein, O. (2013). Making death "good": Instructional tales for dying in newspaper accounts of Jade Goody's death. *Sociology of Health and Illness, 35*(3), 419–33.

Gort, E. (1986). A social history of naturopathy in Ontario: The formation of an occupation. MA thesis, University of Toronto.

Harden, B.L., & Harden, C.R. (1997). *Alternative health care: The Canadian directory*. Noble Ages Publishing.

Hirschkorn, K.A., & Bourgeault, I.L. (2005). Conceptualizing mainstream healthcare providers' behaviours in relation to complementary and alternative medicine. *Social Science and Medicine, 61*, 157–70.

Howell, W.L.J. (2012, Feb.). More medical schools offer instruction in complementary and alternative therapies. *AAMC Reporter*. https://www.aamc.org/newsroom/reporter/feb2012/273812/therapies.html

Imman, W. (1996, Dec.). Alternate treatments gaining ground. *Globe and Mail*.

Kelner, M., Hall, O., Welsh, S., & Boon, H. (2006). How far can complementary and alternative medicine go? The case of chiropractic and homeopathy. *Social Science and Medicine, 63*, 2617–27.

——, Wellman, B., Boon, H., & Welsh, S. (2004). Responses of established healthcare to the professionalization of complementary and alternative medicine in Ontario. *Social Science and Medicine, 59*, 915–30.

Lahave River Chiropractic and Health Centre. (2018). What is chiropractic. https://www.lahaveriverchiro.com/include/about_chiropractic.htm

Langone, J. (1982). *Chiropractors*. Addison-Wesley.

Lawrence, D.J., & Meeker, W.C. (2007). Chiropractic and CAM utilization: A descriptive review. *Chiropractic and Osteopathy, 15*(2), 1–27. www.chiroandosteo.com/content/pdf/1746-1340-15-2.pdf

Lerner, B.H. (2006). *When illness goes public: Celebrity patients and how we look at medicine*. Johns Hopkins University Press.

Linde, K., Clausius, N., Ramirez, G., Melchart, D., Eitel, F., Hedges, L.V., & Jonas, W.B. (1997). Are the clinical effects of homoeopathy placebo effects? A meta-analysis of placebo-controlled trials. *The Lancet, 350*(9081), 834–43.

Liu, F., Li, Z.M., Jiang, Y.J., & Chen, L.D. (2014). A meta-analysis of acupuncture use in the treatment of cognitive impairment after stroke. *Journal of Alternative and Complementary Medicine, 20*(7), 535–44.

May, C., & Sirur, D. (1998). Art, science and placebo: Incorporating homeopathy in general practice. *Sociology of Health and Illness, 20*(2), 168–90.

Montbriand, M.J. (1994). An overview of alternate therapies chosen by patients with cancer. *Oncology Nursing Forum, 21*(9), 1547–54.

Nahin, R.L., Barnes, P.M., Stussman, B.J., & Bloom, B. (2009, 30 July). Costs of complementary and alternative medicine (CAM) and frequency of visits to CAM practitioners: United States, 2007. *National Health Statistics Report, 18*, 1–14.

Noar, S.M., Willoughby, J.F., Myrick, J.G., & Brown, J. (2014). Public figure announcements about cancer and opportunities for cancer communication: A review and research agenda. *Health Communication, 29*, 445–61.

Ontario Naturopathic Association (ONA). (1983, July). *Naturopathic medicine and health care in Ontario*. A Brief Prepared by the ONA and the Board of Directors of Drugless Therapy for the Honorable Keith Norton, Minister of Health.

Picard, A. (2015). We're aiding and abetting homeopathic quackery. *Globe and Mail*. https://www.theglobeandmail.com/opinion/were-aiding-and-abetting-homeopathic-quackery/article23701139/

Qureshi, N.A., & Al-Bedah, A.M. (2013). Mood disorders and complementary and alternative medicine: A literature review. *Neuropsychiatric Disease and Treatment, 3*(9), 639–58.

Reilly, D.T, Taylor, M.A., McSharry, C., & Aitchison, T. (1986). Is homoeopathy a placebo response? Controlled trial of homoeopathic potency, with pollen in hay fever as model. *The Lancet, 2*(8512), 881–6.

Rose, N. (1999). *Powers of freedom reframing political thought*. Cambridge University Press.

Rothouse, H. (1997, June). History of homeopathy reveals discipline's excellence. *Alternative and Complementary Therapies*, 223–7.

Salmon, J.W. (Ed.). (1984). *Alternative medicines: Popular and policy perspectives*. Tavistock.

Specter, M. (2013, Jan.). The operator. *The New Yorker*. https://www.newyorker.com/magazine/2013/02/04/the-operator

Statistics Canada. (2005). Health reports: Use of alternative health care. www.statcan.ca/Daily/English/050315/d050315b.htm

Studdert, D.M., Eisenberg, D.M., Miller, F.H., Curto, D.A., Kaptchuk, T.J., & Brennan, T.A. (1998). Medical malpractice implications of alternative medicine. *Journal of the American Medical Association, 280*(18), 1610–15.

Valji, R., Adams, D., Dagenais, S., Clifford, T., Baydala, L., King, W.J., & Vohra, S. (2013). Complementary and alternative medicine: A survey of its use in pediatric oncology. *Evidence-Based Complementary and Alternative Medicine*.

Verhoef, M.J., Boon, H.S., & Mutasingwa, D.R. (2006). The scope of naturopathic medicine in Canada: An emerging profession. *Social Science and Medicine, 63*, 409–17.

Verhoef, M.J., & Sutherland, L.R. (1995). Alternative medicine and general practitioners. *Canadian Family Physician, 41*, 1005.

Vickers, A., Wilson, P., & Kleijnen, J. (2002). Acupuncture. *Quality and Safety in Health Care, 11*, 92–7.

Wardell, W. (1988). Chiropractors: Evolution to acceptance. In N. Gentz (Ed.), *Other healers: Unorthodox medicine in America* (pp. 174–84). Johns Hopkins University Press.

Weil, A. (1983). *Health and healing: Understanding conventional and alternative medicine*. Houghton Mifflin.

World Federation of Chiropractic. (2012). The current status of the chiropractic profession. https://www.wfc.org/website/images/wfc/WHO_Submission-Final_Jan2013.pdf

Chapter 14

Abraham, J. (1995). *Science, politics, and the pharmaceutical industry*. St Martin's Press.

Acosta, D., Plant, J., Boulette, M., & Owusu-Sarfo, S. (2017). Anti-psychotic medications in long term care. *Hospital News*. https://hospitalnews.com/antipsychotic-medications-in-long-term-care/

Armstrong, P., & Armstrong, H. (1996, 2003). *Wasting away: The undermining of Canadian health care*. Oxford University Press.

Barker, K.N., Flynn, E.A., Pepper, G.A., Bates, D.W., & Mikeal, R.L. (2002). Medication errors observed in 36 health care facilities. *Archives of Internal Medicine, 162*(16), 1897–1903.

Batt, S. (1994). *Patient no more: The politics of breast cancer*. Gynergy Books.

Bell, R.W., & Osterman, J. (1983). The compendium of pharmaceuticals and specialties: A critical analysis. *International Journal of Health Services, 13*, 107–18.

Belzak, L., & Halverson, J. (2018). Evidence synthesis—the opioid crisis in Canada: A national perspective. *Health Promotion and Chronic Disease Prevention in Canada: Research, Policy and Practice, 38*(6), 224.

Bombardier, C., Laine, L., Reicin, A., Shapiro, D., Burgos-Vargas, R., Davis, B., Day, R., Ferraz, M.B., Hawkey, C.J., Hochberg, M.C., Kvien, T.K., & Schnitzer, T.J. (2000). Comparison of upper gastrointestinal toxicity of rofecoxib and naproxen in patients with rheumatoid arthritis. *New England Journal of Medicine, 343*(21), 1520–8.

Branswell, H. (2002, July). Superbug genie is out of the bottle. *National Post*.

Budnitz, D.S., Lovegrove, M.C., Shehab, N., & Richards, C.L. (2011). Emergency hospitalizations for adverse drug reactions in older Americans. *New England Journal of Medicine, 365*, 2002–12.

Butt, A.R. (2010). Medical error in Canada: Issues relating to reporting of medical error and methods to increase reporting. *McMaster University Medical Journal, 7*(1), 15–18.

Canadian Foundation for Healthcare Improvement (CFHI). (2010). Myth: If a drug makes it to market, it's safe for everyone. http://www.cfhi-fcass.ca/searchresultsnews/2010/10/01/f1ca3fcf-f9aa-4dcb-a64c-a95f2bbadd8d.aspx

———. (2013). Myth: When It comes to drugs and devices, newer is always better. Retrieved from http://www.cfhi-fcass.ca/SearchResultsNews/13-03-13/7081e550-fed8-4c8c-84c6-bfd360e48f19.aspx

Canadian Health Coalition. (2006). *More for less: A national pharmacare strategy*. www.nursesunions.ca/cms/updir/moreforless-6.pdf

Canadian Institute for Health Information (CIHI). (2007). *Quality of healthcare in Canada: A chartbook*. CIHI.

———. (2008). *Health care in Canada 2008*. Ottawa, ON: CIHI.

Canadian Institute for Health Information (CIHI). (2010). *Healthcare in Canada: A chartbook*. CIHI.

———. (2018). Drug spending at a glance, fact sheet. https://www.cihi.ca/sites/default/files/document/nhex-drug-infosheet-2018-en-web.pdf

———. (2019). *National health expenditure trends, 1975 to 2019*. https://www.cihi.ca/en/national-health-expenditure-trends-1975-to-2019

CBC News. (2013). Yaz, Yasmin birth control pills suspected in 23 deaths. https://www.cbc.ca/news/canada/british-columbia/yaz-yasmin-birth-control-pills-suspected-in-23-deaths-1.1302473

Centers for Disease Control and Prevention. (2019). Therapeutic drug use. https://www.cdc.gov/nchs/fastats/drug-use-therapeutic.htm

Chong. Y., Fryar, C., & Gu, Q. (2013, Aug.). Prescription sleep aids use among adults: United States 2005–2010. *NCHS Data Brief* (127).

Clarke, J.N. (2013). Surplus suffering: The search for help when a child has mental health issues. *Child and Family Social Work, 18*(2), 217–25.

College of Physicians and Surgeons of Ontario. (2019). Barwin, Bernard Norman. https://doctors.cpso.on.ca/DoctorDetails/Bernard-Norman-Barwin/0023874-28666?type=num&term=28666

Dewa, C.S., Hoch, J.S., & Steele, L. (2005). Prescription drug benefits and Canada's uninsured. *International Journal of Law and Psychiatry, 28*(5), 496–513.

DiManno, R. (2013, 4 Feb.). Wrong-sperm doctor Barwin took shortcuts in career and races, too: DiManno. *Toronto Star*. https://www.thestar.com/news/gta/2013/02/04/wrong-sperm_doctor_barwin_took_shortcuts_in_career_and_races_too_dimanno.html

Dove, F. (2011). What's happened to thalidomide babies? *BBC News Online*. www.bbc.co.uk/news/magazine-15536544.

Dowell, D., Noonan, R.K., & Houry, D. (2017). Underlying factors in drug overdose deaths. *Jama, 318*(23), 2295–6.

Eggertson, L. (2005). Drug approval system questioned in US and Canada. *CMAJ, 172*(3), 317–18.

Eichler, M. (1988). *Families in Canada Today*. Gage.

Elmi, A.V., Tierney, Y.M., & Petch, J. (2015). Improving appropriateness of anti-psychotic use in long term care.

Healthy Debate. https://healthydebate.ca/2015/06/topic/community-long-term-care/antipsychotics

Esmail, N. (2015). Drug coverage for low-income families in Canada. *The Fraser Institute.* https://www.fraserinstitute.org/sites/default/files/drug-coverage-for-low-income-families-rev.pdf

Foster, M., & Huffman, E. (1995). The portrayal of the elderly in medical journals. Paper written for Qualitative Methods sociology course at Wilfrid Laurier University.

Freidson, E. (1975). *The profession of medicine: Study in the sociology of applied knowledge.* Dodd Mead.

Friday, F. (2018, Jan.). Opioids from China are flooding the US. *The Observer.*

Fuller, C. (2010). Reporting adverse drug reactions: What happens in the real world? In A.R. Ford and D. Saibil (Eds), *The push to prescribe: Women and Canadian drug policy* (pp. 139–60). Women's Press.

Gagnon, M.A. (2012). Drug shortages: Searching for a cure. *Healthcare Policy, 7*(4), 10.

——— & Lexchin, J. (2008). The cost of pushing pills: New estimate of the cost of pharmaceutical promotion expenditures in the United States. *PLOS Medicine, 5*(1).

Gerum, K., & Choo, E. (2015, Jan.). Gender and prescription opioid abuse. *American Women's Medical Association.*

Glauser, W. (2013). Pharma influence widespread at medical schools: Study. *CMAJ, 185*(13), 1121–2.

Globe and Mail. (1989, Feb.). Thalidomide's after-effects today.

Golden, R.L. (2009). William Osler, urolithiasis, and God's own medicine. *Urology, 74*(3), 517–21.

Government of Canada. (2019). Fertility. https://www.canada.ca/en/public-health/services/fertility/fertility.html

Harding, J. (1987). The pharmaceutical industry as a public health hazard and an institution of social control. In D. Coburn, C. D'Arcy, & G. Torrance (Eds), *Health and Canadian society* (pp. 314–32). University of Toronto Press.

———. (1994). Social basis of the over prescribing of mood-modifying pharmaceuticals to women. In B.S. Bolaria & R. Bolaria (Eds), *Women, medicine, and health* (pp. 157–81). Fernwood.

Insel, T.R. (2010). Psychiatrists' relationships with pharmaceutical companies. *Journal of the American Medical Association, 303*(12), 1192.

Jüni, P., Nartey, L., Reichenbach, S., Sterchi, R., Dieppe, P.A., & Egger, M. (2004). Risk of cardiovascular events and rofecoxib: Cumulative meta-analysis. *The Lancet, 364*(9450), 2021–9.

Kirkey, S. (2016, July). Switched embryos and wrong sperm: IVF mix-ups lead to babies born with "unintended parentage." *National Post.* https://nationalpost.com/health/ivf-mix-ups-lead-to-babies-born-with-unintended-parentage

Kitchener-Waterloo Record. (1972, Sept.). Thalidomide tragedy, labelling snag linked.

Klass, A. (1975). *There's gold in them thar pills.* Penguin Books.

Kondro, W. (2010a). Drug industry cash. *CMAJ, 182*(6), E266.

———. (2010b). Pfizer handouts. *CMAJ, 182*(8), E345.

Koskie Minsky LLP. (2020). Thalidomide Survivors Contribution Program class action. https://kmlaw.ca/cases/thalidomide-survivors-contribution-program-class-action/

Law, M.R., Cheng, L., Worthington, H., Majumdar, S.R., McGrail, K.M., Chan, F., Laba, T.-L., & Mamdani, M. (2019). Impact of a household-level deductible on prescription drug use among lower-income adults: A quasi-experimental study. *CMAJ Open, 7*(1), E167.

Lexchin, J. (1984). *The real pushers: A critical analysis of the Canadian drug industry.* New Star Books.

Lexchin, J. (1988). Profits first: The pharmaceutical industry in Canada. In B.S. Bolaria & H.D. Dickinson (Eds), *Health, illness, and health care in Canada* (pp. 497–513). Harcourt Brace Jovanovich.

———. (1994a). Profits first: The pharmaceutical industry in Canada. In B.S. Bolaria and H.D. Dickinson (Eds), *Health, illness, and health care in Canada* (pp. 700–20). Harcourt Brace Jovanovich.

———. (1994b). Canadian marketing codes: How well are they controlling pharmaceutical promotion. *International Journal of Health Services, 24*(1), 91–104.

———. (1996). Cost-effective pharmaceutical care for the elderly and the formulation of pharmaceutical policy in Canada. *Health and Canadian Society, 391*(2), 119–33.

———. (2005). Drug withdrawals from the Canadian market for safety reasons, 1963–2004. *CMAJ, 172*(6), 765–7.

———. (2009). *Drug safety and Health Canada: Going, going . . . gone?* Canadian Centre for Policy Alternatives. http://www.policyalternatives.ca/sites/default/files/uploads/publications/National_Office_Pubs/2009/Drug_Safety_and_Health_Canada.pdf

———. (2012). The pharmaceutical industry and Health Canada: Values in conflict. In J. Germov & J. Hornosty (Eds), *Second opinion: An introduction to health sociology, Canadian edn* (pp. 277–95). Oxford University Press.

——— & Wiktorowicz, M.E. (2009). Profits first: The pharmaceutical industry in Canada. In B.S. Bolaria and H.D. Dickinson (Eds), *Health, illness, and health care in Canada* (pp. 437–57). Harcourt Brace Jovanovich.

McIntyre, R.S., Konarski, J.Z., Grigoriadis, S., Fan, N.C., Mancini, D.A., Fulton, K.A., Stewart, D.E., & Kennedy, S.H. (2005). Hormone replacement therapy and antidepressant prescription patterns: A reciprocal relationship. *CMAJ, 172*(1), 57–9.

McVeigh, K. (2013, 13 June). US supreme court rules human genes cannot be patented. *The Guardian.* https://www.theguardian.com/law/2013/jun/13/supreme-court-genes-patent-dna

Makary, M., & Daniel, M. (2016). Medical error—the third leading cause of death in US. *British Medical Journal, 353*, i2139.

Mariani, M. (2015, 4 Mar.). How the American opiate epidemic was started by one pharmaceutical company. *The Week: Pacific Standard.* https://theweek.com/articles/541564/how-american-opiate-epidemic-started-by-pharmaceutical-company

Mather, C. (2005). The pipeline and the porcupine: Alternate metaphors of the physician–industry relationship. *Social Science and Medicine, 60*, 1323–34.

Miller, J.A. (1996). Money for mischief: USAID and pathfinder tag-team women in the developing world. *Population Reserve Institute, 6*, 5.

Mintzes, B. (2010). Ask your doctor: Women and direct-to-consumer advertising. In A.R. Ford and D. Saibil (Eds), *The push to prescribe: Women and Canadian drug policy* (pp. 17–46). Women's Press.

——, Barer, M.L., & Kravitz, R.L. (2002). Influence of direct-to-consumer pharmaceutical advertising and patients' requests on prescribing decisions: Two-site cross-sectional survey. *British Medical Journal, 324*, 278–9.

——, ——, & ——. (2003). How does direct-to-consumer advertising (DTCA) affect prescribing? A survey in primary care environments with and without legal DTCA. *CMAJ, 169*(5), 405.

Morgan, S.G., Martin, D., Gagnon, M.A., Mintzes, B., Daw, J.R., & Lexchin, J. (2015). Pharmacare 2020: The future of drug coverage in Canada. Pharmaceutical Policy Research Collaboration, University of British Columbia.

Motluk, A. (2017). Lawsuit claims fertility doctor used his own sperm to inseminate patients. *Globe and Mail.* https://www.theglobeandmail.com/news/national/lawsuit-claims-fertility-doctor-used-his-own-dna-to-inseminate-patients/article32640067/

O'Grady, K. (2003). New evidence about hormone replacement therapy turning the tide in the menopause wars. *Women's Studies Quarterly,* 1 & 2, 137–44.

Olivieri, N. (2010). Foreword. In A.R. Ford and Saibil, D. (Eds), *The push to prescribe: Women and Canadian drug policy* (pp. ix–xii). Women's Press.

Ollila, E., & Hemminki, E. (1997). Does licensing of drugs in industrialized countries guarantee drug quality and safety for Third World countries? The case of norplant licensing in Finland. *International Journal of Health Services, 27*(2), 309–25.

Organisation for Economic Co-operation and Development (OECD). (2018). Pharmaceutical spending (indicator). https://data.oecd.org/healthres/pharmaceutical-spending.htm

Payne E. (2018, May). Barwin's babies: The remarkable story of a disgraced Ottawa fertility doctor and those who say they are his children. *Ottawa Citizen.* https://ottawacitizen.com/news/local-news/barwins-babies

Peritz, I. (2010). Cursed by miracle drug, they wait for an apology. *Globe and Mail.* Retrieved from https://www.theglobeandmail.com/news/national/thalidomide-victims-wait-for-canadas-apology/article4352125/

Perou, R., Bitsko, R., Blumberg, S.J., Pastor, P., Ghandour, R.M., Gfroerer, J.C., Hedden, S.L., Crosby, A.E., Visser, S.N., Schieve, L.A., Parks, S.E., Hall, J.E., Brody, D., Simile, C.M., Thompson, W.W., Baio, J., Avenevoli, S., Kogan, M.D., & Huang, L.N. (2013). Mental health surveillance among children—United States, 2005–2011. *Morbidity and Mortality Weekly Report, 62*(2), 1–35. https://www.cdc.gov/mmwr/preview/mmwrhtml/su6202a1.htm

Rachlis, M., & Kushner, C. (1989). *Second opinion: What's wrong with Canada's health care system.* HarperCollins.

Ramage-Morin, P.L. (2009). Medication use among senior Canadians. *Health Reports, 20*(1), 1–8.

Robbins, R. (2016, 9 Mar.). Drug makers now spend 5 billion a year on advertising. *Stat News.* https://www.statnews.com/2016/03/09/drug-industry-advertising/

Rath A. (2017). Lethal opiates delivered by mail from China, killing addicts in the US. *Kazu.* https://www.kazu.org/post/lethal-opiates-delivered-mail-china-killing-addicts-us

Roughead, E.E., Gilbert, A.L., & Harvey, K.J. (1998). Self-regulatory codes of conduct: Are they effective in controlling pharmaceutical representatives' presentation to general practitioners? *International Journal of Health Services, 282*, 269–79.

Senate of Canada. (2001, Mar.). *The health of Canadians—The federal role. Volume One—The story so far.* Interim report on the state of health care system in Canada (Kirby Report). https://www.canada.ca/en/health-canada/services/health-care-system/health-human-resources/strategy/kirby-report.html

Shield, K.D., Ialomiteanu, A., Fischer, B., & Mann, R.E. (2011). Non-medical use of prescription opioids among Ontario adults: Data from the 2008/2009 CAMH monitor. *Canadian Review of Public Health, 102*(5), 330–5.

Silversides, A. (2010). Lifting the curtain on the drug approval process. In A.R. Ford and D. Saibil (Eds), *The push to prescribe: Women and Canadian drug policy* (pp. 115–38). Women's Press.

Smith, B.L. (2012). Inappropriate prescribing. *Monitor on Psychology, 43*(6).

Stelfox, H.T., Chua, G., O'Rourke, K., & Detsky, A.S. (1998). Conflict of interest in the debate over calcium-channel antagonists. *New England Journal of Medicine, 338*(2), 101–6.

Tannenbaum, C., & Tsuyiki, R.T. (2013). The expanding scope of pharmacists' practice: Implications for physicians. *CMAJ, 185*(4), 1228–32.

Talmazan, Y. (2017, Jan.). B.C. woman advocates for genetic testing after sister nearly dies of adverse drug reaction. *Global News.* https://globalnews.ca/news/3141824/b-c-woman-advocates-for-genetic-testing-after-sister-nearly-dies-of-adverse-drug-reaction/

Usher, W., & Skinner, J. (2012). EMPIRE and health website recommendations: Technologies of control. *Social Theory & Health, 10*(1), 20–41.

Van Zee, A. (2009). The promotion and marketing of OxyContin: Commercial triumph, public health tragedy. *American Journal of Public Health, 99*(2), 221–7.

Vavasour, M., & Mennie, Y. (1984). *For health or profit.* World Inter-Action Ottawa and Inter-Paris.

Ventola, C.L. (2015). The antibiotic resistance crisis: Part 1, causes and threats. *Pharmacy & Therapeutics, 40*(4), 277–83.

Votova, K., Blais, R., Penning, M.J., & MacLure, M.K. (2013). Polypharmacy meets polyherbacy: Pharmaceutical, over-the-counter, and natural health product use among Canadian adults. *Canadian Journal of Public Health, 104*(3), 222–8.

Weeks, C. (2017, June). How hospitals are seeking to prevent medical error deaths. *Globe and Mail.* https://www.theglobeandmail.com/life/health-and-fitness/health/toronto-hospitals-embark-on-safety-initiative-to-prevent-medical-error-deaths/article30610569/

Whitaker, R. (2010). *Anatomy of an epidemic: Magic bullets, psychiatric drugs, and the astonishing rise of mental illness in America.* Crown.

Williams, A.P., Dominick, K., & Vayda, E. (1993). Women in medicine: Toward a conceptual understanding of the potential for change. *Journal of the American Medical Women's Association, 48*(4), 115–23.

Willison, D.J., & MacLeod, S.M. (2002). Patenting of genetic material: Are the benefits to society being realized? *CMAJ, 167*(3), 259–63.

Willmsen, C. (2019). How OxyContin's maker sought to influence mass legislators. *Common Health.* https://www.wbur.org/commonhealth/2019/04/25/purdue-pharma-state-house-lobbying

Winsor, H. (1973, Mar.). Thalidomide. *Globe and Mail.*

Zitner, D. (2002). Drug use in Canada: Opportunity lost. *Atlantic Insitute for Market Studies (AIMS).*

Zlomislic, D., & Teotonio, I. (2013, 31 Jan.). Diane 34 deaths of 11 Canadian women linked to acne drug, compared to four in France. *Toronto Star.* https://www.thestar.com/news/canada/2013/01/31/diane35_deaths_of_11_canadian_women_linked_to_acne_drug_compared_to_four_in_france.html

Chapter 15

Alexander, R. (2012). Which is the world's biggest employer? *BBC News.* https://www.bbc.com/news/magazine-17429786

Breiman, R.F. (2020, 27 Mar.). The Covid-19 culprit is us, not pangolins. *CNN.* https://www.cnn.com/2020/03/27/opinions/pangolins-coronavirus-pandemic-breiman/index.html

Brueck, H., Miller, A.M., & Feder, S. (2020, 24 Mar.). China took at least 12 strict measures to control the coronavirus. *Business Insider.* https://news.yahoo.com/11-extreme-measures-china-took-161600502.html

Business Tech. (2016, Jan.). Capetown is now among the 10 most violent cities in the world. https://businesstech.co.za/news/general/110133/cape-town-is-now-among-the-10-most-violent-cities-in-the-world/

Castano, A. (2018, Dec.). Brazilian spiritual healer "John of God" indicted for rape, accused of sexually abusing nearly 600 women. *ABC News.* https://abcnews.go.com/International/brazilian-spiritual-healer-john-god-indicted-rape-accused/story?id=60019325

Centers for Disease Control and Prevention. (2017). Health insurance coverage. https://www.cdc.gov/nchs/fastats/health-insurance.htm

Collinson, P. (2017, 16 Jan.). Private health insurance sales soar amid NHS crisis. *The Guardian.* https://www.theguardian.com/business/2017/jan/16/private-medical-insurance-sales-surge-health-nhs

Countrymeters. (2020). Brazil population. https://countrymeters.info/en/Brazil

Couttolenc, B., & Alexandre, N. (2007). Private health insurance in Brazil: Features and impact on access and utilization. Paper presented at IHEA 6th World Congress: Explorations in Health Economics.

CTV News. (2017, July). 63,000 Canadians left the country for medical treatment last year: Fraser Institute. https://www.ctvnews.ca/health/63-000-canadians-left-the-country-for-medical-treatment-last-year-fraser-institute-1.3486635

Davidson, H. (2020, 13 Mar.). First Covid-19 case happened in November, China government records show—report. *The Guardian.* https://www.theguardian.com/world/2020/mar/13/first-covid-19-case-happened-in-november-china-government-records-show-report

Davis, K., Schoen, C., & Stremikis, K. (2010). Mirror, mirror on the wall: An international update on the comparative performance of American health care. *Commonwealth Fund.* www.commonwealthfund.org/~/media/Files/Publications/Fund%20Report/2010/Jun/1400_Davis_Mirror_Mirror_on_the_wall_2010.pdf

Dennis, J. (2012). 2012 International herb & botanical trends. *Nutraceuticals World.* https://www.nutraceuticalsworld.com/issues/2012-07/view_features/2012-international-herb-botanical-trends

De Vogli, R. (2011). Neoliberal globalisation and health in a time of economic crisis. *Social Theory & Health, 9*(4), 311–25.

Durrani, T. (2020, 21 Mar.). COVID-19 disproportionately affects those living in poverty. And this impacts us all. *Healthy Debate.* https://healthydebate.ca/2020/03/topic/covid-19-low-income-poverty

Export.gov. (2018). Brazil healthcare. https://www.export.gov/article?id=Brazil-Healthcare

Fallon, A. (2013, Oct.). Rags to riches. *Chatelaine,* 161–2.

Finch, S. (2014a). Thailand top destination for medical tourists. *CMAJ, 186*(1), 1–2.

———. (2014b). Medical tourism driving health care disparity in Thailand. *CMAJ, 186*(1), 11.

Frydman, C., & Saks, S. (2005). Historical trends in executive compensation, 1936–2003. Working paper, cited in De Vogli (2011).

Garrett, L. (1995). *The coming plague: Newly emerging diseases in a world out of balance.* Penguin.

Glover, L. (2015, 26 Jan.). Inside the clinical research machine. *US News and World Report.* https://health.usnews.com/health-news/patient-advice/articles/2015/01/26/inside-the-clinical-research-machine

Gragnolati, M., Lindelow, M., & Bernard, C. (2013). Twenty years of health system reform in Brazil: An assessment of the Sistema Único de Saúde. *Directions in development—human development.* World Bank. https://openknowledge.worldbank.org/handle/10986/15801

Helman, C.G. (2007). *Culture, health and illness,* 5th edn. Hodder Arnold.

Herrick, D.M. (2007). *Medical tourism: Global competition in health care*. NCPA Policy Report No. 304, Nov.

Hodgson, P. (2015, 22 June). Top CEOs make more than 300 times average worker. *Fortune*. http://fortune.com/2015/06/22/ceo-vs-worker-pay/

Kapoor, I. (2012). *Celebrity humanitarianism: The ideology of global charity*. Routledge.

McIntyre, D., & Gilson, L. (2000). Redressing disadvantage: Promoting vertical equity within South Africa. *Health Care Analysis, 8*(3), 235–58.

Makary, M., & Daniel, M. (2016). Medical error—the third leading cause of death in US. *British Medical Journal, 353*, i2139.

Market Research Future. (2019). Herbal market value to surpass USD 129 billion revenue mark by 2023 at 5.88% CAGR predicts Market Research Future. *Globe News Wire*. https://www.globenewswire.com/news-release/2019/04/03/1796359/0/en/Herbal-Medicine-Market-Value-to-Surpass-USD-129-Billion-Revenue-Mark-by-2023-at-5-88-CAGR-Predicts-Market-Research-Future.html

Mishel, L., & Schieder, J. (2018, 16 Aug.). CEO compensation surged in 2017. *Economic Policy Institute*. https://www.epi.org/publication/ceo-compensation-surged-in-2017/

Nahin, R.L., Dahlhamer, J.M., & Stussman, B.J. (2010). Health need and the use of alternative medicine among adults who do not use conventional medicine. *BMC Health Services Research, 10*, 220.

National Health Service. (2017). Clinical evidence for homeopathy. https://www.england.nhs.uk/wp-content/uploads/2017/11/sps-homeopathy.pdf

Organisation for Economic Co-operation and Development (OECD). (2017a). *Health at a glance 2017*. http://www.oecd.org/health/health-systems/health-at-a-glance-19991312.htm

———. (2017b). OECD data computed tomography scanners (CT). https://data.oecd.org/healtheqt/computed-tomography-ct-scanners.htm

———. (2017c). OECD data magnetic resonance imaging units (MRI). https://data.oecd.org/healtheqt/magnetic-resonance-imaging-mri-units.htm

O'Neill, J., Wilson, D., Purushothaman, R., & Stupnytska, A. (2005). How strong are the BRICs? Global Economics Paper No. 134.

Paim, J., Travassos, C., Almeida, C., Bahia, L., & Macinko, J. (2011). The Brazilian health system: History, advances, and challenges. *The Lancet, 377*, 1778–97. www.thelancet.com/journals/lancet/article/PIIS0140-6736%2811%2960054-8/fulltext#

Patwardhan, B. (2005). Traditional medicine: Modern approach for affordable global health. *World Health Organization*. https://www.who.int/intellectualproperty/studies/traditional_medicine/en/

Petryna, A. (2009). *When experiments travel: Clinical trials and the global search for human subjects*. Princeton University Press.

Rainey, S. (2013, Nov.). Prince Charles and homeopathy: Crank or revolutionary? *The Telegraph*. https://www.telegraph.co.uk/news/uknews/prince-charles/10433939/Prince-Charles-and-homeopathy-crank-or-revolutionary.html

Reinhart, R.J. (2018, Feb.). In the news: Americans' satisfaction with their healthcare. *Health Care*. https://news.gallup.com/poll/226607/news-americans-satisfaction-healthcare.aspx

Roberts, A., Marshall, L., & Charlesworth, A. (2012). A decade of austerity? The funding pressures facing the NHS from 2010/11 to 2021/22. *Nuffield Trust*. https://www.nuffieldtrust.org.uk/research/a-decade-of-austerity-the-funding-pressures-facing-the-nhs-from-2010-11-to-2021-22

Sanders, D., & Chopra, M. (2006). Key challenges to achieving health for all in an inequitable society: The case of South Africa. *American Journal of Public Health, 96*(1), 73–8.

Sartorius, B., Sartorius, K., Chirwa, T., & Fonn, S. (2011). Infant mortality in South Africa—distribution association and policy implications, 2007: An ecological spatial analysis. *International Journal of Health Geography, 10*, 61.

Schneider, E.C., Sarnak, D.O., Squires, D., Shah, A., & Doty, M.M. (2017). Mirror, mirror: How the U.S. health care system compares internationally at time of radical change. *Commonwealth Fund*. https://www.commonwealthfund.org/chart/2017/health-care-system-performance-rankings

Seear, M. (2007). *An introduction to global health*. Canadian Scholars' Press.

Shah, A. (2011). Health care around the world. *Global Issues*. http://www.globalissues.org/article/774/health-care-around-the-world

Siegel, K.R., Feigl, A.B., Kishore, S.P., & Stuckler, D. (2011, 9 May). Misalignment between perceptions and actual burden of disease: Evidence from the US population. *Global Health Action, 4*. www.ncbi.nlm.nih.gov/pmc/articles/PMC3092698/

Stuckler, D., Basu, S., & McKee, M. (2011). Health care capacity and allocation among South Africa's provinces: Infrastructure-inequality traps after the end of apartheid. *American Journal of Public Health, 101*(1), 165–72.

Turner, L. (2007). First World health care at Third World prices: Globalization, bioethics and medical tourism. *BioSocieties, 2*, 303–25.

UNICEF. (2015). Progress on sanitation and drinking water: 2015 assessment and MDG update. https://data.unicef.org/resources/progress-on-sanitation-and-drinking-water-2015-assessement-and-mdg-update/

Viergever, R., & Keyang, L. (2015). Trends in global clinical trial registration: An analysis of the numbers of registered clinical trials in different parts of the world 2004 to 2013. *BMJ Open, 5*(9). https://www.ncbi.nlm.nih.gov/pmc/articles/PMC4593134/

Weiss, G.L., & Lonnquist, L.E. (2012). *The sociology of health, illness and healing*, 7th edn. Prentice-Hall.

Wermuth, L. (2003). *Global inequality and human needs.* Allyn & Bacon.

Whitaker, R. (2010). *Anatomy of an epidemic: Magic bullets, psychiatric drugs, and the astonishing rise of mental illness in America.* Crown.

Woodward, A. (2020). At least 5 people in China have disappeared, gotten arrested, or been silenced after speaking out about the coronavirus. *Business Insider.* https://www.businessinsider.com/china-coronavirus-whistleblowers-speak-out-vanish-2020-2

World Bank. (2018). *Poverty and shared prosperity.* http://www.worldbank.org/en/publication/poverty-and-shared-prosperity

———. (2019). The World Bank in Brazil. https://www.worldbank.org/en/country/brazil/overview

World Bank Group. (2017). Data for South Africa, upper middle income. https://data.worldbank.org/?locations=ZA-XT

World Health Organization (WHO). (2002). *WHO traditional medicine strategy 2002–2005.* Retrieved from whqlibdoc.who.int/hq/2002/who_edm_trm_2002.1.pdf

———. (2008). Traditional medicine: Fact sheet No. 134. www.who.int/mediacentre/factsheets/fs134/en/index.html

———. (2017). Violence against women. https://www.who.int/news-room/fact-sheets/detail/violence-against-women

Index

abnormality, 224, 230–1
Aboriginal Healing Fund, 131
abortion pill, 204
abortions, worldwide, 43
accidents, 82–3, 84
acupressure, 326
acupuncture, 323
Aday, L.A., 91
addiction, 53, 221, 345, 364–5
Adelson, N., 139, 140
adenosis, 362
ADHD (attention deficit hyperactive disorder): and boys, 206, 229; description and discovery, 227, 228; diagnosis impact, 231; medicalization, 206, 227–8, 229; prescriptions, 203; social construction, 228
administrators, in hospitals, 282
adolescents. *see* youth
adults, social value, 172
advertisements for drugs, 343, 347, 350, 356; direct-to-consumer, 211, 347, 351; Purdue for opioids, 364, 365
Affordable Care Act (US), 210
Afghanistan combat mission, 51
Africa, menstruation in girls, 374
Afripads, 374
age, 116, 120–2, 134–5
Age of Degenerative and Man-Made Diseases, 36
Age of Pestilence and Famine, 36
Age of Receding Pandemics, 36
aging, and cost of health care, 99
aging populations. *see* elderly
agricultural work, 82
AIDS, 57, 181, 182, 183, 218; *see also* HIV/AIDS
air pollution, 62, 67–8, 69–73; in Canada, 70–2
Alberta, 279, 280, 348
alcohol: and drugs, 367; impact, 52, 152; as precursor in Canada, 52;

at schools and colleges, 54; views of addiction, 221
Algonquian peoples, pre-contact medicine, 240
alienation in medical education, 278
allopathic medicine: and CAM, 323–4, 325; *vs.* chiropractic, 329–30; criticisms, 10, 318, 325; description and goal, 10, 318, 335; discoveries, 222–4; division of labour, 267; early organization in Canada, 243, 245; history, 219–21; *vs.* homeopathy, 332, 333; *vs.* naturopathy, 335; power, 235–6; threats to dominance, 270–1
"allostasis" and allostatic load, 147
Alma-Alta forum and Accord, 377
alternative medicine. *see* complementary and alternative medicine
Alzheimer's disease, 92
American Journal of Obstetrics and Gynecology, 361
American Medical Association (AMA), and CAM, 328, 329, 333
Anaguayan troopship, 244
"anatomical acupuncture," 323
anorexia, and sexual politics, 184, 185
anti-aging medicine, 185
antibiotic resistance, 354
anti-racist theory. *see* critical race theory
anti-vaccine or "anti-vax" movement, 10, 46
Antonovsky, A., 157
apothecaries, 220, 242
Apple company, 203
Arctic, and climate change, 64, 65
Arizona Center for Integrative Medicine, 324
arthritis, 20–1
asbestos, 71
aspiration, illness as, 185–6
aspirational health, 170, 185, 232–3

asthma, 71
attachment process, and medicalization, 224–5
Australia, 356–7
authoritarian personality in medical education, 278
automobiles. *see* cars
autopsies, 221

babies, and nutrition, 40, 41
bacterial diseases and resistance, 354
baldness, as disease, 203
Balshem, M., 208–9
Banting, Frederick G., 273
barber-surgeons, 220, 242
bariatric surgeries, 210–11
Barwin, Norman, 359–60
Baumgart, Alice, 298
BBC chain (bibliography, body, and self-conception), 191
beauty, 226
Becker, Howard S., and colleagues, 275, 277
Beers list, 344
behaviour (human), medicalization, 227–34
being able to cope, 157–8
benzodiazepines, 345, 355
Best, Charles E., 273–4
Bethune, Norman, 268–9
Bethune family history, 268
Bhopal (India), 68
bibliography, body, and self-conception (BBC chain), 191
Biggs, C.I., 313, 314
big pharma. *see* pharmaceutical industry
biodiversity decline, 75
bioengineering, 367–8
biologistic view of the body, 198
biomedical equipment, 367
biomedicalization, 32, 229–31
biopower, 24, 31